Mathematics in Action

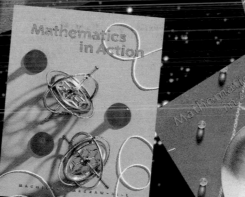

Audrey L. Jackson

Martin L. Johnson

Steven J. Leinwand

Richard D. Lodholz

Gary L. Musser

Walter G. Secada

Macmillan/McGraw-Hill Publishing Company
New York • Columbus

Self Confidence built on success is the most important objective

Mathematics in Action.

T-2

… Mathematics is taught via Problem Solving …

"Problem Solving is the focus of Mathematics in Action. Our students take risks in finding solutions to problems in a classroom where thought provoking questions center around motivating real world situations."

Dr. Richard D. Lodholz, Mathematics Coordinator K-12 of the Parkway School District, Missouri, supervises mathematics instruction in a nationally known, forward-looking school district. Dr. Lodholz is a member of the Board of Directors of the National Council of Teachers of Mathematics and is a frequent presenter at national and regional meetings. He has a particular expertise in the areas of estimation, mental math, and middle school.

… Communicating Ideas helps students Solve Problems …

"Our students listen to, read about, write about, speak about, reflect on, and demonstrate mathematical ideas. They interact with classmates and clarify their own thinking while learning other ways to think about ideas."

Dr. Martin L. Johnson, Professor of Mathematics Education at the University of Maryland, College Park, has special expertise in diagnosis and remediation in mathematics and its application to the learning of minority children. Dr. Johnson has been an advisor, consultant, and writer and is a contributor to many professional journals.

… Cooperative Learning Activities Build Confidence …

"As students explore, create, and discover mathematics through activity centered instruction, they construct their own mathematics understanding."

Audrey L. Jackson, Mathematics Specialist, Parkway School District, Missouri, specializes in developmental learning in the primary grades. She is a frequent speaker at national and regional meetings of the National Council of Teachers of Mathematics.

TABLE OF CONTENTS

...Mathematics is Cross-Disciplinary... and Cross-Cultural...

"*Students have many opportunities to develop an awareness and an appreciation of the interaction of mathematical ideas among each other and to other disciplines. Students appreciate the contribution of their cultures to the creation of mathematical ideas.*"

Dr. Walter G. Secada, Associate Professor of Mathematics Education at the University of Wisconsin at Madison, is a specialist in multicultural and bilingual education. He has conducted extensive research in the area of equity in mathematics education and is a consultant to school districts around the country.

Every student can engage in mathematics successfully.

...Performance Assessment looks at the Process and the Products...

"*Critical thinking is at the heart of mathematics. Students learn that explaining and justifying their thinking is important and how a problem is solved is as important as its answers.*"

Steven J. Leinwand, Mathematics Consultant for the Connecticut State Department of Education, is responsible for the development of a statewide program in mathematics. He is the author of many articles in professional journals, and a member of the Curriculum Framework Task Force of the Mathematical Sciences Education Board.

...Confident Teachers are Successful Teachers...

"*Teachers need to have models of good mathematics teaching, knowledge of mathematical pedagogy, and knowledge of how students learn mathematics.*

All teachers are given comprehensive support as they ensure lifelong mathematical learning for all students."

Dr. Gary L. Musser, Professor of Mathematics at Oregon State University in Corvallis, is the author of the highly successful Mathematics for Elementary Teachers, published by Macmillan's College Division. Dr. Musser has taught mathematics to students from elementary schools through universities. His current research is in problem solving.

Make every lesson an event! Hands-on, *activity-rich*, Mathematics in Action will delight your students with opportunities to d i s c o v e r cooperatively, to think creatively, and - as they move beyond the classroom - to confidently apply what they've learned.

Mathematics in Action

ACTIVITY-RICH...EVERY LESSON, EVERY DAY!

Students first encounter new concepts and skills through high-interest activities. They deal with all new material in concrete terms — by working with manipulatives — before they deal with it abstractly.

▲ Cooperative Learning

Working together to develop concepts, students trade opinions, clarify each other's thinking, and share in decision making.

② Versatile Manipulatives

Using connecting cubes, spinners, and a variety of other simple manipulatives, students connect mathematics with the real world. They visualize numbers, develop an understanding of the basic operations, explore concepts of shape, size, and more.

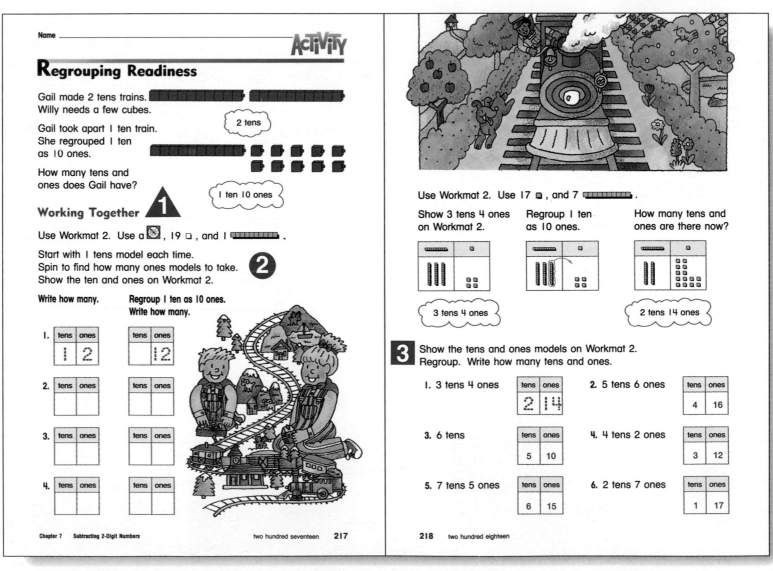

Grade 2, Pages 217-218

Artful Questioning

Guided by carefully designed question sequences, students experience the satisfaction of exploring and developing an understanding of mathematical concepts on their own.

Powerful Features

Through relevant and subject-linking lesson features, students become involved in and retain what they've learned. This helps to build confidence and to develop more creative thinking skills.

"Talk about..." provides opportunities for students to communicate mathematically and to reinforce their grasp of the main point of the lesson.

Mixed Review keeps students sharp with ongoing review at pivotal points throughout each chapter.

Practice is built into each lesson, enabling students to apply what they've learned in a variety of ways.

Extra Practice and *Practice Plus* provide still more reinforcement at the end of each chapter, where it's needed most.

Fully Meets NCTM Standards

Communication

Students communicate with each other, and with their teacher as they question, clarify, and explain their thinking...deepening their mathematical understanding and sharpening their mathematical skills.

Reasoning

Activities are designed to exercise both mental and visual abilities...inviting students to think logically, work systematically, and thoroughly test their procedures.

Problem Solving

Whether it's programming a VCR or measuring ingredients for a recipe...students are quick to see how mathematics relates to their everyday lives.

Connections

Language arts, music, social studies, art, and more... wherever mathematics connects with other disciplines, students are engaged in activities that make those connections clear and meaningful.

PROBLEM SOLVING...THE CREATIVE APPROACH

Given high-interest, imaginative problems, students learn to reason creatively and apply skills in innovative ways.

Creative Problem Solving Strategies

Students develop a highly flexible approach to problem solving. Their basic five-step approach—**understand, plan, try, check, and extend**—allows them to be truly inventive in selecting and combining those skills that are best suited to the situation at hand.

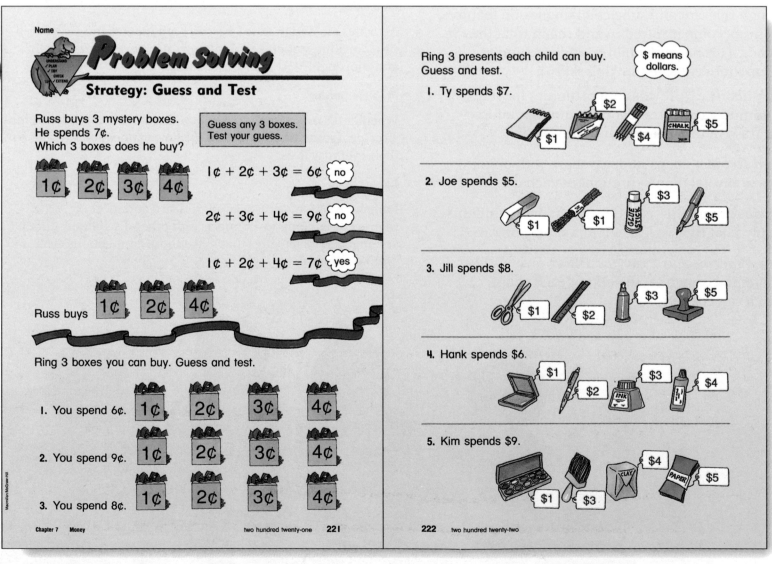

Thinking Mathematically

To help students learn to *think mathematically* and apply the skills that they've learned, they're given motivating, non-routine problems that challenge them to pursue solutions in new innovative ways.

Decision Making

Students have many opportunities to work cooperatively on problems that involve tangible, real-life situations. With data to analyze and options to consider, they're on their way to becoming effective decision makers!

Name

Toy Hunt

Use the clues.
Ring the correct toy.

PROBLEM SOLVING

THINKING MATHEMATICALLY

ACTIVITY

I paid

My toy is round.

30¢

25¢

30¢

23¢

23¢

13¢

brown.

Grade 1, Page 215

Name

Decision Making

Problem Solving:
Planning a Trip to the Zoo

You want to go to the zoo.
Here are some things to think about.

You have 70¢.

It costs 30¢ to get into the zoo.

A bus ride costs 20¢.
You can park your bike for 10¢.

A can of juice costs 20¢.
A bag of peanuts costs 10¢.

1. How will you get to the zoo?

2. How will you spend your money?

3. Compare your dec___ with a ___tne___

Grade 1,
Page 411

Chapter 13   Adding and Subtracting 2-Dig

CONNECTIONS ... CROSS-DISCIPLINARY, CROSS-CULTURAL

Open your students' eyes to the whole world of mathematics. Here's how to show them its connections with other disciplines, with cultures from around the world ... as well as fascinating connections within mathematics itself.

Mathematics and Literature

Literature often serves as a springboard to exploring various math concepts, further reinforcing and dramatizing the vital connection between mathematics and everyday living.

Grade 2 TE, Pages 214Q-214R

Math Anthology

This multicultural treasury of guaranteed-to-please stories, poetry, and music from around the world provides a vital link between mathematics and literature.

Curriculum Connections

Students discover how mathematics is applied in language arts, the fine arts, science, and social studies.

Technology

Simulations and various other chapter activities make it easy for you to integrate computers and calculators into your program as tools for problem solving.

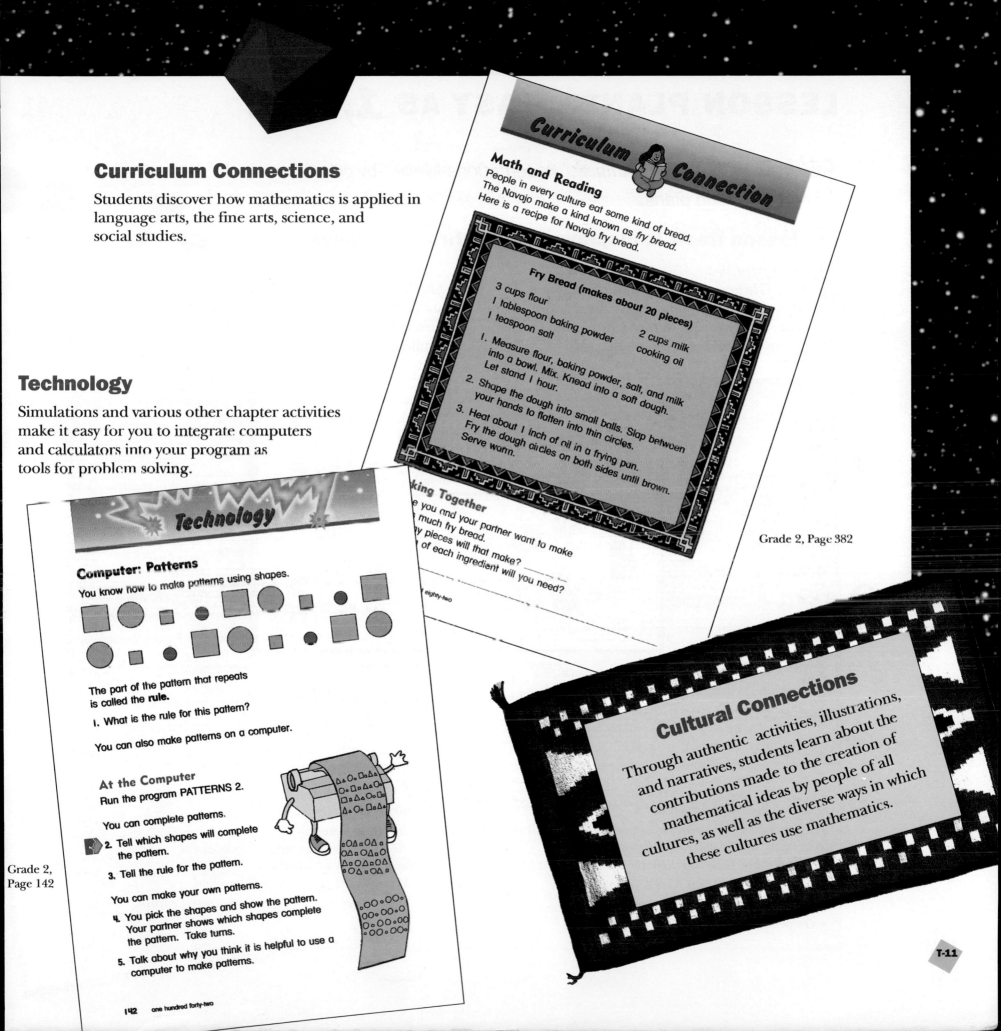

Curriculum Connection

Math and Reading

People in every culture eat some kind of bread. The Navajo make a kind known as *fry bread*. Here is a recipe for Navajo fry bread.

Fry Bread (makes about 20 pieces)

3 cups flour
1 tablespoon baking powder
1 teaspoon salt

2 cups milk
cooking oil

1. Measure flour, baking powder, salt, and milk into a bowl. Mix. Knead into a soft dough. Let stand 1 hour.
2. Shape the dough into small balls. Slap between your hands to flatten into thin circles.
3. Heat about 1 inch of oil in a frying pan. Fry the dough circles on both sides until brown. Serve warm.

king Together
e you and your partner want to make
t much fry bread.
y pieces will that make? _____
of each ingredient will you need?

eighty-two

Grade 2, Page 382

Technology

Computer: Patterns

You know how to make patterns using shapes.

The part of the pattern that repeats is called the **rule**.

1. What is the rule for this pattern?

You can also make patterns on a computer.

At the Computer
Run the program PATTERNS 2.

You can complete patterns.

2. Tell which shapes will complete the pattern.

3. Tell the rule for the pattern.

You can make your own patterns.

4. You pick the shapes and show the pattern. Your partner shows which shapes complete the pattern. Take turns.

5. Talk about why you think it is helpful to use a computer to make patterns.

Grade 2,
Page 142

Cultural Connections

Through authentic activities, illustrations, and narratives, students learn about the contributions made to the creation of mathematical ideas by people of all cultures, as well as the diverse ways in which these cultures use mathematics.

LESSON PLANS...EASY AS *1, 2, 3!*

Preparations are made simpler, presentations livelier, by consistent four-page lesson plans.

The lesson itself is displayed on the first two pages.

1 **At A Glance.** A concise outline of lesson objectives, assignment suggestions, and teaching materials. Notes on Manipulatives and Teacher Resources make management easy.

2 **Skills Trace.** Lesson by lesson, you know where you are in the overall instructional cycle...and where to turn for additional development, practice, and applications.

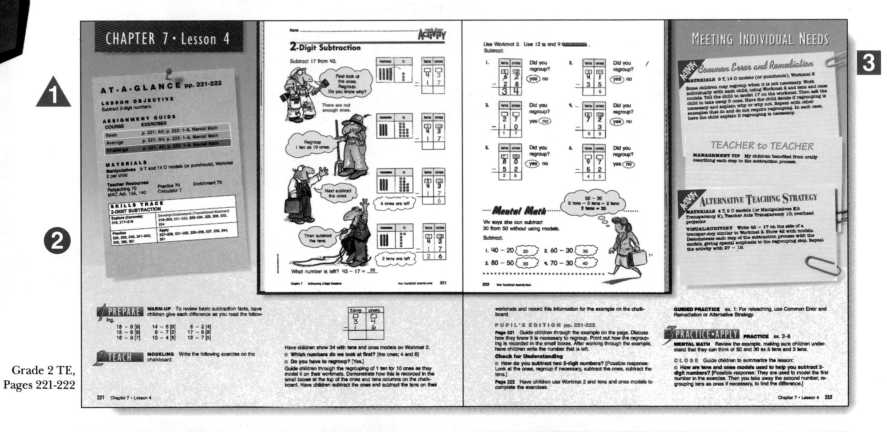

Grade 2 TE,
Pages 221-222

3 **Meeting Individual Needs**

These teaching tips provide opportunities for all students to become *mathematically literate.*

- *Alternative Teaching Strategy*
- *Common Error and Remediation*
- *For Students Acquiring English*
- *Ongoing Assessment*

- *Cultural Diversity*
- *Teacher to Teacher*
  Practical tips that guarantee a successful mathematics environment.
  + *Management*
  + *Manipulatives*
  + *Calculator*
  + *Estimation*
  + *Cooperative Learning*

T-12

The third and fourth pages organize all your follow-up activities.

④ MAC Activities. They're fun for your students and convenient for you...just tear off and distribute. Only minimum supervision is required...giving you more time to work with students individually.

⑤ Practice, Reteaching, Enrichment supplements are pictured in the Teacher's Edition in a size that is LARGE ENOUGH FOR YOU TO READ THEM EASILY!

⑥ Problem of the Day, a handy resource to begin or end a lesson that keeps problem solving skills sharp, is available on a tear-off pad.

Grade 2 TE, Pages 222A-222B

TEACHING SUPPORT...EACH STEP OF THE WAY

Chapter Organizers offer support in a time-saving, easy-to-read format. They help you provide students of every aptitude and interest with the very best mathematics experience imaginable.

Notes from the Author — give you a chapter preview and tips on what to expect from your students.

Chapter Planning Guide — In this comprehensive chart (correlated to NCTM standards), you see what, when, how– *and with what options*– you'll be teaching.

Assessment Options — both formal and informal — There's a method to meet every need: pre-teaching activities, ongoing observation, portfolios, journal writing, computer management ...as well as instruments correlated to specific chapter objectives. You'll know how your students think before, during, and after each concept is taught.

Manipulatives Workshop helps you create a stimulating classroom environment where students can explore "without threat." It focuses on the specific manipulatives used in the current chapter, illustrating how to use them both with individuals and with groups.

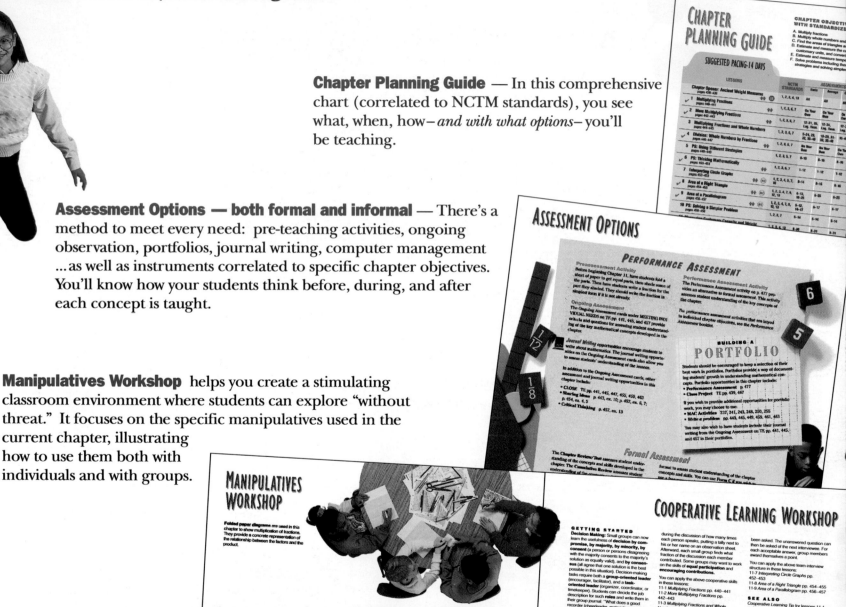

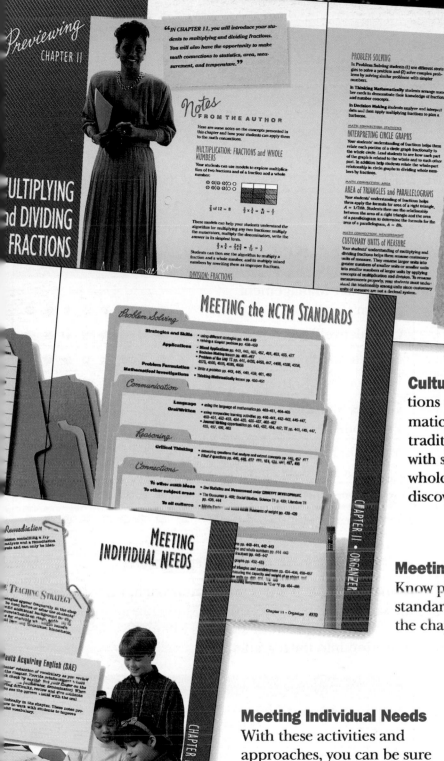

Professional Handbook

Turn to this convenient resource for up-to-date information on Problem Solving, Communication and Reasoning, Mental Math, Estimation, Patterns, Algebra, Data Collection and Analysis, Connections, Technology...and many other major issues in mathematics education.

- Learning Stages
- Manipulatives
- Cooperative Learning
- Assessment
- Meeting Individual Needs
- Cultural Diversity
- Problem Solving
- Communication and Reasoning
- Connections
- Technology
- Data Collection and Analysis
- Algebra
- Patterns
- Mental Math
- Estimation and Number Sense
- Home Involvement

AND MORE...

Cultural Diversity The contributions of various cultures to mathematics–through art, literature, traditions, and more–are shared with students as they experience a whole new world of learning and discovery.

Meeting the NCTM Standards. Know precisely where and how the standards are addressed throughout the chapter.

Meeting Individual Needs With these activities and approaches, you can be sure that all students have equal opportunities to learn...and succeed.

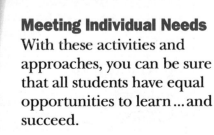

Cooperative Learning Workshop These *Workshops* illustrate the ins-and-outs of utilizing a methodology that researchers have found can improve the performance of *all* children.

PROGRAM COMPONENTS

Everything you need to provide rewarding mathematical experiences for all your students.

Mathematics in Action

	K	1	2	3	4	5	6	7	8
Pupil's Edition (Consumable)	●	●	●						
Pupil's Edition (Hard Cover)				●	●	●	●	●	●
Teacher's Edition	●	●	●	●	●	●	●	●	●
Big Book and Clings	●								
Math Anthology	●	●	●	●	●	●	●		
Read Aloud Cassettes	●	●	●						
Practice		●	●	●	●	●	●	●	●
Reteaching Activities		●	●	●	●	●	●	●	●
Enrichment Activities		●	●	●	●	●	●	●	●
Problem Solving Activities		●	●	●	●	●	●	●	●
Testing Program		●	●	●	●	●	●	●	●
Performance Assessment Activities		●	●	●	●	●	●	●	●
Critical Thinking	●	●	●	●	●	●	●	●	●
Home Involvement				●	●	●	●	●	●
Calculator Workshop		●	●	●	●	●	●	●	●
Computer Workshop Software		●	●	●	●	●	●	●	●
Teacher Aids	●	●	●	●	●	●	●	●	●
MAC Activity Pads	●	●	●	●	●	●	●	●	●
Problem of the Day Pads	●	●	●	●	●	●	●	●	●
Create-A-Kit Manipulatives		●	●	●	●	●	●	●	●
Posters	●	●	●	●	●	●	●	●	●
Manipulatives Kit Transparencies		●	●	●	●	●	●	●	●
Teacher Aids Transparencies	●	●	●	●	●	●	●	●	●
Calculator Kit		●	●	●	●	●	●	●	●
Overhead Calculator	●	●	●	●	●	●	●	●	●
Overhead Manipulatives	●	●	●	●	●	●	●	●	●

	K	1	2	3	4	5	6	7	8
Computer Management System		●	●	●	●	●	●	●	●
Cumulative Record Book	●	●	●	●	●	●	●	●	●
Mathematics Skills Software		●	●	●	●	●	●	●	●
The Pyramid Software			●	●	●	●	●	●	●
Graphs, Statistics and Probability Software		●	●	●	●	●	●	●	●
Math On-Line Masters for Springboard Publisher 2						●	●	●	●
Staff Development Videos	●	●	●	●	●	●	●	●	●
Professional Handbook	●	●	●	●	●	●	●	●	●

I Can! Math Activity Program

A non-textbook, child-centered approach, *I Can!* follows the same Chapter Objectives as Mathematics in Action, so you can be assured your students will make a smooth transition into third grade.

	K	1	2
Jumbo Book and Clings	●	●	●
Teacher's Guide	●	●	●
My Activity Book	●	●	●
Workmats	●	●	●
Floormats	●	●	●
Literature Big Books	●	●	●
Math Anthology	●	●	●
Math Songs Audio Cassette	●	●	●
Read Aloud Audio Cassette	●	●	●
Posters	●	●	●
Computer Workshop		●	●

PUPIL'S EDITION

This section contains the following pages from the Pupil's Edition:

Table of Contents
Chapters 1-6
Picture Glossary

This section also contains teacher commentary for all lessons and Chapter Organizer pages that preview the chapter's content. In addition, Manipulatives Plus activities and Read-Aloud selections are provided for each chapter.

iii

4 MONEY *Page 125*

LITERATURE *CONNECTION:* PENELOPE GETS WHEELS

5 MEASUREMENT *Page 151*

LITERATURE *CONNECTION:* HOW BIG IS A FOOT?

v

6 ADDING 2-DIGIT NUMBERS *Page 185*

LITERATURE *CONNECTION:* NINETY-NINE POCKETS

vii

ix

13 EXPLORE ADDING AND SUBTRACTING 3-DIGIT NUMBERS *Page 391*

LITERATURE *CONNECTION:* TOO MANY BOOKS!

Mathematics in Action

GRADE 2 • PART 1

MACMILLAN/McGRAW-HILL SCHOOL PUBLISHING COMPANY
New York   Columbus

GETTING STARTED

AT·A·GLANCE p.1

LESSON OBJECTIVE
Develop a sense of mathematical curiosity and reasoning.

PROBLE

GETTING STARTED

Look around you. Name some things that are longer than your shoe. Name some things that are shorter than your desk.

Find some round things. Find some square things. Name some things you only see one of.

Name some things you see a lot of.

This book has games, puzzles, and activities. You can do them alone or with a partner.

The stories and poems at the beginning of each chapter will help you to think about sizes, shapes, and numbers.

Have fun!

Audrey Jackson   *Richard Lodholz*

Martin Johnson   *Gary L Musser*

Steve Leinwand   *Walter G. Secad*

1

PLAN   **AIMS AND ATTITUDES**   This page begins the development of number skills. Emphasize to children that mathematics is special to all of us and that the activities in this book will be fun. Your enthusiasm will help children develop a positive attitude toward learning mathematics.

MANAGEMENT   This page is intended for all children and has been designed for whole-class work.

GUIDE   Display the pupil's edition and explain to children that this is their mathematics book. Discuss the picture on the cover and have children identify objects they recognize.

Explain to children that they will use this book to learn about numbers and how to use numbers.

■ **Where do you see numbers in the classroom?** [Possible responses: on the clock; on books; on the calendar; on the classroom door]

■ **Did you use mathematics today? How?** [Guide children to possible responses: checked the time before leaving the house; checked the temperature to know how to dress; bought lunch; and so on.]

Read the letter on page 1 aloud to the children. Stop after each statement and encourage children to find objects that the statement describes.

EXTEND   Have children share their ideas with the class about what they think they will learn about in mathematics and what kinds of special tools or materials they may use to help them learn about mathematics.

BUTT⊙N UP

Cut out the buttons.
Sort them on the jackets.
How many ways can you sort?
Show your favorite way
to sort.
Sorting will vary.

 Talk about the different ways to sort.

2 Children should note that the buttons can be sorted by color, shape, and number of holes.

AT·A·GLANCE p. 2

LESSON OBJECTIVE
Sort objects.

ASSIGNMENT GUIDE

COURSE	EXERCISES
Basic	p. 2: All
Average	p. 2: All
Challenge	p. 2: All

MATERIALS
Classroom Materials 3 red crayons, 1 blue crayon; scissors
Manipulatives 4 ⚪ (or punchouts), 4 ◼ and 4 ▢ (or square counter punchouts), stickers for p. 2 per child

---

1 PLAN **AIMS AND ATTITUDES** This activity develops logical reasoning through the skill of sorting. Encourage children to verbalize their reasons for sorting as they do since some children may come up with different ways to sort other than by the usual attributes of size, shape, or color. A child may, for example, put buttons with two holes in one group and buttons with four holes in another group. Stress that there are many ways to sort, and praise the uniqueness of each method.

MANAGEMENT The activity is intended for all children and has been designed for independent work but is appropriate for pairs of children as well.

2 GUIDE Before beginning page 2, hold up 3 red crayons and 1 blue crayon.

■ **Which crayon does not belong in the group? Why?** [the blue crayon; it is a different color.]

Read the directions on page 2 aloud and discuss the pictures. Have children cut out the buttons or use stickers and sort them on the coats.

3 EXTEND Distribute 4 two-color counters, 4 red cubes, and 4 yellow cubes to each child or pair of children. Have children sort them. Afterward, have them explain how they sorted the materials.

GETTING STARTED

AT·A·GLANCE p. 3

LESSON OBJECTIVE
Make designs with shapes.

ASSIGNMENT GUIDE

COURSE	EXERCISES
Basic	p. 3: All
Average	p. 3: All
Challenge	p. 3: All

MATERIALS
Classroom Materials drawing paper, crayons
Manipulatives 1 set of pattern blocks (or punchouts) per child

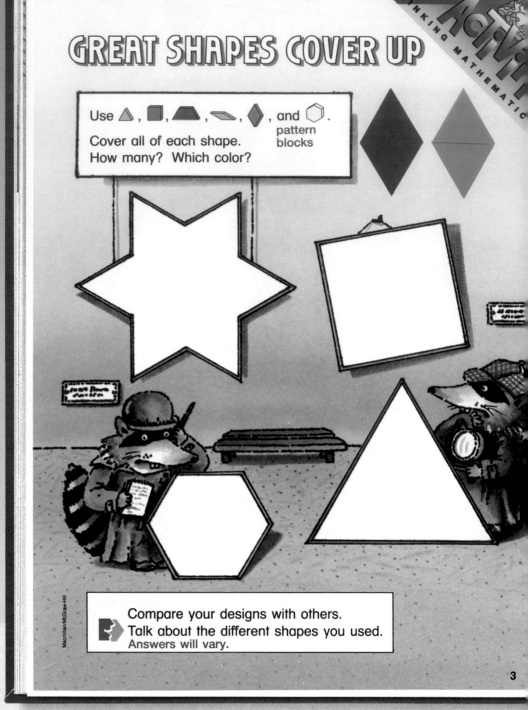

Name _____

GREAT SHAPES COVER UP

Use △, ▮, ⬟, ▬, ◆, and ⬡.
pattern blocks
Cover all of each shape.
How many? Which color?

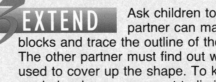

Compare your designs with others.
Talk about the different shapes you used.
Answers will vary.

Macmillan/McGraw-Hill

3

PLAN — **AIMS AND ATTITUDES** This activity develops visual reasoning by having children find geometric shapes that cover up larger shapes. Emphasize the investigative nature of the activity by comparing it to finding the pieces of a puzzle.

MANAGEMENT The activity is intended for all children and has been designed for independent work but is also appropriate for pairs of children.

GUIDE — Draw the pattern block shapes shown on page 3 on the chalkboard. Have volunteers identify the shapes.

Read the directions on page 3 to the children. Then distribute pattern blocks to each child or pair of children. Remind children to use blocks to cover the shapes in as many ways as they can.

Have a follow-up discussion after children have been allowed sufficient time to work with the pattern blocks. Emphasize that several variations of blocks can be used to cover the shapes.

EXTEND — Ask children to work in pairs. Hidden from view, one partner can make up a shape from some pattern blocks and trace the outline of the overall shape onto drawing paper. The other partner must find out which pattern block pieces may be used to cover up the shape. To keep the activity appropriate to the grade level, you may want to limit the number of pieces used to four.

NONSENSE IN NUMBERVILLE

Something strange is going on in Numberville.
What is missing? Fill in the missing things.

 Tell what a world without numbers would be like.

In their own words, children should note that many commonplace activities involving the measurement of length, weight, time, money, temperature, etc., would be more difficult.

4

A·T·A·GLANCE p. 4

LESSON OBJECTIVE
Recognize the importance of numbers.

ASSIGNMENT GUIDE

COURSE	EXERCISES
Basic	p. 4: All
Average	p. 4: All
Challenge	p. 4: All

 **PLAN** **AIMS AND ATTITUDES** This activity develops number sense through recognizing the many ways that numbers are used in everyday life.

An appreciation for numbers may be developed by pointing out the use of numbers whenever possible. You may point out such examples as keeping score during games, the liquid and weight amounts on food packaging, and so on.

MANAGEMENT The activity is intended for all children and has been designed for independent work. It is also appropriate for pairs of children.

GUIDE Read the directions aloud on page 4 and identify the pictures.

■ **What is missing from the things in the picture?** [numbers]
Have children write any numbers they wish on each pictured object.

EXTEND Have pairs of children make a list of some of the ways numbers are used every day. After pairs have made their lists, have groups share their ideas with the rest of the class. Keep a running list of their responses. Then discuss what the world would be like without numbers. [Without numbers, people would not be able to measure things, find their friends' houses, know the prices in a store, and so on.]

GETTING STARTED

AT·A·GLANCE p. 5

LESSON OBJECTIVE
Compare lengths.

ASSIGNMENT GUIDE

COURSE	EXERCISES
Basic	p. 5: All
Average	p. 5: All
Challenge	p. 5: All

MATERIALS
Manipulatives 10 ▱ per pair

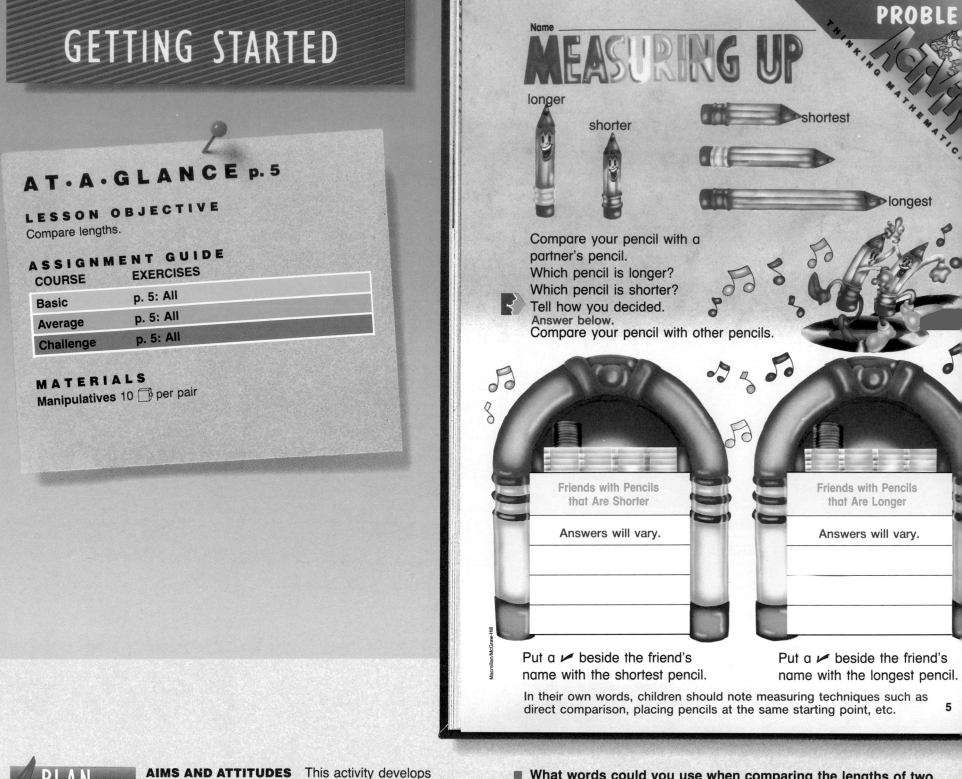

MEASURING UP

Name _____

longer
shorter
shortest
longest

Compare your pencil with a
partner's pencil.
Which pencil is longer?
Which pencil is shorter?
Tell how you decided.
Answer below.
Compare your pencil with other pencils.

Friends with Pencils that Are Shorter	Friends with Pencils that Are Longer
Answers will vary.	Answers will vary.

Put a ✔ beside the friend's
name with the shortest pencil.

Put a ✔ beside the friend's
name with the longest pencil.

In their own words, children should note measuring techniques such as
direct comparison, placing pencils at the same starting point, etc.

Macmillan/McGraw-Hill

5

**PLAN** **AIMS AND ATTITUDES** This activity develops
measuring sense by having children compare the
lengths of objects.

Encourage children to develop their own techniques for comparing
lengths. Children can compare by direct observation, by lining up objects at the same starting point, or by using a standard measure. Encourage children to be consistent by using the same method throughout the activity.

MANAGEMENT The activity is intended for all children and has been
designed for pairs.

GUIDE Before beginning page 5, ask:

■ **What words could you use when comparing the lengths of two
objects? when comparing the lengths of three objects?** [shorter,
longer; shortest, longest]

Remind children when to use the terms *shorter* and *longer* and *shortest* and *longest*. Then assign children partners and have them compare the lengths of their pencils. Call on volunteers to explain the
methods they used.

EXTEND Continue to have children work in pairs. Distribute
10 cubes to each pair. Have each partner make a
cube train. They can then discuss the lengths of the trains and the
methods they used to compare the lengths. Repeat the process by
having them compare three cube trains.

PICK A PET

Make this graph.
Ask 7 children to pick one
of these pets.
Color one box to show each choice.

Pets We Picked

bird

cat

dog

fish

Which pet did the most children pick? <u>Check students' answers</u>.

Which pet did the least children pick? <u>Check students' answers</u>.

6   Check that exactly 7 boxes are colored.

AT·A·GLANCE p. 6

LESSON OBJECTIVE
Make a graph.

ASSIGNMENT GUIDE

COURSE	EXERCISES
Basic	p. 6: All
Average	p. 6: All
Challenge	p. 6: All

MATERIALS
Classroom Materials drawing paper, crayons

**PLAN**   **AIMS AND ATTITUDES** This activity develops data recording through the use of a graph and number sense through the skill of counting.

Children can begin to appreciate the usefulness of recording data on graphs if you ask for a show of hands to see how many children live in houses, mobile homes, and apartment buildings. Stress that it is easier to record the information than it is to remember who raised their hands for each question.

MANAGEMENT The activity is intended for all children and has been designed for independent work. It is also appropriate for pairs of children.

**GUIDE**   Have children help you read the directions at the top of the page. When the graphs are completed, have children discuss the answers to the questions presented. Also, discuss the graph as a useful and quick way to recall information.

**EXTEND**   Give each child drawing paper and crayons. Have them repeat the activity, but this time ask 7 classmates which color is their favorite—red, yellow, blue, or green. Discuss the results.

GETTING STARTED

AT·A·GLANCE p. 7

LESSON OBJECTIVE
Use nickels, dimes, and pennies.

ASSIGNMENT GUIDE

COURSE	EXERCISES
Basic	p. 7: 1–4
Average	p. 7: 1–4
Challenge	p. 7: 1–4

MATERIALS
Classroom Materials paper, crayons
Manipulatives 3 D, 6 N, and 30 P coins (or punchouts) per child

Name _____

CRAZY CRITTERS

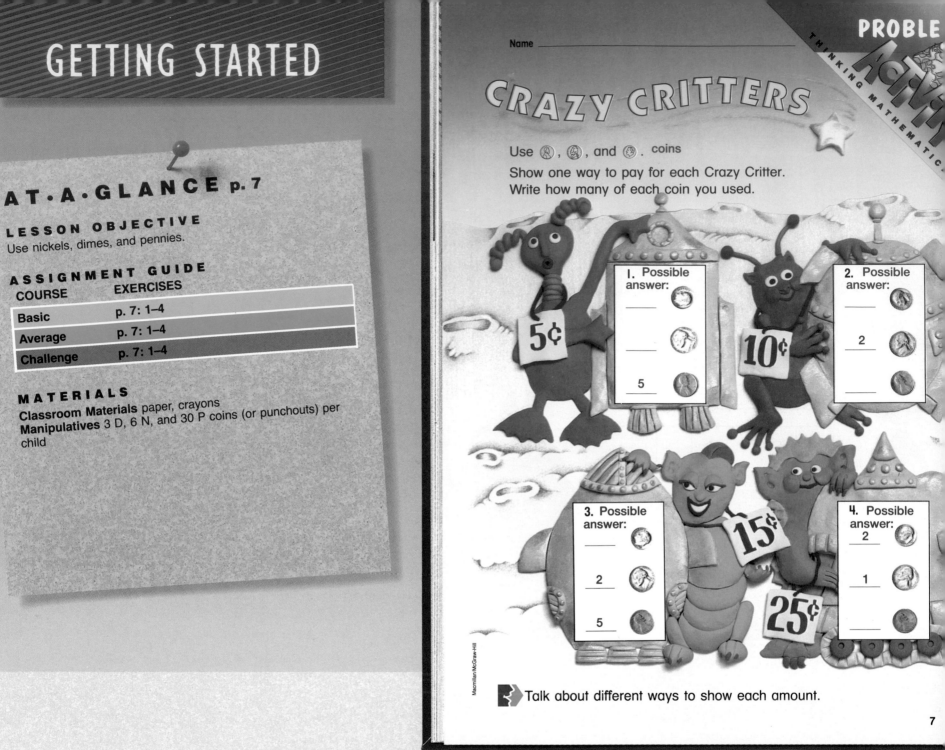

Use 🪙, 🪙, and 🪙. coins
Show one way to pay for each Crazy Critter.
Write how many of each coin you used.

1. Possible answer:
___
5

2. Possible answer:
___
2

3. Possible answer:
___
2
5

4. Possible answer:
2
1

 Talk about different ways to show each amount.

Macmillan/McGraw-Hill

7

PLAN

AIMS AND ATTITUDES This activity develops number sense through the skill of counting money. Encourage children to use their own way to show which coins are needed in the activity. Accept all combinations of coins, even if a child uses only pennies to show the coins needed. The opportunity to discuss possible combinations will help children learn new combinations in a nonthreatening way.

MANAGEMENT The activity is intended for all children and has been designed for independent work. It is also appropriate for pairs of children.

GUIDE

Display several play dimes, nickels, and pennies. Draw a hat on the chalkboard with a price tag for 6¢. Ask children which coins you could use to buy the hat. [1 nickel, 1 penny; 6 pennies] Repeat the activity by changing the price.

Give each child 3 dimes, 6 nickels, and 30 pennies in play coins. Have children use their coins to find combinations to pay for each critter. Afterward, have children tell which coins they used as you list them on the chalkboard. Point out that each combination, though different, equals the amount on the card the critter is holding.

EXTEND

Have children repeat the activity for 8¢, 19¢, and 30¢, recording possible combinations on paper. Then discuss each combination.

FIND FRED

Use the clues to find Fred.
Ring your answer.

Fred wears a hat.

He does not wear glasses.

He uses wheels to get around the park.

Make up clues about another person in the park.
Ask a friend to find the person.

8

AT·A·GLANCE p. 8

LESSON OBJECTIVE
Use logical reasoning.

ASSIGNMENT GUIDE

COURSE	EXERCISES
Basic	p. 8: All
Average	p. 8: All
Challenge	p. 8: All

 PLAN   **AIMS AND ATTITUDES** This activity develops logical reasoning. Children make choices among illustrated characters being described only after considering several clues about that character. Emphasize the fun of trying to determine which character is being described. Stress that clues, and not guessing, be used to identify Fred.

MANAGEMENT The activity is intended for all children and has been designed for independent work. It is also appropriate for pairs of children. If pairing children, it may be particularly effective to pair a child having strong problem-solving and language skills with one having weaker skills.

GUIDE   Before beginning page 8, model the activity by having three volunteers come to the front of the room. Give clues about one of the children while the class uses the clues to name the child described. Repeat the procedure.

Read the directions and clues on page 8 with the children. Encourage children to use only the clues and the picture to figure out which character is Fred.

EXTEND   Ask children to work in pairs to repeat the activity about another person pictured on the page. Partners may then switch roles. Children should then tell in their own words the process they used to identify the person being described. Encourage them to describe any problems they may have encountered.

Previewing CHAPTER 1

ADDING and SUBTRACTING FACTS to 10

Martin L. Johnson

> **❝IN CHAPTER 1, you will introduce your children to adding and subtracting facts to 10. You will also have the opportunity to explore part-part-whole relationships and fact families.❞**

Notes FROM THE AUTHOR

Here are some notes on the concepts presented in this chapter and how your children can apply them to solve problems.

UNDERSTANDING ADDITION

Your children should make cube trains to explore joining and to demonstrate their understanding that addition means putting together two sets of objects (*parts*) to find a total (*whole*). Children write addition sentences for their models.

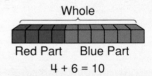

Whole

Red Part   Blue Part

4 + 6 = 10

Children were introduced to part-part-whole models, as shown above, in Grade 1. Using these models helps children review basic addition facts to 10. Children also review the counting-on strategy.

UNDERSTANDING SUBTRACTION

Children make cube trains to explore separating and to demonstrate their understanding that subtraction means taking away some objects (a *part*) from a set (*whole*) and finding how many are left (a *part*). Children write subtraction sentences for their models.

Whole

Red Part   Blue Part

9 − 2 = 7

Using part-part-whole models helps children review basic subtraction facts to 10. Children also review the counting-back strategy.

ADDITION and SUBTRACTION RELATIONSHIPS

Your children should use models such as the one below to help them understand how the operations of addition and subtraction are related. Children use the model to help them understand the concept of *part + part = whole* for addition and then see the related form of *whole - part = part* for subtraction. The number sentences help children focus on the related facts and on the patterns that emerge as the facts for a number are developed.

9 + 0 = 9	9 − 0 = 9
8 + 1 = 9	9 − 1 = 8
7 + 2 = 9	9 − 2 = 7
6 + 3 = 9	9 − 3 = 6
5 + 4 = 9	9 − 4 = 5
4 + 5 = 9	9 − 5 = 4
3 + 6 = 9	9 − 6 = 3
2 + 7 = 9	9 − 7 = 2
1 + 8 = 9	9 − 8 = 1
0 + 9 = 9	9 − 9 = 0

FACT FAMILIES

Help children understand that if they know one fact in a fact family, they can find the other sums or differences by using that known fact. Models enable children to see the addition and subtraction relationships that exist among three numbers in a fact family. Models also illustrate the order property of addition.

Part + Part = Whole

5 + 3 = 8   3 + 5 = 8

Whole − Part = Part

8 − 3 = 5   8 − 5 = 3

PROBLEM SOLVING

In **Problem Solving** your children are introduced to a plan for solving problems. Encourage them to use this plan as a tool to (1) write an addition or subtraction sentence to solve problems and (2) solve problems by choosing the operation.

In **Thinking Mathematically** children use number cubes and counters to find missing addends for sums to 7. Children use number sense to play Hocus Pocus.

In **Decision Making** your children use information to decide what craft they will make and what craft materials they can buy with 10 cents.

Mathematics and Literature

To use literature in the application of mathematics
■ To promote appreciation of the contributions of all cultures to mathematics. ■ Children are introduced to a Haitian story in the K–2 *Math Anthology* on page 128. By reading *The Banza,* children build addition, subtraction, and counting skills. ■ In the Curriculum Connection on page 42, children learn counting words in the Cheyenne language and in the *Twi* language of the Ashanti people of Ghana.

CULTURAL DIVERSITY

CHAPTER 1 • ORGANIZER

CHAPTER PLANNING GUIDE

A. Add, facts to 10	MAT, CAT, SAT, ITBS, CTBS
B. Subtract, facts to 10	MAT, CAT, SAT, ITBS, CTBS
C. Add three 1-digit numbers	MAT, CAT, SAT, ITBS, CTBS
D. Solve problems including those that involve writing an addition or subtraction sentence and choosing the correct operation	MAT, CAT, SAT, ITBS, CTBS

SUGGESTED PACING–16 DAYS

LESSONS	NCTM STANDARDS	ASSIGNMENTS Basic/Average/Challenge	STUDENT EDITION Extra Practice/ Practice Plus	Manip. Plus	Reteach	Practice	Enrich	MAC Activities
Chapter Opener: *The Banza* page 9 **CC**	1, 2, 3, 4, 7	p. 9: All						
✔ 1 Adding and Subtracting Facts to 10 page 10	1, 2, 3, 7, 8	p. 10: 1–5						
✔ 2 Addition Facts to 5 page 11	1, 2, 3, 8	p. 11: 1–6		1	1	1	1	1, 2
✔ 3 Subtraction Facts to 5 page 12	1, 2, 3, 8	p. 12: 1–6			2	2	2	3, 4
✔ 4 Informal Algebra: Fact Families pages 13–14	1, 2, 3, 8	p. 13: 1–5; p. 14: 1–3, Mental Math		2, 3	3	3	3	5, 6
✔ 5 Addition and Subtraction Patterns pages 15–16	1, 2, 3, 8, 13	p. 15: 2–4, 6–9; p. 16: 2–12		4	4	4	4	7, 8
6 PS: Using the Five-Step Plan pages 17–18	1, 2, 3, 6	p. 17: All; p. 18: All			5	5	5	9, 10
✔ 7 Facts to 6 pages 19–20	1, 2, 3, 8	p. 19: 2–8; p. 20: 1–8		5	6	6	6	11, 12
✔ 8 Facts to 7 pages 21–22	1, 2, 3, 8	p. 21: 2–9; p. 22: 1–5, Reasoning	pp. 28, 44		7	7	7	13, 14
9 Counting On and Counting Back pages 23–24	1, 2, 3, 8	p. 23: 1–3; p. 24: 1–5		6, 7	8	8	8	15, 16
10 PS: Addition or Subtraction Sentence p. 25–26	1, 2, 3, 7, 8	p. 25: 1–2; p. 26: 1–2	p. 28		9	9	9	17, 18
✔ 11 PS: Thinking Mathematically page 27	1, 2, 3, 7, 8	p. 27: All						
✔ 12 Facts to 8 pages 29–30	1, 2, 3, 8	p. 29: 2–10; p. 30: 1–4, Mental Math			10	10	10	19, 20
✔ 13 Adding Three Numbers pages 31–32	1, 2, 3, 8	p. 31: 1–3; p. 32: 1–4	p. 43	8	11	11	11	21, 22
✔ 14 Facts to 9 pages 33–34	1, 2, 3, 8	p. 33: 2–9; p. 34: 1–5, Reasoning			12	12	12	23, 24
✔ 15 Facts to 10 pages 35–36	1, 2, 3, 8	p. 35: 2–9; p. 36: 3–5, Estimation	pp. 43, 44		13	13	13	25, 26
16 Adding and Subtracting Money page 37	1, 2, 3, 8	p. 37: 1–2, Reasoning			14	14	14	27, 28
✔ 17 Choosing a Computation Method page 38	1, 2, 3, 6, 8	p. 38: 1–5			15	15	15	29, 30
18 PS: Choosing the Operation pages 39–40	1, 2, 3, 7, 8	p. 39: 1–2; p. 40: 1–6	p. 43		16	16	16	31, 32
19 PS: Decision Making page 41	1, 2, 3, 6, 8	p. 41: 1–3						
Curriculum Connection: Social Studies page 42 **CC**								
Chapter Review/Test pages 45–46								
Performance Assessment page 47								
Cumulative Review page 49								
Enrichment for All/Home Activity pages 48, 50								

NATIONAL COUNCIL OF TEACHERS OF MATHEMATICS Grades K–4

1. Problem Solving
2. Communication
3. Reasoning
4. Connections
5. Estimation
6. Number Sense and Numeration
7. Concepts of Whole Number Operations
8. Whole Number Computation
9. Geometry and Spatial Sense
10. Measurement
11. Statistics and Probability
12. Fractions and Decimals
13. Patterns and Relationships

✔ Activity   **Cooperative Learning**   **CC** Cultural Connection

MEETING the NCTM STANDARDS

Problem Solving

Strategies and Skills
- using the five-step plan pp. 17–18
- writing an addition or subtraction sentence pp. 25–26
- choosing the operation pp. 39-40

Applications
- **Decision Making** lesson p. 41
- **Problem of the Day** TE pp. 10, 11C, 12C, 14B, 16B, 18B, 20B, 22B, 24B, 26B, 30B, 32B, 34B, 36B, 37C, 38C, 40B

Mathematical Investigations
- **Thinking Mathematically** lesson p. 27

Communication

Language
- using the language of mathematics TE pp. 11, 12, 13–14, 19–20, 23–24, 29–30, 35–36, 37

Oral/Written
- using cooperative learning activities pp. 10, 19–20, 27, 31–32, 33–34, 41, 42; TE pp. 8I-8P
- **Journal Writing** opportunities TE pp. 12A, 14, 16, 22, 26, 32, 36, 38A

Reasoning

Critical Thinking
- answering questions that analyze and extend concepts pp. 9, 10, 11, 12, 13, 15, 16, 19, 20, 21, 23, 29, 41

Connections

To other subject areas
- Literature p. 9, Social Studies p. 42; Literature TE pp. 9–10, 11, 15, 17

To all cultures
- Haitian story, *The Banza*, *Math Anthology* p. 128
- Cheyenne and Ashanti counting words p. 42

Concept Development

Whole Number Computation
- adding facts to 10 pp. 10, 11, 13–14, 19–20, 21–22, 23–24, 29–30, 35–36; TE pp. 8I–8K, 8M–8O
- adding three 1-digit numbers pp. 33–34; TE p. 8P
- subtracting facts to 10 pp. 13–14, 19–20, 21–22, 23–24, 29–30, 35–36
- adding and subtracting money amounts p. 37

Patterns and Relationships
- finding patterns in addition and subtraction pp. 15–16; TE p. 8L

ASSESSMENT OPTIONS

PERFORMANCE ASSESSMENT

Preassessment Activity

Before beginning Chapter 1, have children use several manipulatives to model and record the number of windows, doors, and light fixtures in the classroom. Have children model, draw pictures, or write number sentences using these numbers to find how many objects there are in all and how many more of one object there are than another.

Ongoing Assessment

The Ongoing Assessment cards under MEETING INDIVIDUAL NEEDS on TE pp. 14 and 36 provide criteria and questions for assessing children's understanding of the key mathematical concepts developed in the chapter.

Journal Writing opportunities encourage children to write about mathematics. Their responses can be recorded either pictorially or in words. The journal writing opportunities on the Ongoing Assessment cards also allow you to assess children's understanding of the lessons.

In addition to the Ongoing Assessment cards, other assessment and journal writing opportunities in this chapter include:

- **CLOSE** TE pp. 12A, 14, 16, 22, 26, 32, 38A

Performance Assessment Activity

The Performance Assessment activity on p. 47 provides an alternative to formal assessment. This activity assesses children's understanding of the key concepts of the chapter.

For performance assessment activities that are keyed to individual chapter objectives, see the *Performance Assessment* booklet.

BUILDING A PORTFOLIO

Children should be encouraged to keep a selection of their best work in portfolios. The portfolios provide a way of documenting children's growth in understanding mathematical concepts. Portfolio opportunities in this chapter include:

- **Performance Assessment** p. 47
- **Class Project** TE p. 41A

If you wish to provide additional opportunities for portfolio work, you may choose to use:

- **MAC Activities** 2, 6, 11, 12, 14, 16

You may also wish to have children include their journal writing from the Ongoing Assessment on TE pp. 14 and 36 in their portfolio.

Formal Assessment

The **Chapter Review/Test** assesses children's understanding of the concepts and skills developed in the chapter. The **Cumulative Review** assesses children's understanding of the concepts and skills developed from the beginning of the year.

You can use **Form A** or **Form B** of the **Chapter Test** found in the *Testing Program Blackline Masters and Teacher's Manual* if you wish to use a multiple-choice format to assess children's understanding of the chapter concepts and skills. You can use **Form C** if you wish to use a free-response format. Any of the forms may be used as a pretest, posttest, or for retesting.

The **COMPUTER MANAGEMENT SYSTEM**, or **CMS**, enables you to score **Forms A** and **B** of the **Chapter Test** quickly and automatically. It also prescribes learning activities based on children's test results.

For more information about Assessment, see the *Professional Handbook*.

Common Error and Remediation

The Teacher's Edition notes for each Develop/Understand (Transitional/Abstract) lesson provide a common error analysis and a remediation activity. Some errors defy quick analysis and can only be identified by interviewing the child.

ALTERNATIVE TEACHING STRATEGY

Alternative Teaching Strategies appear frequently in the chapter. These strategies provide other presentations of the lessons for children who might benefit from instruction in different learning modalities: kinesthetic, visual, and/or auditory.

For Students Acquiring English (SAE)

SAE children will need representation (visual and dramatizations) of the following words: **join, add, separate, subtract, take away, equals, addition sentence, subtraction sentence, pattern,** and **number line.** Also introduce and have children practice saying the names of any manipulatives you may be using to illustrate concepts.

SAE notes appear periodically in the chapter. These notes provide suggestions for how to work with children to improve comprehension and build vocabulary.

MANIPULATIVES WORKSHOP

Connecting cubes are used in this chapter to explore number facts to 10. They provide concrete representations of the part-part-whole relationship in addition and the whole-part-part relationship in subtraction.

USING MANIPULATIVES

Here a child is modeling 4 + 3. The child uses connecting cubes to show each addend.

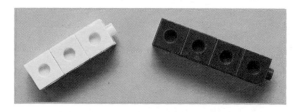

The child joins the addends to form a single "train."

The model shows that 4 + 3 = 7.

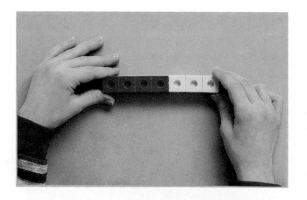

Here is a child's model for 5 − 2.

The child begins with a train of 5 connecting cubes.

The child separates 2 cubes.

The model shows that 5 − 2 = 3.

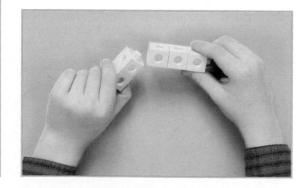

MAKING MANIPULATIVES See the Manipulatives section of the *Professional Handbook* for materials that can be used as a substitute for connecting cubes.

COOPERATIVE LEARNING WORKSHOP

GETTING STARTED

The Classroom Community: Establishing a cooperative classroom community will create a foundation of trust for working in groups. Sitting children with a small "family group" will give a safe home base for sharing and support. Help children get acquainted by using an activity to learn names and collect information about everyone in the class—a **people hunt:** Each child gets a list of pictures with spaces for others to mark. Everyone must "find somebody who . . . ." ("likes baseball," "walks to school," "has a cat," and so on) and asks him or her to mark the sheet next to the appropriate picture. Make it a **group challenge:** No one is finished until everyone has found someone for every blank on the list. Talk in a **community circle** about what the children have learned about each other.

IDEAS TO TRY

Let Us Count the Ways: Working in pairs, children can learn to praise one another for successful work and encourage each other to try again when mistakes are made. Help your children "count the ways" they can give praise ("great job!" "right on!" thumbs up, handshake) or encouragement ("you've almost got it," "that's close—try again!" smiling, nodding). Write both verbal and non-verbal responses on the chalkboard for pairs to refer to as they work together.

You can apply the above pair-encouragement techniques in these lessons:
1-1 *Adding and Subtracting Facts to 10* p. 10
1-2 *Addition Facts to 5* p. 11
1-3 *Subtraction Facts to 5* p. 12

Turn to Your Partner: Seating children in family groups of four produces a number of pair arrangements. Vary working partners for each activity so that the children work with many children. Ask each child to think about a question. After an appropriate "wait time," ask him or her to turn to a partner and share ideas or answers. Then call on either partner to share what the other said. This teaches the cooperative skills of **attentive listening** and **respecting differing answers.**

You can apply the preceding partner-building structure in these lessons:
1-4 *Informal Algebra: Fact Families* pp. 13–14
1-5 *Addition and Subtraction Patterns* pp. 15–16

SEE ALSO

Cooperative Learning Tip for lessons 1-6 Problem Solving p. 18; 1-10 Problem Solving p. 26; 1-18 Problem Solving p. 40

The Cooperative Learning section of the *Professional Handbook* for additional information

---

INTERACTIVE BULLETIN BOARD

(As a variation) have children write a subtraction fact on their rabbits and tack them next to the correct rabbit hole.

SETUP Use oaktag to make a rabbit pattern. Trace the pattern onto white construction paper, making enough rabbits to give one to each child. Have volunteers cut out the rabbits. Then make six rabbit holes out of brown construction paper. Write each of the following numbers on a different rabbit hole: 5, 6, 7, 8, 9, 10. Attach the holes to the bulletin board in random order, as shown in the illustration.

PROCEDURE 👥 Assign a sum from 5 through 10 to each child. Ask children to write a fact for their assigned sums on their rabbits. Then collect the rabbits. Place the rabbits in a large envelope and attach it to the board.

Have children take the rabbits out of the envelope and match the facts on the rabbits to the sums on the rabbit holes. Have them tack each rabbit near the appropriate hole.

For use before LESSON 1.2, p. 11

PART–PART–WHOLE

OBJECTIVE
Explore addition and subtraction using a part-part-whole model.

MATERIALS
Manipulatives 5 🟥 and 5 ⬜ per group

WHOLE GROUP ACTIVITY 🕐

Begin by working with the class as a group. Connect 5 cubes, 3 red and 2 yellow, to make a "cube train."

Hold up the 5 cubes.

■ **What can you say about this cube train?**
[Possible responses: There is a red part and a yellow part. The red part has 3 cubes, the yellow part has 2 cubes.]

Next separate the cubes into two parts by color.

■ **What do you see?** [You separated the train into two parts. The red part has 3 cubes, the yellow part has 2 cubes. They are the same as before, except the parts are now separated.]

Reconnect 5 red cubes. Then "break" the train, taking away 2 cubes.

■ **I have taken away one part of the whole train. What is left?** [one part]

■ **How many cubes are left?** [3 cubes]

SMALL GROUP ACTIVITY 🕐 👥

Have children work in groups of three. Distribute 5 cubes each of two different colors to each group. Assign roles to children. One child can make a train using 3, 4, or 5 cubes. The other children can describe the train, using the words *part* and *whole*. Have them switch roles.

EXTENDING THE ACTIVITY

Read this problem to the whole group: Elsie had a pack of 4 juice boxes. Then she drank part of the pack. She has 2 juice boxes in the part that is left. How many juice boxes are in the part that she drank? Have children solve the problem, using models if they wish. Have them make up their own story problem using the word *part*.

ONGOING ASSESSMENT

✔ Are children able to describe parts by discerning the color and number of cubes?

MANIPULATIVES plus ACTIVITY

For use before LESSON 1.4, pp. 13-14

2 DEVELOPING FACTS

OBJECTIVE
Use a part-part-whole model to develop facts.

MATERIALS
Manipulatives 5 ▢ per child; 4 ▭ and 4 ▭ and 1 crayon to match each of the two colors per pair (EXTENDING THE ACTIVITY only)

SMALL GROUP ACTIVITY 🕐 👥

Have children work in groups of three. Distribute 5 cubes of one color to each child in a group. Have each child connect the 5 cubes to make a train. Then have them break the train to make two parts. Have children record what they have done and write addition sentences.

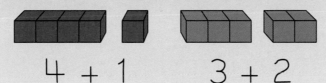

$$4 + 1 \qquad 3 + 2$$

Have members within a group compare their trains and discuss how their trains are different and the same. [They all have the same number of cubes in the whole. The number of cubes in each part is different.]

Challenge children to find other ways to break apart their trains. You will need to prompt them to find 5 + 0 and 0 + 5. Accept addition sentences with more than two addends, also. Discuss that each sentence is a name for 5.

Repeat the activity by having children make trains with 4 cubes and then with 3 cubes.

EXTENDING THE ACTIVITY

Have children work in pairs. Provide each pair with 4 cubes in each of two colors and crayons to match the two colors. Read this problem: Walt is making up designs for flags. He wants to use 4 squares in a row. Two of the squares should be in one color. Two of the squares should be in another color. In how many different ways can he place the squares? [6]

Have children solve the problem and record their solutions. You may wish to assign roles to each child in a pair, while having both children involved in sharing their strategies for solving. One child can show the solutions with models. One child can record.

ONGOING ASSESSMENT

✔ Are children able to describe parts and wholes by discerning color and number?

MANIPULATIVES plus ACTIVITY

For use before LESSON 1.4, pp. 13-14

3

ADDITION AND SUBTRACTION PATTERNS

OBJECTIVE
Identify related addition and subtraction facts.

MATERIALS
Classroom Materials
colored chalk in two different colors
Manipulatives 5 ▣
and 5 ▣ per child

WHOLE GROUP ACTIVITY ⬍

Distribute 5 cubes in each of two different colors to each child. Draw a 5-by-5 grid on the chalkboard. Use two different colors of chalk to color in the first row, as shown:

▦▦▦▦▦

Ask children to use their cubes to copy the drawing you made on the grid. Then discuss the arrangement. Point to each part of the row:

■ **How many in this part?** [4]
■ **How many in this part?** [1]
■ **What number sentences can you make up for this row?** [4 blue + 1 red = 5 in all; 5 in all − 1 red = 4 blue]

Write children's responses on the chalkboard. Point out that these two facts are **related**. Continue this development with all the rows except the last row on the grid.

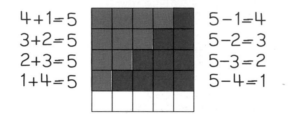

4+1=5	5−1=4
3+2=5	5−2=3
2+3=5	5−3=2
1+4=5	5−4=1

Point to the last row and have children describe it.

■ **How can we talk about this row?**
Help children understand that the number sentences 0 + 5 = 5 and 5 − 5 = 0 can both be used to tell about the last row of colored boxes: 0 blue + 5 red = 5 in all; 5 in all − 5 red = 0 blue.

EXTENDING THE ACTIVITY

Challenge children to make their own arrangements of patterns for 4 and for 3, using 4-by-4 and 3-by-3 grids.

ONGOING ASSESSMENT

✓ Are children able to indicate the related addition and subtraction number sentences for an arrangement of cubes?

MANIPULATIVES plus ACTIVITY

For use before LESSON 1.5, pp. 15-16

4

ORDER PROPERTY

OBJECTIVE
Explore the order property of addition.

MATERIALS
Classroom Materials
construction paper
Manipulatives 20 ⬤
(or punchouts) per pair

PAIRS ACTIVITY

Use construction paper to make three-part work-mats as shown below. Have children work in pairs. Distribute 20 counters and 2 three-part workmats to each pair.

The first child can use 5 counters to show an addition fact that has the sum of 5. The second child can show another fact with the same addends. Children should use one color in the first part of the mat to show the first addend and the other color in the second part of the mat to show the second addend. In the third part of the mat, they can use one color to show the sum. Have children write the sentences they have modeled and then check that the sums are the same.

Have children switch roles each time as they continue to develop facts for 5. Have them record their sentences.
[4 + 1, 1 + 4, 3 + 2, 2 + 3, and so on.]

When children have recorded all the addition facts for 5, call on volunteers to write their sentences on the chalkboard. Then have a volunteer point to the two addition sentences with the addends 3 and 2.

numb ... ch you add these two
Continue th ... ? [No.]
... her pairs of facts.

EXTENDING THE ACTIVITY

Read this problem to children: 5 ... sent on Monday. 3 of the children were ... ab-of them were boys. 5 children were absent and 2 Tuesday. 2 of the children were girls. How many of the children were boys? Have children solve the problem. Then have them choose two related facts and make up a story problem for partners to solve.

ONGOING ASSESSMENT

✓ Are children able to change the order of the addends to show the related fact?

**For use before
LESSON 1.7,
pp. 19-20**

5

MORE ORDER PROPERTY

OBJECTIVE
Use the order property of addition.

MATERIALS
Manipulatives 1 set of number cards for 0–5* per pair; 2 sets of number cards for 0–5 per pair (EXTENDING THE ACTIVITY only)
Teacher Resources
*Teacher Aid 11

PAIRS ACTIVITY

Have children work in pairs. Give each pair 1 set of number cards for 0 through 5. Tell children that they will play a version of the game "Concentration."

Assign roles to children. One player can mix up the cards and place them facedown in any arrangement on the table. Then he or she chooses two cards and turns them faceup. That player reads the numbers aloud and makes up an addition sentence, for example, 4 + 1 = 5.

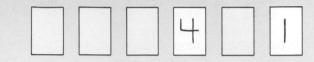

The first child turns the cards facedown again. Then the other player can turn over the same cards but in reverse order. For example, the second player must turn over the 1 card first and then the 4 card. Then he or she says the correct addition sentence for those cards. [1 + 4 = 5]

Have players switch roles.

EXTENDING THE ACTIVITY

Provide each pair with a total of 2 sets of cards. Each player gets a chance to turn over four cards to find a set of matching addends. For example, 4, 1, 1, and 4. Children each take turns until a set of matching addends is found. The game ends when all the matching addends are found.

ONGOING ASSESSMENT

✓ Are children able to say the appropriate addition sentence for the cards and find the addends in reverse?

6
NUMBER LINE

OBJECTIVE
Add and subtract on a
number line.

MATERIALS
Classroom Materials
1 floor number line or tape;
toys (EXTENDING THE
ACTIVITY only)
Manipulatives number
cards for 0 10*
Teacher Resources
*Teacher Aid 11

WHOLE GROUP ACTIVITY

Place a number line on the classroom floor or make
one with tape and number cards.

Call on volunteers, in turn, to act out adding and
subtracting on the number line. Children should
start at the 0 as you say an addition fact, such as
2 + 7. Have a child hop 2 lines and then 7 more
lines.

- **What number are you standing on?** [9]
- **What is the sum of 2 + 7?** [9]

Now say a subtraction fact aloud, such as 9 − 2.
Call on another child to hop to the number 9 and
then hop back 2 lines.

- **What number are you standing on?** [7]
- **What is the difference for 9 − 2?** [7]

Continue by allowing children to take turns using
the number line for adding and subtracting.

EXTENDING THE ACTIVITY

Place the number line on a table Have children use
toy animals or dolls to show the action of adding
and subtracting on a number line. You may wish to
read aloud problems, such as the following:
Scamper Squirrel jumped ahead 5 branches. Then
Scamper jumped back 2 branches. On which
branch did Scamper land?

ONGOING ASSESSMENT

✔ Are children able to determine the
appropriate direction in which to hop on
the number line for each operation?

MANIPULATIVES plus ACTIVITY

For use before LESSON 1.9, pp. 23-24

7

MENTAL MATH READINESS

OBJECTIVE
Count on and count back.

WHOLE GROUP ACTIVITY 🕒

Draw a number line with numbers from 1 through 10 on the chalkboard. Allow children to refer to the number line during the activity.

<------|---|---|---|---|---|---|---|---|---|------>
    1   2   3   4   5   6   7   8   9   10

This activity will prepare children to use counting strategies as one way of solving addition and subtraction examples. Recite the following examples:

■ **Count to 5. Where are you?** [5]

■ **Start at 4 and count on 1. Where are you?** [5]

■ **Start at 3 and count on 1. Where are you?** [4]

■ **Start at 3 and count on 2. Where are you?** [5]

■ **Start at 1 and count on 2. Where are you?** [3]

Then present these examples:

■ **Start at 3 and count back 2. Where are you?** [1]

■ **Start at 5 and count back 1. Where are you?** [4]

■ **Start at 4 and count back 1. Where are you?** [3]

Repeat with other numbers.

EXTENDING THE ACTIVITY

Challenge children to solve these examples "in their heads":

■ **5 − 1** [4]
■ **4 − 1** [3]
■ **5 − 2** [3]
■ **3 − 2** [1]
■ **3 − 1** [2]
■ **4 − 2** [2]

Pause after each example. Allow pairs of children to whisper their answers to each other. Then have volunteers share their answers and their strategies for solving.

ONGOING ASSESSMENT

✔ Are children beginning to use mental math to solve addition and subtraction situations?

MANIPULATIVES plus ACTIVITY

For use before LESSON 1.13, pp. 31-32

8
THREE
ADDENDS

OBJECTIVE
Explore addition with three addends.

MATERIALS
Classroom Materials
overhead projector
Manipulatives 8 beans
per child

WHOLE GROUP ACTIVITY 🕐

Distribute 8 beans to each child. Tell children to separate the beans into three groups, or parts. Then call on volunteers to show their groups on the overhead projector and tell how many beans are in each of their groups. Write the numbers on the chalkboard. For example, children may come up with the following arrangements:

2 3 3   3 2 3   4 3 1

If children do not identify 0 as a possible group, show these groups on the overhead projector: 6 and 2. You may wish to draw rings around the groups, including around the group of 0, as you indicate:

■ **There are really three groups here. One group has 6 beans. One group has 2 beans. How many beans do you think there are in the third group?** [0]

Write the numbers on the chalkboard: 6 2 0. Children should realize that there are 8 beans in all.

Repeat the activity with 7 beans.

EXTENDING THE ACTIVITY

Have children write addition sentences for their arrangements.

ONGOING ASSESSMENT

✓ Are children able to separate the whole into three groups?

THE BANZA
By Diane Wolkstein

Mathematics and Literature

Listening and Speaking

The Read-Aloud selection can be used with the Chapter 1 Opener and Lesson 1-1 on pages 9-10.

Tape 1, Side 1
Selection 1

◆ THE BANZA ◆

BY DIANE WOLKSTEIN

On the island of Haiti there once lived a little tiger named Teegra and a little goat named Cabree. Usually tigers and goats are enemies, but these two were best friends.

They had met during a thunderstorm when they had each run into the same cave for shelter. The storm had lasted all night, and when they came out in the morning, everything seemed strange to them, for they had come out of the cave by a different entrance and were lost.

They were both quite small, lonely, and afraid.

They looked at each other.

Cabree brayed, "Be-be. . . ."

Teegra roared, "Rrr. . . ."

"Do you want to be friends?" Cabree asked.

"Now!" Teegra answered.

So they wandered over the countryside, playing together, sharing whatever food they found, and sleeping close to each other at night for warmth.

Then one morning they found themselves in front of the cave where they had first met.

"rrRRRRRR!"

Cabree turned. But it was not Teegra who had roared.

"RRRRRRRrr-rrRR!"

It was a roar of another tiger.

"Mama! Papa! *Auntie!*" Teegra cried joyfully as three huge tigers bounded out of the bushes.

Cabree ran into the cave without waiting.

After a while Teegra went to find Cabree, but Cabree refused to come out of the cave, so Teegra went home with his family.

The next morning Teegra went to the cave alone.

"Cabree!" he called. "I brought you a banza."

Cabree poked her head out of the cave.

"A *ban-za*? What's that?"

"A little banjo," Teegra said. "It belonged to my uncle, but I want you to have it—so it will protect you."

"How will the banza protect me?" Cabree asked.

"Auntie says, 'The banza belongs to the heart, and there is no stronger protection than the heart.' When you play the banza, Auntie says to place it over your heart, and 'one day the heart and banza will be one.'"

"Is that true?"

"Oh, Cabree, I don't really know, but I know I shall not forget you."

Teegra placed the banza around his friend's neck, then he turned to go.

"Where are you going?" Cabree asked.

"Home!" Teegra answered, and the little tiger ran back to his family without stopping.

Cabree stepped out of the cave so she could see the banza more clearly. It was a beautiful banza, and when the sun shone on it, it gleamed. Cabree held the banza over her heart.

She stroked it gently. A friendly, happy sound came out. She stroked it again—and again—and before she realized it, she was trotting through the forest, humming to herself and stopping now and then to play a tune on the banza.

One afternoon Cabree came to a spring. She wanted to drink, but she was afraid the banza would get wet, so she took it off and carefully laid it down in the bushes. As she drank the cool sweet water she heard a low growl behind her.

"rrrRRrrr. . . ."

Turning quickly, Cabree saw four large hungry tigers. Cabree wanted to leap across the stream and run away, but the banza was in the bushes behind the tigers. No! She would not leave the banza Teegra had given her.

Slowly and fiercely Cabree walked toward the banza.

Another tiger appeared. Now there were five.

Cabree kept walking.

"Where are you going?" the leader shouted.

Cabree reached the bushes. She picked up the banza and hung it around her neck. Then she turned to the tigers. Five more jumped out of the bushes.

Now there were ten!

"What have you put around your neck?" asked the leader.

And Cabree, trying to quiet her thundering, pounding heart, brought her foreleg to her chest and, by mistake, plucked the banza.

"A musician!" said the chief, laughing. "So you wish to play us a song?"

"No!" said Cabree.

"No?" echoed the leader. And all the tigers took a step closer to Cabree.

Teegra! Cabree wanted to shout. But Teegra was far away, and she was alone, surrounded by the tigers. No, she was not completely alone. She still had the banza Teegra had given her.

Cabree's heart beat very fast, but in time to her heartbeat she stroked the banza. She opened her mouth, and a song came out. To her own surprise it was a loud, low, ferocious song:

> Ten fat tigers, ten fat tigers,
> Cabree eats tigers raw.
> Yesterday Cabree ate ten tigers;
> Today Cabree eats ten more.

The tigers were astonished.

"Who is Cabree? And where did you learn that song?" demanded the chief.

"I am Cabree." Cabree answered in a new deep voice, and noticing how frightened the tigers looked, she added, "And that is *my* song.

I always sing it before dinner."

The tiger chief realized that three of his tigers had suddenly disappeared.

"Madame Cabree," he said, "you play beautifully. Permit me to offer you a drink."

"Very well," said Cabree.

"Bring Madame Cabree a drink!" he ordered the two tigers closest to him, and as they started to leave he whispered, "and don't come back."

Five tigers stared at Madame Cabree.

Cabree stared back. Then she stroked her banza and sang, a little slower, but just as intently:

> Five fat tigers, five fat tigers,
> Cabree eats tigers raw.
> Yesterday Cabree ate ten tigers;
> Today Cabree eats five more.

"Oh! Oh-h-h! Something dreadful must have happened to my tigers," said the leader. "You." He motioned to the two tigers nearest him. "Go fetch Madame Cabree a drink." And again he whispered, "And don't come back."

Now only three tigers quaked before Madame Cabree. Cabree sang again:

> Three fat tigers, three fat tigers,
> Cabree eats tigers raw.
> Yesterday Cabree ate ten tigers;
> Today Cabree eats three more.

When she finished her song, only the leader remained. Cabree began:

> One fat tiger—

"Please," whispered the leader, "please let me go. I promise no tiger will ever bother you again."

Cabree looked at the trembling tiger. All she had done was to play the banza and sing what was in her heart. So Teegra's Auntie was right. Her heart had protected her. Her heart and her banza.

"Please!" begged the leader. "I'll do whatever you wish."

"Then go at once to Teegra, the little tiger who lives near the cave. Tell Teegra: 'Today Cabree's heart and the banza are one.'"

"Yes, yes," said the tiger. "'Today Cabree's heart and the banza are one.'" And the tiger chief ran off to find Teegra.

With her banza gleaming around her neck, Cabree went trotting through the forest. But every now and then she would stop. She would stroke her banza and sing, for her heart would have a new song.

8R

AT·A·GLANCE pp. 9-10

LESSON OBJECTIVES

Explore mathematical concepts through literature.
Explore addition and subtraction facts.

ASSIGNMENT GUIDE

COURSE	EXERCISES
Basic	p. 9: All; p. 10: 1–5
Average	p. 9: All; p. 10: 1–5
Challenge	p. 9: All; p. 10: 1–5

MATERIALS

Classroom Materials picture of banjo
Manipulatives spinner for 1–9 (or punchouts), Workmat 1, 9 tiger punchouts per pair

Teacher Resources
Teacher Aid 11 *Math Anthology*, pp. 128–131
Read-Aloud Cassette 1, Side 1, Selection 1
Computer Software *Mathematics Skills*: Disk 1 Act. 1–5

SKILLS TRACE
FACTS TO 10

Explore (Concrete)	Develop/Understand (Transitional/Abstract)
10	11, 12, 13–14, 15–16, 19–20, 21–22, 23–24, 29–30, 31–32, 33–34, 35–36, 37, 38
Practice 20, 28, 32, 43, 44, 45–46, 49, 60	**Apply** 17–18, 25–26, 27, 39–40, 41, 42

Adding and Subtracting Facts to 10

READ ALOUD
THE BANZA
By Diane Wolkstein

🦻 Listen to the story The Banza.

🗣 Tell how many tigers frightened Cabree by the stream. 4, 1, and 5; 10 in all
Tell how many tigers Cabree scared away. 3, 2, 2, and 3; 10 in all

9

---

1 PREPARE **WARM-UP** To review numbers to ten, hold up from 1 through 9 fingers. Have children identify the number of fingers shown on each hand as well as the total number.

2 TEACH **DISCUSSING** Before reading the story *The Banza,* display a picture of a banjo. Explain that a banjo is a stringed instrument that is played by plucking the strings.

Write *The Banza* on the chalkboard and pronounce it. Explain that a banza is an old instrument that was played many years ago on the island of Haiti. Tell childen that the story they are about to hear is an old Haitian folktale about friendship and courage.

Mathematics and Literature **CULTURAL CONNECTION**

PUPIL'S EDITION pp. 9-10

Page 9 Read *The Banza* found on pages 8Q–8R or in *Math Anthology* to children, or play Read-Aloud Cassette 1, Side 1, Selection 1 for them.

Discuss the questions on the page. After recalling the number of tigers, have children count to find the answers.

Page 10 ■ Working Together Assign each child a partner. Give each pair Workmat 1, 9 punchout tigers, and a spinner. Have children use their punchout tigers to copy the combination of tigers in the picture at the top of the page.

Check for Understanding

■ The picture shows 7 tigers in all with 3 in the cave and 4 in the clearing. What is another way to show 7 tigers in all? [Possible

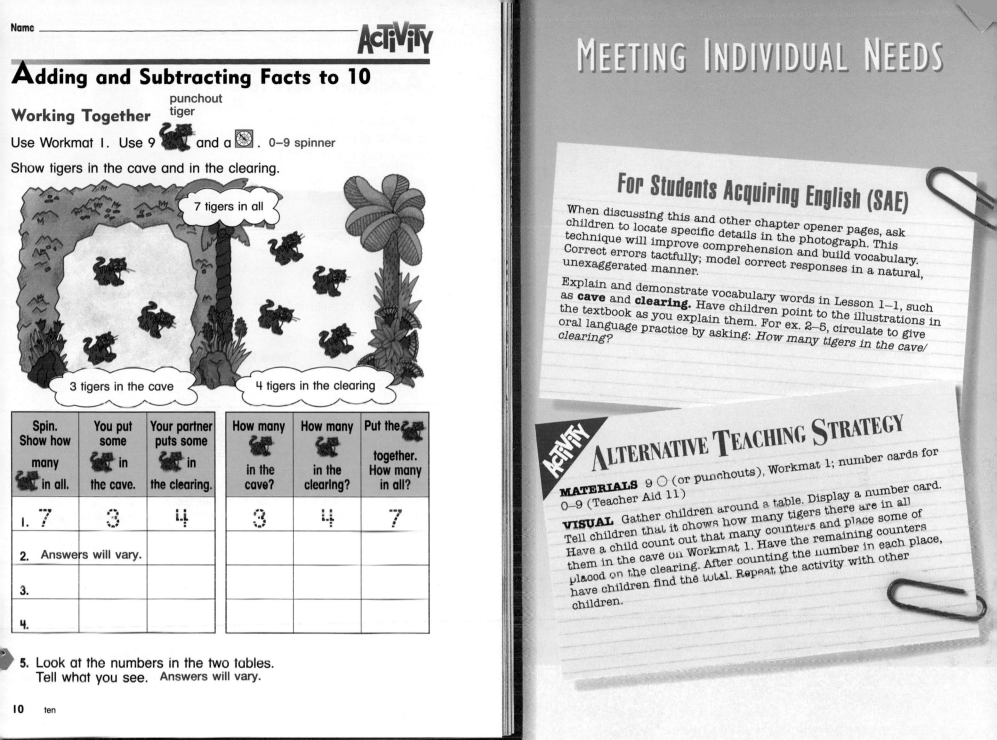

Name _____

Adding and Subtracting Facts to 10

Working Together

Use Workmat I. Use 9 🐅 punchout tiger and a 🎡 . 0–9 spinner

Show tigers in the cave and in the clearing.

7 tigers in all

3 tigers in the cave

4 tigers in the clearing

Spin. Show how many 🐅 in all.	You put some 🐅 in the cave.	Your partner puts some 🐅 in the clearing.	How many 🐅 in the cave?	How many 🐅 in the clearing?	Put the 🐅 together. How many in all?
1. 7	3	4	3	4	7
2. Answers will vary.					
3.					
4.					

5. Look at the numbers in the two tables.
Tell what you see. Answers will vary.

10 ten

For Students Acquiring English (SAE)

When discussing this and other chapter opener pages, ask children to locate specific details in the photograph. This technique will improve comprehension and build vocabulary. Correct errors tactfully; model correct responses in a natural, unexaggerated manner.

Explain and demonstrate vocabulary words in Lesson 1–1, such as **cave** and **clearing**. Have children point to the illustrations in the textbook as you explain them. For ex. 2–5, circulate to give oral language practice by asking: *How many tigers in the cave/clearing?*

ACTIVITY ALTERNATIVE TEACHING STRATEGY

MATERIALS 9 ◯ (or punchouts), Workmat 1; number cards for 0–9 (Teacher Aid 11)

VISUAL Gather children around a table. Display a number card. Tell children that it shows how many tigers there are in all. Have a child count out that many counters and place some of them in the cave on Workmat 1. Have the remaining counters placed on the clearing. After counting the number in each place, have children find the total. Repeat the activity with other children.

---

responses: 1 tiger in the cave, 6 in the clearing; 2 tigers in the cave and 5 in the clearing]

GUIDED PRACTICE ex. 1: Have children refer to the picture at the top of the page as you work through ex. 1 with them.

For reteaching, use Alternative Strategy.

3 PRACTICE•APPLY

PRACTICE ex. 2–5: When discussing ex. 5, have children compare the same line in both tables.

CLOSE Guide children to summarize the lesson:

■ **If there were 9 tigers in all and 2 tigers were in the cave, how many tigers would be in the clearing?** [7 tigers]

Problem of the Day

There are 3 tigers by the stream. Then 5 more tigers come out of the bushes. How many tigers are there in all? [8 tigers]

AT·A·GLANCE p. 11

LESSON OBJECTIVE
Write addition sentences for facts to 5.

ASSIGNMENT GUIDE

COURSE	EXERCISES
Basic	p. 11: 1–6
Average	p. 11: 1–6
Challenge	p. 11: 1–6

MATERIALS
Manipulatives 5 ■, 5 ▢ (or square counter punchouts) per child

Teacher Resources
Reteaching 1   Practice 1   Enrichment 1
MAC Act. 1, 2   Teacher Aid 4
Math Anthology p. 133

SKILLS TRACE
ADDITION FACTS TO 5

Explore (Concrete)	Develop/Understand (Transitional/Abstract)
10	11, 13–14, 15–16, 19–20, 21–22, 23–24, 29–30, 31–32, 33–34, 35–36, 37, 38
Practice 20, 28, 32, 43, 44, 45–46, 49, 60	**Apply** 17–18, 25–26, 27, 39–40, 41, 42

See **MANIPULATIVES PLUS 1,** p. 8l.

Addition Facts to 5

Joe put 2 red cubes and
3 yellow cubes together.
How many cubes in all?

2 red   3 yellow   5 in all

Use 4 ■ and 3 ▢. connecting cubes

$$2 + 3 = 5$$

addend   addend   sum

Use cubes to build the train.
Complete.

	Red Part	Yellow Part	In All	Addition Sentence
1.	2	2	4	2 + 2 = 4
2.	3	1	4	3 + 1 = 4
3.	1	2	3	1 + 2 = 3
4.	4	1	5	4 + 1 = 5

Build a cube train.
Write the addition sentence.

5. Lisa has 3 red cubes.
   She has 2 yellow cubes.
   How many cubes does she
   have in all?

   $3 + 2 = 5$

6. Tell an addition story of
   your own. Answers will vary.

PREPARE

WARM-UP To prepare children for modeling addition sentences, have children make arrangements with cubes. Give each child 5 cubes. Tell children to arrange the cubes in various ways to show 5 and then to compare their arrangements.

TEACH

MODELING Give each child 5 yellow and 5 red cubes. Have children use 3 yellow cubes and 2 red cubes to build a train of 5 cubes. Have them discuss their combinations using **part-part-whole** language by describing the number of cubes in the whole train and the number in each color part of the train. Write 3 + 2 = 5 on the chalkboard and identify it as an **addition sentence.** Explain that 3 + 2 = 5 tells about the train. Identify the 3 and 2 as **addends** and the 5 as the **sum.** Point out the **plus sign** and

equal sign, and have children read the addition sentence as 3 plus 2 equals 5.

PUPIL'S EDITION p. 11
Using 5 cubes, guide children through the example at the top of the page as you tell this story.

Joe closed his eyes and chose 2 red and 3 yellow cubes. Then he put the cubes together to make a train.

■ **How many cubes are in the red part of Joe's train?** [2]
■ **How many cubes are in the yellow part of Joe's train?** [3]
■ **How many cubes are there in all?** [5]

ACTIVITY

Common Error and Remediation

MATERIALS 5 ◯ (or punchouts)

Some children may not grasp the concept of addition. Work individually with each child. Have the child use red and yellow counters to show facts to 5. While the child is modeling, guide him or her to tell about the activity.

■ **How many red counters are you showing?**
■ **How many yellow counters are you showing?** [Answers will vary.]

As each model is completed, have child tell how many counters in all.

ALTERNATIVE TEACHING STRATEGY

MATERIALS inch graph paper (Teacher Aid 4), crayons

VISUAL/KINESTHETIC Write these sentences on the board.

4 + 1 = —[5] 2 + 3 = —[5] 1 + 1 = —[2] 2 + 1 — —[3]
2 + 2 = —[4] 4 + 0 = —[4] 3 + 2 = —[5] 5 + 0 = —[5]

Have children work in pairs to illustrate each sentence with two different colors on graph paper, then write it.

4+1=5

Have children read the addition sentence. Make sure that they understand that the addends represent the parts and the sum represents the whole.

Check for Understanding

■ **Which addition sentence tells about 2 red cubes and 1 yellow cube, 2 + 1 = 3 or 2 + 2 = 4?** [2 + 1 = 3]

GUIDED PRACTICE ex. 1–4: For reteaching, use Common Error and Remediation or Alternative Strategy.

Mathematics and Literature

PRACTICE ex. 5–6: Point out that ex. 5 is an example of an addition story. Call on volunteers to tell their addition stories for ex. 6.

Have children listen as you read the poem "There Was an Old Man Who Said" found in *Math Anthology*. Have them use connecting cubes to show and explain, as if speaking to the man in the poem, how to add 2 and 2.

CLOSE Guide children to summarize the lesson:

■ **What addition sentence tells about 3 red cubes and 2 yellow cubes?** [3 + 2 = 5]

**MAC Activity 1:
Basic-to-Average**
▼

MAC Activity 1

On Your Own   Pair and Share   In a Group

SPEAKING MATHEMATICALLY ▪ ADDITION STORIES

Materials   counters or punchout counters

Tell children that you will tell them some stories. Have them use counters to model each problem. Then call on volunteers to give the answer for each problem and say the addition sentence they used to find the answer.

1. Lynn washed 2 dishes.
   Bob washed 3 dishes.
   How many dishes did they wash all together?
   [5; 2 + 3 = 5]
2. Jason delivers 3 newspapers each day.
   Alice delivers 1 newspaper each day.
   How many newspapers do they deliver each day?
   [4; 3 + 1 = 4]

Call on volunteers to make up addition problems for the rest of the class to solve.

**MAC Activity 2:
Average-to-Challenge**
▼

MATH AND ART ▪ PICTURE THIS!

MAC Activity 2

On Your Own   Pair and Share   In a Group

Materials   drawing paper, paste, scissors, magazines

Write addition sentences for facts to 5 on the chalkboard.

2 + 3 = 5	1 + 4 = 5	2 + 2 = 4
3 + 1 = 4	1 + 2 = 3	1 + 1 = 2

Read the sentences with the children. Distribute a set of materials to groups of children. Have each child choose one addition sentence to illustrate. Tell children to draw or cut out pictures of objects to model each sentence. Call on volunteers to show and explain their pictures.

1 + 4 = 5

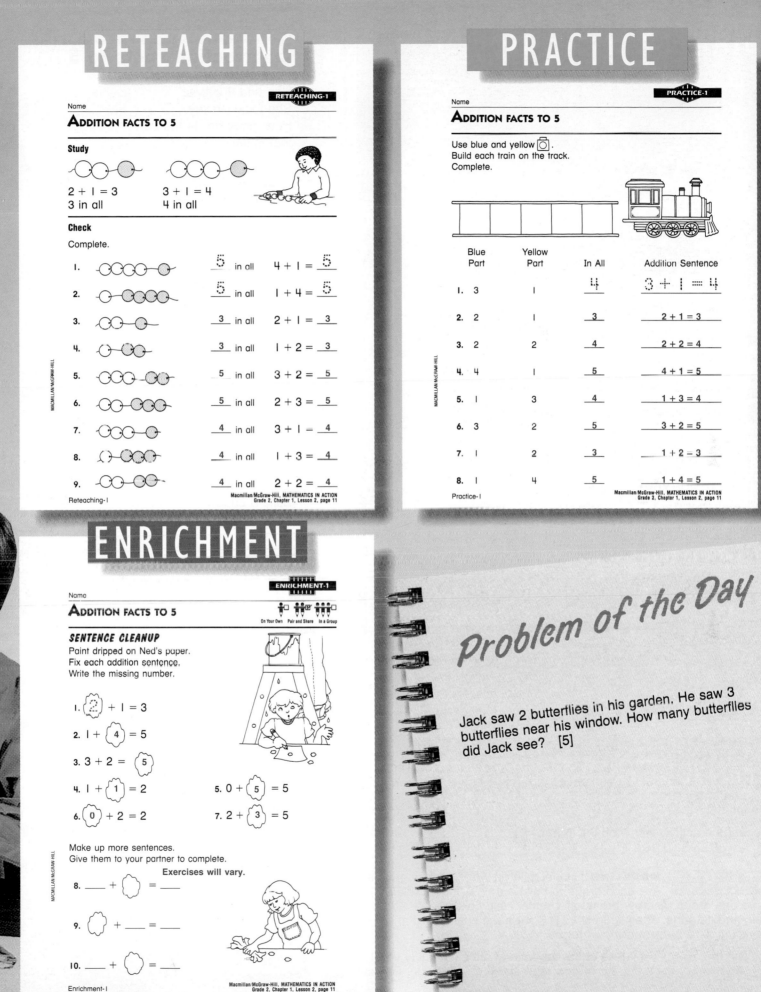

RETEACHING

RETEACHING-1

Name

ADDITION FACTS TO 5

Study

2 + 1 = 3   3 + 1 = 4
3 in all   4 in all

Check

Complete.

1. 5 in all $4 + 1 = 5$
2. 5 in all $1 + 4 = 5$
3. 3 in all $2 + 1 = 3$
4. 3 in all $1 + 2 = 3$
5. 5 in all $3 + 2 = 5$
6. 5 in all $2 + 3 = 5$
7. 4 in all $3 + 1 = 4$
8. 4 in all $1 + 3 = 4$
9. 4 in all $2 + 2 = 4$

Reteaching-1

Macmillan/McGraw-Hill, MATHEMATICS IN ACTION
Grade 2, Chapter 1, Lesson 2, page 11

PRACTICE

PRACTICE-1

Name

ADDITION FACTS TO 5

Use blue and yellow.
Build each train on the track.
Complete.

	Blue Part	Yellow Part	In All	Addition Sentence
1.	3	1	4	$3 + 1 = 4$
2.	2	1	3	$2 + 1 = 3$
3.	2	2	4	$2 + 2 = 4$
4.	4	1	5	$4 + 1 = 5$
5.	1	3	4	$1 + 3 = 4$
6.	3	2	5	$3 + 2 = 5$
7.	1	2	3	$1 + 2 = 3$
8.	1	4	5	$1 + 4 = 5$

Practice-1

Macmillan/McGraw-Hill, MATHEMATICS IN ACTION
Grade 2, Chapter 1, Lesson 2, page 11

ENRICHMENT

ENRICHMENT-1

Name

ADDITION FACTS TO 5

On Your Own   Pair and Share   In a Group

SENTENCE CLEANUP

Paint dripped on Ned's paper.
Fix each addition sentence.
Write the missing number.

1. $2 + 1 = 3$
2. $1 + 4 = 5$
3. $3 + 2 = 5$
4. $1 + 1 = 2$
5. $0 + 5 = 5$
6. $0 + 2 = 2$
7. $2 + 3 = 5$

Make up more sentences.
Give them to your partner to complete.

Exercises will vary.

8. ___ + ⬜ = ___

9. ⬜ + ___ = ___

10. ___ + ⬜ = ___

Enrichment-1

Macmillan/McGraw-Hill, MATHEMATICS IN ACTION
Grade 2, Chapter 1, Lesson 2, page 11

Problem of the Day

Jack saw 2 butterflies in his garden. He saw 3 butterflies near his window. How many butterflies did Jack see?   [5]

AT·A·GLANCE p. 12

AT·A·GLANCE p. 12

LESSON OBJECTIVE
Write subtraction sentences for facts to 5.

ASSIGNMENT GUIDE

COURSE	EXERCISES
Basic	p. 12: 1–6
Average	p. 12: 1–6
Challenge	p. 12: 1–6

MATERIALS
Manipulatives 5 ▢ (or square counter punchouts) per child

Teacher Resources
Reteaching 2   Practice 2   Enrichment 2
MAC Act. 3, 4   Teacher Aid 4

SKILLS TRACE
SUBTRACTION FACTS TO 5

Explore (Concrete)	Develop/Understand (Transitional/Abstract)
10	12, 13–14, 15–16, 19–20, 21–22, 23–24, 29–30, 31–32, 33–34, 35–36, 37, 38

Practice	Apply
20, 28, 32, 43, 44, 45–46, 49, 60	17–18, 25–26, 27, 39–40, 41, 42

Subtraction Facts to 5

Nan had 4 cubes.
She took 1 away.
How many are in the part
that is left?

4 in all   Take 1 away   3 are left   4 − 1 = 3

difference

Use 5 ▢.

Use cubes to build the train.
Complete.

	Start with	Part to Take Away	Part Left	Subtraction Sentence
1.	5	1	4	5 − 1 = 4
2.	4	3	1	4 − 3 = 1
3.	2	2	0	2 − 2 = 0
4.	3	0	3	3 − 0 = 3

Build a cube train.
Write the subtraction sentence.

5. Cal had 5 cubes.
He put 2 cubes away.
How many cubes are left?

   5 − 2 = 3

6. Tell a subtraction story of
your own. **Answers will vary.**

---

1 PREPARE   **WARM-UP** To prepare children for modeling subtraction sentences, arrange 5 chairs in a row. Ask 2 children to each remove a chair. Have children tell how many chairs are left. [3]

Repeat the activity with 4 chairs in a row.

2 TEACH   **MODELING** Have children work in small groups. Ask each group to build a train using 5 cubes. Then have one group member break off 1 cube. Help children talk about the train and its parts. Then write 5 − 1 = 4 on the chalkboard and identify it as a **subtraction sentence.**

Explain that 5 − 1 = 4 tells about the train of cubes. Identify the 4 as the **difference.** Point out the **minus sign** and the equal sign. Review their meanings. Finally have children read the sentence as 5 minus 1 equals 4.

PUPIL'S EDITION p. 12
Have children use 4 cubes to work through the example at the top of the page as you tell this story.

Nan made a train of 4 cubes on her desk. Then she took 1 cube from the end of the train and gave it to Sue.

■ **How many cubes are left in Nan's train?** [3]
Have children read the subtraction sentence.

ACTIVITY Common Error and Remediation

MATERIALS 5 ○ (or punchouts)

Some children may not grasp the concept of subtraction. Work individually with each child. Have the child show 5 counters of one color. Then have him or her take away any number of counters.

■ **How many counters did you take away?**
■ **How many counters are left?** [Answers will vary.]

Repeat the activity with 4 counters; 3 counters.

ALTERNATIVE TEACHING STRATEGY

MATERIALS inch graph paper (Teacher Aid 4), crayons

VISUAL/KINESTHETIC Write these sentences on the board.

4 − 2 = —[2] 3 − 2 = —[1] 5 − 2 = —[3] 3 − 1 = —[2]
4 − 4 = —[0] 5 − 1 = —[4] 2 − 1 = —[1] 4 − 3 = —[1]

Distribute graph paper and crayons. Have children color and mark squares and then write the sentences.

4 − 2 = 2

Check for Understanding

■ **What subtraction sentence could you use to show the following?**

There were 4 cubes on the table.
I took 2 cubes away.
How many are left? [4 − 2 = 2]

GUIDED PRACTICE ex 1–4: For reteaching, use Common Error and Remediation or Alternative Strategy.

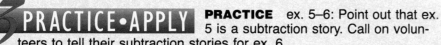

3 PRACTICE•APPLY **PRACTICE** ex. 5–6: Point out that ex. 5 is a subtraction story. Call on volunteers to tell their subtraction stories for ex. 6.

CLOSE Guide children to summarize the lesson:

■ **What does the subtraction sentence 4 − 3 = 1 tell you?** [Possible response: There were 4 things. 3 were taken away, so 1 thing is left.]

MAC Activity 3:
Basic-to-Average
▼

SPEAKING MATHEMATICALLY ■ SUBTRACTION STORIES

MAC Activity 3

On Your Own   Pair and Share   In a Group

Materials   counters or punchout counters

Tell children that you will tell them some stories. Have them use counters to model each problem. Then call on volunteers to give the answer for each problem and say the subtraction sentence they used to find the answer.

1. Kim had a 5-piece puzzle.
   She lost 2 pieces.
   How many pieces were left? [3; 5 − 2 = 3]
2. Fred has 3 hats.
   He gives 1 hat to Gene.
   How many hats does Fred have left?
   [2; 3 − 1 = 2]

Call on volunteers to make up subtraction stories for the rest of the class to solve.

MAC Activity 4:
Average-to-Challenge
▼

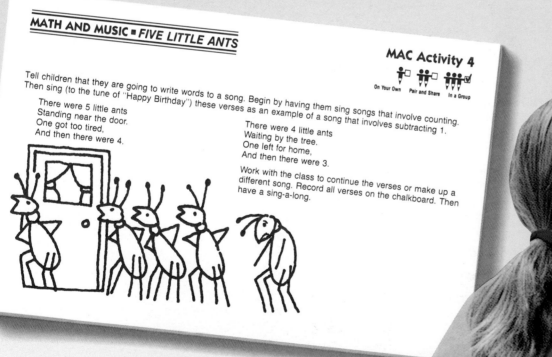

MATH AND MUSIC ■ FIVE LITTLE ANTS

MAC Activity 4

On Your Own   Pair and Share   In a Group

Tell children that they are going to write words to a song. Begin by having them sing songs that involve counting. Then sing (to the tune of "Happy Birthday") these verses as an example of a song that involves subtracting 1.

There were 5 little ants
Standing near the door.
One got too tired,
And then there were 4.

There were 4 little ants
Waiting by the tree.
One left for home,
And then there were 3.

Work with the class to continue the verses or make up a different song. Record all verses on the chalkboard. Then have a sing-a-long.

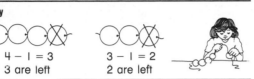

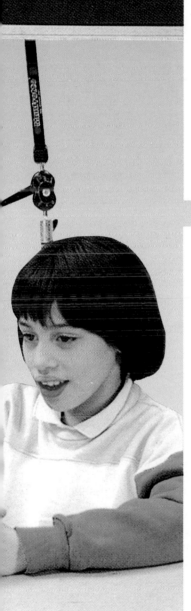

RETEACHING-2

Name

SUBTRACTION FACTS TO 5

Study

4 − 1 = 3
3 are left

3 − 1 = 2
2 are left

Check

Complete.

1.	4	left	5 − 1 = 4
2.	2	left	4 − 2 = 2
3.	1	left	4 − 3 = 1
4.	1	left	5 − 4 = 1
5.	1	left	2 − 1 = 1
6.	0	left	3 − 3 = 0
7.	3	left	5 − 2 = 3
8.	2	left	3 − 1 = 2
9.	3	left	4 − 1 = 3

Macmillan/McGraw-Hill, MATHEMATICS IN ACTION
Grade 2, Chapter 1, Lesson 3, page 12

Reteaching-2

PRACTICE-2

Name

SUBTRACTION FACTS TO 5

Use blue ▢.
Build each train on the track.
Complete.

	Start With	Part to Take Away	Part Left	Subtraction Sentence
1.	3	2	1	3 − 2 = 1
2.	2	2	0	2 − 2 = 0
3.	2	1	1	2 − 1 = 1
4.	5	3	2	5 − 3 = 2
5.	4	2	2	4 − 2 = 2
6.	3	1	2	3 − 1 = 2
7.	5	2	3	5 − 2 = 3
8.	4	4	0	4 − 4 = 0

Macmillan/McGraw-Hill, MATHEMATICS IN ACTION
Grade 2, Chapter 1, Lesson 3, page 12

Practice-2

ENRICHMENT-2

Name

SUBTRACTION FACTS TO 5

On Your Own   Pair and Share   In a Group

MORE SENTENCE CLEANUP

The baby colored Nora's paper.
Fix each subtraction sentence.
Write the missing number.

1. 5 − 1 = 4

2. 4 − 2 = 2

3. 3 − 1 = 2

4. 5 − 3 = 2

5. 4 − 3 = 1

6. 4 − 1 = 3

7. 5 − 2 = 3

Make up more sentences.
Give them to your partner to complete.

Exercises will vary.

8. ___ − ☐ = ___

9. ☐ − ___ = ___

10. ___ − ☐ = ___

Macmillan/McGraw-Hill, MATHEMATICS IN ACTION
Grade 2, Chapter 1, Lesson 3, page 12

Enrichment-2

Problem of the Day

Kim saw 5 birds at the feeder. 3 flew away. How many birds were left at the feeder? [2]

AT·A·GLANCE pp. 13-14

LESSON OBJECTIVE
Complete addition and subtraction fact families.

ASSIGNMENT GUIDE

COURSE	EXERCISES
Basic	p. 13: 1–5; p. 14: 1–3, Mental Math
Average	p. 13: 1–5; p. 14: 1–3, Mental Math
Challenge	p. 13: 1–5; p. 14: 1–3, Mental Math

MATERIALS
Classroom Materials domino cards*

Teacher Resources
Reteaching 3   Practice 3   Enrichment 3
MAC Act. 5, 6   *Teacher Aid 19

SKILLS TRACE
FACTS TO 10

Explore (Concrete)	Develop/Understand (Transitional/Abstract)
10	11, 12, 13–14, 15–16, 19–20, 21–22, 23–24, 29–30, 31–32, 33–34, 35–36, 37, 38
Practice 20, 28, 32, 43, 44, 45–46, 49, 60	**Apply** 17–18, 25–26, 27, 39–40, 41, 42

See **MANIPULATIVES PLUS 2–3**, pp. 81J–81K.

① PREPARE
WARM-UP To prepare children for work with fact families, write these exercises on the chalkboard.

$3 + 1 = 4$ $1 + 3 = 4$
$4 - 1 = 3$ $4 - 3 = 1$

Have children look at the **facts** carefully. Ask them what they notice about all four facts. [They each have the same numbers: 4, 1, and 3.]

② TEACH
DISCUSSING Display a domino card, such as:

■ **What fact does this card show?** [$2 + 1 = 3$]
Turn the card around to show the **related addition fact**.
■ **What is the fact for this card?** [$1 + 2 = 3$]

Informal Algebra: Fact Families

$2 + 3 = 5$ $5 - 3 = 2$

$3 + 2 = 5$ $5 - 2 = 3$

You can show 4 facts with 1 domino. The 4 facts make a **fact family**.

Write facts that you can show with each domino.

1. $3 + 2 = 5$ $5 - 2 = 3$
    $2 + 3 = 5$ $5 - 3 = 2$

2. $4 + 1 = 5$ $5 - 1 = 4$
    $1 + 4 = 5$ $5 - 4 = 1$

3. $1 + 1 = 2$ $2 - 1 = 1$

4. Tell which domino shows only two facts. Why? **Exercise 3; because the addends are the same.**
5. Draw another domino that also shows only two facts.

> Answers will vary. Possible answers:

Then cover the card one side at a time to develop the **related subtraction facts,** $3 - 1 = 2$ and $3 - 2 = 1$. Remind children that related addition and subtraction facts with the same three numbers are called a **fact family.**

Then display this domino card: . Discuss with children why there are only two facts in this family, $2 + 2 = 4$ and $4 - 2 = 2$.

PUPIL'S EDITION pp. 13-14
Page 13 Guide children through the example at the top of the page. Have volunteers read the number sentences.

Check for Understanding
■ **What fact family does a domino with 2 dots and 1 dot show?**
[$2 + 1 = 3, 1 + 2 = 3, 3 - 2 = 1, 3 - 1 = 2$]

$1 + 2 = 3$ $\begin{array}{r} 1 \\ +2 \\ \hline 3 \end{array}$ $3 - 2 = 1$ $\begin{array}{r} 3 \\ -2 \\ \hline 1 \end{array}$

Complete each fact family.
Use cubes if you need help.

1. $\begin{array}{r} 4 \\ +1 \\ \hline 5 \end{array}$ $\begin{array}{r} 1 \\ +4 \\ \hline 5 \end{array}$ $\begin{array}{r} 5 \\ -1 \\ \hline 4 \end{array}$ $\begin{array}{r} 5 \\ -4 \\ \hline 1 \end{array}$

2. $\begin{array}{r} 3 \\ +1 \\ \hline 4 \end{array}$ $\begin{array}{r} 1 \\ +3 \\ \hline 4 \end{array}$ $\begin{array}{r} 4 \\ -1 \\ \hline 3 \end{array}$ $\begin{array}{r} 4 \\ -3 \\ \hline 1 \end{array}$

3. $\begin{array}{r} 2 \\ +3 \\ \hline 5 \end{array}$ $\begin{array}{r} 3 \\ +2 \\ \hline 5 \end{array}$ $\begin{array}{r} 5 \\ -3 \\ \hline 2 \end{array}$ $\begin{array}{r} 5 \\ -2 \\ \hline 3 \end{array}$

···· *Mental Math* ························

Write the missing number.

1. $2 + \boxed{2} = 4$ 2. $\boxed{1} + 1 = 2$

    $4 - \boxed{2} = 2$ $\boxed{2} - 1 = 1$

ACTIVITY   *Common Error and Remediation*

MATERIALS 10 ○ (or felt shapes); oaktag, glue

When completing fact families, some children may not recognize the relationship between the facts. Have each child make a large domino with 2 and 3 dots by gluing counters or felt shapes on an oaktag card. Ask the children to say each of the 4 facts for the model as they turn or cover part of the domino card. Repeat with $4 + 1$.

ONGOING ASSESSMENT

INTERVIEW Give the child a domino showing 4 dots and 3 dots. **(1) What addition facts can you show with this domino? (2) What subtraction facts can you show? (3)** Give the child a domino showing 5 dots and 5 dots. **What facts could you show with this domino?**

JOURNAL WRITING You may wish to have children record their responses in their math journals.

ACTIVITY   ALTERNATIVE TEACHING STRATEGY

MATERIALS 1 ■, 1 ▢ por child

KINESTHETIC Distribute connecting cubes to each child. Tell children to make a two-color cube train to show $3 + 1$. Ask a volunteer to give the sum and write the addition sentence on the chalkboard. Have children turn their cube trains to show $1 + 3$.

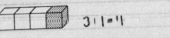

Then have children take 3 cubes off their train and then 1 cube off their train to develop the subtraction facts $4 - 3$ and $4 - 1$. Repeat the activity to show $1 + 1$ and $2 - 1$.

GUIDED PRACTICE   ex. 1–5: For reteaching, use Common Error and Remediation or Alternative Strategy.

Page 14 Explain that an addition or subtraction fact can be written as a sentence or with one number above the other.

3 PRACTICE•APPLY   **PRACTICE**   ex. 1–3

MENTAL MATH Help children understand that they can use what they know about fact families to find the missing numbers.

C L O S E Guide children to summarize the lesson:
- **Why are $3 + 1 = 4$, $1 + 3 = 4$, $4 - 3 = 1$, and $4 - 1 = 3$ a fact family?** [They are related facts with the same numbers.]

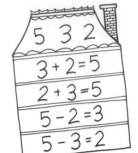

MAC Activity 6

On Your Own   Pair and Share   In a Group

MATH AND ART ▪ AT HOME WITH THE FACTS

Materials construction paper, crayons, cards with fact family numbers

Distribute construction paper to each child. Have children draw a "Fact Family House" with four floors, a roof, and a chimney.

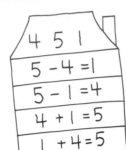

Then have each child choose from a deck of cards on which you have written fact family numbers, such as 4 5 1. Tell the children to write the numbers on the roof of their house. On each floor, they should write an addition or a subtraction fact for the fact family.

MAC Activity 5

On Your Own   Pair and Share   In a Group

CALCULATOR ▪ CALCULATOR PAIRS

Materials calculator

Children can practice addition and subtraction facts to 5 with a calculator. Have children work in pairs. As one child says a fact, such as 5 − 4, and enters it into the calculator, the other child gives the answer orally. Then he or she presses the = key. Both children check the calculator to see if the response is correct. Have children keep a record of each fact that was answered incorrectly. Have them use these facts to do this activity on another day.

▲
MAC Activity 6:
Average-to-Challenge

▲
MAC Activity 5:
Basic-to-Average

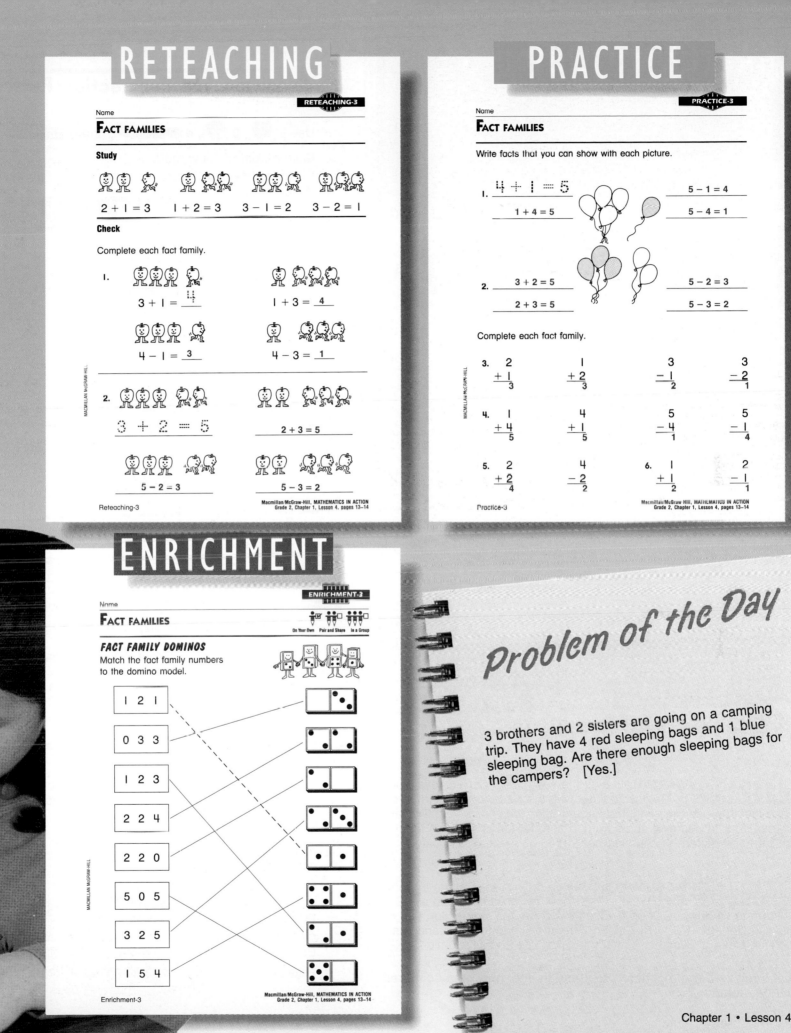

RETEACHING-3

Name

FACT FAMILIES

Study

2 + 1 = 3   1 + 2 = 3   3 − 1 = 2   3 − 2 = 1

Check

Complete each fact family.

1. 3 + 1 = 4   1 + 3 = 4

   4 − 1 = 3   4 − 3 = 1

2. 3 + 2 = 5   2 + 3 = 5

   5 − 2 = 3   5 − 3 = 2

Reteaching-3

Macmillan/McGraw-Hill, MATHEMATICS IN ACTION
Grade 2, Chapter 1, Lesson 4, pages 13–14

PRACTICE-3

Name

FACT FAMILIES

Write facts that you can show with each picture.

1. 4 + 1 = 5   5 − 1 = 4
   1 + 4 = 5   5 − 4 = 1

2. 3 + 2 = 5   5 − 2 = 3
   2 + 3 = 5   5 − 3 = 2

Complete each fact family.

3. 2   1   3   3
   + 1   + 2   − 1   − 2
   ___   ___   ___   ___
    3   3   2   1

4. 1   4   5   5
   + 4   + 1   − 4   − 1
   ___   ___   ___   ___
    5   5   1   4

5. 2   4   6. 1   2
   + 2   − 2   + 1   − 1
   ___   ___   ___   ___
    4   2   2   1

Practice-3

Macmillan/McGraw-Hill, MATHEMATICS IN ACTION
Grade 2, Chapter 1, Lesson 4, pages 13–14

ENRICHMENT-3

Name

FACT FAMILIES

On Your Own   Pair and Share   In a Group

FACT FAMILY DOMINOS

Match the fact family numbers
to the domino model.

1 2 1

0 3 3

1 2 3

2 2 4

2 2 0

5 0 5

3 2 5

1 5 4

Enrichment-3

Macmillan/McGraw-Hill, MATHEMATICS IN ACTION
Grade 2, Chapter 1, Lesson 4, pages 13–14

Problem of the Day

3 brothers and 2 sisters are going on a camping trip. They have 4 red sleeping bags and 1 blue sleeping bag. Are there enough sleeping bags for the campers?   [Yes.]

AT·A·GLANCE pp. 15-16

LESSON OBJECTIVES
Apply the order property of addition.
Add and subtract with zero.

ASSIGNMENT GUIDE

COURSE	EXERCISES
Basic	p. 15: 2–4, 6–9; p. 16: 2–12
Average	p. 15: 2–4, 6–9; p. 16: 2–12
Challenge	p. 15: 2–4, 6–9; p. 16: 2–12

MATERIALS

Classroom Materials red and blue crayons
Manipulatives 5 ▥, 2 ▥ (or punchout squares) per child

Teacher Resources
Reteaching 4   Practice 4   Enrichment 4
MAC Act. 7, 8
Math Anthology p. 134
Math Songs Cassette, Side 2, Selection 7

SKILLS TRACE
FACTS TO 10

Explore (Concrete)	Develop/Understand (Transitional/Abstract)
10	11, 12, 13–14, 15–16, 19–20, 21–22, 23–24, 29–30, 31–32, 33–34, 35–36, 37, 38
Practice 20, 28, 32, 43, 44, 45–46, 49, 60	**Apply** 17–18, 25–26, 27, 39–40, 41, 42

See *MANIPULATIVES PLUS 4*, p. 8L.

Mathematics and Literature

1 PREPARE **WARM-UP** Sing the song "Five Fat Turkeys" found in *Math Anthology* with the class, or play the tape. Have children use their fingers to count back, beginning with five fat turkeys, four fat turkeys, and so on, to zero fat turkeys. Guide them to describe the pattern of counting back. [You subtract 1 each time.]

2 TEACH **DISCUSSING** Call on 5 children to stand in front of the classroom. Count the children. Then ask 2 children to sit down. Call on a volunteer to say the subtraction fact for this situation. [5 − 2 = 3] Call on 2 other children to come and join the line. Have a volunteer say the addition fact for this situation. [3 + 2 = 5]

■ **If I call zero more children to stand in line, how many children will be standing?** [5]

Addition and Subtraction Patterns

Use 5 ▥ , 2 ▥ , a ⬭ red ⬭ , and a ⬭ blue ⬭ .

Build a train to show the fact.
Color to show your train.
Write the sum.

1. 4 + 1 = 5
    1 + 4 = 5

2. 2 + 1 = 3
    1 + 2 = 3

r	r	b
b	r	r

3. 2 + 2 = 4
    2 + 2 = 4

r	r	b	b
b	b	r	r

🗣 **4.** Talk about the pattern you see.
In their own words, children should note order property.

Build a train to show the fact.
Color to show your train.
Write the sum.

5. 2 + 0 = 2

6. 3 + 0 = 3

r	r	r

7. 0 + 5 = 5

r	r	r	r	r

8. 1 + 0 = 1

r

✊ **9.** Do you see a pattern?
Write what you know about adding 0.

In their own words, children should note that when 0

is one of the addends, the sum is the same as the other addend.

Chapter 1   Adding and Subtracting Facts to 10   fifteen **15**

Call on a volunteer to say the addition fact for this situation. [5 + 0 = 5] Phrase another question for the subtraction fact 5 − 0 = 5.

PUPIL'S EDITION pp. 15-16

Page 15 Guide children through ex. 1 and 5. Remind them that they do not show any cubes for zero.

Check for Understanding

■ **3 + 2 can be shown with 3 blue and 2 red cubes. What other fact can you show with these cubes?** [2 + 3]

GUIDED PRACTICE ex. 2–4, 6–9: For reteaching, use Common Error and Remediation or Alternative Strategy.

Page 16 Work through ex. 1 with the children.

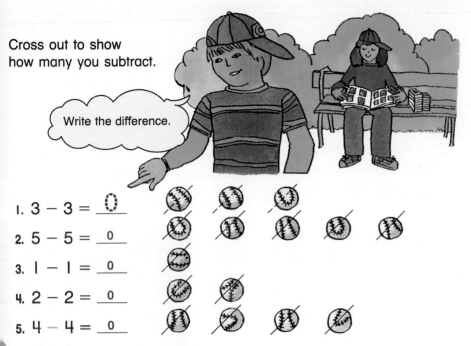

Cross out to show
how many you subtract.

Write the difference.

1. $3 - 3 = \underline{0}$

2. $5 - 5 = \underline{0}$

3. $1 - 1 = \underline{0}$

4. $2 - 2 = \underline{0}$

5. $4 - 4 = \underline{0}$

6. Talk about the pattern you see. **In their own words, children should note that when they subtract a number from itself, the answer is zero.**

Subtract.
Cross out if you have to.

7. $3 - 0 = \underline{3}$

8. $1 - 0 = \underline{1}$

9. $5 - 0 = \underline{5}$

10. $2 - 0 = \underline{2}$

11. $4 - 0 = \underline{4}$

12. Look for a pattern.
Write what you know about subtracting 0.

<u>In their own words, children should note that when they</u>

<u>subtract 0 from a number, the answer is that number.</u>

16   sixteen

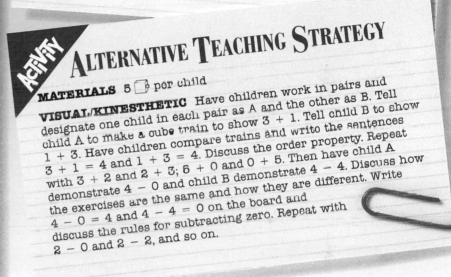

Common Error and Remediation

MATERIALS 5 ○ (or punchouts)

Some children may consistently subtract zero from a number and get a difference of zero. Work individually with each child, using a set of counters. Have him or her model a set of subtraction exercises in which zero is subtracted. Have the child describe what happens when you take away zero. The child should observe that, in such an instance, no counters are moved. Emphasize that when you subtract zero the difference is always the same as the starting number.

ALTERNATIVE TEACHING STRATEGY

Activity

MATERIALS 5 ▢ per child

VISUAL/KINESTHETIC Have children work in pairs and designate one child in each pair as A and the other as B. Tell child A to make a cube train to show 3 + 1. Tell child B to show 1 + 3. Have children compare trains and write the sentences 3 + 1 = 4 and 1 + 3 = 4. Discuss the order property. Repeat with 3 + 2 and 2 + 3; 5 + 0 and 0 + 5. Then have child A demonstrate 4 − 0 and child B demonstrate 4 − 4. Discuss how the exercises are the same and how they are different. Write 4 − 0 = 4 and 4 − 4 = 0 on the board and discuss the rules for subtracting zero. Repeat with 2 − 0 and 2 − 2, and so on.

PRACTICE • APPLY   **PRACTICE**   ex. 2–12

CLOSE   Guide children to summarize the lesson:

■ **What happens when you add or subtract zero?** [Possible response: When you add 0 the sum is the same as the other addend. When you subtract 0 the difference is the same as the number from which you subtracted.]

MAC ACTIVITY CENTER

MAC Activity 7:
Basic-to-Average
▼

SPEAKING MATHEMATICALLY ▪ TELL A ZERO STORY

MAC Activity 7
On Your Own Pair and Share In a Group

Have children work in pairs. Explain that one child is to say a number sentence that includes zero, such as 0 + 4 = 4 or 3 − 0 = 3. The other child is to tell an addition or subtraction story for the sentence:

I didn't have any crayons. Then I got 4.
Now I have 4 crayons.

Have children reverse roles and repeat the activity.

MAC Activity 8:
Average-to-Challenge ▶

MENTAL MATH ▪ BATTER UP!

MAC Activity 8
On Your Own Pair and Share In a Group

Briefly discuss the number of balls and strikes a batter is allowed during a turn in baseball. [4 balls, 3 strikes] Explain that "the count" in baseball refers to the number of balls and strikes against the batter. A count of 3 and 1 means 3 balls and 1 strike.

Tell children that for this activity, they are to add the number of balls and strikes together to find the total count. Say the following counts aloud and have children tell the total count.

1 and 2	2 and 1
2 and 0	0 and 2
3 and 2	2 and 3
3 and 0	0 and 3

1 and 2
2 and 0
3 and 2
3 and 0

Name

ADDITION AND SUBTRACTION PATTERNS

Study

$3 + 0 = 3$

$0 + 3 = 3$

$3 - 0 = 3$

$3 - 3 = 0$

Check

Draw dots to help. Write the sum.

1. $1 + 0 = \underline{1}$

$0 + 1 = \underline{1}$

2. $3 + 0 = \underline{3}$

$0 + 3 = \underline{3}$

3. $0 + 2 = \underline{2}$

$2 + 0 = \underline{2}$

4. $0 + 4 = \underline{4}$

$4 + 0 = \underline{4}$

Cross out. Write the difference.

5. $1 - 1 = \underline{0}$

$2 - 2 = \underline{0}$

$4 - 4 = \underline{0}$

6. $1 - 0 = \underline{1}$

$2 - 0 = \underline{2}$

$3 - 0 = \underline{3}$

Macmillan/McGraw-Hill, MATHEMATICS IN ACTION
Grade 2, Chapter 1, Lesson 5, pages 15–16

Reteaching-4

Name

ADDITION AND SUBTRACTION PATTERNS

Color to show each fact.
Write the sum.

1. $3 + 1 = \underline{4}$

$1 + 3 = \underline{4}$

2. $2 + 3 = \underline{5}$

$3 + 2 = \underline{5}$

3. $3 + 0 - \underline{3}$

$0 + 3 = \underline{3}$

Match. Write the difference.

4. $5 - 5 = \underline{0}$

5. $2 - 0 = \underline{2}$

6. $4 - 4 = \underline{0}$

7. $4 - 0 - \underline{4}$

8. $3 - 3 = \underline{0}$

Macmillan/McGraw-Hill, MATHEMATICS IN ACTION
Grade 2, Chapter 1, Lesson 5, pages 15–16

Practice-4

Name

ADDITION AND SUBTRACTION PATTERNS

On Your Own   Pair and Share   In a Group

SIGN IN

Complete each number sentence.
Write + or −.

1. $3 \overset{---}{} 3 = 0$

2. $2 \overset{+}{} 1 = 3$

3. $5 \overset{\pm}{} 0 = 5$

4. $4 \overset{-}{} 4 = 0$

5. $3 \overset{+}{} 1 = 4$

6. $1 \overset{+}{} 4 = 5$

7. $5 \overset{-}{} 5 = 0$

8. $1 \overset{\pm}{} 0 = 1$

9. $2 \overset{-}{} 2 = 0$

10. $2 \overset{\pm}{} 0 = 2$

11. $4 \overset{\pm}{} 0 = 4$

12. $1 \overset{+}{} 2 = 3$

13. $1 \overset{-}{} 1 = 0$

14. $0 \overset{+}{} 4 = 4$

15. $3 \overset{\pm}{} 0 = 3$

16. $0 \overset{+}{} 5 = 5$

17. $4 \overset{\pm}{} 1 = 5$

18. $0 \overset{+}{} 2 = 2$

19. $1 \overset{+}{} 1 = 2$

20. $1 \overset{+}{} 3 = 4$

Which sentences can have + and −?

3, 8, 10, 11, 15

Macmillan/McGraw-Hill, MATHEMATICS IN ACTION
Grade 2, Chapter 1, Lesson 5, pages 15–16

Enrichment-4

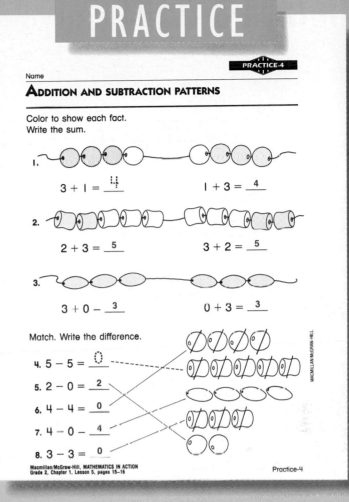

Problem of the Day

Rick's team scored 1 run and then 3 runs. Jill's team scored 3 runs and then 1 run. Who won the game? [The game was tied. Children may work it out this way: $1 + 3 = 4$, $3 + 1 = 4$.]

AT·A·GLANCE pp. 17-18

LESSON OBJECTIVE
Use a problem-solving plan to solve problems.

ASSIGNMENT GUIDE

COURSE	EXERCISES
Basic	p. 17: All; p. 18: All
Average	p. 17: All; p. 18: All
Challenge	p. 17: All; p. 18: All

MATERIALS
Manipulatives 10 ○ (or punchouts) per child

Teacher Resources
Reteaching 5   Practice 5   Enrichment 5
Prob. Solv. 1   MAC Act. 9, 10
Math Anthology, p. 132

Name _____

Problem Solving
Using the Five-Step Plan

You can use a plan to solve problems.

There were 3 ants on a rock.
2 more ants came.
How many ants were there
in all?

Understand What do I know?	There were 3 ants. 2 more came.
What do I need to find out?	How many in all?
Plan What can I do?	I need to join the groups. I can add.
Try Try the plan.	3 + 2 = 5 5 ants in all.
Check Does my answer make sense?	Yes. The answer shows I joined the groups to make a larger group.
Extend What have I learned?	I can add to find how many in all.

Macmillan/McGraw-Hill

Chapter 1   Adding and Subtracting Facts to 10   seventeen **17**

PREPARE **WARM-UP** To prepare children for using a five-step plan to solve problems, have them give the following sums and differences:

2 + 3 [5]   5 − 1 [4]   4 − 3 [1]   2 + 2 [4]

Mathematics and Literature

TEACH **MODELING** Read "There Was an Old Man with a Beard" from *Math Anthology*. Tell children that they will use counters to model the number of birds that live in the old man's beard. As you read this poem again, have children model the numbers.

■ **What do we know?** [Many birds live in the old man's beard.]

■ **What do we need to find out?** [how many birds in all]

■ **How can you use the counters?** [Make groups of 2 counters for the owls, 1 for the hen, 4 for the larks, and 1 for the wren.]

■ **How can we find how many birds in all?** [Combine all counters.]

PUPIL'S EDITION pp. 17-18

Page 17 Read the problem. Call attention to the steps of the plan.

■ **What do you know?** [There were 3 ants on a rock and 2 more ants came.]

Guide children to see that the groups of ants can be added to find how many in all. Have children use counters to try the plan.

■ **Why is it important to understand the problem first?** [You know what information you already have and what information you need.]

■ **What does a plan help you to do?** [answer the question]

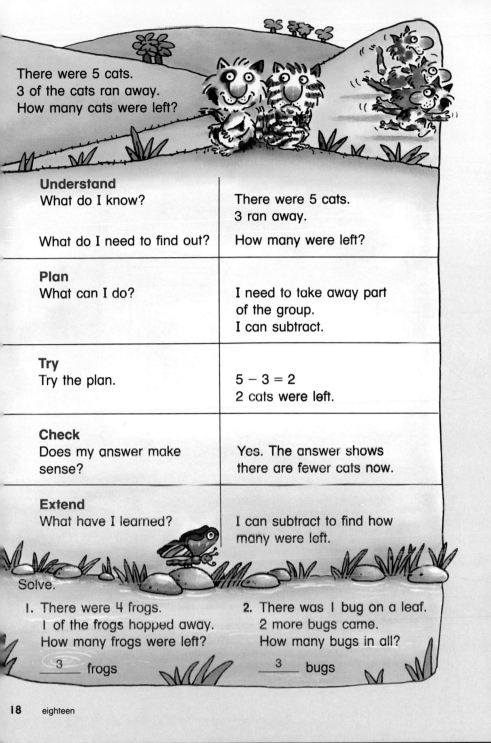

There were 5 cats.
3 of the cats ran away.
How many cats were left?

Understand	
What do I know?	There were 5 cats. 3 ran away.
What do I need to find out?	How many were left?
Plan	
What can I do?	I need to take away part of the group. I can subtract.
Try	
Try the plan.	5 − 3 = 2 2 cats were left.
Check	
Does my answer make sense?	Yes. The answer shows there are fewer cats now.
Extend	
What have I learned?	I can subtract to find how many were left.

Solve.

1. There were 4 frogs.
   1 of the frogs hopped away.
   How many frogs were left?

   __3__ frogs

2. There was 1 bug on a leaf.
   2 more bugs came.
   How many bugs in all?

   __3__ bugs

18   eighteen

For Students Acquiring English (SAE)

Scan the pages for vocabulary that may be new to SAE students. As the lesson is read aloud, introduce new words by using visuals, gestures, and body movements to convey meaning. Ask questions frequently to check comprehension. Complete the pages as a directed lesson, having some children act out the problems while another child answers them.

TEACHER to TEACHER

COOPERATIVE LEARNING TIP To accustom my students to working with different people during the early weeks of class, I have them form new pairs before each lesson. I might use random methods for forming pairs, such as matching number families, or I might use more purposeful ones, such as asking them to **line up** according to how much they enjoy the kind of work in that lesson. If students in the lower half of the line form pairs with students in the upper half of the line, each pair varies with respect to comfort doing this type of lesson.

■ **Why is it important to check your answer?** [to see if the plan works]

■ **Why is it important to think about what you have learned?** [you can remember the plan for later use.]

Check for Understanding

■ **What if there was 1 ant on a rock and 3 more ants came? How many ants would there be in all?** [4]

GUIDED PRACTICE   All: Work through the problems with children.

Page 18   Read the problem at the top of the page. Discuss the steps.

■ **What do you know?** [There were 5 cats and 3 ran away.]

Discuss the questions on the page. Guide children to see that they have to find out how many cats were left. Discuss separating groups by subtracting. Have children use counters to try the plan.

3 PRACTICE·APPLY   PRACTICE   ex. All

CLOSE   Guide children to summarize the lesson:

■ **How do you use a plan to solve problems?** [Possible response: Think about what you already know and what you need to find out. Plan what to do. Try the plan. Check that the answer makes sense.]

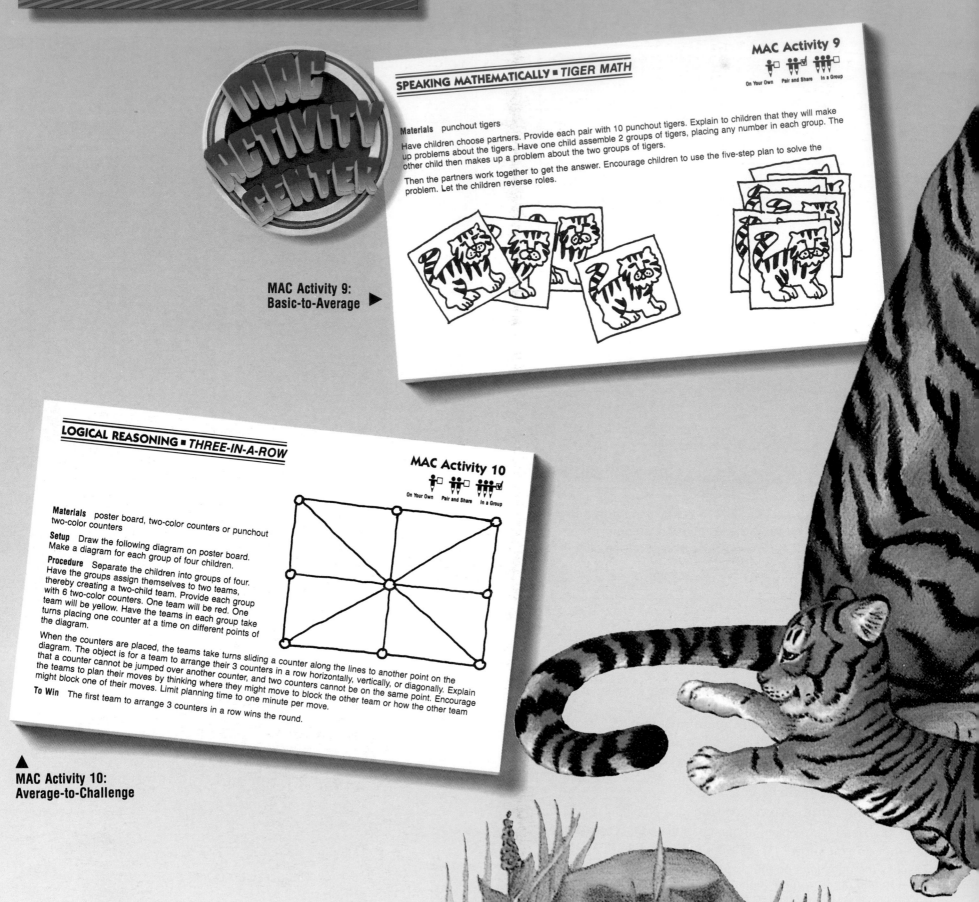

SPEAKING MATHEMATICALLY ■ TIGER MATH

MAC Activity 9

On Your Own   Pair and Share   In a Group

Materials   punchout tigers

Have children choose partners. Provide each pair with 10 punchout tigers. Explain to children that they will make up problems about the tigers. Have one child assemble 2 groups of tigers, placing any number in each group. The other child then makes up a problem about the two groups of tigers.

Then the partners work together to get the answer. Encourage children to use the five-step plan to solve the problem. Let the children reverse roles.

MAC Activity 9:
Basic-to-Average ▶

LOGICAL REASONING ■ THREE-IN-A-ROW

MAC Activity 10

On Your Own   Pair and Share   In a Group

Materials   poster board, two-color counters or punchout two-color counters

Setup   Draw the following diagram on poster board. Make a diagram for each group of four children.

Procedure   Separate the children into groups of four. Have the groups assign themselves to two teams, thereby creating a two-child team. Provide each group with 6 two-color counters. One team will be red. One team will be yellow. Have the teams in each group take turns placing one counter at a time on different points of the diagram.

When the counters are placed, the teams take turns sliding a counter along the lines to another point on the diagram. The object is for a team to arrange their 3 counters in a row horizontally, vertically, or diagonally. Explain that a counter cannot be jumped over another counter, and two counters cannot be on the same point. Encourage the teams to plan their moves by thinking where they might move to block the other team or how the other team might block one of their moves. Limit planning time to one minute per move.

To Win   The first team to arrange 3 counters in a row wins the round.

▲
MAC Activity 10:
Average-to-Challenge

RETEACHING

Name

PROBLEM SOLVING STRATEGY: USING THE FIVE-STEP PLAN

Study

1 pig was in the pen. 3 more came. How many in all?

Understand	There was 1 pig. 3 more came. Find out how many pigs there are.
Plan	Add to find how many.
Try	1 pig + 3 pigs = 4 pigs in all.
Check	The answer shows a larger group.
Extend	Add to find how many in all.

Check

Use the plan to solve.

1. There were 4 rabbits in the field.
   2 rabbits hopped away.
   How many rabbits were left?

   _2_ rabbits

2. There were 3 hens in the yard.
   2 more hens came into the yard.
   How many hens in all?

   _5_ hens

Reteaching-5

Macmillan/McGraw-Hill, MATHEMATICS IN ACTION
Grade 2, Chapter 1, Lesson 6, pages 17–18

PRACTICE

Name

PROBLEM SOLVING STRATEGY: USING THE FIVE-STEP PLAN

Understand
Plan
Try
Check
Extend

Use the plan to solve the problem.

1. There were 2 cars on the street.
   1 more car drove up.
   How many cars in all?

   _3_ cars

2. There were 5 buses in the parking lot.
   1 bus left.
   How many buses were still in the lot?

   _4_ buses

3. 3 trucks picked up boxes.
   2 more trucks came for boxes.
   How many trucks carried boxes?

   _5_ trucks

4. 4 cars stopped at the stoplight.
   2 cars turned right.
   How many cars did not turn right?

   _2_ cars

Practice-5

Macmillan/McGraw-Hill, MATHEMATICS IN ACTION
Grade 2, Chapter 1, Lesson 6, pages 17–18

ENRICHMENT

Name

PROBLEM SOLVING

On Your Own   Pair and Share   In a Group

COUNTING SHEEP

Tell your partner a story about the picture.
Write 1, 2, 3, 4, 5 to put the steps in order.
Then do each step.

☐1 **Understand.** Ring what you know about the picture.

   (5 sheep eat grass.)   2 sheep eat grass.
   (2 ran away.)   2 more came.

☐4 **Check.** Ring the words about the answer.

   2 more   (2 fewer)

☐3 **Try.** Ring the plan you will try.

   (5 – 2 = 3)   3 – 2 = 1

☐2 **Plan.** Ring what you can do.

   join groups   (take away part of a group)

☐5 **Extend.** Ring the sentence that tells what you did.

   Added to find   (Subtracted to find
   how many in all.   how many are left.)

Enrichment-5

Macmillan/McGraw-Hill, MATHEMATICS IN ACTION
Grade 2, Chapter 1, Lesson 6, pages 17–18

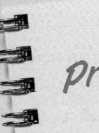

Problem of the Day

Jim has 5 fish.
He has 3 fish in one bowl.
Does he have more than 2 fish in a second bowl?
[No; 3 + 2 = 5 fish.]

AT·A·GLANCE pp. 19-20

LESSON OBJECTIVE
Add and subtract facts to 6.

ASSIGNMENT GUIDE

COURSE	EXERCISES
Basic	p. 19: 2–8; p. 20: 1–8
Average	p. 19: 2–8; p. 20: 1–8
Challenge	p. 19: 2–8; p. 20: 1–8

MATERIALS
Classroom Materials red and blue crayons
Manipulatives 6 🔲 and 6 🔲 (or square counter punchouts)
per pair

Teacher Resources
Reteaching 6   Practice 6   Enrichment 6
MAC Act. 11, 12

SKILLS TRACE
FACTS TO 10

Explore (Concrete)	Develop/Understand (Transitional/Abstract)
10	11, 12, 13–14, 15–16, 19–20, 21–22, 23–24, 29–30, 31–32, 33–34, 35–36, 37–38
Practice 20, 28, 32, 43, 44, 45–46, 49, 60	**Apply** 17–18, 25–26, 27, 39–40, 41, 42

See **MANIPULATIVES PLUS 5**, p. 8M.

PREPARE **WARM-UP** To review addition facts for 5, draw a large flower with six petals on the chalkboard, and write the number 5 in the center. Ask children to name a fact for 5, such as 1 + 4, and write it on one of the petals. Call on volunteers to write another fact for 5 on each of the other petals.

TEACH **MODELING** Have children make a train using 3 red and 2 blue cubes. Then have them snap on one more cube of either color and discuss the train, using the words **part-part-whole**: "The red part has 4 cubes; the blue part has 2 cubes. My whole train has 6 cubes." Repeat this modeling process using other facts for 5, and then add one more cube, arriving at a fact for 6.

Name _____

ACTIVITY

Facts to 6

Working Together

Use 6 🔲 , 6 🔲 , a ✏️ red ,

and a ✏️ blue .

You build a train to show the fact.
Your partner colors to show the train.
Take turns. Complete.

Write the sum.   Write the difference.

1. 6 + 0 = _6_   [train] 6 − 0 = _6_

2. 5 + 1 = _6_   [r r r r r b] 6 − 1 = _5_

3. 4 + 2 = _6_   [r r r r b b] 6 − 2 = _4_

4. 3 + 3 = _6_   [r r r b b b] 6 − 3 = _3_

5. 2 + 4 = _6_   [r r b b b b] 6 − 4 = _2_

6. 1 + 5 = _6_   [r b b b b b] 6 − 5 = _1_

7. 0 + 6 = _6_   [b b b b b b] 6 − 6 = _0_

8. Talk about the patterns. Answers will vary. Possible answer: the numbers in the addition fact are the same as the numbers in the subtraction fact.

Chapter 1   Adding and Subtracting Facts to 10   nineteen **19**

PUPIL'S EDITION pp. 19-20

Page 19 ■ Working Together Assign children to work in pairs, using red and blue cubes. Guide children through ex. 1. Have volunteers read the number sentences.

Check for Understanding

■ **Which addition and subtraction sentences are shown by a cube train of 5 red cubes and 1 blue cube?** [5 + 1 = 6 and 6 − 1 = 5]

GUIDED PRACTICE ex. 2–8: For reteaching, use Common Error and Remediation or Alternative Strategy.

Page 20 Review the way in which addition and subtraction sentences can be written horizontally or vertically.

Write the fact family for each picture.

1. $5 + 1 = 6$ $6 - 1 = 5$
   $1 + 5 = 6$ $6 - 5 = 1$

2. $2 + 4 = 6$ $6 - 4 = 2$
   $4 + 2 = 6$ $6 - 2 = 4$

3. $3 + 3 = 6$ $6 - 3 = 3$

Add or subtract.

4.
$\begin{array}{r} 2 \\ +1 \\ \hline 3 \end{array}$
$\begin{array}{r} 1 \\ +2 \\ \hline 3 \end{array}$
$\begin{array}{r} 2 \\ +3 \\ \hline 5 \end{array}$
$\begin{array}{r} 3 \\ +2 \\ \hline 5 \end{array}$
$\begin{array}{r} 3 \\ +1 \\ \hline 4 \end{array}$
$\begin{array}{r} 1 \\ +3 \\ \hline 4 \end{array}$

5.
$\begin{array}{r} 6 \\ -1 \\ \hline 5 \end{array}$
$\begin{array}{r} 6 \\ -5 \\ \hline 1 \end{array}$
$\begin{array}{r} 4 \\ -0 \\ \hline 4 \end{array}$
$\begin{array}{r} 4 \\ -4 \\ \hline 0 \end{array}$
$\begin{array}{r} 5 \\ -2 \\ \hline 3 \end{array}$
$\begin{array}{r} 5 \\ -3 \\ \hline 2 \end{array}$

6.
$\begin{array}{r} 5 \\ +0 \\ \hline 5 \end{array}$
$\begin{array}{r} 0 \\ +5 \\ \hline 5 \end{array}$
$\begin{array}{r} 4 \\ +0 \\ \hline 4 \end{array}$
$\begin{array}{r} 0 \\ +4 \\ \hline 4 \end{array}$
$\begin{array}{r} 0 \\ +6 \\ \hline 6 \end{array}$
$\begin{array}{r} 6 \\ +0 \\ \hline 6 \end{array}$

7. Look at each row of facts.
   Talk about any patterns you see.
   Children may note order property
   and zero property.

Mixed Review 〰〰〰〰〰〰〰〰〰

Add or subtract.

8. $3 + 1 = \underline{4}$ $1 + 4 = \underline{5}$ $5 - 2 = \underline{3}$

ACTIVITY
Common Error and Remediation

MATERIALS 6 ○ (or punchouts)

Some children may guess when they cannot recall a fact. Work individually with each child, using a set of counters. Explain to the child that using counters is a better strategy than guessing because guesses are often wrong. Have the child use counters to work through facts that he or she wrote incorrectly in the previous activity. Help the child to verbalize each action using the words **part-part-whole**: "One part has 3, one part has 2, there are 5 in the whole group."

ACTIVITY
Alternative Teaching Strategy

VISUAL/AUDITORY Ask 6 children to stand in a row at the front of the room. Tell 1 child to sit down and have a volunteer give the subtraction sentence for this action. [$6 - 1 = 5$] Tell the child to stand up again and have another volunteer give the addition sentence. [$5 + 1 = 6$] Repeat the activity with different groups of six children to develop $6 - 2 = 4$ and $4 + 2 = 6$, $6 - 3 = 3$ and $3 + 3 = 6$, $6 - 4 = 2$ and $2 + 4 = 6$, $6 - 5 = 1$ and $1 + 5 = 6$. Next, have all 6 children sit down and have a volunteer give the subtraction sentence for the action. [$6 - 6 = 0$] Then ask the 6 children to stand up again and have another volunteer give the addition sentence. [$0 + 6 = 6$]

3 PRACTICE·APPLY   **PRACTICE**   ex. 1–5

CLOSE   Guide children to summarize the lesson:

■ **What fact family is modeled by a domino with 1 dot and 5 dots?** [$1 + 5 = 6$, $5 + 1 = 6$, $6 - 1 = 5$, $6 - 5 = 1$]

MAC ACTIVITY CENTER

MAC Activity 11

CAREER—FIREFIGHTER ▪ FIRE STORY TIME

On Your Own Pair and Share In a Group

Discuss the work of firefighters with the children. Take children on a walk around the school and point out fire exit signs, smoke alarms, and fire extinguishers. Then ask children to write an addition or subtraction story about firefighters or their equipment. Encourage them to use pictures for words they cannot spell. Present the following example to get children started.

There were 6 fire engines in the firehouse. 2 engines went to a fire. How many fire engines were still in the firehouse? [4]

Have children read their stories aloud.

▲
MAC Activity 11:
Basic-to-Average

MAC Activity 12:
Average-to-Challenge
▼

LOGICAL REASONING ▪ MYSTERY FACTS

MAC Activity 12

On Your Own Pair and Share In a Group

Assign each child a partner. Have partners write a riddle that contains two clues about a mystery fact for 6. To get children started, present the following examples.

One addend is 4.
The other addend is less than 3.
What is the mystery fact for 6?
[4 + 2 = 6 or 2 + 4 = 6]

One number is 6.
I take away more than 3 to get 2.
What is the mystery fact for 6? [6 − 4 = 2]

Have pairs of children exchange riddles to solve.

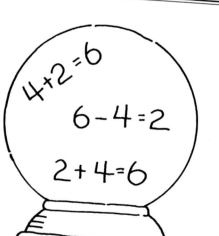

$4 + 2 = 6$

$6 - 4 = 2$

$2 + 4 = 6$

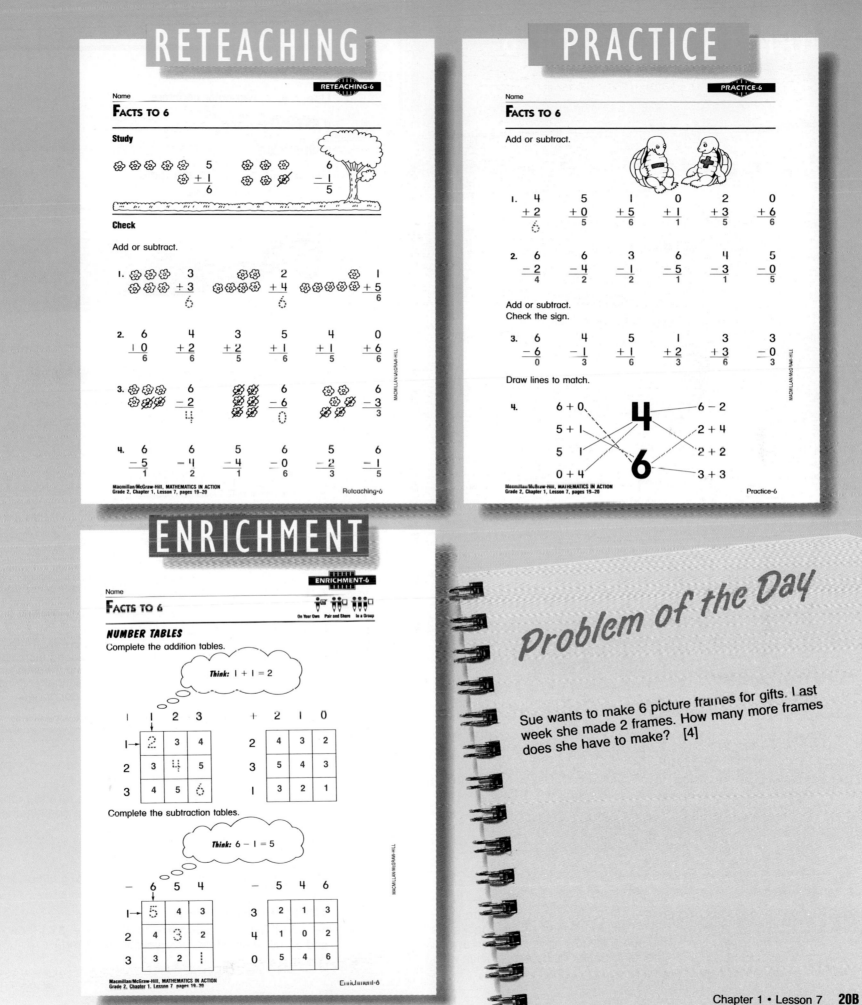

RETEACHING-6

Name

FACTS TO 6

Study

🌸🌸🌸🌸🌸   5   🌸🌸   🌸🌸   6
            🌸 +1   🌸🌸 🌸🌸   −1
            ───   ───
             6   5

Check

Add or subtract.

1. 🌸🌸🌸 3   🌸🌸 2   🌸 1
    🌸🌸🌸 +3   🌸🌸🌸 +4   🌸🌸🌸🌸 +5
          ───   ───   ───
           6   6   6

2. 6   4   3   5   4   0
   +0   +2   +2   +1   +1   +6
   ───   ───   ───   ───   ───   ───
    6   6   5   6   5   6

3. 🌸🌸🌸 6   🌸🌸 6   🌸🌸 6
    🌸🌸🌸 −2   🌸🌸🌸🌸 −6   🌸🌸 −3
          ───   ───   ───
           4   0   3

4. 6   6   5   6   5   6
   −5   −4   −4   −0   −2   −1
   ───   ───   ───   ───   ───   ───
    1   2   1   6   3   5

Macmillan/McGraw-Hill, MATHEMATICS IN ACTION
Grade 2, Chapter 1, Lesson 7, pages 19–20   Reteaching-6

MACMILLAN/McGRAW-HILL

PRACTICE-6

Name

FACTS TO 6

Add or subtract.

1. 4   5   1   0   2   0
   +2   +0   +5   +1   +3   +6
   ───   ───   ───   ───   ───   ───
    6   5   6   1   5   6

2. 6   6   3   6   4   5
   −2   −4   −1   −5   −3   −0
   ───   ───   ───   ───   ───   ───
    4   2   2   1   1   5

Add or subtract.
Check the sign.

3. 6   4   5   1   3   3
   −6   −1   +1   +2   +3   −0
   ───   ───   ───   ───   ───   ───
    0   3   6   3   6   3

Draw lines to match.

4.   6 + 0   **4**   6 − 2
      5 + 1   2 + 4
      5   1   2 + 2
      0 + 4   **6**   3 + 3

Macmillan/McGraw-Hill, MATHEMATICS IN ACTION
Grade 2, Chapter 1, Lesson 7, pages 19–20   Practice-6

MACMILLAN/McGRAW-HILL

ENRICHMENT-6

Name

FACTS TO 6

On Your Own   Pair and Share   Is a Group

NUMBER TABLES

Complete the addition tables.

Think: 1 + 1 = 2

1	1	2	3
1	2	3	4
2	3	4	5
3	4	5	6

+	2	1	0
2	4	3	2
3	5	4	3
1	3	2	1

Complete the subtraction tables.

Think: 6 − 1 = 5

−	6	5	4
1	5	4	3
2	4	3	2
3	3	2	1

−	5	4	6
3	2	1	3
4	1	0	2
0	5	4	6

Macmillan/McGraw-Hill, MATHEMATICS IN ACTION
Grade 2, Chapter 1, Lesson 7, pages 19–20   Enrichment-6

MACMILLAN/McGRAW-HILL

Problem of the Day

Sue wants to make 6 picture frames for gifts. Last week she made 2 frames. How many more frames does she have to make?   [4]

AT·A·GLANCE pp. 21-22

LESSON OBJECTIVE
Add and subtract facts to 7.

ASSIGNMENT GUIDE

COURSE	EXERCISES
Basic	p. 21: 2–9; p. 22: 1–5, Reasoning
Average	p. 21: 2–9; p. 22: 1–5, Reasoning
Challenge	p. 21: 2–9; p. 22: 1–5, Reasoning
Extra Practice, p. 28	Practice Plus, p. 44

MATERIALS
Classroom Materials red and yellow crayons
Manipulatives 7 ◐ (or punchouts) per child

Teacher Resources
Reteaching 7   Practice 7   Enrichment 7
MAC Act. 13, 14

SKILLS TRACE
FACTS TO 10

Explore (Concrete)	Develop/Understand (Transitional/Abstract)
10	11, 12, 13–14, 15–16, 19–20, 21–22, 23–24, 29–30, 31–32, 33–34, 35–36, 37, 38
Practice 20, 28, 32, 43, 44, 45–46, 49, 60	**Apply** 17–18, 25–26, 27, 39–40, 41, 42

Facts to 7

Use 7 ◐ , two-color counters

a ▰▰ red ▰ , and

a ▰▰ yellow ▰ .

Use counters to show the facts.
Color to show the facts.

Write the sum.   Write the difference.

1. $7 + 0 = \underline{7}$ ●●●●●●● $7 - 0 = \underline{7}$

2. $6 + 1 = \underline{7}$ ⓡⓡⓡⓡⓡⓡⓨ $7 - 1 = \underline{6}$

3. $5 + 2 = \underline{7}$ ⓡⓡⓡⓡⓡⓨⓨ $7 - 2 = \underline{5}$

4. $4 + 3 = \underline{7}$ ⓡⓡⓡⓡⓨⓨⓨ $7 - 3 = \underline{4}$

5. $3 + 4 = \underline{7}$ ⓡⓡⓡⓨⓨⓨⓨ $7 - 4 = \underline{3}$

6. $2 + 5 = \underline{7}$ ⓡⓡⓨⓨⓨⓨⓨ $7 - 5 = \underline{2}$

7. $1 + 6 = \underline{7}$ ⓡⓨⓨⓨⓨⓨⓨ $7 - 6 = \underline{1}$

8. $0 + 7 = \underline{7}$ ⓨⓨⓨⓨⓨⓨⓨ $7 - 7 = \underline{0}$

9. Talk about the patterns.

In their own words, children should note that as one addend increases and the other decreases, the sum remains the same. As the subtrahend increases the difference decreases.

Chapter 1   Adding and Subtracting Facts to 10   twenty-one   21

---

① PREPARE   **WARM-UP** To review facts to 6, write the following numbers on the chalkboard. Have children ring pairs of numbers that add to 6.

4	2	1	2	5
1	2	4	3	1
3	5	1	3	2
3	0	6	2	4
2	2	4	1	5

② TEACH   **DISCUSSING** Ask 7 children to stand in a line. Turn the last 3 children around so their backs are to the rest of the class. Have volunteers tell how many children are facing forward and how many have their backs to the class. Then help them relate the activity to subtraction.

■ **There are 7 children in line; 4 are facing forward. How many are facing in the opposite direction?** [3]

Have a volunteer say the subtraction sentence for the problem. [7 − 4 = 3] Repeat the activity with a different combination of children.

PUPIL'S EDITION pp. 21-22

Page 21 Tell children that in this lesson they will use counters rather than cubes. Guide them through ex. 1.

Check for Understanding

■ **How could you use counters to show 4 + 3?** [Show 4 red counters and 3 yellow counters, or 4 yellow and 3 red.]

Write the fact family for each picture.

1.

2 + 5 = 7   7 − 5 = 2

5 + 2 = 7   7 − 2 = 5

2.

7 + 0 = 7   7 − 0 = 7

0 + 7 = 7   7 − 7 = 0

Add or subtract.

3.
$$\begin{array}{c} 5 \\ +2 \\ \hline 7 \end{array} \quad \begin{array}{c} 2 \\ +5 \\ \hline 7 \end{array} \qquad \begin{array}{c} 3 \\ +4 \\ \hline 7 \end{array} \quad \begin{array}{c} 4 \\ +3 \\ \hline 7 \end{array} \qquad \begin{array}{c} 2 \\ +3 \\ \hline 5 \end{array} \quad \begin{array}{c} 3 \\ +2 \\ \hline 5 \end{array}$$

4.
$$\begin{array}{c} 4 \\ -3 \\ \hline 1 \end{array} \quad \begin{array}{c} 4 \\ -1 \\ \hline 3 \end{array} \qquad \begin{array}{c} 7 \\ -2 \\ \hline 5 \end{array} \quad \begin{array}{c} 7 \\ -5 \\ \hline 2 \end{array} \qquad \begin{array}{c} 6 \\ -4 \\ \hline 2 \end{array} \quad \begin{array}{c} 6 \\ -2 \\ \hline 4 \end{array}$$

5.
$$\begin{array}{c} 5 \\ -0 \\ \hline 5 \end{array} \quad \begin{array}{c} 5 \\ -5 \\ \hline 0 \end{array} \qquad \begin{array}{c} 2 \\ -0 \\ \hline 2 \end{array} \quad \begin{array}{c} 2 \\ -2 \\ \hline 0 \end{array} \qquad \begin{array}{c} 7 \\ -0 \\ \hline 7 \end{array} \quad \begin{array}{c} 7 \\ -7 \\ \hline 0 \end{array}$$

Reasoning

Write the facts that continue the pattern.

1 + 1 = 2	2 + 1 = 3	3 + 1 = 4
4 + 1 = 5	5 + 1 = 6	6 + 1 = 7

Extra Practice, page 28 *Practice Plus,* page 44

ACTIVITY — Common Error and Remediation

MATERIALS 4 red and 3 blue punchout squares

Some children may have problems finding a related subtraction fact. Work with each child, having the child display 4 red squares and 3 blue squares in a row.

■ **How many red squares do you have?** [4]
■ **How many blue squares do you have?** [3]

Then present several "take-away" subtraction problems in which the child covers squares of one color with his or her hand to represent "take away."

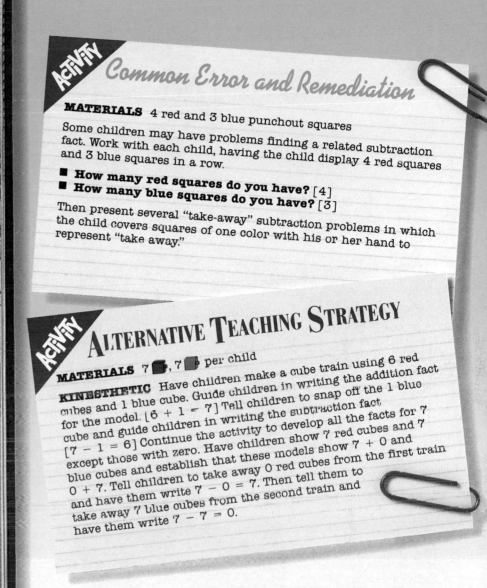

ACTIVITY — ALTERNATIVE TEACHING STRATEGY

MATERIALS 7 ■, 7 ■ per child

KINESTHETIC Have children make a cube train using 6 red cubes and 1 blue cube. Guide children in writing the addition fact for the model. [6 + 1 = 7] Tell children to snap off the 1 blue cube and guide children in writing the subtraction fact [7 − 1 = 6] Continue the activity to develop all the facts for 7 except those with zero. Have children show 7 red cubes and 7 blue cubes and establish that these models show 7 + 0 and 0 + 7. Tell children to take away 0 red cubes from the first train and have them write 7 − 0 = 7. Then tell them to take away 7 blue cubes from the second train and have them write 7 − 7 = 0.

GUIDED PRACTICE   ex. 2–9: For reteaching, use Common Error and Remediation or Alternative Strategy.

Page 22   Remind children to pay special attention to addition and subtraction signs when completing ex. 3–5.

3 PRACTICE•APPLY   **PRACTICE**   ex. 1–5

REASONING   Discuss the pattern and help children to understand that 1 is an addend in each fact, that the other addend increases by 1 from the previous fact, and that each sum also increases by 1.

C L O S E   Guide children to summarize the lesson:

■ **How would you model 2 + 5 to find the sum?** [Possible response: 2 red counters and 5 yellow counters]

■ **What subtraction fact is shown with the same model?** [7 − 5 = 2]

MAC ACTIVITY CENTER

MATH AND SOCIAL STUDIES ■ TO MARKET, TO MARKET

MAC Activity 14

On Your Own   Pair and Share   In a Group

Materials paper for a mural, paint or crayons, pieces of oaktag

Briefly discuss a current or recent social studies topic. Tell children to use the topic to create a mural showing facts to 7. For example, if a current topic were how farm goods reach city markets, children could create a mural showing 2 red farm trucks and 5 blue farm trucks hauling crops to market.

Assign children to work in small groups to plan and create their murals. First have each group decide on a subject for their mural. After the murals have been planned and painted or colored, have children write the addition or subtraction fact for the mural on a strip of oaktag. Display children's murals and facts separately and have volunteers match them.

▲ **MAC Activity 14: Average-to-Challenge**

MATH AND CONSUMERS ■ FAIRY TALE RESTAURANT

MAC Activity 13

On Your Own   Pair and Share   In a Group

Materials oaktag, punchout pennies

Write the following menu for the "Fairy Tale Restaurant" on the chalkboard or on a large sheet of oaktag.

Baby Bear hot cereal	3¢
Chicken Little burger	5¢
Stone soup	3¢
Little Red Hen muffins	4¢
Rapunzel salad	4¢
Sleeping Beauty taco	5¢
Three Pigs cocoa	2¢
Goldilocks juice	1¢

Have each child select a food item and something to drink and tell how much his or her two choices cost in all. Then give each child 7 punchout pennies. Have volunteers point to various items on the menu. Ask others to use the pennies to buy each item, one at a time, and then show how much change they have left.

▲ **MAC Activity 13: Basic-to-Average**

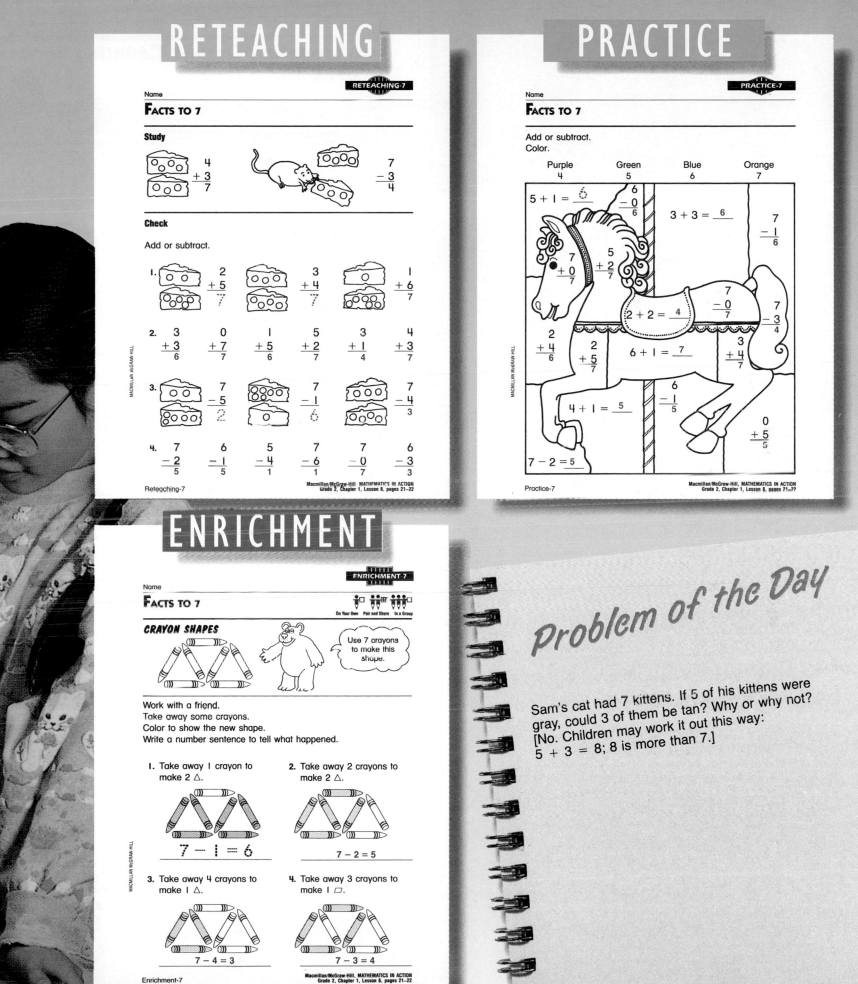

RETEACHING

FACTS TO 7

Study

$$\begin{array}{r} 4 \\ +\ 3 \\ \hline 7 \end{array}$$

$$\begin{array}{r} 7 \\ -\ 3 \\ \hline 4 \end{array}$$

Check

Add or subtract.

1. $\begin{array}{r} 2 \\ +5 \\ \hline 7 \end{array}$ $\begin{array}{r} 3 \\ +4 \\ \hline 7 \end{array}$ $\begin{array}{r} 1 \\ +6 \\ \hline 7 \end{array}$

2. $\begin{array}{r} 3 \\ +3 \\ \hline 6 \end{array}$ $\begin{array}{r} 0 \\ +7 \\ \hline 7 \end{array}$ $\begin{array}{r} 1 \\ +5 \\ \hline 6 \end{array}$ $\begin{array}{r} 5 \\ +2 \\ \hline 7 \end{array}$ $\begin{array}{r} 3 \\ +1 \\ \hline 4 \end{array}$ $\begin{array}{r} 4 \\ +3 \\ \hline 7 \end{array}$

3. $\begin{array}{r} 7 \\ -5 \\ \hline 2 \end{array}$ $\begin{array}{r} 7 \\ -1 \\ \hline 6 \end{array}$ $\begin{array}{r} 7 \\ -4 \\ \hline 3 \end{array}$

4. $\begin{array}{r} 7 \\ -2 \\ \hline 5 \end{array}$ $\begin{array}{r} 6 \\ -1 \\ \hline 5 \end{array}$ $\begin{array}{r} 5 \\ -4 \\ \hline 1 \end{array}$ $\begin{array}{r} 7 \\ -6 \\ \hline 1 \end{array}$ $\begin{array}{r} 7 \\ -0 \\ \hline 7 \end{array}$ $\begin{array}{r} 6 \\ -3 \\ \hline 3 \end{array}$

PRACTICE

FACTS TO 7

Add or subtract.
Color.

Purple	Green	Blue	Orange
4	5	6	7

$5 + 1 = 6$

$\begin{array}{r} 6 \\ -0 \\ \hline 6 \end{array}$

$3 + 3 = 6$

$\begin{array}{r} 7 \\ -1 \\ \hline 6 \end{array}$

$\begin{array}{r} 7 \\ +0 \\ \hline 7 \end{array}$ $\begin{array}{r} 5 \\ +2 \\ \hline 7 \end{array}$

$2 + 2 = 4$

$\begin{array}{r} 7 \\ -0 \\ \hline 7 \end{array}$

$\begin{array}{r} 7 \\ -3 \\ \hline 4 \end{array}$

$\begin{array}{r} 2 \\ +4 \\ \hline 6 \end{array}$ $\begin{array}{r} 2 \\ +5 \\ \hline 7 \end{array}$ $6 + 1 = 7$ $\begin{array}{r} 3 \\ +4 \\ \hline 7 \end{array}$

$4 + 1 = 5$

$\begin{array}{r} 6 \\ -1 \\ \hline 5 \end{array}$

$\begin{array}{r} 0 \\ +5 \\ \hline 5 \end{array}$

$7 - 2 = 5$

ENRICHMENT

FACTS TO 7

On Your Own   Pair and Share   In a Group

CRAYON SHAPES

Use 7 crayons to make this shape.

Work with a friend.
Take away some crayons.
Color to show the new shape.
Write a number sentence to tell what happened.

1. Take away 1 crayon to make 2 △.

$7 - 1 = 6$

2. Take away 2 crayons to make 2 △.

$7 - 2 = 5$

3. Take away 4 crayons to make 1 △.

$7 - 4 = 3$

4. Take away 3 crayons to make 1 ▢.

$7 - 3 = 4$

Problem of the Day

Sam's cat had 7 kittens. If 5 of his kittens were gray, could 3 of them be tan? Why or why not? [No. Children may work it out this way: $5 + 3 = 8$; 8 is more than 7.]

AT·A·GLANCE pp. 23-24

LESSON OBJECTIVES

Count on to add.
Count back to subtract.

ASSIGNMENT GUIDE

COURSE	EXERCISES
Basic	p. 23: 1–4; p. 24: 1–5
Average	p. 23: 1–4; p. 24: 1–5
Challenge	p. 23: 1–4; p. 24: 1–5

Teacher Resources
Reteaching 8
MAC Act. 15, 16
Practice 8
Teacher Aids 11, 12
Enrichment 8
Calculator 1

SKILLS TRACE

FACTS TO 10

Explore (Concrete)	Develop/Understand (Transitional/Abstract)
10	11, 12, 13–14, 15–16, 19–20, 21–22, 23–24, 29–30, 31–32, 33–34, 35–36, 37, 38
Practice 20, 28, 32, 43, 44, 45–46, 49, 60	**Apply** 17–18, 25–26, 27, 39–40, 41, 42

See **MANIPULATIVES PLUS 6–7**, pp. 8N–8O.

Counting On and Counting Back

Flo will roll the yarn forward 1 more.

What number will she stop on? __5__

You can count on to add.

> I want to find 4 + 2.

Start with 4.
Count on to add 2.
4 + 2 = 6

Count on to add.

1. 4 + 1 = __5__   6 + 1 = __7__   5 + 2 = __7__

2. 2 + 1 = __3__   5 + 1 = __6__   3 + 2 = __5__

3. 3 + 1 = __4__   2 + 2 = __4__   4 + 3 = __7__

4. Tell how you can count on to add 2 + 5.

In their own words, children should note that the order of the addends can be changed.

Chapter 1   Adding and Subtracting Facts to 10

Macmillan/McGraw-Hill

twenty-three   **23**

---

1 PREPARE

WARM-UP To review fact families, write these pairs of addition and subtraction sentences on the chalkboard.

    4 + 2 = 6   6 − 4 = 2
    [2 + 4 = 6,   6 − 2 = 4]
    3 + 4 = 7   7 − 3 = 4
    [4 + 3 = 7,   7 − 4 = 3]
    2 + 1 = 3   3 − 2 = 1
    [1 + 2 = 3,   3 − 1 = 2]

Have children tell the two related number sentences that complete each fact family.

2 TEACH

DISCUSSING Write an addition sentence on the chalkboard below a number line.

    0 1 2 3 4 5 6 7 8 9 10

3 + 2 = ____

Guide children in discussing how they could use the number line to help them find the sum if they could not remember a fact. Have a volunteer point to each number on the number line as the class counts from 1 to 3 and then 4, 5 to find the sum. Explain that an easier and faster way to count is by starting at 3 and then **counting on** 4, 5. Repeat several times with other facts.

Flo will roll the yarn back 1.

What number will she stop on? __5__

You can count back to subtract.

I want to find 6 − 2.

Start at 6.
Count back to subtract 2.
6 − 2 = 4

6 – 5 – 4

Count back to subtract.

1. 6 − 1 = __5__   7 − 2 = __5__   5 − 1 = __4__

2. 2 − 1 = __1__   4 − 2 = __2__   5 − 2 = __3__

3. 4 − 1 = __3__   3 − 1 = __2__   7 − 3 = __4__

Write the subtraction sentence.

4. Jane has 5 🧢 .

She gives 1 🧢 to Ed.

How many 🧢 does

she have left?

__5 − 1 = 4__

5. Bob had 7 🧣 .

He gave 2 🧣 away.

How many 🧣

does he have left?

__7 − 2 = 5__

Write a subtraction sentence on the chalkboard below a number line.

0 1 2 3 4 5 6 7 8 9 10

5 − 2 = ____

Demonstrate **counting back** by placing your finger or a pointer on 5 and counting back 4, 3. Repeat this procedure with several more facts, asking volunteers to demonstrate counting back on the number line.

PUPIL'S EDITION pp. 23-24

Page 23 Guide children through the examples at the top of the page.

MEETING INDIVIDUAL NEEDS

ACTIVITY **ALTERNATIVE TEACHING STRATEGY**

MATERIALS punchout inch rulers

KINESTHETIC Demonstrate how to use an inch ruler as a number line. Present the exercise 6 + 1. Have children point to the 6 and count on 1 to find the sum of 7. Repeat the activity for 7 − 1 and have children count back. Continue to present pairs of related addition and subtraction facts.

| 5 + 2 [7] | 4 + 3 [7] | 3 + 4 [7] | 2 + 5 [7] |
| 7 − 2 [5] | 7 − 3 [4] | 7 − 4 [3] | 7 − 5 [2] |

TEACHER to TEACHER

MANIPULATIVES TIP I had my children tape number lines to their desks. This helped remind them to use strategies rather than guessing.

ACTIVITY *Common Error and Remediation*

MATERIALS 7 ○ (or punchouts)

Some children may count on to find the sum but then get an answer that is one number less than the correct sum. Work individually with each child. Have the child solve addition problems using counters. Listen as the child verbalizes the process to make sure he or she is not counting on starting with the addend. For example, for 5 + 2, the child push the first 5 count on 5, 6 instead of 6, 7. Have the child push the first 5 counters aside as he or she says 5. Then have the child count the remaining counters as 6, 7.

Check for Understanding

■ **Where do you begin to count on for the fact 4 + 3?** [from 4]

GUIDED PRACTICE ex. 1–4: For reteaching, use Common Error and Remediation or Alternative Strategy.

Page 24 Guide children through the example at the top of the page.

PRACTICE・APPLY **PRACTICE** ex. 1–5

CLOSE Guide children to summarize the lesson:

■ **Show how you count on to solve 3 + 3.** [Child should point to 3 on number line and counts 4, 5, 6.] **to solve 6 − 2.** [Child should point to 6 on number line and counts 5, 4.]

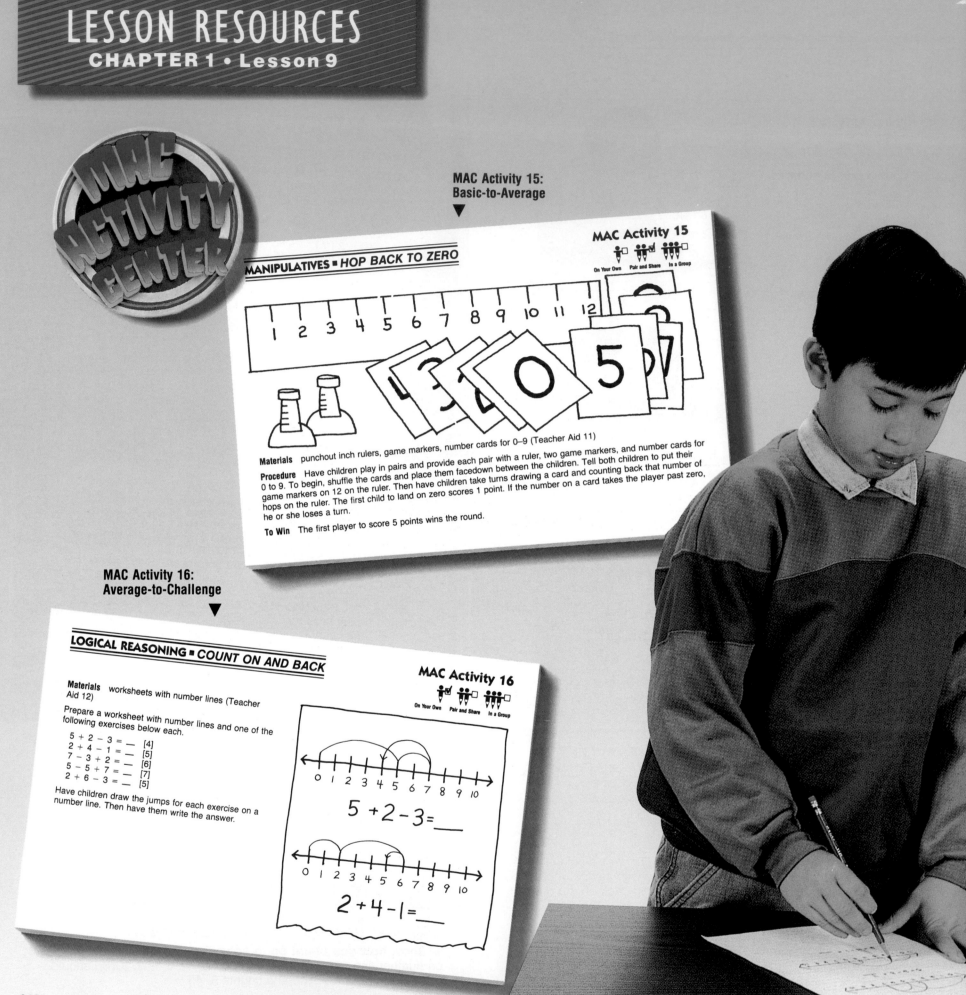

**MAC Activity 15:
Basic-to-Average**
▼

MANIPULATIVES ■ HOP BACK TO ZERO

MAC Activity 15

On Your Own   Pair and Share   In a Group

Materials   punchout inch rulers, game markers, number cards for 0–9 (Teacher Aid 11)

Procedure   Have children play in pairs and provide each pair with a ruler, two game markers, and number cards for 0 to 9. To begin, shuffle the cards and place them facedown between the children. Tell both children to put their game markers on 12 on the ruler. Then have children take turns drawing a card and counting back that number of hops on the ruler. The first child to land on zero scores 1 point. If the number on a card takes the player past zero, he or she loses a turn.

To Win   The first player to score 5 points wins the round.

**MAC Activity 16:
Average-to-Challenge**
▼

LOGICAL REASONING ■ COUNT ON AND BACK

MAC Activity 16

On Your Own   Pair and Share   In a Group

Materials   worksheets with number lines (Teacher Aid 12)

Prepare a worksheet with number lines and one of the following exercises below each.

5 + 2 − 3 = —   [4]
2 + 4 − 1 = —   [5]
7 − 3 + 2 = —   [6]
5 − 5 + 7 = —   [7]
2 + 6 − 3 = —   [5]

Have children draw the jumps for each exercise on a number line. Then have them write the answer.

0 1 2 3 4 5 6 7 8 9 10

5 + 2 − 3 = __

0 1 2 3 4 5 6 7 8 9 10

2 + 4 − 1 = __

RETEACHING

Name

COUNTING ON AND COUNTING BACK

Study

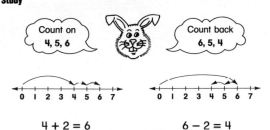

Count on
4, 5, 6

Count back
6, 5, 4

$$4 + 2 = 6 \qquad 6 - 2 = 4$$

Check

Count on to add. | Count back to subtract.

1. $5 + 1 = 6$ | 6. $5 - 2 = 3$

2. $4 + 3 = 7$ | 7. $7 - 1 = 6$

3. $6 + 1 = 7$ | 8. $7 - 2 = 5$

4. $5 + 2 = 7$ | 9. $6 - 1 = 5$

5. $3 + 2 = 5$ | 10. $5 - 3 = 2$

Macmillan/McGraw-Hill, MATHEMATICS IN ACTION
Grade 2, Chapter 1, Lesson 9, pages 23–24

Reteaching-8

PRACTICE

Name

COUNTING ON AND COUNTING BACK

Count on to add.

1. $1 + 1 = 2$ $\qquad$ $3 + 2 = 5$

2. $5 + 2 = 7$ $\qquad$ $4 + 1 = 5$

3. $4 + 2 = 6$ $\qquad$ $4 + 3 = 7$

4. $6 + 1 = 7$ $\qquad$ $3 + 3 = 6$

Count back to subtract.

5. $7 - 1 = 6$ $\qquad$ $5 - 2 = 3$

6. $6 - 2 = 4$ $\qquad$ $4 - 1 = 3$

7. $4 - 2 = 2$ $\qquad$ $5 - 1 = 4$

8. $3 - 1 = 2$ $\qquad$ $7 - 2 = 5$

Macmillan/McGraw-Hill, MATHEMATICS IN ACTION
Grade 2, Chapter 1, Lesson 9, pages 23–24

Practice-8

ENRICHMENT

On Your Own Pair and Share In a Group

Name

COUNTING ON AND COUNTING BACK

WHERE IS WILLIAM?

William and 7 of his friends live on the same street.

Solve.

1. William went to Ned's house. Then he walked back 2 houses. Where is he now? — **Joe's house**

2. William went to Kim's house. Then he walked on 3 houses. Where is he now? — **Nan's house**

Write your own William problems.
Share them with a friend.

3. _____ **Answers will vary.** _____

4. _____

Macmillan/McGraw-Hill, MATHEMATICS IN ACTION
Grade 2, Chapter 1, Lesson 9, pages 23–24

Enrichment-8

Problem of the Day

Eva had 7 books. She gave away 4 books. Then she got 2 more books. How many books does she have now? [5. Children may work it out this way: $7 - 4 = 3; 3 + 2 = 5$.]

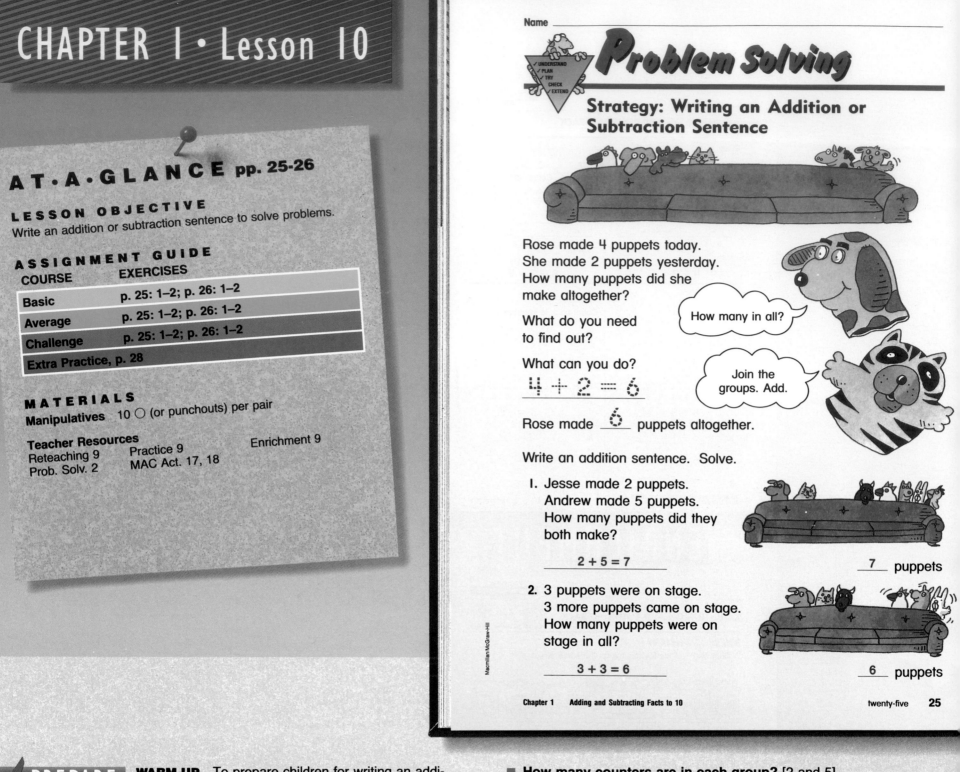

AT·A·GLANCE pp. 25-26

LESSON OBJECTIVE
Write an addition or subtraction sentence to solve problems.

ASSIGNMENT GUIDE

COURSE	EXERCISES
Basic	p. 25: 1–2; p. 26: 1–2
Average	p. 25: 1–2; p. 26: 1–2
Challenge	p. 25: 1–2; p. 26: 1–2
Extra Practice, p. 28	

MATERIALS
Manipulatives 10 ○ (or punchouts) per pair

Teacher Resources
Reteaching 9   Practice 9   Enrichment 9
Prob. Solv. 2   MAC Act. 17, 18

PREPARE   **WARM-UP**   To prepare children for writing an addition or subtraction sentence to solve a problem, have them give the following sums and differences.

$3 + 5$ [8] $7 + 2$ [9] $9 - 2$ [7] $6 - 5$ [1]

TEACH   **DISCUSSING**   Assign children to work in pairs. Give each pair of children a set of ten counters. Explain that you will read a problem aloud and then they will use their counters to model the numbers in the problem.

Tanya baked 2 pies today.
She baked 5 pies yesterday.
How many pies did she bake in all?

■ **How many groups of counters did you make?** [2]

■ **How many counters are in each group?** [2 and 5]
■ **What do we need to find out?** [the number of pies in all]
■ **How can we find how many in all?** [Combine 2 counters and 5 counters or add $2 + 5 = 7$.]

PUPIL'S EDITION pp. 25-26

Page 25   Have a volunteer read the problem at the top of the page.
■ **What do you know?** [Rose made 4 puppets and 2 puppets.]
Discuss the questions on the page. Guide children to see that they must find the total number of puppets made, or how many in all. Discuss joining groups by adding.

■ **Does the answer 6 make sense?** [Yes, joining 4 and 2, gives 6.]
■ **What did you learn?** [Add to find how many in all.]

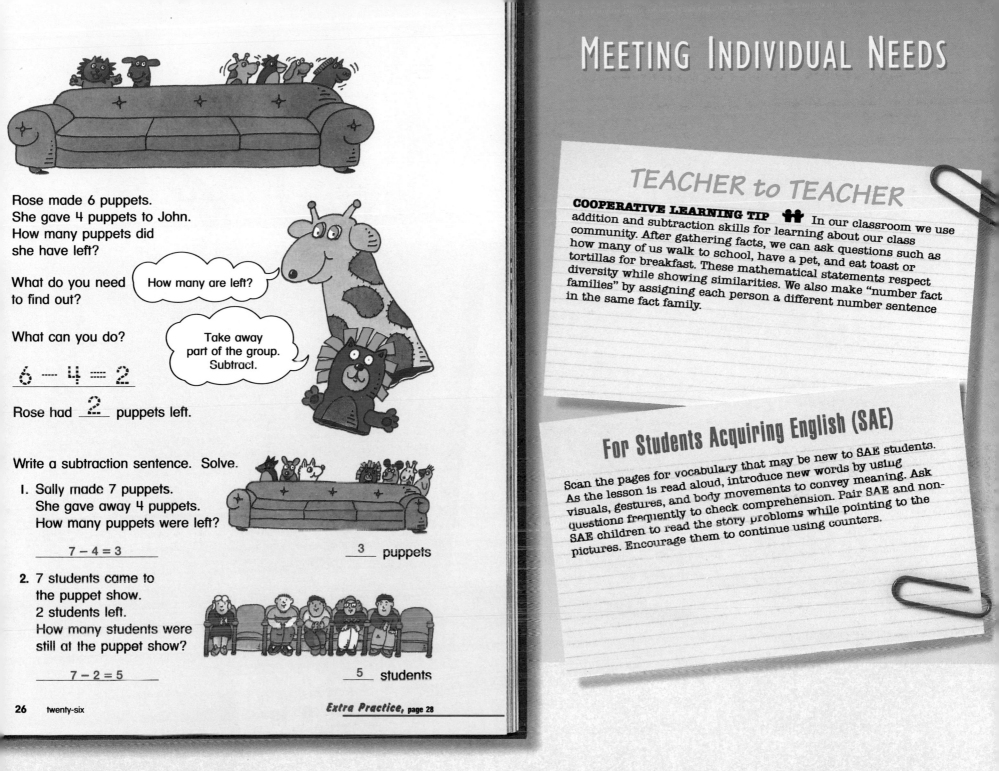

Encourage children to explain other ways to solve this problem.

Check for Understanding

■ **What if Rose made 3 puppets yesterday and 1 puppet today? How many puppets would she have made?** [4]

GUIDED PRACTICE ex. 1–2: Work through problem 1 with the children. Make sure they understand how to solve the problem by writing an addition sentence.

Page 26 Have a volunteer read the problem at the top of the page.

■ **What do you know?** [Rose made 6 puppets and she gave 4 away.]

Discuss the questions on the page. Guide children to see that they have to find how many puppets Rose has left. Have a volunteer tell how to find the answer by subtracting.

■ **What did you learn?** [When you have a group of things and you take some away, you subtract to find how many things are left.]

Encourage children to explain other ways to solve the problem.

3 PRACTICE•APPLY **PRACTICE** ex. 1–2

CLOSE Guide children to summarize the lesson:

■ **How do you know if you should add or subtract to solve a problem?** [Possible response: You add to join two groups; you subtract when you separate a group and take some away.]

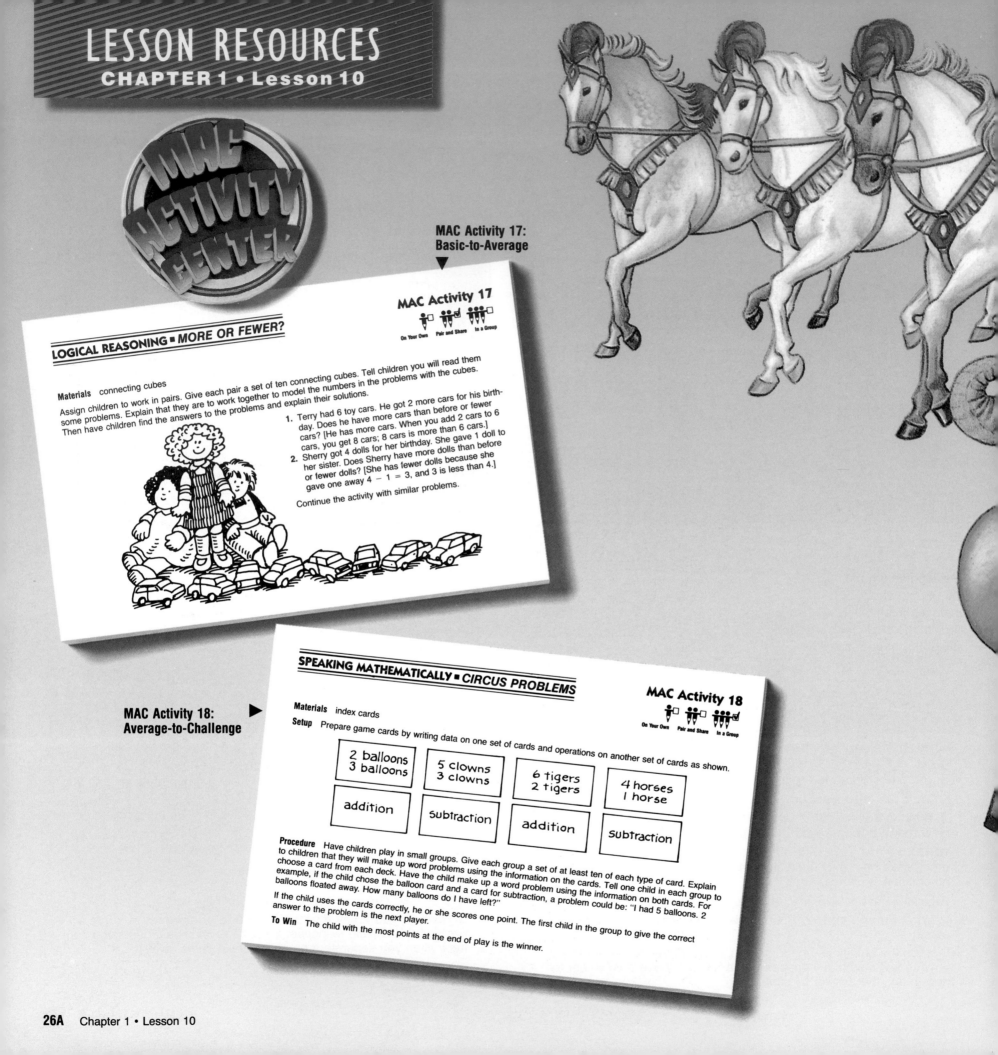

MAC Activity 17:
Basic-to-Average

MAC Activity 17

On Your Own   Pair and Share   In a Group

LOGICAL REASONING ▪ MORE OR FEWER?

Materials connecting cubes

Assign children to work in pairs. Give each pair a set of ten connecting cubes. Tell children you will read them some problems. Explain that they are to work together to model the numbers in the problems with the cubes. Then have children find the answers to the problems and explain their solutions.

1. Terry had 6 toy cars. He got 2 more cars for his birthday. Does he have more cars than before or fewer cars? [He has more cars. When you add 2 cars to 6 cars, you get 8 cars; 8 cars is more than 6 cars.]
2. Sherry got 4 dolls for her birthday. She gave 1 doll to her sister. Does Sherry have more dolls than before or fewer dolls? [She has fewer dolls because she gave one away 4 − 1 = 3, and 3 is less than 4.]

Continue the activity with similar problems.

MAC Activity 18:
Average-to-Challenge

SPEAKING MATHEMATICALLY ▪ CIRCUS PROBLEMS

MAC Activity 18

On Your Own   Pair and Share   In a Group

Materials index cards

Setup Prepare game cards by writing data on one set of cards and operations on another set of cards as shown.

2 balloons 3 balloons	5 clowns 3 clowns	6 tigers 2 tigers	4 horses 1 horse
addition	subtraction	addition	subtraction

Procedure Have children play in small groups. Give each group a set of at least ten of each type of card. Explain to children that they will make up word problems using the information on the cards. Tell one child in each group to choose a card from each deck. Have the child make up a word problem using the information on both cards. For example, if the child chose the balloon card and a card for subtraction, a problem could be: "I had 5 balloons. 2 balloons floated away. How many balloons do I have left?"

If the child uses the cards correctly, he or she scores one point. The first child in the group to give the correct answer to the problem is the next player.

To Win The child with the most points at the end of play is the winner.

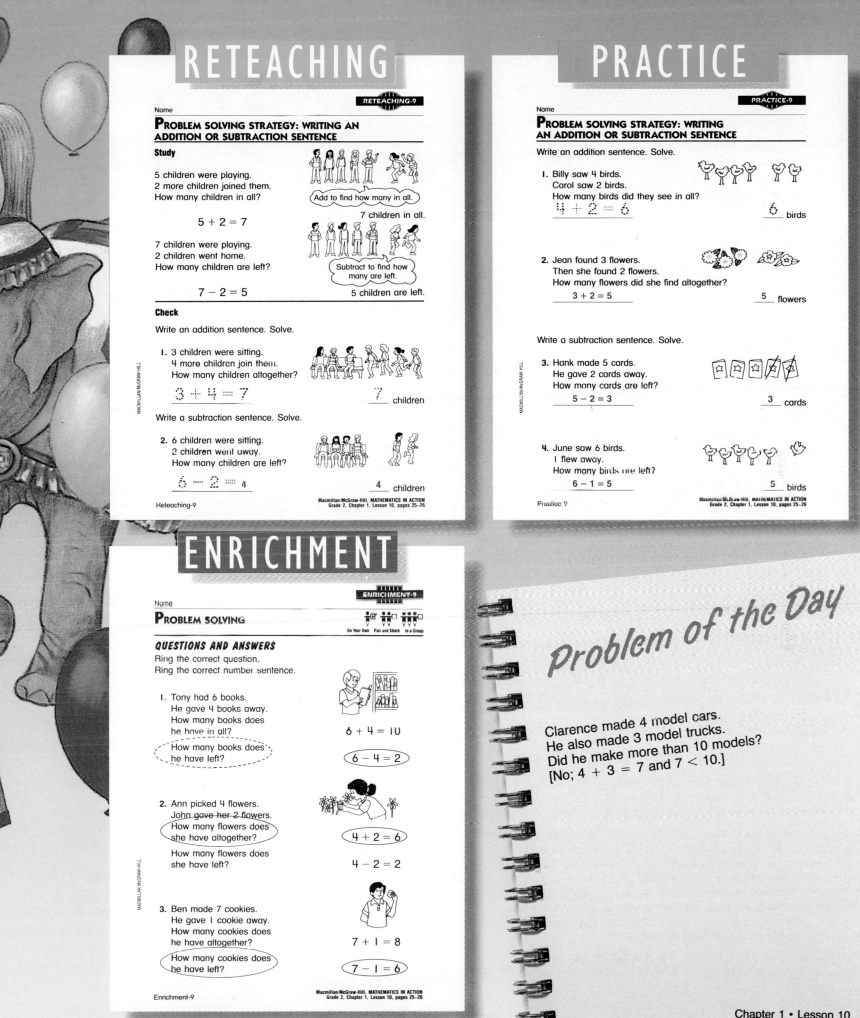

RETEACHING

Name

PROBLEM SOLVING STRATEGY: WRITING AN ADDITION OR SUBTRACTION SENTENCE

Study

5 children were playing.
2 more children joined them.
How many children in all?

Add to find how many in all.

$5 + 2 = 7$

7 children in all.

7 children were playing.
2 children went home.
How many children are left?

Subtract to find how many are left.

$7 - 2 = 5$

5 children are left.

Check

Write an addition sentence. Solve.

1. 3 children were sitting.
4 more children join them.
How many children altogether?

$3 + 4 = 7$

_7_ children

Write a subtraction sentence. Solve.

2. 6 children were sitting.
2 children went away.
How many children are left?

$6 - 2 = 4$

_4_ children

Reteaching-9

Macmillan/McGraw-Hill, MATHEMATICS IN ACTION
Grade 2, Chapter 1, Lesson 10, pages 25–26

PRACTICE

Name

PROBLEM SOLVING STRATEGY: WRITING AN ADDITION OR SUBTRACTION SENTENCE

Write an addition sentence. Solve.

1. Billy saw 4 birds.
Carol saw 2 birds.
How many birds did they see in all?

$4 + 2 = 6$

_6_ birds

2. Jean found 3 flowers.
Then she found 2 flowers.
How many flowers did she find altogether?

$3 + 2 = 5$

_5_ flowers

Write a subtraction sentence. Solve.

3. Hank made 5 cards.
He gave 2 cards away.
How many cards are left?

$5 - 2 = 3$

_3_ cards

4. June saw 6 birds.
1 flew away.
How many birds are left?

$6 - 1 = 5$

_5_ birds

Practice-9

Macmillan/McGraw-Hill, MATHEMATICS IN ACTION
Grade 2, Chapter 1, Lesson 10, pages 25–26

ENRICHMENT

Name

PROBLEM SOLVING

On Your Own   Pair and Share   Is a Group

QUESTIONS AND ANSWERS

Ring the correct question.
Ring the correct number sentence.

1. Tony had 6 books.
He gave 4 books away.
How many books does
he have in all?

$6 + 4 = 10$

How many books does
he have left?

$6 - 4 = 2$

2. Ann picked 4 flowers.
John gave her 2 flowers.
How many flowers does
she have altogether?

$4 + 2 = 6$

How many flowers does
she have left?

$4 - 2 = 2$

3. Ben made 7 cookies.
He gave 1 cookie away.
How many cookies does
he have altogether?

$7 + 1 = 8$

How many cookies does
he have left?

$7 - 1 = 6$

Enrichment-9

Macmillan/McGraw-Hill, MATHEMATICS IN ACTION
Grade 2, Chapter 1, Lesson 10, pages 25–26

Problem of the Day

Clarence made 4 model cars.
He also made 3 model trucks.
Did he make more than 10 models?
[No; $4 + 3 = 7$ and $7 < 10$.]

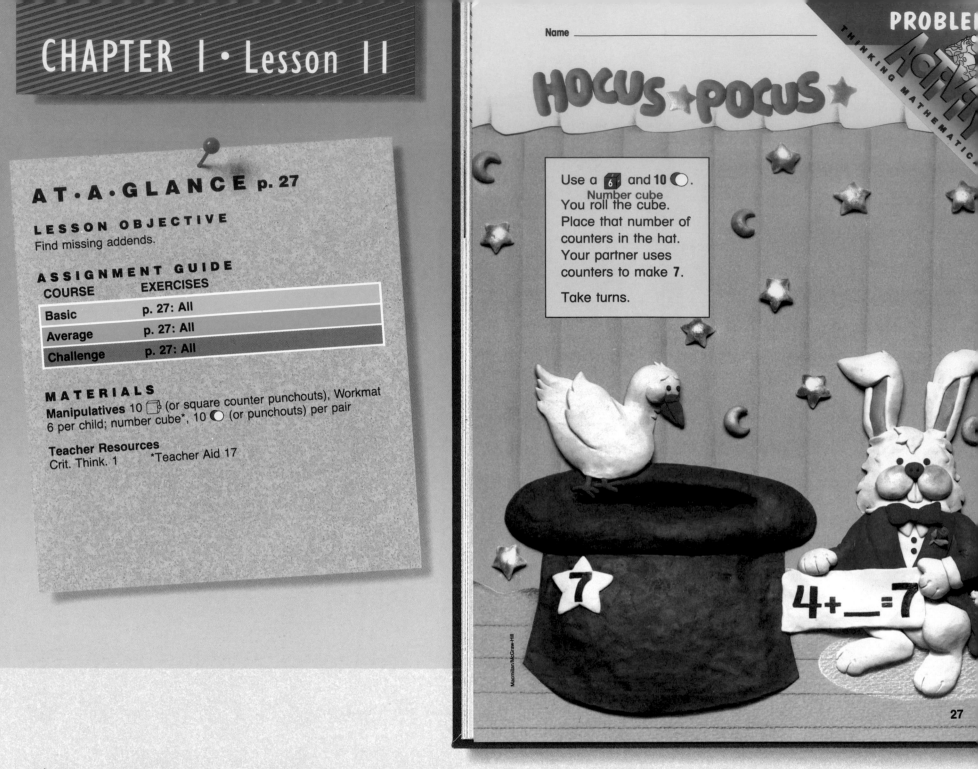

Name _____

HOCUS ★POCUS★

Use a 🎲 and 10 ⚪.
Number cube
You roll the cube.
Place that number of
counters in the hat.
Your partner uses
counters to make **7**.

Take turns.

7

4+__=7

Macmillan/McGraw-Hill

27

AT·A·GLANCE p. 27

LESSON OBJECTIVE
Find missing addends.

ASSIGNMENT GUIDE

COURSE	EXERCISES
Basic	p. 27: All
Average	p. 27: All
Challenge	p. 27: All

MATERIALS
Manipulatives 10 ⬜ (or square counter punchouts), Workmat 6 per child; number cube*, 10 ⚪ (or punchouts) per pair

Teacher Resources
Crit. Think. 1   *Teacher Aid 17

1 **PLAN**   **AIMS AND ATTITUDES** This lesson develops number sense by having children play a game involving missing addends. Stress the gamelike quality of the activity.

Encourage children to verbalize the method they use to find the missing addend. Some children may see the problem as addition (count on from the number shown on the number cube until the number 7 is reached). Other children may see the problem as subtraction (minus the number shown on the number cube). Asking a child to verbalize the process used will give you some insight into the child's reasoning process and help other children understand that there are often several ways to approach the same problem.

MANAGEMENT The activity is intended for all children and has been designed for pairs of children. It is also appropriate for small-group

work. Pairing a child having strong problem-solving skills with one having weaker skills may be particularly effective.

2 **GUIDE**   Give each child 10 connecting cubes. Have children place 5 cubes on Workmat 6.

■ **How many more cubes are needed to make 7?** [2]

Have children clear the workmats and place 3 cubes on the mats.

■ **How many more cubes are needed to make 6?** [3]

After the workmats are clear, let them place 1 cube on the mats.

■ **How many more cubes are needed to make 6?** [5]

Identify the pictures on page 27 with the children. Point out the number 7 on the hat.

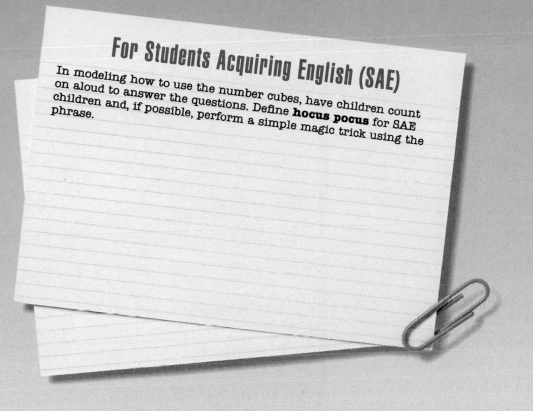

For Students Acquiring English (SAE)

In modeling how to use the number cubes, have children count on aloud to answer the questions. Define **hocus pocus** for SAE children and, if possible, perform a simple magic trick using the phrase.

■ **How many counters in all must be put on the hat?** [7]

■ **How many counters do you start with?** [the number rolled on the cube]

Assign children to work in pairs. Give each pair a number cube and 10 counters. Remind children to take turns rolling the cube. Have them describe how they went about finding the missing addends. Discuss differences in approaches with the class.

 **EXTEND** Have pairs play the game again. This time, have them find the number of counters needed to make 9 counters in all on the hat.

EXTRA PRACTICE

Extra Practice items are provided so that children may have an opportunity for further practice.

The *Additional Practice* section also provides practice you may wish to assign.

Extra Practice

Facts to 7, pages 21–22 . . . .
Write the fact family for the picture.

1.
$4 + 3 = 7$ $7 - 4 = 3$

$3 + 4 = 7$ $7 - 3 = 4$

2.
$5 + 1 = 6$ $6 - 1 = 5$

$1 + 5 = 6$ $6 - 5 = 1$

Add or subtract.

3.
4	2	6	1	5	2
$+2$	$+4$	$+1$	$+6$	$+2$	$+5$
6	6	7	7	7	7

4.
6	6	7	7	6	6
-0	-6	-2	-5	-4	-2
6	0	5	2	2	4

Problem Solving: Writing an Addition or Subtraction Sentence, pages 25–26 . . . .
Write an addition sentence. Solve.

1. 4 children were singing.
3 more children came.
How many children in all?

$4 + 3 = 7$ 7 children

ADDITIONAL PRACTICE

p. 21 *Write the fact family for the picture.*

1.

[4 + 2 = 6]
[2 + 4 = 6]
[6 − 4 = 2]
[6 − 2 = 4]

2.

[1 + 6 = 7]
[6 + 1 = 7]
[7 − 6 = 1]
[7 − 1 = 6]

Add or subtract.

1.
6	6	7	0	3	4
-1	-5	$+0$	$+7$	$+4$	$+3$
[5]	[1]	[7]	[7]	[7]	[7]

2.
7	7	7	7	4	1
-4	-3	-6	-1	$+1$	$+4$
[3]	[4]	[1]	[6]	[5]	[5]

3.
5	1	6	6	4	4
$+1$	$+5$	-1	-5	-3	-1
[6]	[6]	[5]	[1]	[1]	[3]

p. 25 *Write a subtraction sentence. Then solve.*

1. Ben has 7 kites. 3 fly away. How many kites does he have left?
   [7 − 3 = 4] [4] kites

2. Sara makes 6 pies. She gives 4 pies to Jack. How many pies does she have left?
   [6 − 4 = 2] [2] pies

Write an addition sentence. Then solve.

3. Ellen buys 2 balloons. Dad gives her 5 more. How many balloons does she have in all?
   [2 + 5 = 7] [7] balloons

4. Zack has 1 toy car. Zack gets 4 more toy cars. How many toy cars does he have in all?
   [1 + 4 = 5] [5] toy cars

AT·A·GLANCE pp. 29-30

LESSON OBJECTIVE
Add and subtract facts to 8.

ASSIGNMENT GUIDE

COURSE	EXERCISES
Basic	p. 29: 2–10; p. 30: 1–4, Mental Math
Average	p. 29: 2–10; p. 30: 1–4, Mental Math
Challenge	p. 29: 2–10; p. 30: 1–4, Mental Math

MATERIALS
Classroom Materials red and yellow crayons
Manipulatives 8 ○ (or punchouts) per child

Teacher Resources
Reteaching 10   Practice 10   Enrichment 10
MAC Act. 19, 20

SKILLS TRACE

FACTS TO 10	
Explore (Concrete) 10	**Develop/Understand (Transitional/Abstract)** 11, 12, 13–14, 15–16, 19–20, 21–22, 23–24, 29–30, 31–32, 33–34, 35–36, 37, 38
Practice 20, 28, 32, 43, 44, 45–46, 49, 60	**Apply** 17–18, 25–26, 27, 39–40, 41, 42

Name _____

Facts to 8

Use 8 ○,

a ▬▬ red ▬▬ , and

a ▬▬ yellow ▬▬ .

Use counters to show the facts.
Color to show the facts.

Write the sum.   Write the difference.

1. 8 + 0 = 8   ●●●●●●●●   8 − 0 = 8

2. 7 + 1 = 8   (r)(r)(r)(r)(r)(r)(r)(y)   8 − 1 = 7

3. 6 + 2 = 8   (r)(r)(r)(r)(r)(r)(y)(y)   8 − 2 = 6

4. 5 + 3 = 8   (r)(r)(r)(r)(r)(y)(y)(y)   8 − 3 = 5

5. 4 + 4 = 8   (r)(r)(r)(r)(y)(y)(y)(y)   8 − 4 = 4

6. 3 + 5 = 8   (r)(r)(r)(y)(y)(y)(y)(y)   8 − 5 = 3

7. 2 + 6 = 8   (r)(r)(y)(y)(y)(y)(y)(y)   8 − 6 = 2

8. 1 + 7 = 8   (r)(y)(y)(y)(y)(y)(y)(y)   8 − 7 = 1

9. 0 + 8 = 8   (y)(y)(y)(y)(y)(y)(y)(y)   8 − 8 = 0

10. **Talk about the patterns.** Answers will vary. Possible answer: the numbers in the addition fact are the same as the numbers in the subtraction fact.

Chapter 1   Adding and Subtracting Facts to 10   twenty-nine   **29**

Macmillan/McGraw-Hill

---

1 PREPARE

WARM-UP To review facts for 7, ask children to give each of the following sums and differences orally.

1 + 6 [7]	7 − 1 [6]	3 + 4 [7]
2 + 5 [7]	7 − 2 [5]	7 − 3 [4]

2 TEACH

MODELING Have children display 1 red counter and 1 yellow counter.

■ **Say the addition fact for the counters.** [1 + 1 = 2]
■ **Say the subtraction fact for the counters.** [2 − 1 = 1]
Have children put down another red and another yellow counter.

■ **Name the addition fact and the subtraction fact for the model.** [2 + 2 = 4, 4 − 2 = 2]

Continue until they have 4 red counters and 4 yellow counters. At this time point out that all these facts are called **doubles** because in all of them both addends are the same.

PUPIL'S EDITION pp. 29-30

Page 29 Guide children through ex. 1.

Check for Understanding
■ **How could you use counters to show 8 − 4?** [Show 4 red counters and 4 yellow counters.]

GUIDED PRACTICE ex. 2–10: For reteaching, use Common Error and Remediation or Alternative Strategy.

Page 30 Have children tell how many facts are in the fact family shown in ex. 2. [2]

Write the fact family for each picture.

1.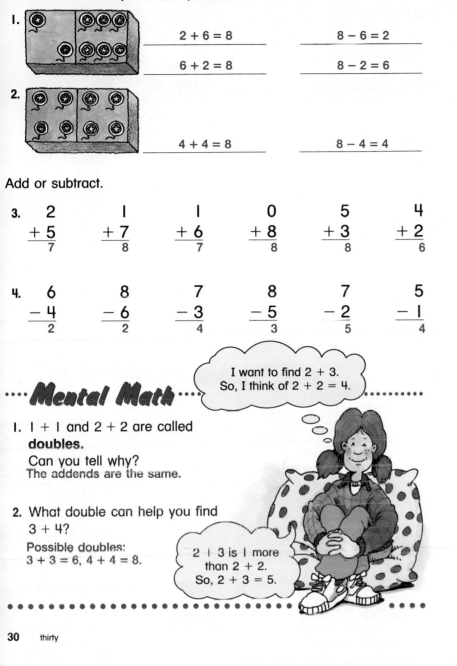

$$2 + 6 = 8 \qquad 8 - 6 = 2$$

$$6 + 2 = 8 \qquad 8 - 2 = 6$$

2.

$$4 + 4 = 8 \qquad 8 - 4 = 4$$

Add or subtract.

3.
$$\begin{array}{r} 2 \\ + 5 \\ \hline 7 \end{array} \qquad \begin{array}{r} 1 \\ + 7 \\ \hline 8 \end{array} \qquad \begin{array}{r} 1 \\ + 6 \\ \hline 7 \end{array} \qquad \begin{array}{r} 0 \\ + 8 \\ \hline 8 \end{array} \qquad \begin{array}{r} 5 \\ + 3 \\ \hline 8 \end{array} \qquad \begin{array}{r} 4 \\ + 2 \\ \hline 6 \end{array}$$

4.
$$\begin{array}{r} 6 \\ - 4 \\ \hline 2 \end{array} \qquad \begin{array}{r} 8 \\ - 6 \\ \hline 2 \end{array} \qquad \begin{array}{r} 7 \\ - 3 \\ \hline 4 \end{array} \qquad \begin{array}{r} 8 \\ - 5 \\ \hline 3 \end{array} \qquad \begin{array}{r} 7 \\ - 2 \\ \hline 5 \end{array} \qquad \begin{array}{r} 5 \\ - 1 \\ \hline 4 \end{array}$$

···· *Mental Math* ····

> I want to find $2 + 3$. So, I think of $2 + 2 = 4$.

1. $1 + 1$ and $2 + 2$ are called **doubles.**
   Can you tell why?
   The addends are the same.

2. What double can help you find $3 + 4$?
   Possible doubles:
   $3 + 3 = 6$, $4 + 4 = 8$.

> $2 + 3$ is 1 more than $2 + 2$. So, $2 + 3 = 5$.

ACTIVITY

ALTERNATIVE TEACHING STRATEGY

VISUAL/AUDITORY Ask 8 children to stand in a row at the front of the room. Tell 1 child to sit down as you say the subtraction sentence for this action, $8 - 1 = 7$. Tell the child to stand up again as you say the addition sentence, $7 + 1 = 8$. Repeat with different groups of 8 children to develop $8 - 2 = 6$ and $6 + 2 = 8$, $8 - 3 = 5$, and $5 + 3 = 8$. Continue the activity to develop other facts for 8.

For Students Acquiring English (SAE)

Practice by reviewing **plus, in all, minus, take away,** and **equals.** Pair SAE and non-SAE children to complete and read aloud ex. 1 to 9 on page 29. In discussing Mental Math, have heterogeneous pairs "build" and present facts with **doubles** using classroom objects.

ACTIVITY

Common Error and Remediation

MATERIALS 7 ◯ (or punchouts)

Some children may add when they should subtract, or vice versa. Work with each child. Tell the child to write a $+$ or $-$ in each answer circle.

$$4 \bigcirc 3 = 7 \; [+] \quad 6 \bigcirc 2 = 4 \; [-] \quad 5 \bigcirc 1 = 4 \; [-] \quad 2 \bigcirc 5 = 7 \; [+]$$

Then have the child use counters to check the sum or difference. Remind the child to think about whether the size of each answer makes sense in relation to the size of the other two numbers in the exercise.

3 PRACTICE•APPLY   **PRACTICE**   ex. 1–4

MENTAL MATH   Discuss how doubles can be used to help children find answers to other facts.

CLOSE   Guide children to summarize the lesson:
- **What fact family can you write for the numbers 1, 7, and 8?**
  $[1 + 7 = 8, \; 7 + 1 = 8, \; 8 - 7 = 1, \; 8 - 1 = 7]$

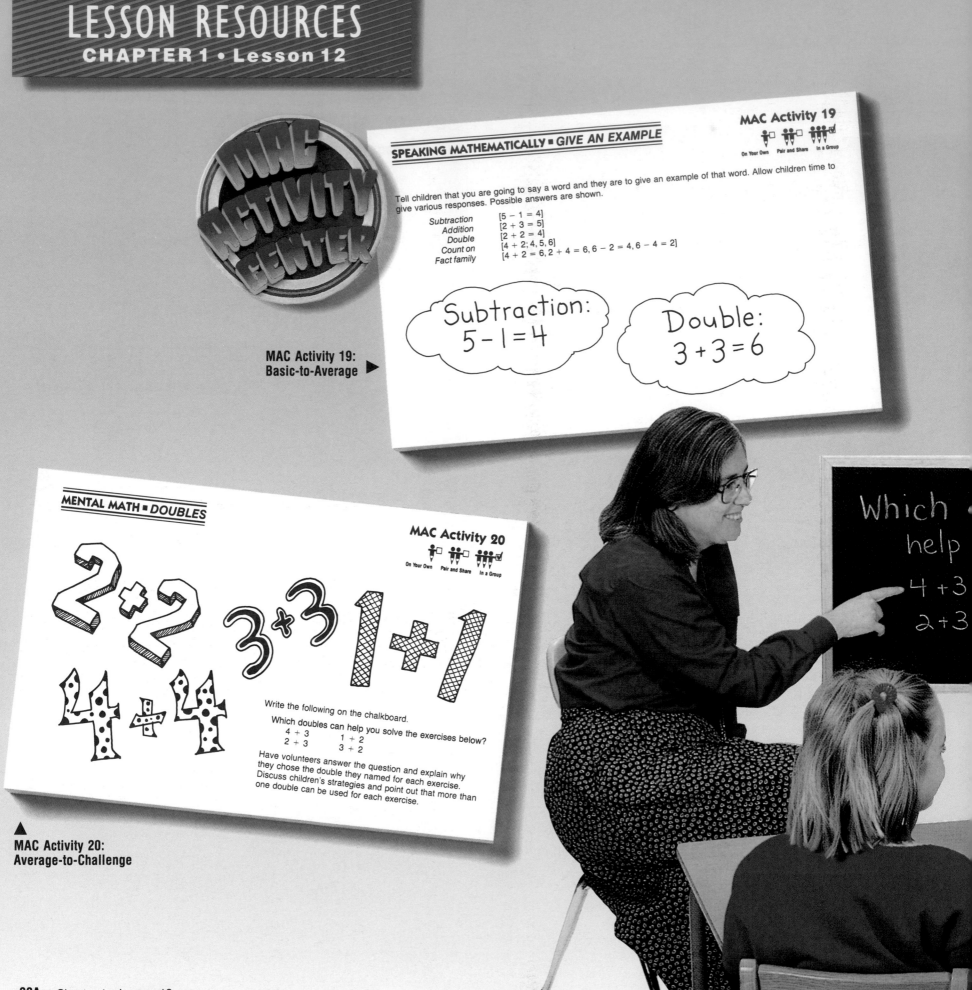

MAC Activity 19

On Your Own   Pair and Share   In a Group

SPEAKING MATHEMATICALLY ▪ GIVE AN EXAMPLE

Tell children that you are going to say a word and they are to give an example of that word. Allow children time to give various responses. Possible answers are shown.

Subtraction	$[5 - 1 = 4]$
Addition	$[2 + 3 = 5]$
Double	$[2 + 2 = 4]$
Count on	$[4 + 2; 4, 5, 6]$
Fact family	$[4 + 2 = 6, 2 + 4 = 6, 6 - 2 = 4, 6 - 4 = 2]$

Subtraction:
5 – 1 = 4

Double:
3 + 3 = 6

MAC Activity 19:
Basic-to-Average ▶

MENTAL MATH ▪ DOUBLES

2 + 2   3 + 3   1 + 1

4 + 4

MAC Activity 20

On Your Own   Pair and Share   In a Group

Write the following on the chalkboard.

Which doubles can help you solve the exercises below?

| 4 + 3 | 1 + 2 |
| 2 + 3 | 3 + 2 |

Have volunteers answer the question and explain why they chose the double they named for each exercise. Discuss children's strategies and point out that more than one double can be used for each exercise.

▲
MAC Activity 20:
Average-to-Challenge

Which
help
4 + 3
2 + 3

RETEACHING

Name _____

FACTS TO 8

Study

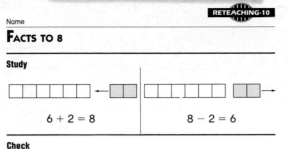

$6 + 2 = 8$ $8 - 2 = 6$

Check

Add or subtract.

1.
$3 + 5 = 8$
$8 - 5 = 3$

2.
$1 + 7 = 8$
$8 - 7 = 1$

3.
$4 + 4 = 8$
$8 - 4 = 4$

---

4. $7 - 2 = 5$
$8 - 1 = 7$
$6 - 2 = 4$
$5 - 0 = 5$
$8 - 8 = 0$

5. $8 + 0 = 8$
$5 + 3 = 8$
$2 + 5 = 7$
$7 + 1 = 8$
$2 + 4 = 6$

6. $8 - 3 = 5$
$7 - 5 = 2$
$8 - 6 = 2$
$6 - 3 = 3$
$7 - 4 = 3$

Macmillan/McGraw-Hill, MATHEMATICS IN ACTION
Grade 2, Chapter 1, Lesson 12, pages 29-30   Reteaching-10

PRACTICE

Name _____

FACTS TO 8

Write the fact family for each picture.

1. $1 + 7 = 8$ $8 - 7 = 1$
   $7 + 1 = 8$ $8 - 1 = 7$

2. $0 + 8 = 8$ $8 - 0 = 8$
   $8 + 0 = 8$ $8 - 8 = 0$

Add or subtract.

3.
2	1	3	4	5	4
+6	+4	+5	+3	+1	+4
8	5	8	7	6	8

4.
8	7	6	8	8	7
-4	-5	-0	-0	-6	-1
4	2	6	8	2	6

Color yellow if the answer is 8.

5.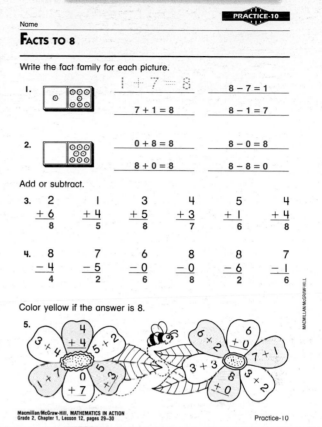

Macmillan/McGraw-Hill, MATHEMATICS IN ACTION
Grade 2, Chapter 1, Lesson 12, pages 29-30   Practice-10

ENRICHMENT

Name _____

FACTS TO 8

On Your Own   Pair and Share   In a Group

BALL GAMES

Each bag must have 8 balls in all.
How many balls are *inside* each bag?

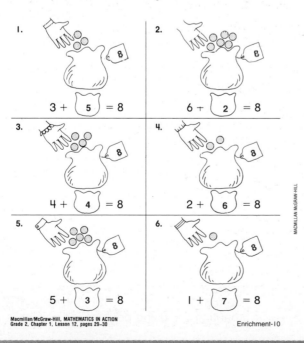

1. $3 + \boxed{5} = 8$
2. $6 + \boxed{2} = 8$
3. $4 + \boxed{4} = 8$
4. $2 + \boxed{6} = 8$
5. $5 + \boxed{3} = 8$
6. $1 + \boxed{7} = 8$

Macmillan/McGraw-Hill, MATHEMATICS IN ACTION
Grade 2, Chapter 1, Lesson 12, pages 29-30   Enrichment-10

Problem of the Day

Kate has 4 heart stickers and 4 flower stickers.
Patty has 4 heart stickers and 3 flower stickers.
Which girl has more stickers?   [Kate. Children
may work it out this way: $4 + 4 = 8$; $4 + 3 = 7$;
$8 > 7$.]

AT·A·GLANCE pp. 31-32

LESSON OBJECTIVE
Add three 1-digit numbers.

ASSIGNMENT GUIDE

COURSE	EXERCISES
Basic	p. 31: 1–3; p. 32: 1–4
Average	p. 31: 1–3; p. 32: 1–4
Challenge	p. 31: 1–3; p. 32: 1–4
Extra Practice, p. 43	

MATERIALS
Classroom Materials red, blue, and yellow crayons
Manipulatives 5 ▣, 5 ▣, 5 ▢ (or punchout square counters) per pair

Teacher Resources
Reteaching 11   Practice 11   Enrichment 11
MAC Act. 21, 22   Teacher Aid 1

SKILLS TRACE
FACTS TO 10

Explore (Concrete)	Develop/Understand (Transitional/Abstract)
10	11, 12, 13–14, 15–16, 19–20, 21–22, 23–24, 29–30, 31–32, 33–34, 35–36, 37, 38
Practice	**Apply**
20, 28, 32, 43, 44, 45–46, 49, 60	17–18, 25–26, 27, 39–40, 41, 42

See **MANIPULATIVES PLUS 8**, p. 8P.

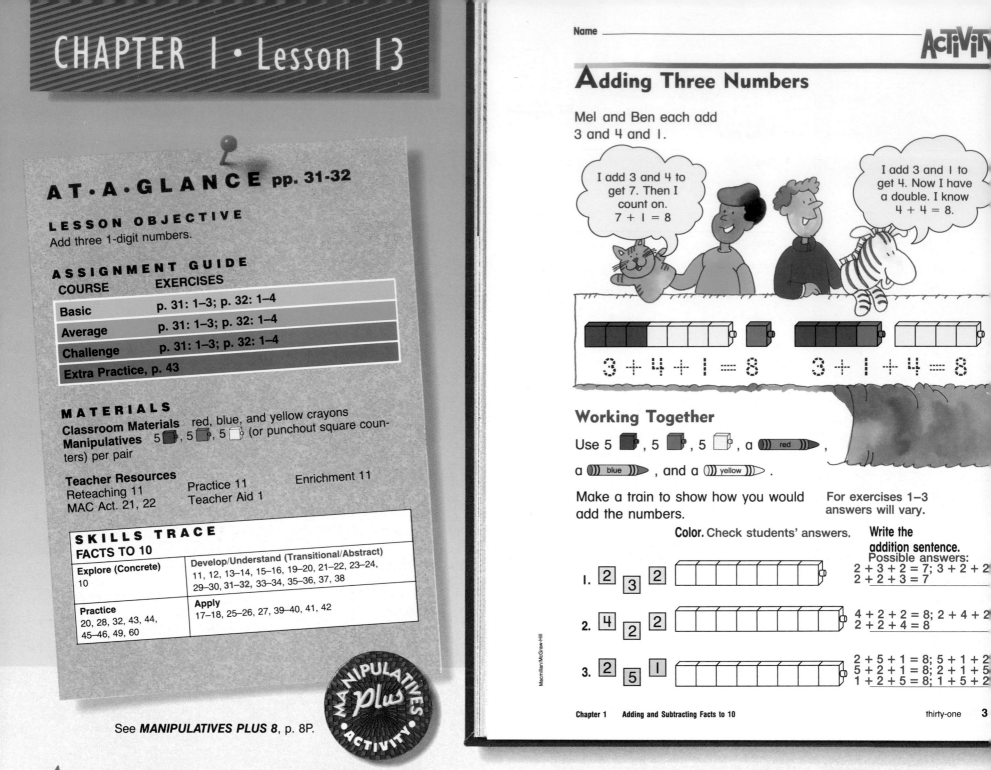

Adding Three Numbers

Mel and Ben each add
3 and 4 and 1.

I add 3 and 4 to get 7. Then I count on. 7 + 1 = 8

I add 3 and 1 to get 4. Now I have a double. I know 4 + 4 = 8.

$3 + 4 + 1 = 8$ $3 + 1 + 4 = 8$

Working Together

Use 5 ▣, 5 ▣, 5 ▢, a ▭ red ▷,
a ▭ blue ▷, and a ▭ yellow ▷.

Make a train to show how you would add the numbers.

For exercises 1–3 answers will vary.

Color. Check students' answers.   **Write the addition sentence.**
Possible answers:

1. [2] [3] [2] $2 + 3 + 2 = 7; 3 + 2 + 2$
                        $2 + 2 + 3 = 7$

2. [4] [2] [2] $4 + 2 + 2 = 8; 2 + 4 + 2$
                        $2 + 2 + 4 = 8$

3. [2] [5] [1] $2 + 5 + 1 = 8; 5 + 1 + 2$
                        $5 + 2 + 1 = 8; 2 + 1 + 5$
                        $1 + 2 + 5 = 8; 1 + 5 + 2$

Macmillan/McGraw-Hill

Chapter 1   Adding and Subtracting Facts to 10   thirty-one   3

---

1 PREPARE

WARM-UP To prepare children for adding three numbers, ask children to say each sum for each pair of facts.

2 + 2	[4]	4 + 2	[6]
3 + 4	[7]	7 + 1	[8]
2 + 3	[5]	5 + 2	[7]
2 + 0	[2]	2 + 4	[6]

2 TEACH

MODELING Tell children the following story.

Mary, Tom, and Greg are all collecting shells. Mary and Greg each find 3 shells. Tom finds 2 shells. How many shells did they find in all?

Have children work in groups and model the three numbers in the story with cubes of three different colors. Then have them find the answer by counting the cubes. [8]

Present a similar problem using the numbers 3, 1, and 2, and write 3 + 1 + 2 on the chalkboard. Have children model the numbers with their cubes.

■ **How could you combine the numbers to count on?** [Possible responses: Add 3 + 2, count on 1; add 3 + 1, count on 2.]

Have children add both ways to show that the sum is the same.

PUPIL'S EDITION pp. 31-32

Page 31 Guide children through the two solutions to the example at the top of the page. Remind them that they can find the sum by either counting on, using doubles, or adding in any order.

How many 🐱 in all?

Number of Tigers We Made	
Wednesday	🐱
Thursday	🐱
Friday	🐱🐱🐱🐱🐱

There are 7 in all.

I like doubles.

Adding 1 more is easy.

1 > 2
  1
+ 5
───
  7

1 > 6
  1
+ 5
───
  7

Add.

1.

```
   5        1        3        2        1        3
   1        4        2        1        2        1
 + 2      + 3      + 2      + 5      + 1      + 2
 ───      ───      ───      ───      ───      ───
   8        8        7        8        4        6
```

2.

```
   2        1        2        1        1        2
   1        1        3        3        1        2
 + 4      + 5      + 1      + 1      + 4      + 3
 ───      ───      ───      ───      ───      ───
   7        7        6        5        6        7
```

3.

```
   4        6        1        2        5        3
   0        1        6        1        0        2
 + 3      + 0      + 1      + 3      + 3      + 3
 ───      ───      ───      ───      ───      ───
   7        7        8        6        8        8
```

Mixed Review

Add or subtract.

4.

```
   4        1        8        7        4        5
 + 2      + 6      - 3      - 5      + 4      - 0
 ───      ───      ───      ───      ───      ───
   6        7        5        2        8        5
```

Extra Practice, page 43

ACTIVITY

Common Error and Remediation

MATERIALS 8 ○; vertical addition exercises

Some children may have difficulty mentally holding the partial sum when adding three digits. Work individually with each child, using counters and a set of addition exercises written vertically. Have the child combine two of the groups of counters and record the partial sum, as shown on page 32. Then have the child count on the remaining counters to find the sum. Relate this activity to counting on the remaining addend from the partial sum.

ALTERNATIVE TEACHING STRATEGY

VISUAL/AUDITORY Write the following on the chalkboard.

```
4 + 2 + 1 = ___      4 + 2 + 1 = ___      4 + 2 + 1 = ___
```

Demonstrate three ways to group the addends to find the sum. Guide children to see that the sum is the same regardless of the order or grouping of the addends. Have children vote on which is the easiest way for them to add the three numbers. Encourage children to explain their choices.

Check for Understanding

■ **How could you add 2 + 2 + 3?** [Add 2 + 2 and count on 3 or add 2 + 3 and count on 2.]

GUIDED PRACTICE ■ **Working Together** Have children work in pairs to do ex. 1–3.

For reteaching, use Common Error and Remediation or Alternative Strategy.

Page 32 Relate the numbers in the examples to the graph. Review each method shown for finding the sum.

3 PRACTICE•APPLY   PRACTICE   ex. 1–4

CLOSE Guide children to summarize the lesson:

■ **Explain what you do to add three numbers.** [Possible responses: Add two numbers, then count on for the third number; look for doubles or ways to make doubles.]

MENTAL MATH ▪ RACE TO THE MOON

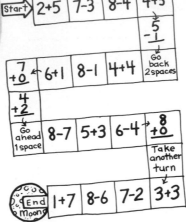

MAC Activity 21

On Your Own   Pair and Share   In a Group

Start→	2+5	7-3	8-4	4+3
				↓ -5 -1
				Go back 2 spaces
7 +0	6+1	8-1	4+4	
4 +2				
Go ahead 1 space	8-7	5+3	6-4 →	8 +0
				Take another turn ↓
End Moon	1+7	8-6	7-2	3+3

Materials game board (Teacher Aid 1), game markers, number cube

Procedure Write addition and subtraction facts to 8 in the spaces of the game board on Teacher Aid 1. Also write statements like *go ahead 1 space* and *go back 2 spaces*. Then duplicate the worksheet for the children.

Have children play in groups of three or four. Provide each group with a game board, game markers, and a number cube. Each player puts his or her marker on *start*. The first player rolls the number cube. The player moves the number of spaces shown, giving the sum or difference for each space as he or she moves. If an answer is incorrect, the player stops on that space. Then the next player takes a turn.

To Win The player who gets to the moon first is the winner.

**MAC Activity 21:
Basic-to-Average** ▶

MENTAL MATH ▪ LETTER CODE

MAC Activity 22

On Your Own   Pair and Share   In a Group

Write the following on the chalkboard.

A	B	C	D	E	F	G	H
1	2	3	4	5	6	7	8

Explain to children that this is a key that shows that each letter stands for the number below it. Then write the following exercises on the chalkboard below the key and have children find the answers.

$$\begin{array}{c} A \\ B \\ +C \\ \hline [F] \end{array} \qquad \begin{array}{c} G \\ -D \\ \hline [C] \end{array} \qquad \begin{array}{c} H \\ -B \\ \hline [F] \end{array} \qquad \begin{array}{c} E \\ +C \\ \hline [H] \end{array} \qquad \begin{array}{c} B \\ D \\ +A \\ \hline [G] \end{array}$$

Have children use the key to make up their own exercises and exchange them with their classmates to solve.

C + C = ?

B +B = ?

$$\begin{array}{c} D \\ -B \\ \hline ? \end{array}$$

$$\begin{array}{c} B \\ -A \\ \hline ? \end{array}$$

A + A = ?

D + D = ?

▲
**MAC Activity 22:
Average-to-Challenge**

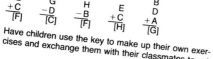

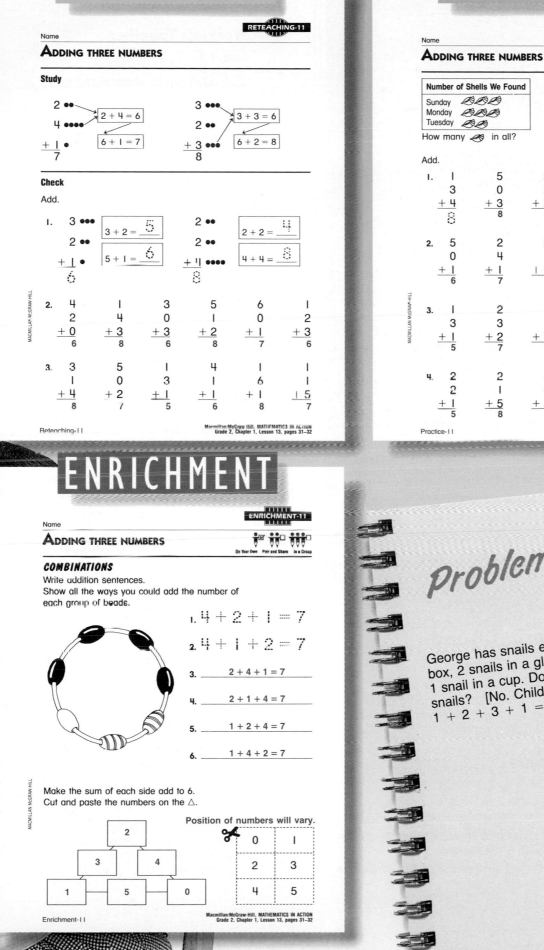

RETEACHING

RETEACHING-11

Name _____

ADDING THREE NUMBERS

Study

```
2 ••            2 + 4 = 6        3 •••            3 + 3 = 6
4 ••••                           2 ••
+ 1 •           6 + 1 = 7       + 3 •••           6 + 2 = 8
___                              ___
7                                8
```

Check

Add.

```
1.   3 •••       3 + 2 = 5       2 ••       2 + 2 = 4
     2 ••                        2 ••
   + 1 •         5 + 1 = 6     + 4 ••••     4 + 4 = 8
    ___                          ___
     6                            8
```

```
2.   4      1      3      5      6      1
     2      4      0      1      0      2
   + 0    + 3    + 3    + 2    + 1    + 3
    ___    ___    ___    ___    ___    ___
     6      8      6      8      7      6
```

```
3.   3      5      1      4      1      1
     1      0      3      1      6      1
   + 4    + 2    + 1    + 1    + 1    + 5
    ___    ___    ___    ___    ___    ___
     8      7      5      6      8      7
```

Reteaching-11

Macmillan/McGraw-Hill, MATHEMATICS IN ACTION
Grade 2, Chapter 1, Lesson 13, pages 31–32

PRACTICE

PRACTICE-11

Name _____

ADDING THREE NUMBERS

Number of Shells We Found	
Sunday	🐚🐚🐚
Monday	🐚🐚
Tuesday	🐚

How many 🐚 in all?

```
  3
  3  >  (6)
+ 2
___
  8
```

Add.

```
1.   1      5      2      2      3      0
     3      0      2      1      2      6
   + 4    + 3    + 2    + 4    + 3    + 2
    ___    ___    ___    ___    ___    ___
     8      8      6      7      8      8
```

```
2.   5      2      3      6      4      1
     0      4      1      1      2      0
   + 1    + 1    + 4    + 1    + 0    + 7
    ___    ___    ___    ___    ___    ___
     6      7      8      8      6      8
```

```
3.   1      2      1      1      5      3      4
     3      3      1      1      2      2
   + 1    + 2    + 4    + 2    + 0    + 2
    ___    ___    ___    ___    ___    ___
     5      7      6      8      5      8
```

```
4.   2      2      3      7      6      4
     2      1      0      1      0      3
   + 1    + 5    + 5    + 0    + 1    + 1
    ___    ___    ___    ___    ___    ___
     5      8      8      8      8      8
```

Practice-11

Macmillan/McGraw-Hill, MATHEMATICS IN ACTION
Grade 2, Chapter 1, Lesson 13, pages 31–32

ENRICHMENT

ENRICHMENT-11

On Your Own Pair and Share In a Group

Name _____

ADDING THREE NUMBERS

COMBINATIONS

Write addition sentences.
Show all the ways you could add the number of
each group of beads.

1. 4 + 2 + 1 = 7
2. 4 + 1 + 2 = 7
3. ____ 2 + 4 + 1 = 7
4. ____ 2 + 1 + 4 = 7
5. ____ 1 + 2 + 4 = 7
6. ____ 1 + 4 + 2 = 7

Make the sum of each side add to 6.
Cut and paste the numbers on the △.

Position of numbers will vary.

```
        2
     3     4
   1    5    0
```

✂

0	1
2	3
4	5

Enrichment-11

Macmillan/McGraw-Hill, MATHEMATICS IN ACTION
Grade 2, Chapter 1, Lesson 13, pages 31–32

Problem of the Day

George has snails everywhere! He has 1 snail in a box, 2 snails in a glass, 3 snails in a bucket, and 1 snail in a cup. Does George have more than 8 snails? [No. Children may work it out this way: 1 + 2 + 3 + 1 = 7; 7 < 8.]

AT·A·GLANCE pp. 33-34

LESSON OBJECTIVE
Add and subtract facts to 9.

ASSIGNMENT GUIDE

COURSE	EXERCISES
Basic	p. 33: 2–11; p. 34: 1–5, Reasoning
Average	p. 33: 2–11; p. 34: 1–5, Reasoning
Challenge	p. 33: 2–11; p. 34: 1–5, Reasoning

MATERIALS
Manipulatives 9 ◯ (or punchouts) per pair

Teacher Resources
Reteaching 12   Practice 12   Enrichment 12
MAC Act. 23, 24   Teacher Aids 4, 12

SKILLS TRACE
FACTS TO 10

Explore (Concrete)	Develop/Understand (Transitional/Abstract)
10	11, 12, 13–14, 15–16, 19–20, 21–22, 23–24, 29–30, 31–32, 33–34, 35–36, 37, 38
Practice 20, 28, 32, 43, 44, 45–46, 49, 60	**Apply** 17–18, 25–26, 27, 39–40, 41, 42

Facts to 9

Working Together
Use 9 ◯ .

Use counters to show sums of 9.

	Write as many addition facts as you can.	Write a subtraction fact for each addition fact.
1.	9 + 0 = 9	9 − 0 = 9
2.	8 + 1 = 9	9 − 1 = 8
3.	7 + 2 = 9	9 − 2 = 7
4.	6 + 3 = 9	9 − 3 = 6
5.	5 + 4 = 9	9 − 4 = 5
6.	4 + 5 = 9	9 − 5 = 4
7.	3 + 6 = 9	9 − 6 = 3
8.	2 + 7 = 9	9 − 7 = 2
9.	1 + 8 = 9	9 − 8 = 1
10.	0 + 9 = 9	9 − 9 = 0

11. Write a fact for 9.

_____ Answers will vary.

Draw a picture for the fact.

Macmillan/McGraw-Hill

---

1 PREPARE
WARM-UP To review doubles, read the following addition sentences. Have children give each sum orally and then give a related subtraction sentence.

4 + 4	[8; 8 − 4 = 4]
2 + 2	[4; 4 − 2 = 2]
1 + 1	[2; 2 − 1 = 1]
3 + 3	[6; 6 − 3 = 3]

2 TEACH
MODELING Have children work in pairs, and provide each pair with 9 counters.

■ **How many counters do you have?** [9] **Take 1 of the counters away. How many are left?** [8]

Next have them add 1 counter and tell how many counters they now have. [9] Repeat the activity, having children first take away and then add 2, 3, 4, and 5 counters.

■ **What pattern do you see?** [Possible response: If you add back the number you have taken away, you end up with the number with which you started.]

PUPIL'S EDITION pp. 33-34

Page 33 Working Together Assign children to work in groups. Ask them to say addition or subtraction sentences that tell about the picture on the page. Guide children through ex. 1, having them use 9 red counters to show 9 + 0 and 9 − 0.

Write the fact family for the picture.

1.

8 + 1 = 9	9 − 1 = 8
1 + 8 = 9	9 − 8 = 1

Add or subtract.

2.

4	5	6	2	0	7
+ 5	+ 4	+ 2	+ 6	+ 7	+ 0
9	9	8	8	7	7

3.

8	8	9	9	6	6
− 3	− 5	− 1	− 8	− 4	− 2
5	3	8	1	2	4

4.

4	4	7	7	5	5
− 1	− 3	− 6	− 1	− 3	− 2
3	1	1	6	2	3

5.

2	6	3	0	1	5
1	1	5	5	5	3
+ 6	+ 2	+ 0	+ 3	+ 3	+ 1
9	9	8	8	9	9

···· **Reasoning** ····

There are 8 beads in all.
Some are in the box.
How many beads are in the box?

__2__ beads

ACTIVITY Common Error and Remediation

MATERIALS fact cards, number line (Teacher Aid 12)

Some children may not be using strategies to find sums and differences for facts they do not know. Work individually with each child, using fact cards and a number line. Have the child begin with an addition card. Tell him or her to start at the greater addend of the fact and count on to find the sum. After working with several addition examples, present a subtraction card. Have the child count back to find the difference. Repeat with other subtraction facts.

ALTERNATIVE TEACHING STRATEGY

MATERIALS graph paper (Teacher Aid 4), crayons

KINESTHETIC/VISUAL Provide children with inch graph paper duplicated from Teacher Aid 4. Have them position the paper so that a row of 9 boxes is at the top of the page. Then guide children in developing the facts for 9 by having them color each row to show a related addition and subtraction fact.

8 + 1 = 9
9 − 1 = 8

Check for Understanding

■ **How would you show 8 + 1 and 9 − 1 using counters?** [8 red counters and 1 yellow counter]

GUIDED PRACTICE ex. 2–11: For reteaching, use Common Error and Remediation or Alternative Strategy.

Page 34 Remind children that they are to use the picture to write a fact family.

3 PRACTICE•APPLY **PRACTICE** ex. 1–5

REASONING Some children may have to draw the missing beads to solve the problem.

C L O S E Guide children to summarize the lesson:
■ **What are three facts for 9?** [Answers will vary.]

MAC ACTIVITY CENTER

MAC Activity 23

MENTAL MATH ▪ DIFFERENCES ADD UP

On Your Own   Pair and Share   In a Group

Materials   counters or punchout counters, number cards for 0–9

Procedure   Have children play in pairs. Give each pair 40 counters and four sets of number cards for 0 to 9. Shuffle the cards and place them facedown between the children. The children each take a card and place it faceup. The child with the lesser number card subtracts it from the greater number. The child with the greater number card takes enough counters to equal the difference.

To Win   The child with the most counters at the end of play wins the round.

▲
**MAC Activity 23:
Basic-to-Average**

**MAC Activity 24:
Average-to-Challenge**
▼

CALCULATOR ▪ NUMBER CHAINS

MAC Activity 24

On Your Own   Pair and Share   In a Group

Materials   calculator

Write the following exercises on the chalkboard. Have children use their calculators to find the answers. Review calculator keying as necessary before the children begin.

1. $2 + 1 + 3 - 2 + 4 = $ ___
2. $5 - 3 + 4 - 6 + 5 = $ ___ [8]
3. $9 - 2 + 1 - 6 - 2 = $ ___ [0]
4. $1 + 7 - 2 + 1 - 6 = $ ___ [1]

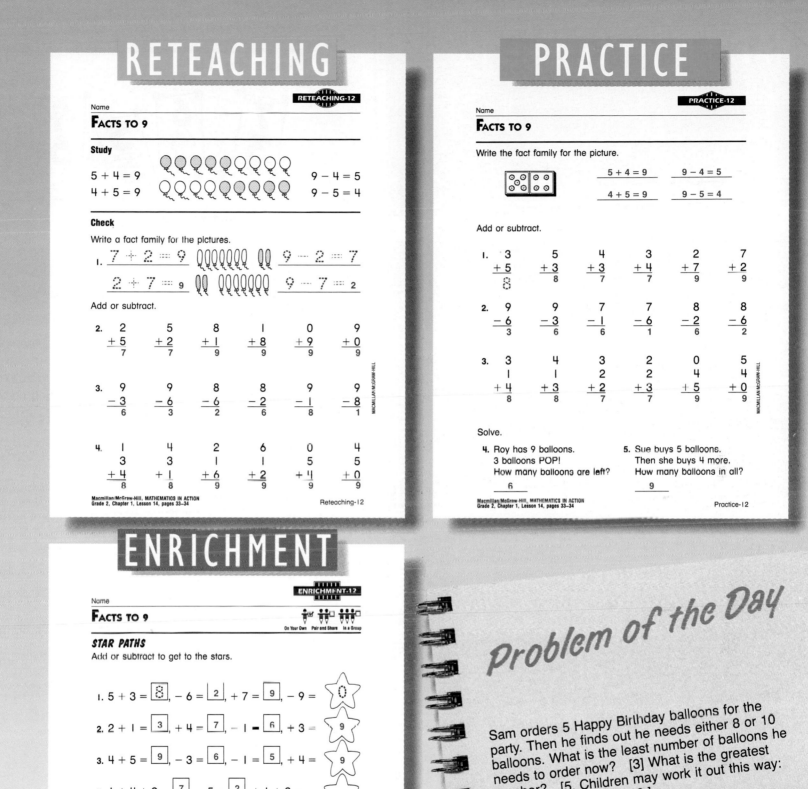

RETEACHING-12

Name

FACTS TO 9

Study

$5 + 4 = 9$ $9 - 4 = 5$
$4 + 5 = 9$ $9 - 5 = 4$

Check

Write a fact family for the pictures.

1. $7 + 2 = 9$ $9 - 2 = 7$
   $2 + 7 = 9$ $9 - 7 = 2$

Add or subtract.

2.
2	5	8	1	0	9
+5	+2	+1	+8	+9	+0
7	7	9	9	9	9

3.
9	9	8	8	9	9
−3	−6	−6	−2	−1	−8
6	3	2	6	8	1

4.
1	4	2	6	0	4
3	3	1	1	5	5
+4	+1	+6	+2	+4	+0
8	8	9	9	9	9

Macmillan/McGraw-Hill, MATHEMATICS IN ACTION
Grade 2, Chapter 1, Lesson 14, pages 33–34   Reteaching-12

PRACTICE-12

Name

FACTS TO 9

Write the fact family for the picture.

$5 + 4 = 9$ $9 - 4 = 5$
$4 + 5 = 9$ $9 - 5 = 4$

Add or subtract.

1.
3	5	4	3	2	7
+5	+3	+3	+4	+7	+2
8	8	7	7	9	9

2.
9	9	7	7	8	8
−6	−3	−1	−6	−2	−6
3	6	6	1	6	2

3.
3	4	3	2	0	5
1	1	2	2	4	4
+4	+3	+2	+3	+5	+0
8	8	7	7	9	9

Solve.

4. Roy has 9 balloons.
   3 balloons POP!
   How many balloons are left?
   __6__

5. Sue buys 5 balloons.
   Then she buys 4 more.
   How many balloons in all?
   __9__

Macmillan/McGraw-Hill, MATHEMATICS IN ACTION
Grade 2, Chapter 1, Lesson 14, pages 33–34   Practice-12

ENRICHMENT-12

Name

FACTS TO 9

On Your Own   Pair and Share   In a Group

STAR PATHS
Add or subtract to get to the stars.

1. $5 + 3 = \boxed{8}$, $- 6 = \boxed{2}$, $+ 7 = \boxed{9}$, $- 9 = \boxed{0}$ ★

2. $2 + 1 = \boxed{3}$, $+ 4 = \boxed{7}$, $- 1 = \boxed{6}$, $+ 3 = \boxed{9}$ ★

3. $4 + 5 = \boxed{9}$, $- 3 = \boxed{6}$, $- 1 = \boxed{5}$, $+ 4 = \boxed{9}$ ★

4. $1 + 4 + 2 = \boxed{7}$, $- 5 = \boxed{2}$, $+ 1 + 3 = \boxed{6}$ ★

5. $7 - 6 = \boxed{1}$
   $+ 5$
   $\boxed{6}$ $+ 3 = \boxed{9}$ $- 2 = \boxed{7}$ $- 7 = \boxed{0}$ ★

6. $9 - 4 = \boxed{5}$
   $+ 2$
   $\boxed{7}$ $+ 2 = \boxed{9}$
   $- 3$
   $\boxed{6}$ $+ 2 = \boxed{8}$ $- 0 = \boxed{8}$ ★

Macmillan/McGraw-Hill, MATHEMATICS IN ACTION
Grade 2, Chapter 1, Lesson 14, pages 33–34   Enrichment-12

Problem of the Day

Sam orders 5 Happy Birthday balloons for the party. Then he finds out he needs either 8 or 10 balloons. What is the least number of balloons he needs to order now? [3] What is the greatest number? [5. Children may work it out this way: $5 + 3 = 8$; $5 + 5 = 10$.]

AT·A·GLANCE pp. 35-36

LESSON OBJECTIVE
Add and subtract facts to 10.

ASSIGNMENT GUIDE

COURSE	EXERCISES
Basic	p. 35: 2–9; p. 36: 3–5
Average	p. 35: 2–9; p. 36: 3–5
Challenge	p. 35: 2–9; p. 36: 3–5
Extra Practice, p. 43	Practice Plus, p. 44

MATERIALS
Manipulatives 10 ⬛, 10 ⬛ or (square counter punchouts) per child

Teacher Resources
Reteaching 13   Practice 13   Enrichment 13
Prob. Solv. 3   MAC Act. 25, 26
Computer Software *Mathematics Skills:* Disk 1 Act. 6, 7;
  Disk 2 Act. 1; Disk 3 Act. 1

SKILLS TRACE
FACTS TO 10

Explore (Concrete)	Develop/Understand (Transitional/Abstract)
10	11, 12, 13–14, 15–16, 19–20, 21–22, 23–24, 29–30, 31–32, 33–34, **35–36**, 37, 38
Practice 20, 28, 32, 43, 44, 45–46, 49, 60	**Apply** 17–18, 25–26, 27, 39–40, 41, 42

Facts to 10

I made these number cards.

Look for a pattern in Maria's cards.
What are the next 3 cards in the pattern?

3		2		1
7		8		9

Use 10 ⬛ and 10 ⬛ to show sums of 10.

Write as many addition facts as you can.   **Write a subtraction fact for each addition fact.**

1. $9 + 1 = 10$ $10 - 1 = 9$

2. $8 + 2 = 10$ $10 - 2 = 8$

3. $7 + 3 = 10$ $10 - 3 = 7$

4. $6 + 4 = 10$ $10 - 4 = 6$

5. $5 + 5 = 10$ $10 - 5 = 5$

6. $4 + 6 = 10$ $10 - 6 = 4$

7. $3 + 7 = 10$ $10 - 7 = 3$

8. $2 + 8 = 10$ $10 - 8 = 2$

9. $1 + 9 = 10$ $10 - 9 = 1$

Macmillan/McGraw-Hill

---

1 PREPARE   **WARM-UP**   To practice adding on, write **+1** on the chalkboard. Explain to children that after you call out a number between 0 and 8, they are to add 1 and give the sum. Then write **+2** and repeat the activity, asking them to add 2 as you call out numbers between 0 and 7.

2 TEACH   **MODELING**   Distribute cubes of two different colors to pairs of children. Ask them to make a 10-cube train using the two colors. Call on children to describe their trains in terms of the colors of the parts as you write the corresponding addition facts on the chalkboard. Then call on volunteers to write a related subtraction fact beside each addition fact.

PUPIL'S EDITION pp. 35-36

Page 35   Discuss the problem at the top of the page with the children.
■ **What is the same about the cards?** [They each have a sum of 10.]

Identify the pattern with the children. [The top number decreases by 1, and the bottom number increases by 1.] Then have them complete the next three cards to continue the pattern.

Check for Understanding
■ **Look at Maria's pattern. What card comes before 7 over 3?** [8 over 2]

■ **What card comes before 8 over 2?** [9 over 1]

GUIDED PRACTICE   ex. 2–9: For reteaching, use Common Error and Remediation or Alternative Strategy.

rite the fact family for the picture.

6 + 4 = 10		10 − 4 = 6
4 + 6 = 10		10 − 6 = 4

5 + 5 = 10		10 − 5 = 5

dd or subtract.

5	4	8	2	9	1	6
+4	+5	+2	+8	+1	+9	+3
9	9	10	10	10	10	9

8	8	7	7	9	9	6
−8	−0	−7	−0	−9	−0	−0
0	8	0	7	0	9	6

2	5	3	3	4	4
3	2	3	1	2	4
+5	+3	+1	+3	+4	+2
10	10	7	7	10	10

Estimation

lan has more brushes than Carl.
Which brushes are Alan's?
ing the box that shows the greater sum.

Extra Practice, page 43 *Practice Plus,* page 44

ACTIVITY Common Error and Remediation

MATERIALS 10 ■, 10 ■

Some children may have difficulty relating addition and subtraction facts. Work individually with each child. Write an addition fact such as 6 + 4. Have the child combine cubes of two colors to make a train showing the fact. Help the child tell a story about the train. Then turn the train around and discuss 4 + 6. Have the child talk about 10 − 6 and 10 − 4.

ONGOING ASSESSMENT
MATH JOURNAL

INTERVIEW (1) What is the sum of 6 + 3? (2) What other facts can you use to make a sum of 9? (3) What is 7 − 2? (4) What other facts can you use to make a difference of 5?

JOURNAL WRITING You may wish to have children record their responses in their math journals.

ACTIVITY ALTERNATIVE TEACHING STRATEGY

MATERIALS 10 ○ (or punchouts); overhead projector

VISUAL/AUDITORY Display 10 counters in a row on an overhead projector. Move 1 counter from the right away from the other 9. Explain that this is a way to show 10 − 1 = 9. Move the 1 counter back and further explain that this is a way to show 9 + 1 = 10. Repeat the action and have children say the facts with you. Continue the activity to develop 10 − 2 = 8 and 8 + 2 = 10, 10 − 3 = 7 and 7 + 3 = 10, 10 − 4 = 6 and 6 + 4 = 10, 10 − 5 = 5 and 5 + 5 = 10.

Page 36 Work through ex. 1 and 2 with the children. Explain that they are to use the pictures to write the fact families.

3 PRACTICE·APPLY
PRACTICE ex. 3–5: Encourage children to tell which row was easiest for them.

ESTIMATION Guide children to understand that it is sometimes possible to find the greater amount by looking, rather than counting.

CLOSE Guide children to summarize the lesson:
■ **Name an addition fact for 10 and a related subtraction fact.**
[Possible response: 6 + 4 = 10; 10 − 4 = 6]

MENTAL MATH ■ ALL IN THE FACT FAMILY

MAC Activity 25

On Your Own   Pair and Share   In a Group

Materials   fact cards

Give pairs of children addition and subtraction cards for facts to 10. Have children mix the cards and place them facedown. The first child draws the top card, reads the fact aloud, and says the sum or difference. The second child names the other members of that fact family. Children take turns until all the cards have been drawn.

$7+3=10$ $3+7=10$ $10-3=7$ $10-7=3$

▲
MAC Activity 25:
Basic-to-Average

MAC Activity 26:
Average-to-Challenge
▼

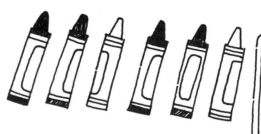

LOGICAL REASONING ■ HOW MANY MORE CRAYONS?

MAC Activity 26

On Your Own   Pair and Share   In a Group

Materials   crayons, tray or mat

Have children work in pairs. The first child places from 0 to 9 crayons on a tray or mat. The second child must tell how many more crayons are needed to make a total of 10. Have children check their answers by adding crayons to the tray while counting on to 10. Then children exchange roles and repeat the activity.

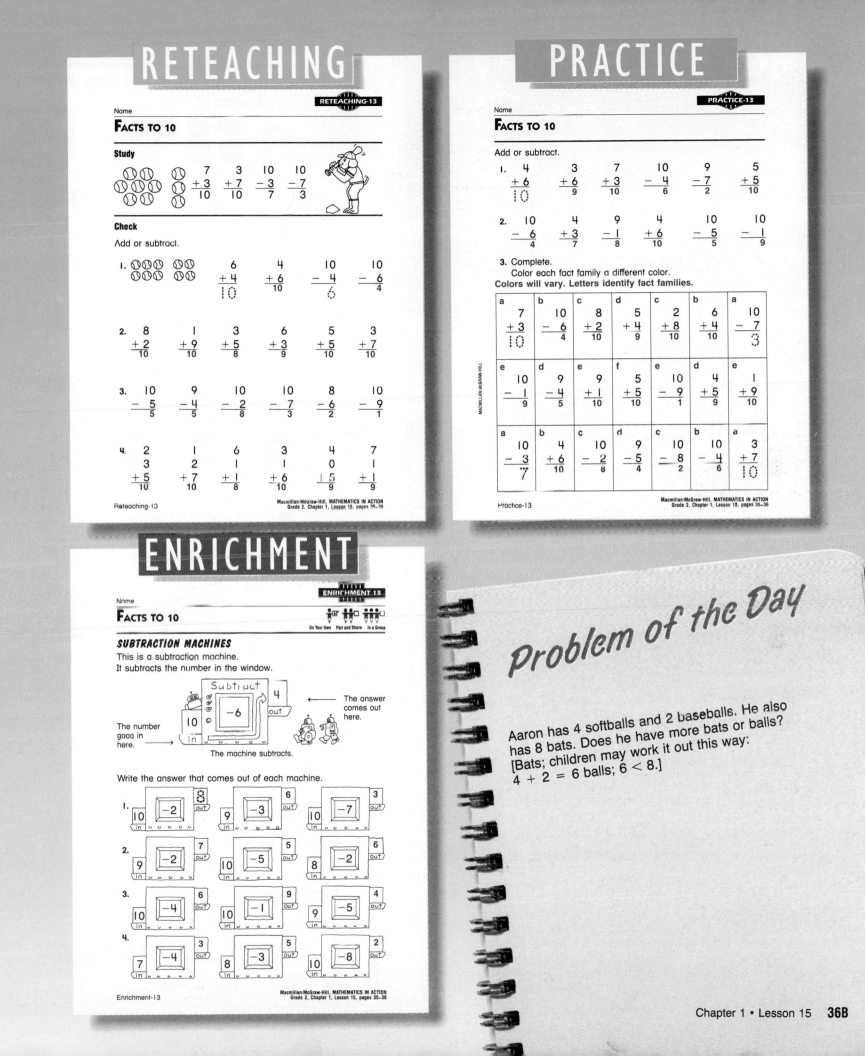

RETEACHING

Name

FACTS TO 10

Study

$$\begin{array}{r} 7 \\ +3 \\ \hline 10 \end{array} \quad \begin{array}{r} 3 \\ +7 \\ \hline 10 \end{array} \quad \begin{array}{r} 10 \\ -3 \\ \hline 7 \end{array} \quad \begin{array}{r} 10 \\ -7 \\ \hline 3 \end{array}$$

Check

Add or subtract.

1. $\begin{array}{r} 6 \\ +4 \\ \hline 10 \end{array}$ $\begin{array}{r} 4 \\ +6 \\ \hline 10 \end{array}$ $\begin{array}{r} 10 \\ -4 \\ \hline 6 \end{array}$ $\begin{array}{r} 10 \\ -6 \\ \hline 4 \end{array}$

2. $\begin{array}{r} 8 \\ +2 \\ \hline 10 \end{array}$ $\begin{array}{r} 1 \\ +9 \\ \hline 10 \end{array}$ $\begin{array}{r} 3 \\ +5 \\ \hline 8 \end{array}$ $\begin{array}{r} 6 \\ +3 \\ \hline 9 \end{array}$ $\begin{array}{r} 5 \\ +5 \\ \hline 10 \end{array}$ $\begin{array}{r} 3 \\ +7 \\ \hline 10 \end{array}$

3. $\begin{array}{r} 10 \\ -5 \\ \hline 5 \end{array}$ $\begin{array}{r} 9 \\ -4 \\ \hline 5 \end{array}$ $\begin{array}{r} 10 \\ -2 \\ \hline 8 \end{array}$ $\begin{array}{r} 10 \\ -7 \\ \hline 3 \end{array}$ $\begin{array}{r} 8 \\ -6 \\ \hline 2 \end{array}$ $\begin{array}{r} 10 \\ -9 \\ \hline 1 \end{array}$

4. $\begin{array}{r} 2 \\ 3 \\ +5 \\ \hline 10 \end{array}$ $\begin{array}{r} 1 \\ 2 \\ +7 \\ \hline 10 \end{array}$ $\begin{array}{r} 6 \\ 1 \\ +1 \\ \hline 8 \end{array}$ $\begin{array}{r} 3 \\ 1 \\ +6 \\ \hline 10 \end{array}$ $\begin{array}{r} 4 \\ 0 \\ 5 \\ \hline 9 \end{array}$ $\begin{array}{r} 7 \\ 1 \\ +1 \\ \hline 9 \end{array}$

Reteaching-13

Macmillan/McGraw-Hill, MATHEMATICS IN ACTION
Grade 2, Chapter 1, Lesson 15, pages 35–36

PRACTICE

Name

FACTS TO 10

Add or subtract.

1. $\begin{array}{r} 4 \\ +6 \\ \hline 10 \end{array}$ $\begin{array}{r} 3 \\ +6 \\ \hline 9 \end{array}$ $\begin{array}{r} 7 \\ +3 \\ \hline 10 \end{array}$ $\begin{array}{r} 10 \\ -4 \\ \hline 6 \end{array}$ $\begin{array}{r} 9 \\ -7 \\ \hline 2 \end{array}$ $\begin{array}{r} 5 \\ +5 \\ \hline 10 \end{array}$

2. $\begin{array}{r} 10 \\ -6 \\ \hline 4 \end{array}$ $\begin{array}{r} 4 \\ +3 \\ \hline 7 \end{array}$ $\begin{array}{r} 9 \\ -1 \\ \hline 8 \end{array}$ $\begin{array}{r} 4 \\ +6 \\ \hline 10 \end{array}$ $\begin{array}{r} 10 \\ -5 \\ \hline 5 \end{array}$ $\begin{array}{r} 10 \\ -1 \\ \hline 9 \end{array}$

3. Complete.
Color each fact family a different color.
Colors will vary. Letters identify fact families.

a	b	c	d	c	b	a
$\begin{array}{r} 7 \\ +3 \\ \hline 10 \end{array}$	$\begin{array}{r} 10 \\ -6 \\ \hline 4 \end{array}$	$\begin{array}{r} 8 \\ +2 \\ \hline 10 \end{array}$	$\begin{array}{r} 5 \\ +4 \\ \hline 9 \end{array}$	$\begin{array}{r} 2 \\ +8 \\ \hline 10 \end{array}$	$\begin{array}{r} 6 \\ +4 \\ \hline 10 \end{array}$	$\begin{array}{r} 10 \\ -7 \\ \hline 3 \end{array}$
e	d	e	f	e	d	e
$\begin{array}{r} 10 \\ -1 \\ \hline 9 \end{array}$	$\begin{array}{r} 9 \\ -4 \\ \hline 5 \end{array}$	$\begin{array}{r} 9 \\ +1 \\ \hline 10 \end{array}$	$\begin{array}{r} 5 \\ +5 \\ \hline 10 \end{array}$	$\begin{array}{r} 10 \\ -9 \\ \hline 1 \end{array}$	$\begin{array}{r} 4 \\ +5 \\ \hline 9 \end{array}$	$\begin{array}{r} 1 \\ +9 \\ \hline 10 \end{array}$
a	b	c	d	c	b	a
$\begin{array}{r} 10 \\ -3 \\ \hline 7 \end{array}$	$\begin{array}{r} 4 \\ +6 \\ \hline 10 \end{array}$	$\begin{array}{r} 10 \\ -2 \\ \hline 8 \end{array}$	$\begin{array}{r} 9 \\ -5 \\ \hline 4 \end{array}$	$\begin{array}{r} 10 \\ -8 \\ \hline 2 \end{array}$	$\begin{array}{r} 10 \\ -4 \\ \hline 6 \end{array}$	$\begin{array}{r} 3 \\ +7 \\ \hline 10 \end{array}$

Practice-13

Macmillan/McGraw-Hill, MATHEMATICS IN ACTION
Grade 2, Chapter 1, Lesson 15, pages 35–36

ENRICHMENT

Name

FACTS TO 10

On Your Own   Pair and Share   In a Group

SUBTRACTION MACHINES

This is a subtraction machine.
It subtracts the number in the window.

The number goes in here.

The machine subtracts.

The answer comes out here.

Write the answer that comes out of each machine.

1. $10 \boxed{-2} = 8$ $9 \boxed{-3} = 6$ $10 \boxed{-7} = 3$

2. $9 \boxed{-2} = 7$ $10 \boxed{-5} = 5$ $8 \boxed{-2} = 6$

3. $10 \boxed{-4} = 6$ $10 \boxed{-1} = 9$ $9 \boxed{-5} = 4$

4. $7 \boxed{-4} = 3$ $8 \boxed{-3} = 5$ $10 \boxed{-8} = 2$

Enrichment-13

Macmillan/McGraw-Hill, MATHEMATICS IN ACTION
Grade 2, Chapter 1, Lesson 15, pages 35–36

Problem of the Day

Aaron has 4 softballs and 2 baseballs. He also has 8 bats. Does he have more bats or balls?
[Bats; children may work it out this way: $4 + 2 = 6$ balls; $6 < 8$.]

AT·A·GLANCE p. 37

LESSON OBJECTIVE
Add and subtract money amounts.

ASSIGNMENT GUIDE

COURSE	EXERCISES
Basic	p. 37: 1–2, Reasoning
Average	p. 37: 1–2, Reasoning
Challenge	p. 37: 1–2, Reasoning

MATERIALS
Manipulatives 10 P coins (or punchouts) per pair

Teacher Resources
Reteaching 14   Practice 14   Enrichment 14
MAC Act. 27, 28

SKILLS TRACE
FACTS TO 10

Explore (Concrete)	Develop/Understand (Transitional/Abstract)
10	11, 12, 13–14, 15–16, 19–20, 21–22, 23–24, 29–30, 31–32, 33–34, 35–36, **37**, 38
Practice 20, 28, 32, 43, 44, 45–46, 49, 60	**Apply** 17–18, 25–26, 27, 39–40, 41, 42

PREPARE   **WARM-UP**   To prepare children for adding and subtracting money amounts, write the following on the chalkboard.

  4¢   10¢   9¢   8¢   7¢

Have volunteers read each amount and tell how many pennies equal that amount.

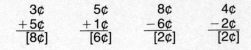

TEACH   **MODELING**   Give pairs of children ten punchout pennies. Write the following exercises on the chalkboard.

3¢	5¢	8¢	4¢
+ 5¢	+ 1¢	− 6¢	− 2¢
[8¢]	[6¢]	[2¢]	[2¢]

Name _____

Adding and Subtracting Money

4¢
+ 2¢
6¢

Add.

1.	5¢	1¢	3¢	2¢	4¢	5¢
	+ 3¢	+ 8¢	+ 7¢	+ 5¢	+ 6¢	+ 4¢
	8¢	9¢	10¢	7¢	10¢	9¢

10¢
− 4¢
6¢

Subtract.

2.	8¢	6¢	9¢	5¢	7¢	10¢
	− 3¢	− 4¢	− 2¢	− 4¢	− 1¢	− 9¢
	5¢	2¢	7¢	1¢	6¢	1¢

Reasoning

Sula spent 8¢ to buy 2 stickers.
Ring the ones that she bought.

Work through each exercise with the children, using pennies as counters. Point out that adding and subtracting amounts of money is the same as adding and subtracting number amounts. Discuss that because the numbers stand for amounts of money, children must include the **cent sign** (¢) in their answer.

PUPIL'S EDITION p. 37

Work through the addition and subtraction examples with the children. Guide them in relating the pictured items to the exercises.

Check for Understanding

■ **How is 5 + 3 the same as 5¢ + 3¢? How is it different?** [same addition; however, second example is about money so answer needs a cent sign]

Activity

Common Error and Remediation

MATERIALS 10 P coins (or punchouts)

Some children may become confused when computing with amounts of money. Work individually with each child, using punchout pennies and exercises similar to those in the lesson. First establish that the value of a penny is 1 cent. Next have the child count sets of pennies and give the value of each set. Then have the child model oral addition facts and give the sums orally. Finally have the child move on to written exercises while still using the pennies. Repeat the activity for subtraction.

ALTERNATIVE TEACHING STRATEGY

VISUAL Write the following exercises on the chalkboard.

4	4¢	6	6¢	2	2¢
+3	+3¢	+3	+3¢	+5	+5¢
[7]	[7¢]	[9]	[9¢]	[7]	[7¢]

Call on volunteers to give the sums. Then write the following.

9	9¢	7	7¢	4	4¢
−2	−2¢	−5	−5¢	−0	−0¢
[7]	[7¢]	[2]	[2¢]	[4]	[4¢]

Guide children to see that adding and subtracting money amounts is the same as adding and subtracting number amounts.

GUIDED PRACTICE ex. 1: For reteaching, use Common Error and Remediation or Alternative Strategy.

PRACTICE•APPLY **PRACTICE** ex. 2

REASONING Have children explain their solutions.

C L O S E Guide children to summarize the lesson:

■ **I had 10¢. I spent 3¢. How much do I have left?** [7¢]

MAC ACTIVITY CENTER

MANIPULATIVES ■ WHO HAS MORE?

MAC Activity 27

Materials punchout pennies

Assign children to work in pairs, and give each pair a set of punchout pennies. Have children work together to solve the following oral problems.

Dan had 10¢ and spent 3¢.
Sue had 9¢ and spent 1¢.
Who has more money now?   [Sue]

Terry had 4¢ and got 2¢.
Sally had 3¢ and got 5¢.
Who has more money now?   [Sally]

Mike had 8¢ and spent 2¢.
Jane had 9¢ and spent 5¢.
Who has more money now?   [Mike]

Lou had 7¢ and spent 1¢.
Fran had 4¢ and got 2¢.
Who has more money now?   [They both have 6¢.]

MAC Activity 27:
Basic-to-Average ▶

MATH FOR SHOPPING ■ BUYING AND SELLING

MAC Activity 28

On Your Own   Pair and Share   In a Group

FOR SALE

Materials punchout pennies

Setup Teacher should have a chart ready with cut-out pictures of items with prices under 10¢. Examples are shown.

Procedure Have children work in pairs, one the "buyer" and one the "seller." The buyer has 10 pennies to spend, and the object is to spend all 10¢ on any combination of items which the seller has "for sale." Examples of possible items for sale:

buttons	2¢	juice	6¢
pencils	3¢	cookies	4¢
box of crayons	7¢	nuts	3¢
scissors	8¢	milk	6¢
		apples	5¢

The buyer decides which items to buy, and the seller totals up the cost. The buyer pays the seller with punchout pennies. Then they trade roles.

▲
MAC Activity 28:
Average-to-Challenge

RETEACHING-14

Name _____

ADDING AND SUBTRACTING MONEY

Study

$$\begin{array}{r} 4¢ \\ + 3¢ \\ \hline 7¢ \end{array}$$

$$\begin{array}{r} 7¢ \\ - 4¢ \\ \hline 3¢ \end{array}$$

Remember to write the cent sign.

Check

Add or subtract.

1.
5¢	4¢	2¢	1¢	3¢	6¢
+ 2¢	+ 6¢	+ 8¢	+ 7¢	+ 6¢	+ 2¢
7¢	10¢	10¢	8¢	9¢	8¢

2.
10¢	9¢	8¢	10¢	9¢	7¢
− 4¢	− 5¢	− 2¢	− 7¢	− 1¢	− 6¢
6¢	4¢	6¢	3¢	8¢	1¢

3.
4¢	3¢	5¢	10¢	6¢	8¢
+ 2¢	+ 1¢	+ 5¢	− 1¢	− 2¢	− 5¢
6¢	4¢	10¢	9¢	4¢	3¢

Macmillan/McGraw-Hill, MATHEMATICS IN ACTION
Grade 2, Chapter 1, Lesson 16, page 37

Reteaching-14

PRACTICE-14

Name _____

ADDING AND SUBTRACTING MONEY

$$\begin{array}{r} 5¢ \\ + 4¢ \\ \hline 9¢ \end{array}$$

Pete and Ann
have 9¢.

Add or subtract.

1.
4¢	2¢	5¢	6¢	4¢	2¢
+ 3¢	+ 8¢	+ 1¢	+ 4¢	+ 5¢	+ 6¢
7¢	10¢	6¢	10¢	9¢	8¢

2.
9¢	5¢	10¢	9¢	10¢	8¢
− 2¢	− 1¢	− 8¢	− 3¢	− 7¢	− 4¢
7¢	4¢	2¢	6¢	3¢	4¢

3.
5¢	5¢	8¢	8¢	7¢	7¢
+ 2¢	− 2¢	+ 1¢	− 1¢	+ 3¢	− 3¢
7¢	3¢	9¢	7¢	10¢	4¢

4.
6¢	9¢	4¢	10¢	5¢	10¢
+ 3¢	− 3¢	+ 6¢	− 6¢	+ 5¢	− 5¢
9¢	6¢	10¢	4¢	10¢	5¢

Macmillan/McGraw-Hill, MATHEMATICS IN ACTION
Grade 2, Chapter 1, Lesson 16, page 37

Practice-14

ENRICHMENT-14

Name _____

ADDING AND SUBTRACTING MONEY

On Your Own   Pair and Share   In a Group

SPENDING PENNIES

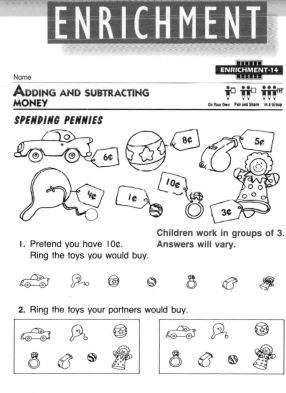

**Children work in groups of 3.
Answers will vary.**

1. Pretend you have 10¢.
   Ring the toys you would buy.

2. Ring the toys your partners would buy.

3. How much money do you have left? _____

4. How much money do your friends have left? _____

5. Combine all the pennies you have left.
   Talk about what else you could buy and share.

Macmillan/McGraw-Hill, MATHEMATICS IN ACTION
Grade 2, Chapter 1, Lesson 16, page 37

Enrichment-14

Problem of the Day

Jerry had 6¢. His grandfather gave him 3¢. He spent 4¢. Then he found a penny. How much money does Jerry have now?   [6¢. Children may work it out this way: 6¢ + 3¢ = 9¢; 9¢ − 4¢ = 5¢; 5¢ + 1¢ = 6¢.]

LESSON OBJECTIVE
Choose a computation method to solve problems.

ASSIGNMENT GUIDE

COURSE	EXERCISES
Basic	p. 38: 1–5
Average	p. 38: 1–5
Challenge	p. 38: 1–5

MATERIALS

Calculator
Manipulatives 10 ◐ (or punchouts) per child

Teacher Resources
Reteaching 15   Practice 15   Enrichment 15
MAC Act. 29, 30
Computer Software *Mathematics Skills:* Disk 2 Act. 1;
 Disk 3 Act. 1

SKILLS TRACE
FACTS TO 10

Explore (Concrete)	Develop/Understand (Transitional/Abstract)
10	11, 12, 13–14, 15–16, 19–20, 21–22, 23–24, 29–30, 31–32, 33–34, 35–36, 37, 38
Practice	**Apply**
20, 28, 32, 43, 44, 45–46, 49, 60	17–18, 25–26, 27, 39–40, 41, 42

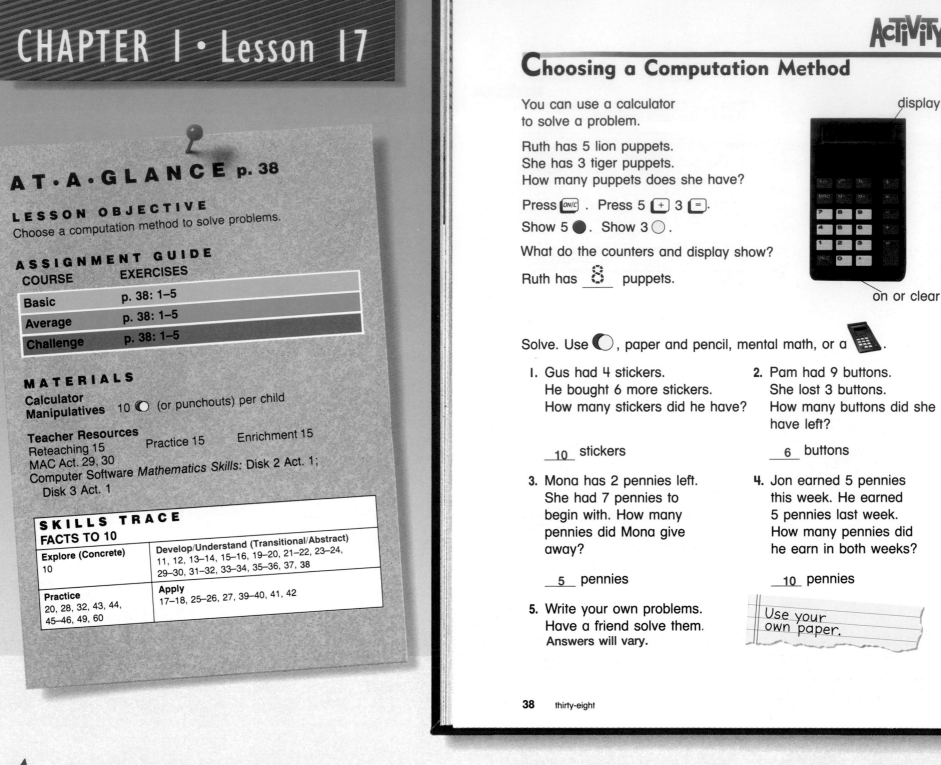

ACTIVITY

Choosing a Computation Method

You can use a calculator
to solve a problem.

display

Ruth has 5 lion puppets.
She has 3 tiger puppets.
How many puppets does she have?

Press [ON/C] . Press 5 [+] 3 [=].
Show 5 ● . Show 3 ○ .

What do the counters and display show?

Ruth has __8__ puppets.

on or clear

Solve. Use ◐, paper and pencil, mental math, or a 🖩.

1. Gus had 4 stickers.
He bought 6 more stickers.
How many stickers did he have?

 __10__ stickers

2. Pam had 9 buttons.
She lost 3 buttons.
How many buttons did she have left?

 __6__ buttons

3. Mona has 2 pennies left.
She had 7 pennies to
begin with. How many
pennies did Mona give
away?

 __5__ pennies

4. Jon earned 5 pennies
this week. He earned
5 pennies last week.
How many pennies did
he earn in both weeks?

 __10__ pennies

5. Write your own problems.
Have a friend solve them.
Answers will vary.

Use your
own paper.

PREPARE
WARM-UP To review word problems, read the following aloud:
There are 2 red apples.
There are 4 yellow apples.
How many apples are there?

Have children use counters to model the problem and find the answer.
[6]

TEACH
DISCUSSING Review that using counters is one
way to find the answer to a problem. Have volunteers describe other ways they can find the answer. Help children describe methods, such as writing a number sentence, using a calculator, using mental math, including counting on and back.

PUPIL'S EDITION p. 38
Distribute a calculator and 10 two-color counters to each child. Point out the location of the "on/clear," "+," "−," "=," and number keys. Have children model the problem at the beginning of the activity with their counters. Then input the problem on a calculator with children. Point out that they should have gotten the same answer using a calculator or counters.

Check for Understanding
■ **Why can you use both a calculator and counters to solve a problem?** [Both ways can help find the same answer.]

GUIDED PRACTICE ex. 1–2: Guide children to add in ex. 1 and subtract in ex. 2. Discuss with children that they may choose a way to find each answer: by using calculators, using counters, using paper and pencil to write number sentences, or by using mental math, such as

ACTIVITY — Common Error and Remediation

MATERIALS calculator per child

Some children may confuse the calculator buttons. Work individually with each child. Using the problems on the pupil page, have the child describe the operation as you write the number sentence on large paper. Have the child say part of the sentence and press the matching calculator key.

ACTIVITY — ALTERNATIVE TEACHING STRATEGY

MATERIALS 10 ⊙, 1 calculator

KINESTHETIC Set up four different stations: counters, calculator, paper and pencil, mental math. Duplicate the same problem to be displayed at each station. Divide the class into four groups. Have children solve the problem using the method established at each station. Have the groups rotate until each group has completed each station.

counting on and counting back. Discuss when and why one might choose each method. For example, it is easier to use mental math when adding 1 or 2, than to use a calculator. For reteaching, use Commmon Error and Remediation or Alternative Strategy.

3 PRACTICE•APPLY   **PRACTICE**   ex. 3–5: Call on volunteers to read their own problems aloud and discuss how they got the answers.

CLOSE   Guide children to summarize the lesson:

■ **What are two different ways to solve a problem?** [Possible answer: by using a calculator or counters]

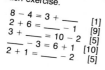

MANIPULATIVES ■ AND CALLED IT MACARONI

MAC Activity 29

On Your Own   Pair and Share   In a Group

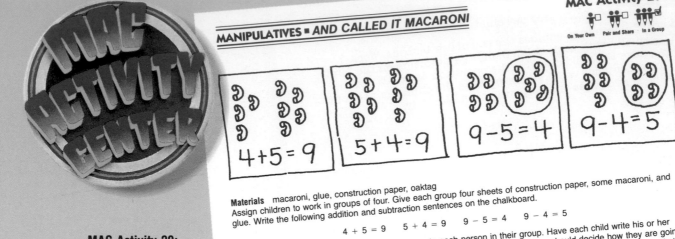

4 + 5 = 9   5 + 4 = 9   9 - 5 = 4   9 - 4 = 5

Materials macaroni, glue, construction paper, oaktag

Assign children to work in groups of four. Give each group four sheets of construction paper, some macaroni, and glue. Write the following addition and subtraction sentences on the chalkboard.

$$4 + 5 = 9 \quad 5 + 4 = 9 \quad 9 - 5 = 4 \quad 9 - 4 = 5$$

Tell children that they are to assign one sentence to each person in their group. Have each child write his or her sentence along the bottom of a sheet of construction paper. Explain that children should decide how they are going to show addition with the macaroni and how they will show subtraction. Then have children glue macaroni on their papers to model each sentence. After the glue has dried, help each group mount the papers on a piece of oaktag. Display each group's work and have volunteers explain the models they made.

**MAC Activity 29:
Basic-to-Average** ▶

LOGICAL REASONING ■ BALANCE IT

MAC Activity 30

On Your Own   Pair and Share   In a Group

Review the meaning of the equal sign with children. Be sure they understand that the total of the numbers on one side of the sign must be the same as the total of the numbers on the other side. Write the following example on the chalkboard.

$$4 + 3 = 9 - 2$$
$$[7 = 7]$$

Then write the following exercises on the chalkboard for the children to copy. Have them find the missing numbers in each exercise.

$8 - 4 = 3 + \underline{\quad}$ [1]
$2 + 6 = \underline{\quad} - 1$ [9]
$3 + \underline{\quad} = 10 - 2$ [5]
$\underline{\quad} - 3 = 6 + 1$ [10]
$2 + 1 = \underline{\quad} - 2$ [5]

4+3   9-2

▲
**MAC Activity 30:
Average-to-Challenge**

RETEACHING

Name

MIXED PRACTICE

Study

Watch those signs!

Add	Subtract	Add	Subtract
7	7	6	6
+2	−2	+3	−3
9	5	9	3

Check

Add or subtract.

1.
$$\begin{array}{c}10\\-5\\\hline 5\end{array}\quad\begin{array}{c}2\\+8\\\hline 10\end{array}\quad\begin{array}{c}10\\-2\\\hline 8\end{array}\quad\begin{array}{c}9\\-9\\\hline 0\end{array}\quad\begin{array}{c}4\\+6\\\hline 10\end{array}\quad\begin{array}{c}10\\-4\\\hline 6\end{array}$$

2.
$$\begin{array}{c}6\\+3\\\hline 9\end{array}\quad\begin{array}{c}5\\+4\\\hline 9\end{array}\quad\begin{array}{c}7\\-4\\\hline 3\end{array}\quad\begin{array}{c}9\\-7\\\hline 2\end{array}\quad\begin{array}{c}5\\+5\\\hline 10\end{array}\quad\begin{array}{c}4\\+2\\\hline 6\end{array}$$

3.
$$\begin{array}{c}10\\-1\\\hline 9\end{array}\quad\begin{array}{c}7\\+3\\\hline 10\end{array}\quad\begin{array}{c}9\\-6\\\hline 3\end{array}\quad\begin{array}{c}5\\+3\\\hline 8\end{array}\quad\begin{array}{c}10\\-6\\\hline 4\end{array}\quad\begin{array}{c}9\\-4\\\hline 5\end{array}$$

4.
$$\begin{array}{c}9\\-8\\\hline 1\end{array}\quad\begin{array}{c}1\\+9\\\hline 10\end{array}\quad\begin{array}{c}10\\-3\\\hline 7\end{array}\quad\begin{array}{c}4\\+4\\\hline 8\end{array}\quad\begin{array}{c}9\\-5\\\hline 4\end{array}\quad\begin{array}{c}10\\-7\\\hline 3\end{array}$$

Reteaching-15

Macmillan/McGraw-Hill, MATHEMATICS IN ACTION
Grade 2, Chapter 1, Lesson 17, page 38

PRACTICE

Name

MIXED PRACTICE

Color sums.

8 🖍 red
9 🖍 yellow

Color differences.

4 🖍 orange
5 🖍 green
6 🖍 brown

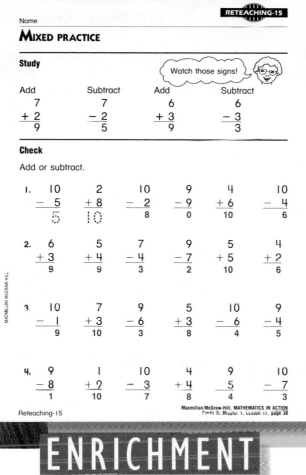

Practice-15

Macmillan/McGraw-Hill, MATHEMATICS IN ACTION
Grade 2, Chapter 1, Lesson 17, page 38

ENRICHMENT

Name

MIXED PRACTICE

On Your Own   Pair and Share   In a Group

BALANCE IT

Write the missing signs.

1. $2 + 2 = 8 \,(-)\, 4$ $5 + 4 = 3 \,(+)\, 6$

2. $2 + 6 = 10 \,(-)\, 2$ $7 + 1 = 9 \,(-)\, 1$

3. $7 - 5 = 3 \,(-)\, 1$ $10 - 7 = 2 \,(+)\, 1$

4. $7 - 4 = 9 \,(-)\, 6$ $8 - 3 = 3 \,(+)\, 2$

5. $10 - 2 = 5 \,(+)\, 3$ $9 - 6 = 5 \,(-)\, 2$

Write more problems.
Have your partner solve them.   **Problems will vary.**

6. $\_\_\_ = \bigcirc$ $\_\_\_ = \bigcirc$

7. $\_\_\_ = \bigcirc$ $\_\_\_ = \bigcirc$

Enrichment-15

Macmillan/McGraw-Hill, MATHEMATICS IN ACTION
Grade 2, Chapter 1, Lesson 17, page 38

Problem of the Day

Laurie had 9 buttons on her jacket. 3 buttons fell off. She found 2 buttons and sewed them back on. How many buttons are still missing? [1; children may work it out this way: 9 − 3 = 6; 6 + 2 = 8; 9 − 8 = 1.]

AT·A·GLANCE pp. 39-40

LESSON OBJECTIVE
Choose the operation to solve problems.

ASSIGNMENT GUIDE

COURSE	EXERCISES
Basic	p. 39: 1–2; p. 40: 1–6
Average	p. 39: 1–2; p. 40: 1–6
Challenge	p. 39: 1–2; p. 40: 1–6
Extra Practice, p. 43	

MATERIALS

Manipulatives 10 ◯ (or punchouts) per child

Teacher Resources
Reteaching 16   Practice 16   Enrichment 16
Prob. Solv. 4   MAC Act. 31, 32

Problem Solving

UNDERSTAND / PLAN / TRY / CHECK / EXTEND

Strategy: Choosing the Operation

6 children were at the table.
2 more children came.
How many children in all?

> Two groups are joined together. Add.

$6 + 2 = 8$ There are 8 children in all.

9 children were at the table.
3 children walked away.
How many children were left?

> Part of the group is taken away. Subtract.

$9 - 3 = 6$ 6 children were left.

Ring the number sentence that solves the problem.

1. 4 children were eating apples.
   I child finished his apple.
   How many children were still
   eating their apples?

   $4 + I = 5$
   $\boxed{4 - I = 3}$

2. 3 friends were eating lunch.
   2 more friends joined them.
   How many friends ate lunch
   together?

   $\boxed{3 + 2 = 5}$
   $3 - 2 = I$

Macmillan/McGraw-Hill

---

1 PREPARE

WARM-UP To prepare children for choosing the operation to solve problems, have them give the following sums and differences.

$7 + 3$ [10] $5 + 3$ [8] $9 - 4$ [5]
$6 + 2$ [8] $7 - 4$ [3] $4 + 5$ [9]
$8 - 5$ [3] $8 + 2$ [10] $6 - 3$ [3]

2 TEACH

QUESTIONING On the chalkboard, write $7 + 2$ and $7 - 2$. Then read aloud the following problem:

Gary has 7 oranges. Barbara has 2 oranges. How many oranges in all?

■ **Who has oranges?** [Gary and Barbara]
■ **How many oranges does Gary have?** [7 oranges]

■ **How many oranges does Barbara have?** [2 oranges]
■ **How can we find how many oranges there are in all?** [We join or add the two groups of oranges.]
■ **Which number sentence on the chalkboard shows what we should do?** [$7 + 2$]

PUPIL'S EDITION pp. 39-40

Page 39 Have a volunteer read the problem at the top of the page.
■ **What do you know?** [6 children were at the table and 2 more children came.]
■ **What do you need to find out?** [the number of children in all]

Discuss adding or joining groups to find how many in all. Provide children with counters and have them model the number sentence to show the addition.

Ring the number sentence that solves the problem.

1. 6 students rode the bus.
   3 students got off the bus.
   How many students were left?

   $6 + 3 = 9$

   $\boxed{6 - 3 = 3}$

2. Sid and Cy were skating.
   Joe and Li joined them.
   How many children in all?

   $\boxed{2 + 2 = 4}$

   $2 - 2 = 0$

3. 7 boys were playing football.
   2 boys went home.
   How many boys were left?

   $7 + 2 = 9$

   $\boxed{7 - 2 = 5}$

4. Eric read 5 books.
   His brother read 4 books.
   How many books altogether?

   $\boxed{5 + 4 = 9}$

   $5 - 4 = 1$

5. 3 girls were in a school play.
   2 boys were in the play.
   How many children were in
   the play altogether?

   $\boxed{3 + 2 = 5}$

   $3 - 2 = 1$

6. 7 children were playing.
   3 children went home.
   How many children were
   still playing?

   $7 + 3 = 10$

   $\boxed{7 - 3 = 4}$

40   forty

Extra Practice, page 43

TEACHER to TEACHER

COOPERATIVE LEARNING TIP 👥 My children enjoy acting out word problems. One pair acts out the problem and all the other groups of two pairs **huddle** to choose the appropriate operation for the problem. Each group is numbered off from one to four. Then when I call a number, for example "Twos," all Number Twos in all groups hold up a symbol for the operation (either a + or a –). Then I ask them to huddle again and think up a number sentence for the story. When I call another number, each student with that number will write their group's number sentence on the chalkboard.

For Students Acquiring English (SAE)

Scan the pages for vocabulary that may be new to SAE children. As the problem on page 39 is read aloud, introduce new words by using visuals, gestures, and body movements to convey meaning. Ask questions frequently to check comprehension. To complete the exercises on pages 39–40, give pairs of SAE and non-SAE children two index cards, one with a large + and the other with a –. Then read the story problems aloud and have children hold up the index card showing the appropriate operation.

Then discuss the second example. Have children use counters to model the number sentence to show subtraction. Guide children to see that they need to choose whether to add or subtract to answer the question. Discuss separating groups by taking away or subtracting.

■ **What did you learn?** [Possible response: Decide whether or not to add or subtract before solving a problem.]

Check for Understanding

■ **What if 5 children were at the table and 4 more joined them? Would you add or subtract to find how many in all?** [Add.]

GUIDED PRACTICE ex. 1–2: Work through problem 1 with the children. Make sure they understand how to solve the problem by choosing the operation.

Page 40 Have a volunteer read the directions at the top of the page.

3 PRACTICE•APPLY **PRACTICE** ex. 1–6

C L O S E Guide children to summarize the lesson:

■ **How do you choose the operation to solve problems?** [Possible response: You read what happens in the problem. Then you decide what you need to do to find the answer to the question.]

LESSON RESOURCES
CHAPTER 1 • Lesson 18

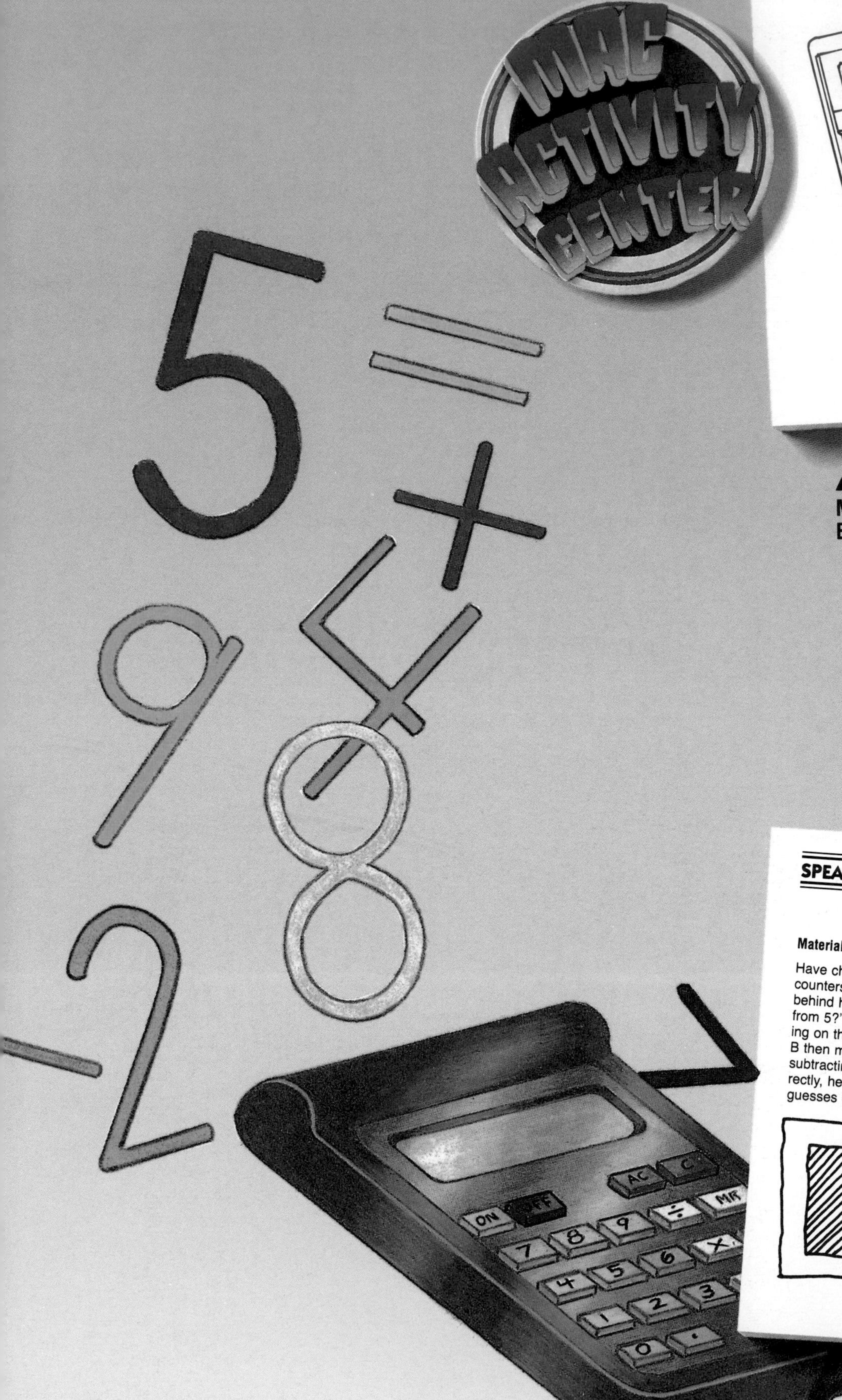

CALCULATOR ▪ *WHAT'S THE NUMBER?*

MAC Activity 31

On Your Own | Pair and Share | In a Group

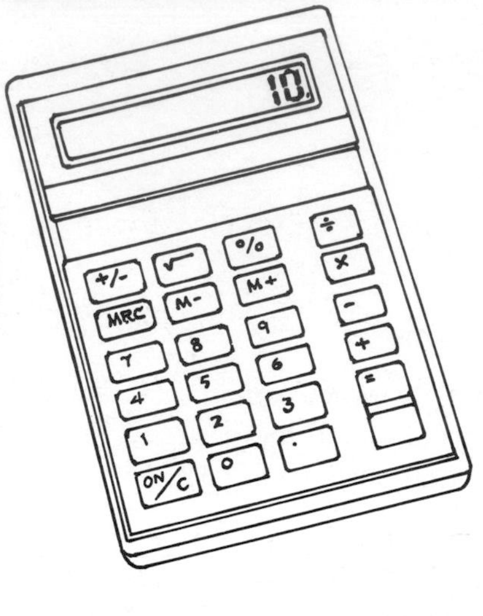

Materials calculator

Assign children to work with a calculator. Have the +, −, =, and clear buttons identified. Tell children that you will read some number riddles aloud. Explain that they are to add or subtract by pressing the keys on the calculator to answer each riddle. Have children identify the number and the operations they used.

1. Press 1 and 0. Make this number 4 less. Press = . Make this number 2 more. Press = . What is the number? [8; 10 − 4 = 6, 6 + 2 = 8; subtract, add]
2. Press 3. Make this number 3 more. Press = . Make this number 1 more. Press = . Make this number 2 less. Press = . What is the number? [5; 3 + 3 = 6, 6 + 1 = 7, 7 - 2 = 5; add, add, subtract]

Continue the activity with similar riddles.

▲ **MAC Activity 31: Basic-to-Average**

MAC Activity 32: Average-to-Challenge ▼

SPEAKING MATHEMATICALLY ▪ *TAKE A GUESS*

MAC Activity 32

On Your Own | Pair and Share | In a Group

Materials counters or punchout counters

Have children play in pairs. Provide each child with 10 counters. Player A hides 1 to 10 counters in one hand behind his or her back. Player B asks "Add to or subtract from 5?" Player A then answers add or subtract, depending on the number of counters in his or her hand. Player B then makes a guess by adding a number up to 5 or subtracting a number from 5. If Player B guesses incorrectly, he or she continues to guess. When Player B guesses correctly, children exchange roles.

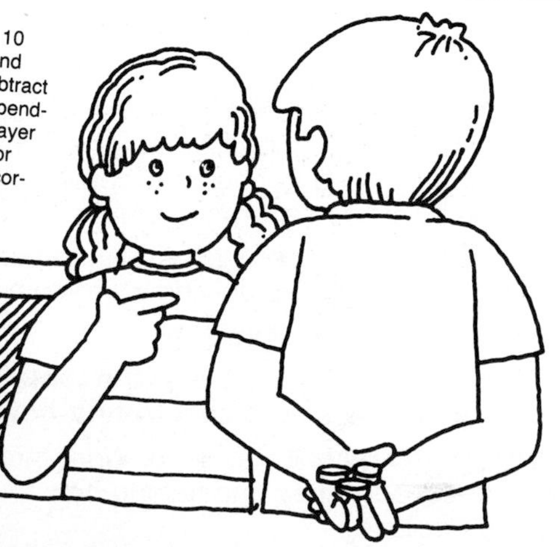

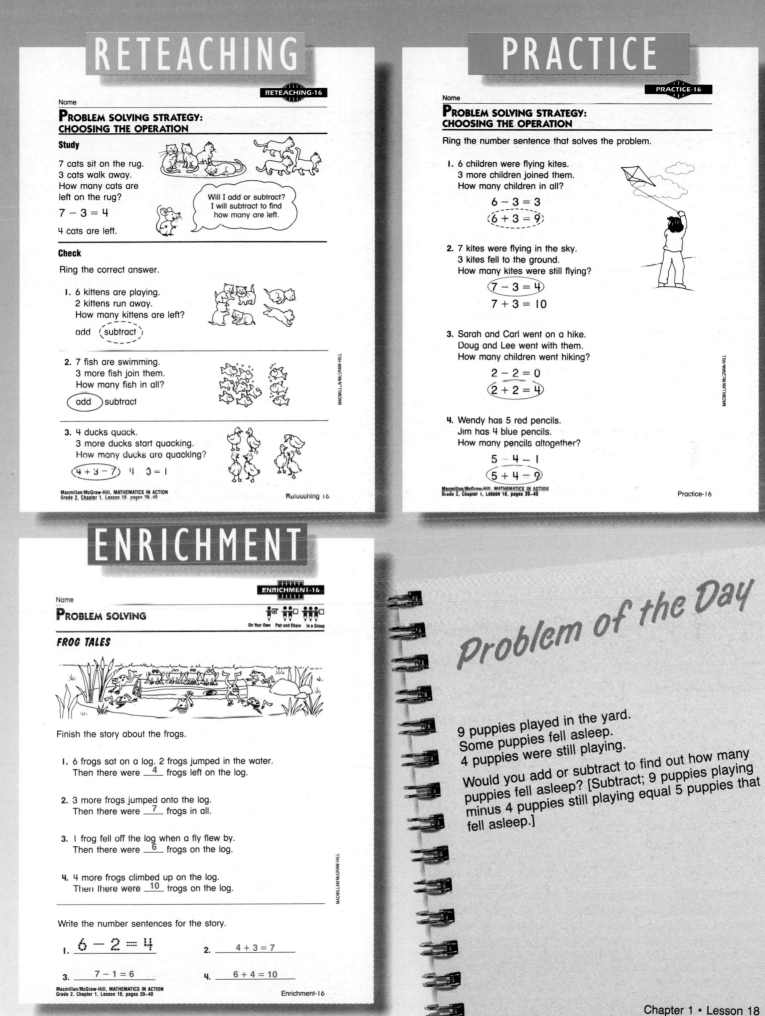

RETEACHING

Name _____

PROBLEM SOLVING STRATEGY:
CHOOSING THE OPERATION

Study

7 cats sit on the rug.
3 cats walk away.
How many cats are
left on the rug?

Will I add or subtract?
I will subtract to find
how many are left.

$7 - 3 = 4$

4 cats are left.

Check

Ring the correct answer.

1. 6 kittens are playing.
   2 kittens run away.
   How many kittens are left?

   add   (subtract)

2. 7 fish are swimming.
   3 more fish join them.
   How many fish in all?

   (add)   subtract

3. 4 ducks quack.
   3 more ducks start quacking.
   How many ducks are quacking?

   $(4 + 3 = 7)$ $4 - 3 = 1$

Macmillan/McGraw-Hill, MATHEMATICS IN ACTION
Grade 2, Chapter 1, Lesson 18, pages 39–40

Reteaching-16

PRACTICE

Name _____

PROBLEM SOLVING STRATEGY:
CHOOSING THE OPERATION

Ring the number sentence that solves the problem.

1. 6 children were flying kites.
   3 more children joined them.
   How many children in all?

   $6 - 3 = 3$
   $(6 + 3 = 9)$

2. 7 kites were flying in the sky.
   3 kites fell to the ground.
   How many kites were still flying?

   $(7 - 3 = 4)$
   $7 + 3 = 10$

3. Sarah and Carl went on a hike.
   Doug and Lee went with them.
   How many children went hiking?

   $2 - 2 = 0$
   $(2 + 2 = 4)$

4. Wendy has 5 red pencils.
   Jim has 4 blue pencils.
   How many pencils altogether?

   $5 - 4 = 1$
   $(5 + 4 = 9)$

Macmillan/McGraw-Hill, MATHEMATICS IN ACTION
Grade 2, Chapter 1, Lesson 18, pages 39–40

Practice-16

ENRICHMENT

Name _____

PROBLEM SOLVING

On Your Own   Pair and Share   In a Group

FROG TALES

Finish the story about the frogs.

1. 6 frogs sat on a log. 2 frogs jumped in the water.
   Then there were __4__ frogs left on the log.

2. 3 more frogs jumped onto the log.
   Then there were __7__ frogs in all.

3. 1 frog fell off the log when a fly flew by.
   Then there were __6__ frogs on the log.

4. 4 more frogs climbed up on the log.
   Then there were __10__ frogs on the log.

Write the number sentences for the story.

1. $6 - 2 = 4$ 2. $4 + 3 = 7$

3. $7 - 1 = 6$ 4. $6 + 4 = 10$

Macmillan/McGraw-Hill, MATHEMATICS IN ACTION
Grade 2, Chapter 1, Lesson 18, pages 39–40

Enrichment-16

Problem of the Day

9 puppies played in the yard.
Some puppies fell asleep.
4 puppies were still playing.

Would you add or subtract to find out how many
puppies fell asleep? [Subtract; 9 puppies playing
minus 4 puppies still playing equal 5 puppies that
fell asleep.]

AT·A·GLANCE p. 41

LESSON OBJECTIVE
Make decisions using information.

ASSIGNMENT GUIDE

COURSE	EXERCISES
Basic	p. 41: 1–3
Average	p. 41: 1–3
Challenge	p. 41: 1–3

Teacher Resources
Crit. Think. 2   Prob. Solv. 5

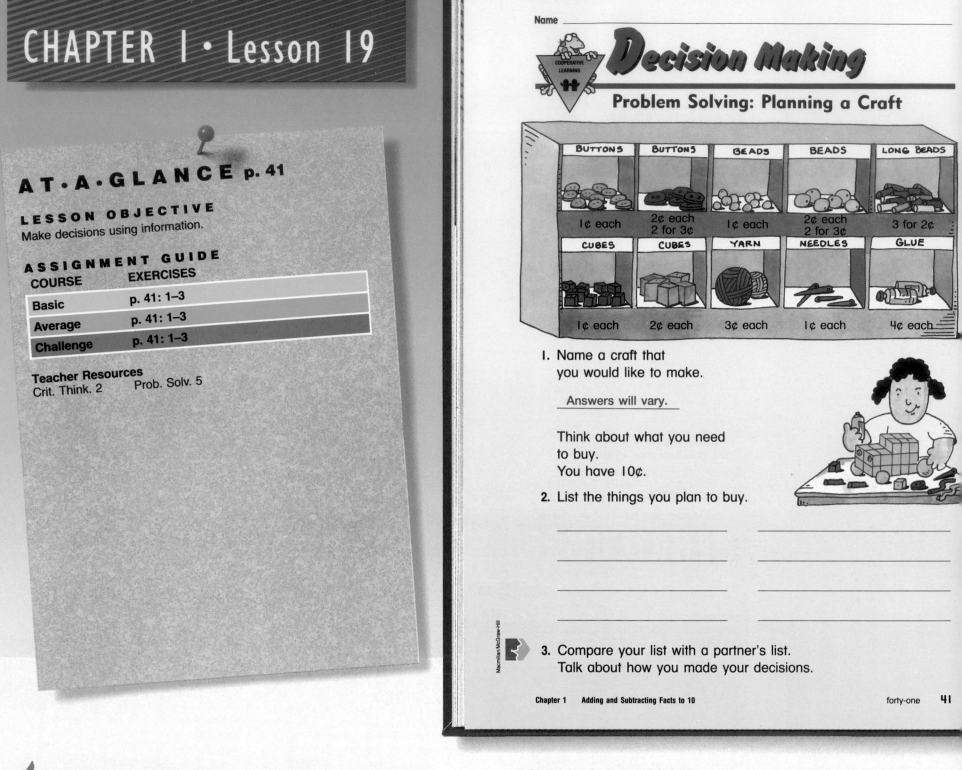

Name _____

Decision Making

Problem Solving: Planning a Craft

BUTTONS	BUTTONS	BEADS	BEADS	LONG BEADS
1¢ each	2¢ each 2 for 3¢	1¢ each	2¢ each 2 for 3¢	3 for 2¢

CUBES	CUBES	YARN	NEEDLES	GLUE
1¢ each	2¢ each	3¢ each	1¢ each	4¢ each

1. Name a craft that you would like to make.

   Answers will vary.

   Think about what you need to buy.
   You have 10¢.

2. List the things you plan to buy.

   _____   _____

   _____   _____

   _____   _____

   _____   _____

3. Compare your list with a partner's list.
   Talk about how you made your decisions.

 **PREPARE** **WARM-UP** To review addition and subtraction facts, have children complete these number sentences.

$10 - 2 =$ ___ [8] $4 + 3 =$ ___ [7]
$6 + 4 =$ ___ [10] $8 + 1 =$ ___ [9]
$9 - 2 =$ ___ [7] $4 + 4 =$ ___ [8]

TEACH **DISCUSSING** Define the word *craft* for the children. Explain that it is something that is planned, designed, and made. Have children name things that they could make. [Possible responses: bead necklaces, buttons, yarn pictures, braided yarn bracelets] List their responses on the chalkboard. Read the completed list with the children. Then discuss with children how they could make each item on the list.

PUPIL'S EDITION p. 41
Identify the pictures and prices at the top of the page with the children.

Check for Understanding

■ **How many blue buttons could you buy with 3¢?** [3]

■ **What could you buy with 4¢?** [Possible responses: glue or yarn and a needle]

■ **How many items are 1¢ each?** [4—buttons, yellow beads, red cubes, needles]

PRACTICE·APPLY Have children complete ex. 1–3. Call on volunteers to tell what craft they will make, how they decided which items to buy, and how many of each item they will need.

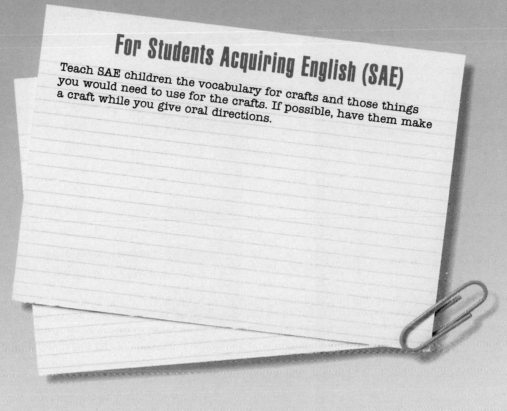

For Students Acquiring English (SAE)

Teach SAE children the vocabulary for crafts and those things you would need to use for the crafts. If possible, have them make a craft while you give oral directions.

CLOSE Guide children to summarize the lesson:
- **What should you do before making a craft?** [Decide what to make and list the things needed. Then see how much money you have and decide if you can buy everything on your list.]

CLASS PROJECT

Materials buttons, beads, yarn, plastic needles, glue, construction paper

Gather the craft materials shown on page 41. Provide the children with a variety of collage materials as well. Then have children make the item that they named, if possible, or encourage them to use the materials to design another craft.

When children have completed the project, call on volunteers to show and tell about their craft.

AT·A·GLANCE p. 42

OBJECTIVE
Read, say, and write counting words in languages other than English.

MULTICULTURAL OUTCOME
Introduce children to words for the numbers 1 to 10 in the Ashanti (Twi) and Cheyenne languages.

MATERIALS
Classroom Materials   green and yellow paper strips

Curriculum Connection

Math and Social Studies

There are many ways to count to ten.
The Ashanti people live in Africa.
The Cheyenne are Native Americans.
Here are Ashanti and Cheyenne counting words.

	ASHANTI		CHEYENNE	
	Write	Say	Write	Say
one	eko	eh KOH	noka	NOH kah
two	eno	eh NOH	nexa	NEKS ah
three	esa	eh SUH	naha	NAH hah
four	enae	ee NYE	neva	NEH vah
five	innum	ih NOOM	nohona	NOH hoh nah
six	insia	ihn SEE ah	naasohtoha	nah SOH toh hah
seven	nso	ehn SOH	nesohtoha	NEH soh toh hah
eight	inwotwie	ihn WAH tweh	nanotoha	nah NOH toh hah
nine	enkoro	ehn KROH	soohtoha	SOH oh toh hah
ten	edu	eh DOO	mahtohtoha	mah TOH toh hah

Write the word to finish each number fact.

1. Add in Ashanti: *eko* + *insia* = _____nso_____

2. Subtract in Cheyenne: *soohtoha* − *neva* = _____nohona_____

Use your own paper.

Working Together

Write an addition fact in Ashanti on green paper.
Write a subtraction fact in Cheyenne on yellow paper.
Trade papers. Write each fact with numbers.

1 PREPARE   **WARM-UP** Ask children when and where they have heard people speaking in words other than English, and if they know any words in other languages. Discuss how people around the world speak many different languages, and some may be able to speak more than one language. Ask:

■ **What happens when people try to talk to each other in different languages?** [They may not understand each other.]

2 TEACH   **DISCUSSING** Count aloud with the class from 1 to 10. Then ask if anyone knows how to count to ten in words other than English. Invite volunteers to count in as many languages as they know.

Then introduce the lesson, using the background information provided. Help the children understand how to read the charts and pronounce the number words. Ask:

■ **How would you say your age in Ashanti (*Twi*)? in Cheyenne?** [Answers will vary.]

■ **If an Ashanti child goes to sleep when her clock says *inwotwie*, what time is it in English?** [8 o'clock]

■ **If a Cheyenne boy has *nohona* cousins, how many is that in English?** [5]

CULTURAL DIVERSITY

ASHANTI AND CHEYENNE LANGUAGES

The Ashanti (or Asante) people form the largest ethnic group in Ghana in western Africa. Most live in the southcentral region where the regional capital, Kumasi, is the country's second largest city. The Ashanti language is called *Twi*, but because English is Ghana's official language, many Ashanti people speak English and Twi.

The Cheyenne originally lived in the area of Lake Superior. The name *Cheyenne* comes from a Sioux word that means "People of Alien Speech." Today, many Cheyenne live in Montana and Oklahoma.

BIBLIOGRAPHY

Feelings, Muriel. *Moja Means One: Swahili Counting Book.* New York: Dial Press, 1971. ISBN 0-8037-5776-X.

3 PRACTICE•APPLY   Have the children refer to the number word charts to complete Questions 1 and 2.

WORKING TOGETHER   Divide the class into pairs. Give each pair green and yellow paper strips. Have them use green for Ashanti and yellow for Cheyenne. When children finish, they exchange number sentences for their partners to translate. The color codes will help guide children to check the correct chart.

CLOSE   Guide children to summarize the lesson:

■ **How would you say the number 4 in Cheyenne?** [*neva*]

■ **What is the Ashanti answer to 4 + 5?** [*enkoro*]

CHAPTER 1

Adding Three Numbers, pages 31–32 ....

Add.

1.
$$
\begin{array}{cccccc}
1 & 4 & 6 & 2 & 3 & 4 \\
2 & 3 & 0 & 1 & 4 & 4 \\
+6 & +1 & +1 & +3 & +2 & +0 \\
\hline
9 & 8 & 7 & 6 & 9 & 8
\end{array}
$$

Facts to 10, pages 35–36 ....

Write the fact family for the picture.

1.
| $3 + 5 = 8$ | $8 - 3 = 5$ |
| $5 + 3 = 8$ | $8 - 5 = 3$ |

2.
| $4 + 5 = 9$ | $9 - 5 = 4$ |
| $5 + 4 = 9$ | $9 - 4 = 5$ |

Problem Solving: Choosing the Operation, pages 39–40 ....

Ring the number sentence that solves the problem.

1. Bill caught 2 butterflies.
   Jean caught 7 butterflies.
   How many butterflies in all?

   $(2 + 7 = 9)$

   $7 - 2 = 5$

2. Maria had 8 fireflies.
   4 fireflies flew away.
   How many fireflies were left?

   $8 + 4 = 12$

   $(8 - 4 = 4)$

Macmillan/McGraw-Hill

Chapter 1   Adding and Subtracting Facts to 10   forty-three   **43**

ADDITIONAL PRACTICE

p. 31   *Add.*

1.
$$
\begin{array}{cccccc}
1 & 0 & 5 & 6 & 4 & 2 \\
1 & 3 & 2 & 0 & 4 & 3 \\
+6 & +4 & +2 & +2 & +1 & +1 \\
\hline
[8] & [7] & [9] & [8] & [9] & [6]
\end{array}
$$

2.
$$
\begin{array}{cccccc}
3 & 1 & 2 & 1 & 4 & 3 \\
2 & 4 & 2 & 3 & 3 & 0 \\
+0 & +3 & +2 & +3 & +2 & +5 \\
\hline
[5] & [8] & [6] & [7] & [9] & [8]
\end{array}
$$

p. 35   *Write the fact family for the picture.*

1.

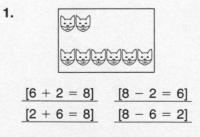

| $[6 + 2 = 8]$ | $[8 - 2 = 6]$ |
| $[2 + 6 = 8]$ | $[8 - 6 = 2]$ |

p. 39   *Ring the number sentence that solves the problem.*

1. Jack had 9 frogs.
   3 hopped away.
   How many frogs were left?
   $9 + 3 = 12$ $[9 - 3 = 6]$

2. Sue made 3 paper hats.
   Dan made 6 paper hats.
   How many paper hats in all?
   $[3 + 6 = 9]$ $6 - 3 = 3$

Practice Plus

Key Skill: Facts to 7, page 22 . . . .

Write the fact family for each picture.

1. $4 + 3 = 7$ $7 - 3 = 4$
   $3 + 4 = 7$ $7 - 4 = 3$

2. $3 + 2 = 5$ $5 - 3 = 2$
   $2 + 3 = 5$ $5 - 2 = 3$

Key Skill: Facts to 10, page 36 . . . .

Add or subtract.

1.
$$
\begin{array}{cccccc}
3 & 6 & 9 & 5 & 4 & 2 \\
+6 & +3 & +1 & +2 & +4 & +8 \\
\hline
9 & 9 & 10 & 7 & 8 & 10
\end{array}
$$

2.
$$
\begin{array}{cccccc}
7 & 9 & 6 & 8 & 9 & 7 \\
-4 & -8 & -0 & -2 & -9 & -2 \\
\hline
3 & 1 & 6 & 6 & 0 & 5
\end{array}
$$

3.
$$
\begin{array}{cccccc}
3 & 3 & 4 & 2 & 5 & 2 \\
1 & 3 & 0 & 7 & 1 & 5 \\
+4 & +3 & +1 & +1 & +1 & +3 \\
\hline
8 & 9 & 5 & 10 & 7 & 10
\end{array}
$$

4.
$$
\begin{array}{cccccc}
10 & 10 & 8 & 8 & 7 & 7 \\
-6 & -4 & -5 & -3 & -1 & -6 \\
\hline
4 & 6 & 3 & 5 & 6 & 1
\end{array}
$$

ADDITIONAL PRACTICE

p. 22 *Write the fact family for each picture.*

1.
[4 + 2 = 6]
[2 + 4 = 6]
[6 − 2 = 4]
[6 − 4 = 2]

2.
[5 + 2 = 7]
[2 + 5 = 7]
[7 − 2 = 5]
[7 − 5 = 2]

p. 36 *Add or subtract.*

1.
$$
\begin{array}{cccc}
4 & 8 & 10 & 7 \\
+6 & +1 & +0 & +2 \\
\hline
[10] & [9] & [10] & [9]
\end{array}
$$

2.
$$
\begin{array}{cccc}
9 & 8 & 10 & 10 \\
-3 & -4 & -2 & -10 \\
\hline
[6] & [4] & [8] & [0]
\end{array}
$$

3.
$$
\begin{array}{cccc}
7 & 8 & 9 & 10 \\
-3 & -6 & -8 & -5 \\
\hline
[4] & [2] & [1] & [5]
\end{array}
$$

4.
$$
\begin{array}{cccc}
2 & 4 & 1 & 9 \\
+2 & +3 & +4 & +1 \\
\hline
[4] & [7] & [5] & [10]
\end{array}
$$

5.
$$
\begin{array}{cccc}
3 & 7 & 2 & 5 \\
3 & 2 & 6 & 1 \\
+2 & +1 & +1 & +1 \\
\hline
[8] & [10] & [9] & [7]
\end{array}
$$

CHAPTER 1

OBJECTIVE
Review/test the concepts and skills presented in Chapter 1.

1A. Add, facts to 10.
1B. Subtract, facts to 10.
1C. Add three 1-digit numbers.
1D. Solve problems including those that involve writing an addition or subtraction sentence and choosing the correct operation.

Teacher Resources
Testing Program, pp. 1–12

Language and Mathematics
Complete. Choose the correct words from the box.

1. The facts

$$2 + 1 = 3 \qquad 3 - 1 = 2$$
$$1 + 2 = 3 \qquad 3 - 2 = 1$$

are called a ____fact family____ .

sum
fact family
difference

2. In $2 + 1 = 3$, 3 is the ____sum____ .

3. When you subtract, the answer is called the

____difference____ .

Concepts and Skills
Complete the fact family for the picture.

4.

$3 + 2 = 5$	$5 - 2 = 3$
$2 + 3 = 5$	$5 - 3 = 2$

Write the fact family for the picture.

5.

$5 + 2 = 7$	$7 - 5 = 2$
$2 + 5 = 7$	$7 - 2 = 5$

6.

$3 + 6 = 9$	$9 - 3 = 6$
$6 + 3 = 9$	$9 - 6 = 3$

USING THE CHAPTER REVIEW/TEST

The Chapter Review/Test may be used as a review to survey children's knowledge and understanding of the chapter material. Or it may be used as a test to formally assess children's understanding of the concepts and skills taught in the chapter. If used as a test, you may wish to assign one or more of the resources listed in *Reinforcement and Remediation* on p. 46 after reviewing children's test results.

If the Chapter Review/Test is used as a review, you may wish to have children work in pairs to complete it. Have them talk about how to count on to find $1 + 7$. Then, you can use the Chapter Tests—Forms A, B, and C—provided in the *Testing Program Blackline Master and Teacher's Manual* testing purposes. Any of these forms may be used for pretesting, posttesting, or retesting.

A performance assessment activity for the key concept in this chapter is provided on page 47.

Add or subtract.

7. $6 + 3 = \underline{9}$ $5 + 0 = \underline{5}$ $8 + 2 = \underline{10}$

8. $7 - 2 = \underline{5}$ $4 - 1 = \underline{3}$ $9 - 9 = \underline{0}$

9.
$$\begin{array}{r} 2 \\ +5 \\ \hline 7 \end{array} \quad \begin{array}{r} 1 \\ +8 \\ \hline 9 \end{array} \quad \begin{array}{r} 3 \\ +2 \\ \hline 5 \end{array} \quad \begin{array}{r} 1 \\ 2 \\ +3 \\ \hline 6 \end{array} \quad \begin{array}{r} 6 \\ 0 \\ +3 \\ \hline 9 \end{array} \quad \begin{array}{r} 3 \\ 4 \\ +3 \\ \hline 10 \end{array}$$

10.
$$\begin{array}{r} 7 \\ -1 \\ \hline 6 \end{array} \quad \begin{array}{r} 9 \\ -4 \\ \hline 5 \end{array} \quad \begin{array}{r} 2 \\ -1 \\ \hline 1 \end{array} \quad \begin{array}{r} 4 \\ -0 \\ \hline 4 \end{array} \quad \begin{array}{r} 8 \\ -3 \\ \hline 5 \end{array} \quad \begin{array}{r} 3 \\ -3 \\ \hline 0 \end{array}$$

Problem Solving

Write a subtraction sentence. Solve.

11. 10 bees are on a flower.
3 bees fly away.
How many bees are left?

$$\underline{\qquad 10 - 3 = 7 \qquad} \qquad \underline{7} \text{ bees}$$

Ring the number sentence that solves the problem.

12. Stan had 6 pencils.
Walt gave him 1 more.
How many pencils did Stan have in all?

$(6 + 1 = 7)$ $6 - 1 = 5$

Reinforcement and Remediation

CHAP. OBJ.	TEST ITEMS	PUPIL'S EDITION pp.			TEACHER'S EDITION pp.	TEACHER RESOURCES	
		Lesson	Extra Practice	Practice Plus	Alt. Teaching Strategy	Reteaching	Practice
1A	1–2, 4–7, 9	11, 13–16, 19–24, 29–30, 33–38	28, 43	44	11A, 14, 16, 20, 22, 24, 30, 34, 36, 37A, 38A	1, 3, 4, 6, 7, 8, 10, 12, 13–15	1, 3, 4, 6, 7, 8, 10, 12–15
1B	1, 3–6, 8, 10	12–16, 19–24, 29–30, 33–38	28, 43	44	12A, 14, 16, 20, 22, 24, 30, 34, 36, 37A, 38A	2, 3, 4, 6, 7, 8, 10, 12, 13–15	2, 3, 4, 6, 7, 8, 10, 12–15
1C	9	31–32	43		32	11	11
1D	11–12	25–26 39–40	28, 43	44		9, 16	9, 16

CHAPTER 1

AT·A·GLANCE p. 47

OBJECTIVE
Assess whether children can add and subtract facts to 10.

MATERIALS
Manipulatives 10 ○ (or punchouts) per pair

Teacher Resources
Performance Assessment booklet, pp. 9–11

For Students Acquiring English (SAE)

Before beginning the performance assessment with SAE children, scan the page for any unfamiliar vocabulary that should be pretaught. You may wish to pair or group SAE children with non-SAE children. You may also wish to repeat some of the activities and techniques for SAE children that were suggested earlier in this chapter.

Performance Assessment

Work with a partner.

Finish this story with an addition or subtraction problem. Draw a picture or write the problem. Write the number sentence that solves the problem.

Manny is juggling 5 balls.
Amy is juggling 4 balls.

You may put this page in your Portfolio.

Macmillan/McGraw-Hill

USING PERFORMANCE ASSESSMENT
The Performance Assessment activity may be used to informally assess children's understanding of the key concept(s) of the chapter. Additional assessment activities and Math Journal Options are provided in the *Performance Assessment* booklet.

Performing the Activity
Assign children to work in pairs. Distribute materials. Have children work together using counters to finish the story. Have them draw or write their problems and write the number sentences individually.

Evaluation Guidelines
Use these criteria to help determine the holistic score for each child. The holistic scoring scale can be found in the Teacher's Reference Section.

• Can children explain how to solve the problem?
• Does the picture (or set of counters) correspond to the numbers in the problem?

[Example Response: 5 − 4 = 1]

If children do not have a full understanding of the key concept(s), you may wish to use the Alternative Teaching Strategies or the MAC Activities within the chapter.

You may wish to have children put their final revised work in their portfolios.

A formal assessment of the concepts and skills taught in this chapter is provided on pages 45–46.

Enrichment For All

Roman Numerals

Many years ago, Romans wrote numbers in a different way.

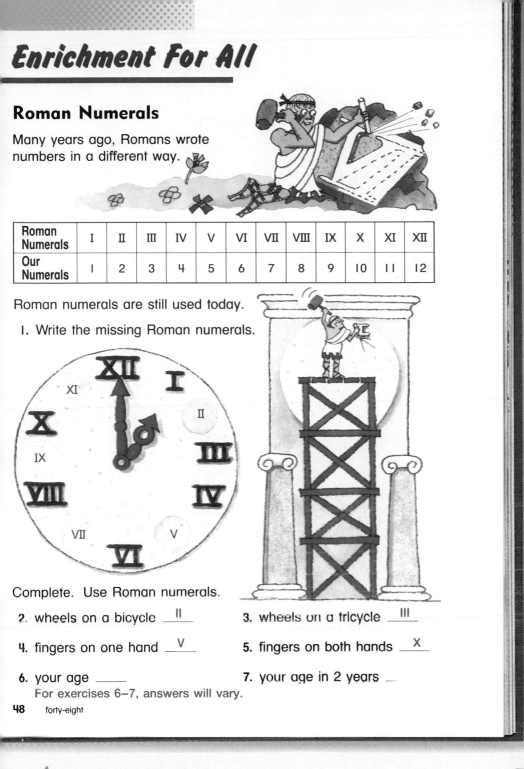

Roman Numerals	I	II	III	IV	V	VI	VII	VIII	IX	X	XI	XII
Our Numerals	1	2	3	4	5	6	7	8	9	10	11	12

Roman numerals are still used today.

1. Write the missing Roman numerals.

Complete. Use Roman numerals.

2. wheels on a bicycle ___II___

3. wheels on a tricycle ___III___

4. fingers on one hand ___V___

5. fingers on both hands ___X___

6. your age _____

7. your age in 2 years ___

For exercises 6–7, answers will vary.

AT·A·GLANCE p. 48

OBJECTIVE
Identify and write Roman numerals.

ASSIGNMENT GUIDE

COURSE	EXERCISES
Basic	p. 48: 1–7
Average	p. 48: 1–7
Challenge	p. 48: 1–7

MATERIALS
Classroom Materials   clocks, watches, and other objects with Roman numerals

CULTURAL DIVERSITY

At one point, the Roman Empire extended from Britain to Western Asia. It is said to have lasted from 27 B.C. to A.D. 475, although the eastern part of the empire existed until A.D. 1453. Roman numerals are believed to have been at least partially derived from numerals used by the Etruscans, a people who at one time had dominated Rome. These numerals are believed to have been derived from letters in the Greek alphabet.

 **PREPARE**   **WARM-UP**   To prepare children to read and write Roman numerals, discuss their origin. Explain that the Romans probably developed their number system by counting on their fingers. If possible, display objects or pictures with Roman numerals for children to study.

TEACH   **DISCUSSING**   Have children study the table on the page. Explain that the Romans combined the same symbols to show different numbers. Have children point to I on the table.

■ **How is Roman numeral three written?** [III]

Help children find patterns. [V is 5; IV is one less than 5; VI is one more than 5.]

 **PRACTICE·APPLY**   Have children complete ex. 1–7. Call on volunteers to explain how they figured out their answers for ex. 6–7.

CLOSE   Guide children to summarize the lesson:

■ **What Roman numeral stands for 9; 11? Write your answers on paper.** [IX; XI]

AT·A·GLANCE p. 49

OBJECTIVE
Review and maintain previously learned concepts and skills.

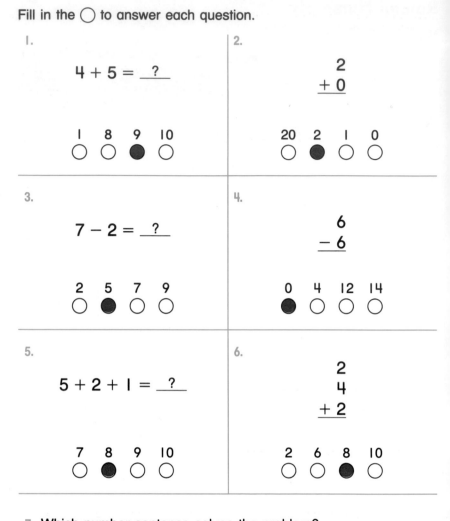

Name _____

Cumulative Review

Fill in the ○ to answer each question.

1.
$$4 + 5 = \underline{\ ?\ }$$

1	8	9	10
○	○	●	○

2.
$$\begin{array}{r} 2 \\ + 0 \\ \hline \end{array}$$

20	2	1	0
○	●	○	○

3.
$$7 - 2 = \underline{\ ?\ }$$

2	5	7	9
○	●	○	○

4.
$$\begin{array}{r} 6 \\ - 6 \\ \hline \end{array}$$

0	4	12	14
●	○	○	○

5.
$$5 + 2 + 1 = \underline{\ ?\ }$$

7	8	9	10
○	●	○	○

6.
$$\begin{array}{r} 2 \\ 4 \\ + 2 \\ \hline \end{array}$$

2	6	8	10
○	○	●	○

7. Which number sentence solves the problem?
Chris had 6 pennies.
He spent 3 pennies.
How many pennies did he have left?

○ $6 + 3 = 9$
● $6 - 3 = 3$

Macmillan/McGraw-Hill

Chapter 1   Adding and Subtracting Facts to 10   forty-nine   **49**

USING THE CUMULATIVE REVIEW

The Cumulative Review is presented in a multiple-choice format to provide practice in taking a standardized test. It gives children an opportunity to review previously learned skills. An answer sheet, similar to those used when taking standardized tests, can be found in the *Testing Program Blackline Masters and Teacher's Manual*.

The table that follows correlates the review items to the lesson pages on which the skills are taught.

Review Items	Text Pages	Review Items	Text Pages
1	33	5	31
2	20	6	32
3	21	7	39–40
4	22		

Testing Program Blackline Masters

In addition to the Cumulative Review in the Pupil's Edition, there are quarterly Cumulative Tests and an End-Year Test. These tests are multiple choice and provide additional opportunities for children to practice taking standardized tests.

Cumulative Tests measure children's performance on major skills and concepts taught during the previous quarters. The **End-Year Test** measures children's performance on major skills and concepts taught throughout the year.

Home Activity

Your child has been learning basic addition and
subtraction facts for sums to 10. Here is a game
that will help your child practice addition facts.

Players:
2

Materials:
2 counters

Directions:
Take turns dropping the 2 counters on the game board.
Your child adds the two numbers on which the counters landed.

5	4	0	3	1
2	3	1	4	5
3	5	4	0	2
0	1	3	2	4
4	0	5	1	3

Variation:
To help your child practice subtraction facts choose a number from 6 to 10.
Take turns dropping just 1 counter on the game board.
Your child subtracts that number from the number that was chosen.

50   fifty

CHAPTER 1

A T · A · G L A N C E p. 50

OBJECTIVE
Give family members an opportunity to share in their child's
mathematics learning.

For Students Acquiring English (SAE)

Before assigning this Home Activity to SAE children, find out if
someone at home will be able to work with them in English. If
not, prepare them to complete the activity independently at
home. Explain the directions of the activity and ask SAE children
to restate them so you can check comprehension. Scan the page
and preteach any difficult vocabulary or phrases that they may
not know. For this first Home Activity, monitor how effectively
SAE children were able to work in English outside the classroom.
Ask to see their work or have them describe it to you.

USING THE ACTIVITY

Have children look at the page. Explain that the page has a game that
an adult in the family can help them complete. Read the page with the
children, making sure that they understand what needs to be done.
Tell children that they will do this page at home.

Previewing
CHAPTER 2

❝IN CHAPTER 2, you will introduce your children to understanding numbers to 100. You will also have the opportunity to explore place value, counting and order, skip-counting, and comparing numbers.❞

Notes
FROM THE AUTHOR

Here are some notes on the concepts presented in this chapter and how your children can apply them to solve problems.

PLACE VALUE

Encouraging children to understand place value helps them avoid most common computation errors.

Your children can use tens and ones models to help them group by ten, and to understand that a 2-digit number is composed of tens and ones. Children begin by modeling 2-digit numbers with ones models. As they trade ten of the ones for 1 ten, they should understand that 10 ones equal 1 ten. Children explore modeling 2-digit numbers, as shown below, to show that a number such as 15 can be shown as 15 ones or as 1 ten 5 ones.

Encourage children to model tens and ones to identify how many tens and ones there are. Then they write the number, first as tens and ones, second in standard form.

3 tens 5 ones   35

UNDERSTANDING
NUMBERS to 100

Walter G. Secada

COUNTING and ORDER

Children use patterns to explore the order of numbers. Help children use the following example to see that when they count by ones, the tens digit stays the same while the ones digit increases from 0-9; then the tens digit increases by one and the count goes on.

40, 41, 42, 43, 44, 45, 46, 47, 48, 49, 50, 51, 52 . . .

Introduce your children to the patterns that emerge when skip-counting by tens, twos, fives, threes, and fours. Understanding skip-counting helps lay the foundation for multiplication. Help children see how skip-counting by twos helps them identify even and odd numbers.

COMPARING NUMBERS

Encourage children to use tens and ones models to compare numbers. Children model to find that when the tens digits are the same, the number with the greater number of ones is the greater number. Help them see that when the tens digits are different, the number with the greater number of tens is the greater number. Children should enjoy the funny characters that introduce the symbols < and >.

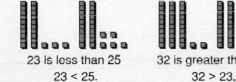

23 is less than 25
23 < 25.

32 is greater than 23
32 > 23.

PROBLEM SOLVING

In **Problem Solving** your children (1) use number sense to solve a problem, (2) solve problems by finding a pattern, and (3) solve problems by making a list.

In **Thinking Mathematically** children use a spinner and a game board to move the Sliding Snails forward and back.

In **Decision Making** children use information, consisting of a game board grid and manipulatives, to plan a game. They decide on how many players are needed, what to do with each game part, and how to play.

Mathematics and Literature

To use literature in the application of mathematics. ■ To promote appreciation of the contributions of all cultures to mathematics. ■ Children are introduced to a story set in Mexico in the K–2 *Math Anthology* on page 140, and a Chinese folk song on page 143. By reading both *A Birthday Basket for Tía* and "Song of the Dragon," children build number sense. ■ In the Curriculum Connection on page 82, children learn to understand and read numbers using the Chinese numeration system and to write Chinese characters for numbers.

CULTURAL DIVERSITY

CHAPTER PLANNING GUIDE

CHAPTER OBJECTIVES WITH STANDARDIZED TEST CORRELATIONS

A. Read, write, and order numbers to 100 — MAT, CAT, SAT, ITBS, CTBS
B. Skip-count by twos, threes, fours, fives, and ten — CAT, SAT, ITBS, CTBS
C. Identify odd and even numbers
D. Compare numbers through 100 — MAT, CAT, SAT, ITBS, CTBS
E. Identify and use ordinal numbers to twentieth — MAT, CAT, SAT, ITBS
F. Solve problems including those that involve finding a pattern

SUGGESTED PACING-16 DAYS

LESSONS	NCTM STANDARDS	ASSIGNMENTS Basic/Average/Challenge	STUDENT EDITION Extra Practice/ Practice Plus	Manip. Plus	Reteach	Practice	Enrich	MAC Activities
Chapter Opener: *The Story Snail* page 51	1, 2, 3, 4, 6	p. 51: All						
✔ **1 Understanding Numbers to 100** page 52	1, 2, 3, 6	p. 52: 1–3						
✔ **2 Tens and Ones** pages 53–54	1, 2, 3, 6	p. 53: 2–11; p. 54: 1–8		9, 10	17	17	17	33, 34
✔ **3 Tens** pages 55–56	1, 2, 3, 6	p. 55: 2–11; p. 56: 1–10			18	18	18	35, 36
✔ **4 More Tens and Ones** pages 57–58	1, 2, 3, 6	p. 57: 3–10; p. 58: 1–14		11, 12	19	19	19	37, 38
5 Order to 100 page 59	1, 2, 3, 6	p. 59: 1–3	p. 68	13	20	20	20	39, 40
6 Counting On and Counting Back page 60	1, 2, 3, 6, 7	p. 60: 2–6, 8–11			21	21	21	41, 42
7 Skip-Counting Patterns pages 61–62	1, 2, 3, 7, 13	p. 61: 2, 4–5; p. 62: 2–4, 6	pp. 68, 84		22	22	22	43, 44
8 Even and Odd Numbers pages 63–64	1, 2, 3, 6	p. 63: 4–10; p. 64: 3–5, Reasoning	p. 68		23	23	23	45, 46
9 PS: Using Number Sense pages 65–66	1, 2, 3, 6	p. 65: 1–2; p. 66: 1–4			24	24	24	47, 48
✔ **10 PS: Thinking Mathematically** page 67	1, 2, 3, 6	p. 67: All						
11 PS: Finding a Pattern pages 69–70	1, 2, 3, 13	p. 69: 1–3; p. 70: 1–4	p. 83		25	25	25	49, 50
12 Graphs pages 71–72	1, 2, 3, 11	p. 71: 1–4; p. 72: 1–5			26	26	26	51, 52
✔ **13 Comparing Numbers to 100** pages 73–74	1, 2, 3, 6	p. 73: 2–6; p. 74: 1–4, Mixed Review		14	27	27	27	53, 54
14 Greater Than and Less Than pages 75–76	1, 2, 3, 6	p. 75: 2–6; p. 76: 1–5, Challenge	pp. 83, 84		28	28	28	55, 56
15 Ordinal Numbers pages 77–78	1, 2, 3, 6	p. 77: 1–2; p. 78: 1–4, Reasoning	p. 83		29	29	29	57, 58
16 PS: Making a List pages 79–80	1, 2, 3, 11	p. 79: All; p. 80: 1–3			30	30	30	59, 60
17 PS: Decision Making page 81	1, 2, 3, 6	p. 81: 1–5						
Curriculum Connection: Writing page 82								
Chapter Review/Test pages 85–86								
Performance Assessment page 87								
Cumulative Review page 89								
Enrichment for All/Home Activity pages 88, 90								

NATIONAL COUNCIL OF TEACHERS OF MATHEMATICS Grades K–4

1. Problem Solving
2. Communication
3. Reasoning
4. Connections
5. Estimation
6. Number Sense and Numeration
7. Concepts of Whole Number Operations
8. Whole Number Computation
9. Geometry and Spatial Sense
10. Measurement
11. Statistics and Probability
12. Fractions and Decimals
13. Patterns and Relationships

✔ Activity ♦♦ Cooperative Learning CC Cultural Connection

MEETING the NCTM STANDARDS

Problem Solving

Strategies and Skills
- using number sense pp. 65–66
- finding a pattern pp. 69–70
- making a list pp. 79-80

Applications
- **Decision Making** lesson p. 81
- **Problem of the Day** TE pp. 52, 54B, 56B, 58B, 59C, 60C, 62B, 64B, 66B, 70B, 72B, 74B, 76B, 78B, 80B

Mathematical Investigations
- **Thinking Mathematically** lesson p. 67

Communication

Language
- using the language of mathematics TE pp. 53–54, 59, 60, 63–64, 69–70, 73–74, 75–76, 77–78

Oral/Written
- using cooperative learning activities pp. 52, 53, 55, 57, 67, 73, 81, 82; TE pp. 50I–50N
- **Journal Writing** opportunities TE pp. 56, 62, 66, 70, 72, 74, 76

Reasoning

Critical Thinking
- answering questions that analyze and extend concepts pp. 51, 53, 54, 55, 61, 63, 71, 73, 81

Connections

To other subject areas
- Literature p. 51, Art p. 82; Literature TE pp. 51–52, 61, 65

To all cultures
- Mexican story, *A Birthday Basket for Tia*, *Math Anthology* p. 140
- Chinese folk song, "Song of the Dragon," *Math Anthology* p. 143
- Japanese numeration p. 82

Concept Development

Number Sense and Numeration
- reading and writing numbers through 100 pp. 52, 53–54, 55–56, 57–58; TE pp. 50I–50L
- ordering numbers through 100 p. 59; TE p. 50M
- comparing numbers through 100 pp. 60, 73–74, 75–76; TE p. 50N
- identifying and using ordinal numbers to twentieth pp. 77–78

Patterns and Relationships
- skip-counting by twos, threes, fours, fives, and tens pp. 61–62
- identifying odd and even numbers pp. 63–64

Statistics
- reading and making a bar graph pp. 71–72

Assessment Options

Performance Assessment

Preassessment Activity

Before beginning Chapter 2, distribute tens and ones models to children. Give them verbal statements describing numbers, for example, "Write and show a number that is less than 42" or "Write and show a number that is between 31 and 44." Have children write responses on a sheet of paper. Select individual children to share their answers and how they modeled.

Ongoing Assessment

The Ongoing Assessment cards under MEETING INDIVIDUAL NEEDS on TE pp. 56, 62, and 74 provide criteria and questions for assessing children's understanding of the key mathematical concepts developed in the chapter.

Journal Writing opportunities encourage children to write about mathematics. Their responses can be recorded either pictorially or in words. The journal writing opportunities on the Ongoing Assessment cards also allow you to assess children's understanding of the lessons.

In addition to the Ongoing Assessment cards, other assessment and journal writing opportunities in this chapter include:

• **CLOSE** TE pp. 66, 70, 72, 76

Performance Assessment Activity

The Performance Assessment activity on p. 87 provides an alternative to formal assessment. This activity assesses children's understanding of the key concepts of the chapter.

For performance assessment activities that are keyed to individual chapter objectives, see the *Performance Assessment* booklet.

BUILDING A PORTFOLIO

Children should be encouraged to keep a selection of their best work in portfolios. The portfolios provide a way of documenting children's growth in understanding mathematical concepts. Portfolio opportunities in this chapter include:

• **Performance Assessment** p. 87
• **Class Project** TE p. 81A

If you wish to provide additional opportunities for portfolio work, you may choose to use:

• **MAC Activities** 34, 35, 36, 49, 50, 51, 52, 55, 58, 59

You may also wish to have children include their journal writing from the Ongoing Assessment on TE pp. 56, 62, and 74 in their portfolio.

Formal Assessment

The **Chapter Review/Test** assesses children's understanding of the concepts and skills developed in the chapter. The **Cumulative Review** assesses children's understanding of the concepts and skills developed from the beginning of the year.

You can use **Form A** or **Form B** of the **Chapter Test** found in the *Testing Program Blackline Masters and Teacher's Manual* if you wish to use a multiple-choice format to assess children's understanding of the chapter concepts and skills. You can use **Form C** if you wish to use a free-response format. Any of the forms may be used as a pretest, posttest, or for retesting.

The **COMPUTER MANAGEMENT SYSTEM**, or **CMS**, enables you to score **Forms A** and **B** of the **Chapter Test** quickly and automatically. It also prescribes learning activities based on children's test results.

For more information about Assessment, see the *Professional Handbook*.

Common Error and Remediation

The Teacher's Edition notes for each Develop/Understand (Transitional/Abstract) lesson provide a common error analysis and a remediation activity. Some errors defy quick analysis and can only be identified by interviewing the child.

ALTERNATIVE TEACHING STRATEGY

Alternative Teaching Strategies appear frequently in the chapter. These strategies provide other presentations of the lessons for children who might benefit from instruction in different learning modalities: kinesthetic, visual, and/or auditory.

For Students Acquiring English (SAE)

SAE children will need extra practice naming the numbers from 1 to 100. Daily practice with rote counting will help them internalize the pattern. Demonstrate the concepts of **ten** and **one** with real objects (pencils and books, for example) before working with the concepts in the text.

SAE notes appear periodically in the chapter. These notes provide suggestions for how to work with children to improve comprehension and build vocabulary.

MANIPULATIVES WORKSHOP

Tens and ones models are used in this chapter to investigate numbers to 100. They provide a concrete representation of the relationship between ones and tens.

USING MANIPULATIVES

Here a child uses tens and ones models to explore the meaning of the number 23. The child counts out 23 ones models.

The child makes a group of 10 ones and then trades the group of ones for a tens model.

The child continues regrouping the 13 ones to make 1 more ten. The final model shows 23 has 2 tens and 3 ones.

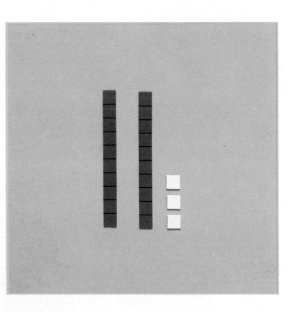

MAKING MANIPULATIVES   See the Manipulatives section of the *Professional Handbook* for materials that can be used as a substitute for tens and ones models.

COOPERATIVE LEARNING WORKSHOP

GETTING STARTED

Common Community Goals: After finding a place for everyone, the community is ready to establish common goals and standards. Each child can **brainstorm** with a partner to develop a list of the traits of a good class community. Pairs share in the family group, and bring their favorite ideas to the community meeting. After the class describes the community, they should discuss what guidelines and standards will help them achieve it. If problems arise later, the children can discuss them as homework and compare possible solutions the next morning in family groups.

Using **concentric circles** (the outside circle faces in, the inside circle faces out, and pairs discuss solutions with a succession of different partners), the class considers the ideas, and then votes on the solutions they wish to try.

IDEAS TO TRY

Meeting My Buddy: You can ask children to **line-up** on some continuous characteristic (such as birthdates or the size of shoes).

Then practice ordinal numbers or skip counting. Ask questions such as "When was the sixth person born?" or have children count by twos and have those children take one step forward, turn around, and then face the line so that pairs are formed.

You may also form heterogeneous pairs with a **grand march** by bringing the ends of the line around to meet and partner-up. When partners are seated, they can get acquainted by calculating the number of months of difference between their birth days.

You can apply the above pairing structures in these lessons:
2-2 *Tens and Ones* pp. 53–54
2-7 *Skip-Counting Patterns* pp. 61–62
2-13 *Comparing Numbers to 100* pp. 73–74
2-15 *Ordinal Numbers* pp. 77–78

Graph It! Graphing lessons are ideal for compiling class data gathered in community-building activities such as **people hunts, line-ups,** or **similarity clusters** (in which children form a series of clusters as you call out traits or preferences). Chil-

dren can make graphs by posting large graph paper around the room for different topics. Family groups can go to each graph in turn and fill in the squares for each of their members in the group's color. When all graphs are filled in, each small group can develop mathematical statements, such as "The number of dog owners is greater than the number of cat owners."

You can apply the above community-building structures in these lessons:
2-12 *Graphs* pp. 71–72
2-13 *Comparing Numbers to 100* pp. 73–74
2-14 *Greater Than and Less Than* pp. 75–76

SEE ALSO

Cooperative Learning Tip for lessons 2-9 Problem Solving p. 66; 2-11 Problem Solving p. 70

The Cooperative Learning section of the *Professional Handbook* for additional information

ACTIVITY
INTERACTIVE BULLETIN BOARD

SETUP Use oaktag to make a sea serpent pattern. Trace the pattern onto sheets of white construction paper, making enough to give each pair of children a sea serpent. Have volunteers cut out the serpents. Then write a number from 50 through 94 on the first segment of each serpent. Cover the bulletin board with blue construction paper.

PROCEDURE 👥 Assign children to work in pairs. Give each pair a sea serpent. Have pairs work together to complete the number sequence by writing a number in sequential order on each segment. Then ask children to decorate their serpents, using crayons. Display the serpents on the bulletin board. Review the number sequences with the children.

MANIPULATIVES *plus* ACTIVITY

For use before LESSON 2.2, pp. 53-54

9

CHIP TRADING

OBJECTIVES
Explore grouping by fives. Regroup based on a given set of rules.

MATERIALS
Classroom Materials yellow, red, and blue crayons per child
Manipulatives 5 blue, red, and yellow square counter punchouts, 1 workmat* per child
Teacher Resources *Teacher Aid 15

WHOLE GROUP ACTIVITY ↕
Duplicate a copy of Teacher Aid 15 workmat for each child. Distribute 1 workmat and 5 yellow, 5 red, and 5 blue punchout squares to each child. Tell children that the squares are chips and the workmat will be used as a trading board. Have children color their trading boards as shown.

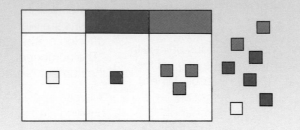

Write the following on the chalkboard:

> 5 blue chips equal 1 red chip
> 5 red chips equal 1 yellow chip

Tell children they are going to do a chip trading activity. Read the information on the chalkboard with the children. Explain that they cannot have 5 or more chips in a column on their chip trading boards. Demonstrate the process.

■ **When I say add 1 chip, put a blue chip in the blue column. Add 1 chip. Add 1. Add 1. Add 1. Add 1. How many chips do you have in your blue column?** [5]

Then repeat the rule to the children.

■ **You cannot have 5 or more chips in any one column. What could you trade 5 blue chips for?** [1 red chip]

Have children make this exchange. Guide them in placing the red chip in the red column.

Continue the activity by saying "Add 1" five times. Restate the rule and demonstrate how to trade if necessary. Children should now have 2 red chips on their boards. Continue until the value of 1 yellow chip has been reached.

EXTENDING THE ACTIVITY
Repeat the activity using instructions that involve combining two sets.

■ **Put down 3 blue chips. Put down 2 blue chips.** [Children trade for 1 red chip.]

■ **Put down 2 blue chips. Put down 4 blue chips.** [Children trade 5 blue chips for 1 red chip with 1 blue chip left.]

Continue the activity with similar numbers.

ONGOING ASSESSMENT
✔ Are children able to trade 5 chips in one color for 1 chip of another color?

For use before LESSON 2.2, pp. 53-54

10

PLACE-VALUE READINESS

OBJECTIVES
Explore grouping by various numbers. Regroup based on a given set of rules.

MATERIALS
Manipulatives 1 number cube*, workmat*, 30 Ⓒ (or punchouts), 30 blue square punchouts, 30 beans per group
Teacher Resources
*Teacher Aids 15, 17

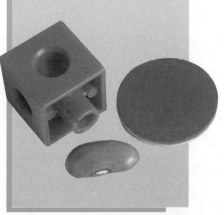

SMALL GROUP ACTIVITY

Have children work in groups of four to play "Banking" which is a version of chip trading. Duplicate a copy of Teacher Aid 15 workmat for each child. Distribute 1 workmat to each child and 30 beans, 30 red counters, and 30 blue squares to each group.

Designate one player in each group to be the BANKER. Have all other children in a group place a blue square at the top of the first column of the workmat, a red counter at the top of the second column, and a bean at the top of the last column, as shown.

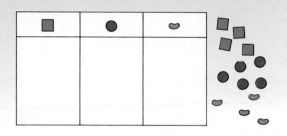

Explain that each player, in turn, rolls the number cube, reads the number, and asks the BANKER for that number of beans. Demonstrate this for children.

Tell children the rule of the game.

■ You cannot have 3 or more of an item in a column. If you have 3 or more beans, you can trade in 3 beans for 1 counter.

■ If you have 3 or more counters you can trade in 3 counters for 1 square.

After each child makes a trade, he or she is to read the number of beans, counters, and squares on his or her mat; for example, 2 counters 1 bean, or 1 square 1 counter 2 beans. The first player to get 3 squares wins the game. Then the winner becomes the BANKER and the game begins again.

EXTENDING THE ACTIVITY

Change the rule of the game. For example, players can have no more than 4 of anything in a column, 3 of anything in a column, and then 10 of anything.

ONGOING ASSESSMENT

✓ Are children able to trade 3 items of one kind for 1 item of another kind?

MANIPULATIVES plus ACTIVITY

For use before LESSON 2.4, pp. 57-58

PLACE OF A DIGIT

OBJECTIVE
Explore the concept of place of a digit.

MATERIALS
Manipulatives 9 T, 9 O models (or punchouts), Workmat 2 per child; 2 spinners for 0–9 per pair (EXTENDING THE ACTIVITY only)
Teacher Resources Teacher Aid 9

WHOLE GROUP ACTIVITY ⬍

Distribute 9 tens and 9 ones models and Workmat 2 to each child. Tell children to model the number 35.

■ **How many tens are in 35?** [3]
■ **How many ones are in 35?** [5]

Draw a place-value box on the chalkboard and write 35 in it.

tens	ones
3	5

Explain that there is a 3 in the **tens place** and a 5 in the **ones place** of 35.

Repeat the activity with the number 53. Guide children in telling how 35 and 53 are the same and how they are different.

Distribute 1 copy of Teacher Aid 9 (place-value charts) to each child. Read the following numbers. Have children model each number on Workmat 2 and write the digits for each on a place-value chart.

2 in the tens place, 4 in the ones place [24]
5 in the ones place, 7 in the tens place [75]
4 in the tens place, 6 in the ones place [46]
8 in the ones place, 1 in the tens place [18]
5 in the tens place, 7 in the ones place [57]
6 in the tens place, 4 in the ones place [64]

EXTENDING THE ACTIVITY

Have children work in pairs with two spinners for 0 to 9. One child spins for the tens place, the other for the ones place. Then each child writes the digits on their own place-value charts on Teacher Aid 9.

ONGOING ASSESSMENT

✓ Are children able to appropriately model and write the digits for a number?

Chapter Four

John walked on until he came to the blue sea. He saw a mermaid sitting on a rock.

"Have you seen a snail with a silver shell? Do you know where it is?" John asked.

"No," said the mermaid. "But I can tell you what the seahorse told me. He has seen the snail with the silver shell."

"Tell me, please tell me!" said John.

"You must do a kind thing and a brave thing, and you must have a magic password. Then you will find the snail with the silver shell. That is what the seahorse told me."

"I have a magic password," said John. "The elf gave it to me. If you tell me what to do I will do it."

But the mermaid swam away.

John walked on. He came to a garden. A little rabbit was sitting in the garden. It looked sad.

"Have you seen the snail with the silver shell? Do you know where it is?" said John.

"How would I know where it is? I do not even know where I am. I am lost," said the rabbit. And it began to cry.

"Don't cry," said John. "I will try to take you home. Where do you live?"

The little rabbit said, "I live at the edge of a dark forest. It is where the green elf lives. A thousand mushrooms grow there. It is far away."

"Poor me," thought John. "I have come so far, and now I must go backward. I will never find the snail now."

But he picked up the lost rabbit and patted its fur. "I will take you home," said John. "I have just come from that forest. I know where it is."

And he took the little rabbit home to its mother.

"You have done a very kind thing," said the mother rabbit and she gave John a carrot.

"Have you seen the snail with the silver shell? Do you know where it is?" said John.

"I have never seen it, but I have heard it from inside my rabbit hole," said the mother rabbit.

She pointed to a big rock and said, "Behind that rock there is a cave, and in that cave lives the snail with the silver shell."

"What have you heard?" said John.

"I have heard words, words, words," said the mother rabbit. "Have some lettuce."

But John ran to the rock.

Chapter Five

John pushed the rock away. Something was growling in the deep, dark cave.

"That is not the snail with the silver shell," thought John.

He was afraid, but he went into the cave. He saw a bright red fire. Then he saw a big green dragon.

"Grrrrrr!" said the dragon. "Who are you? I do not like the looks of you. I might as well eat you up!"

"Please don't," said John. "I am John, and I have come to find the snail with the silver shell."

"I know that snail," said the dragon. "It lives in this cave with me, but it will not tell me any stories. It says I spit fire and growl and eat things up. I will not let you find it."

And the dragon growled.

"If I tell you a story," said John, "will you let me see the snail?"

"No!" said the dragon and he growled again.

"Two stories?" said John.

"No!" said the dragon and spit fire.

"Ten?" said John.

"One hundred!" shouted the dragon.

And so John told the dragon all the stories the snail had given him. And the dragon did not spit fire or eat John up. The dragon growled softly as he listened.

When John had told the last story, the dragon said, "Walk ten steps forward. Take twenty jumps to the right. Take one giant step backward. Close your eyes and you will see a golden door. Knock once loudly and twice softly. Then say the magic password."

"And what is that?" said John.

"I do not know," said the dragon sadly. "The snail will not tell me."

But John knew.

Chapter Six

John walked ten steps forward and took twenty jumps to the right. He took one giant step backward, closed his eyes, and jumped up three times.

When he opened his eyes he saw a golden door. He knocked once loudly and twice softly. Then he said, "Fuzzbuzzoncethorowas!"

The golden door opened, and John saw the snail with the silver shell. It was eating a green leaf.

"Hello, snail," said John. "I have come to ask you for a new story. I have told all the stories you gave me. Even the dragon has heard them. No one wants to hear them again."

The snail stopped eating. It looked at John and poked out its little horns.

"I cannot give you a new story," the snail said. "There are many new stories to tell, that is true. But now you must find them for yourself. You have come so far, though, that I will send you safely home."

Softly the snail whispered, "Fuzzbuzzoncetherewas!" and John fell asleep at once.

Chapter Seven

When John woke up he was home.

"Have you found a new story, John?" everybody asked.

But John had no new story to tell.

Then he heard a bee buzz. Suddenly John smiled.

He said, "Fuzzbuzzoncetherewas a boy named John. John was good and kind but he could not do anything well. Nothing at all. And everyone laughed at him. So one day he ran away."

And John told about the magic snail with the silver shell, the story snail. He told about the Wild West Wind and the green elf. He told about the mermaid and the lost rabbit. He told about the dragon in the deep, dark cave. John told the story you have just read.

And after that, whenever he wanted, John told a new story. And everyone said, "John tells stories very well indeed!"

AT·A·GLANCE pp. 51-52

LESSON OBJECTIVES
Explore mathematical concepts through literature.
Explore the concept of tens.

ASSIGNMENT GUIDE

COURSE	EXERCISES
Basic	p. 51: All; p. 52: 1–3
Average	p. 51: All; p. 52: 1–3
Challenge	p. 51: All; p. 52: 1–3

MATERIALS
Classroom Materials large hundreds chart, stapler

Teacher Resources
Math Anthology, pp. 135–139
Read-Aloud Cassette 1, Side 1, Selection 1

SKILLS TRACE
NUMBERS TO 100

Explore (Concrete) 52	Develop/Understand (Transitional/Abstract) 53–54, 55–56, 57–58, 59, 60, 61–62, 63–64, 71–72, 73–74, 75–76, 77–78
Practice 68, 83, 84, 85–86, 89, 98, 136	Apply 65–66, 69–70, 82, 88, 90

CHAPTER 2

Understanding Numbers to 100

THE STORY SNAIL
By Anne Rockwell

READ ALOUD

👂 Listen to The Story Snail.

🗣 Suppose John told 1 story each day.
Tell how many days he would need
to tell all of the snail's stories. **100 days**

---

1 PREPARE
WARM-UP To review numbers to 100, display a hundreds chart. Have children count in unison as you point to each number. Guide children in finding number patterns on the chart by reading the numbers in various rows, columns, and diagonals.

2 TEACH
DISCUSSING Before reading the story *The Story Snail,* discuss the difference between reading a story and telling a story. Encourage children who have heard a professional storyteller to describe their experiences. Explain that in olden days, before there were printed books, people always listened to storytellers. Mention that stories were passed down from older to younger people, and that many of our favorite folk and fairy tales were part of this oral tradition.

Mathematics and Literature

PUPIL'S EDITION pp. 51-52

Page 51 Read *The Story Snail* found on pages 50M–50N or in *Math Anthology* to children, or play Read-Aloud Cassette 1, Side 1, Selection 2 for them.

■ **What was Jack's big problem?** [Everyone laughed at him because he could not do anything well.]

■ **How did the magic snail help Jack?** [The snail gave Jack 100 stories so all of his friends would listen to him.]

■ **What did the snail mean when it told Jack that he must find new stories for himself?** [Jack should make up his own stories.]

Discuss the question on the page.

Page 52 ■ **Working Together** Have children count to find the number of children in the class.

ACTIVITY

Understanding Numbers to 100

ou can put stories together to
ake a book.

Working Together

se sheets of paper.
ow many books can your class make?
uppose each child writes 1 story.

Put 10 stories
in each book.

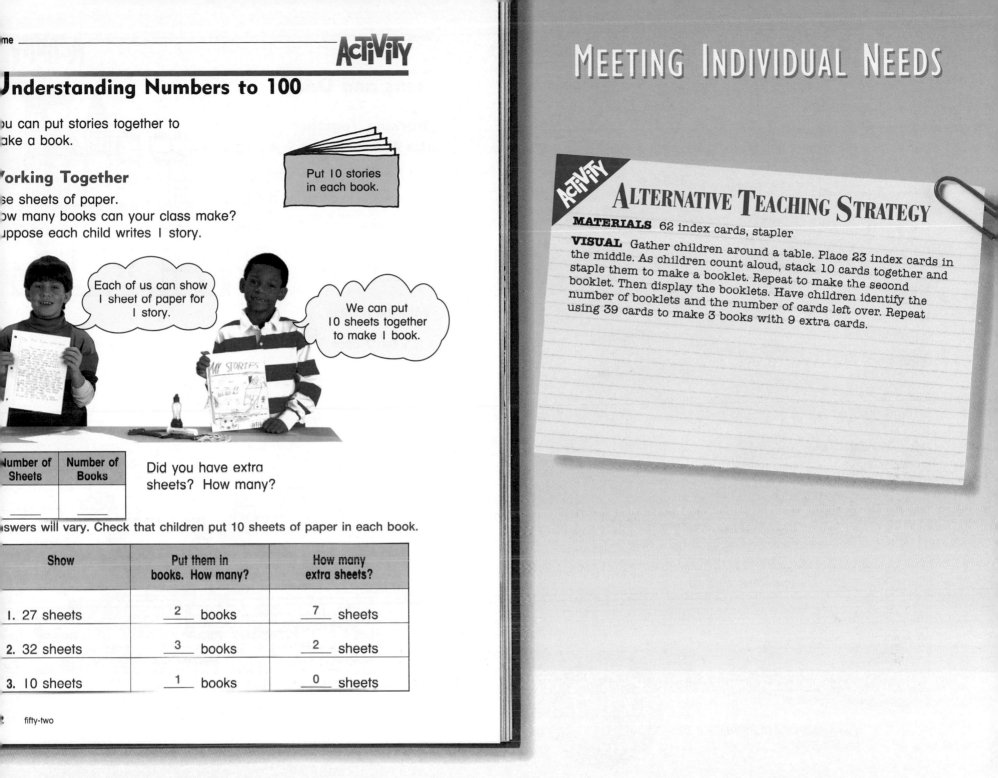

Each of us can show
1 sheet of paper for
1 story.

We can put
10 sheets together
to make 1 book.

| Number of
Sheets | Number of
Books |
|---|---|
| | |

Did you have extra
sheets? How many?

swers will vary. Check that children put 10 sheets of paper in each book.

| Show | Put them in
books. How many? | How many
extra sheets? |
|---|---|---|
| 1. 27 sheets | 2 books | 7 sheets |
| 2. 32 sheets | 3 books | 2 sheets |
| 3. 10 sheets | 1 books | 0 sheets |

ACTIVITY

ALTERNATIVE TEACHING STRATEGY

MATERIALS 62 index cards, stapler

VISUAL Gather children around a table. Place 23 index cards in
the middle. As children count aloud, stack 10 cards together and
staple them to make a booklet. Repeat to make the second
booklet. Then display the booklets. Have children identify the
number of booklets and the number of cards left over. Repeat
using 39 cards to make 3 books with 9 extra cards.

Check for Understanding

■ **How many sheets of paper would the class use in all?** [Responses should reflect 1 sheet per child.]

GUIDED PRACTICE Suggest that each child write a brief story on
paper. Collect all the sheets of paper and display them along the
chalkboard ledge. Have children count off ten sheets in unison to
make each book. Then have them identify the number of extra sheets
left over. Help them staple each book of 10 sheets together.

For reteaching, use Alternative Strategy.

PRACTICE·APPLY **PRACTICE** ex. 1–3: Have children
work as a class to make each book.

CLOSE Guide children to summarize the lesson:

■ **If there were 58 sheets of paper, how many books and extra
sheets would you have?** [5 books, 8 sheets]

Problem of the Day

Jack wrote down the 100 stories from the story
snail. He used 1 sheet of paper for each story.
How many books could he make if he put 10
sheets of paper in each book? [10 books]

CHAPTER 2 • Lesson 2

AT·A·GLANCE pp. 53-54

LESSON OBJECTIVE
Read and write a number for tens and ones.

ASSIGNMENT GUIDE

COURSE	EXERCISES
Basic	p. 53: 2–11; p. 54: 1–8
Average	p. 53: 2–11; p. 54: 1–8
Challenge	p. 53: 2–11; p. 54: 1–8

MATERIALS
Manipulatives 2 T and 10 O models (or punchouts); Workmats 2, 6 per pair

Teacher Resources
Reteaching 17
MAC Act. 33, 34
Practice 17
Teacher Aid 11
Enrichment 17

SKILLS TRACE
NUMBERS TO 100

Explore (Concrete)	Develop/Understand (Transitional/Abstract)
52	53–54, 55–56, 57–58, 59, 60, 61–62, 63–64, 71–72, 73–74, 75–76, 77–78
Practice	Apply
68, 83, 84, 85–86, 89, 98, 136	65–66, 69–70, 82, 88, 90

See *MANIPULATIVES PLUS 9–10*, pp. 50I–50J.

1 PREPARE
WARM-UP To prepare children for working with tens, read the following exercises to the class. Ask children to give each sum orally.

5 + 5 [10]	7 + 3 [10]	1 + 9 [10]
6 + 4 [10]	2 + 8 [10]	3 + 7 [10]

2 TEACH
MODELING Provide pairs of children with **ones** models and Workmat 2. Write several single-digit numbers on the chalkboard, one at a time. Have children model each number on their workmats. Then tell children to show 10 ones.

Distribute **tens** models to the children. Demonstrate exchanging 10 ones for 1 ten, and then place the 1 ten in the tens column on a workmat. Have children do the same.

Tens and Ones

Working Together
Use Workmat 2. Use 9 ■ ones model

and 2 ▭▭▭▭ . tens model

Use models to show the numbers.

10 ones = 1 ten

Write the number.

1. 1 ten 7 ones __17__

2. 1 ten 3 ones __13__

3. 1 ten 9 ones __19__

4. 1 ten 0 ones __10__

5. 1 ten 4 ones __14__

6. 1 ten 8 ones __18__

7. 1 ten 1 one __11__

8. 1 ten 5 ones __15__

9. 2 tens 1 one __21__

10. 1 ten 2 ones __12__

11. Try this with a partner.

> I choose a ten and some ones.

> I say the number.

Talk about the numbers. Take turns.

■ **How many tens equal 10 ones?** [1]

Instruct children to leave the 1 ten in place on their workmats, and place a ones model on their mats.

■ **How many tens and ones are on your mats?** [1 ten 1 one] **What number has 1 ten 1 one?** [11]

Repeat this activity for numbers 12 and 13.

PUPIL'S EDITION pp. 53-54

Page 53 ■ Working Together Have children work in pairs to do the activity. Guide them through ex. 1.

Check for Understanding

■ **What number is shown with 1 ten and 6 ones?** [16]

Keith begins with 1 ten 0 ones.
Then he makes a pattern. Write the number words.

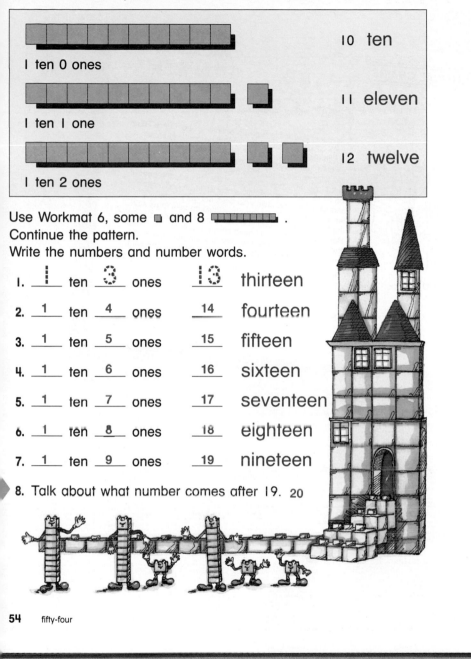

1 ten 0 ones	10 ten
1 ten 1 one	11 eleven
1 ten 2 ones	12 twelve

Use Workmat 6, some ▫ and 8 ▭.
Continue the pattern.
Write the numbers and number words.

1. __1__ ten __3__ ones   __13__ thirteen
2. __1__ ten __4__ ones   __14__ fourteen
3. __1__ ten __5__ ones   __15__ fifteen
4. __1__ ten __6__ ones   __16__ sixteen
5. __1__ ten __7__ ones   __17__ seventeen
6. __1__ ten __8__ ones   __18__ eighteen
7. __1__ ten __9__ ones   __19__ nineteen

8. Talk about what number comes after 19. 20

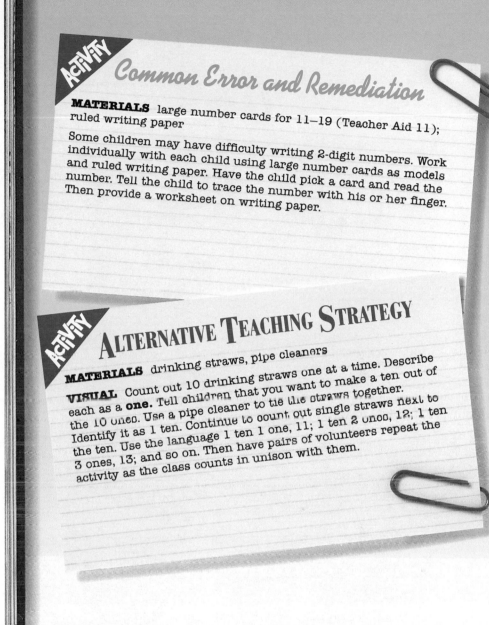

ACTIVITY

Common Error and Remediation

MATERIALS large number cards for 11–19 (Teacher Aid 11); ruled writing paper

Some children may have difficulty writing 2-digit numbers. Work individually with each child using large number cards as models and ruled writing paper. Have the child pick a card and read the number. Tell the child to trace the number with his or her finger. Then provide a worksheet on writing paper.

ACTIVITY

ALTERNATIVE TEACHING STRATEGY

MATERIALS drinking straws, pipe cleaners

VISUAL Count out 10 drinking straws one at a time. Describe each as a **one**. Tell children that you want to make a ten out of the 10 ones. Use a pipe cleaner to tie the straws together. Identify it as 1 ten. Continue to count out single straws next to the ten. Use the language 1 ten 1 one, 11; 1 ten 2 ones, 12; 1 ten 3 ones, 13; and so on. Then have pairs of volunteers repeat the activity as the class counts in unison with them.

GUIDED PRACTICE   ex. 2–11: Discuss ex. 11 with the children before they begin the activity.

For reteaching, use Common Error and Remediation or Alternative Strategy.

Page 54   Distribute Workmat 6. Do the three examples with the children. Point out the pattern of increasing by one. Have children trace the number words.

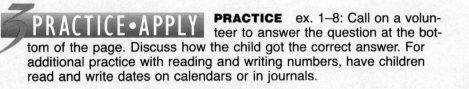

PRACTICE·APPLY   **PRACTICE**   ex. 1–8: Call on a volunteer to answer the question at the bottom of the page. Discuss how the child got the correct answer. For additional practice with reading and writing numbers, have children read and write dates on calendars or in journals.

CLOSE   Guide children to summarize the lesson:
■ **How would you model the number 18?** [1 ten 8 ones]

MAC ACTIVITY CENTER

MATH AND MUSIC ▪ MUSICAL CHAIRS

MAC Activity 33

On Your Own   Pair and Share   In a Group

Materials number cards for 0–9 (Teacher Aid 11) and 1 ten

Procedure Assemble a group of chairs. Label each chair with a card for **1 ten**. There should be one less chair than the total number of children. Give each child a number card from 0 to 9. Explain to children that they are to add 1 ten to the number on their card when it is their turn. Have children walk around the chairs to the beat of the music. When the music stops, children find a chair and sit down. The child who does not get a seat must leave the game. Then the other children take turns saying their number aloud, for example: "1 ten 6 ones is 16." Remove one chair and have children walk around. When the music stops, have them find a chair, pass the card to their right, and then add 1 ten to their new number card.

To Win The game continues until only one child is left.

MAC Activity 33:
Basic-to-Average ▶

LOGICAL REASONING ▪ NUMBER RIDDLES

MAC Activity 34

On Your Own   Pair and Share   In a Group

Tell children that they will work in pairs to make up a riddle about a number from 11 to 19. Explain that they should give three clues for each riddle. Write the following example on the chalkboard.

I am before the number 20.
I am after the number 17.
I do not have 9 ones.
What number am I?   [18]

Remind children that their riddles should always end with a question.

What number am I?

MAC Activity 34:
Average-to-Challenge

RETEACHING

RETEACHING-17

Name ___

TENS AND ONES

Study

| 1 ten 0 ones | 10 |
| 1 ten 1 one | 11 |

Check

Ring to make ten.
Write the numbers.

1. 1 ten 2 ones 12
2. 1 ten 3 ones 13
3. 1 ten 4 ones 14
4. 1 ten 5 ones 15
5. 1 ten 6 ones 16
6. 1 ten 7 ones 17
7. 1 ten 8 ones 18
8. 1 ten 9 ones 19

Reteaching-17

Macmillan/McGraw-Hill, MATHEMATICS IN ACTION
Grade 2, Chapter 2, Lesson 2, pages 53–54

PRACTICE

PRACTICE-17

Name ___

TENS AND ONES

Write the numbers.

1. 1 ten 6 ones 16 sixteen
2. 1 ten 4 ones 14 fourteen
3. 1 ten 1 one 11 eleven
4. 1 ten 7 ones 17 seventeen
5. 1 ten 3 ones 13 thirteen
6. 1 ten 9 ones 19 nineteen
7. 1 ten 0 ones 10 ten
8. 1 ten 5 ones 15 fifteen
9. 1 ten 8 ones 18 eighteen
10. 1 ten 2 ones 12 twelve

Practice-17

Macmillan/McGraw-Hill, MATHEMATICS IN ACTION
Grade 2, Chapter 2, Lesson 2, pages 53–54

ENRICHMENT

ENRICHMENT-17

On Your Own   Pair and Share   In a Group

Name ___

TENS AND ONES

READING IN SPACE

Toby is reading a book about space.
She made this chart to show how many
pages she read.

A ☆ equals 10 pages. A ☾ equals 1 page.

Number of Pages Read

Monday	☆☾	Thursday	☆☾☾☾☾☾☾☾☾☾
Tuesday	☾☾☾☾☾☾☾☾	Friday	☆☾☾
Wednesday	☆☾☾☾	Saturday	☆☾☾☾☾☾☾

Work with a friend.
Use the chart to answer the questions.

1. How many pages did Toby read on
   Wednesday? ___ 13

2. On which day did Toby read 16 pages? ___ Saturday

3. On which day did Toby read the most
   pages? ___ Thursday

4. On how many days did Toby read more
   than 12 pages? ___ 3

5. Toby read 18 pages on Sunday. How
   would she show this on her chart? ___ ☆☾☾☾☾☾☾☾☾

Enrichment-17

Macmillan/McGraw-Hill, MATHEMATICS IN ACTION
Grade 2, Chapter 2, Lesson 2, pages 53–54

Problem of the Day

Marta has 2 boxes of crayons with 8 crayons in
each box. Can she give a friend 10 crayons and
still keep 8 for herself?   [No. Children may work it
out this way: 8 + 8 = 16; 16 − 10 = 6; 6 < 8.]

AT·A·GLANCE pp. 55-56

LESSON OBJECTIVE
Read and write numbers for tens.

ASSIGNMENT GUIDE

COURSE	EXERCISES
Basic	p. 55: 2–11; p. 56: 1–10
Average	p. 55: 2–11; p. 56: 1–10
Challenge	p. 55: 2–11; p. 56: 1–10

MATERIALS
Classroom Materials large number cards for 1–99, word cards for one–ninety-nine
Manipulatives 9 T, 10 O models (or punchouts), Workmat 2 per pair

Teacher Resources
Reteaching 18   Practice 18   Enrichment 18
MAC Act. 35, 36

SKILLS TRACE

NUMBERS TO 100	
Explore (Concrete) 52	**Develop/Understand (Transitional/Abstract)** 53–54, **55–56**, 57–58, 59, 60, 61–62, 63–64, 71–72, 73–74, 75–76, 77–78
Practice 68, 83, 84, 85–86, 89, 98, 136	**Apply** 65–66, 69–70, 82, 88, 90

Name _____

Tens

ACTIVITY

Working Together
Use Workmat 2. Use 9 ◾ ,

and 9 ▮▮▮▮▮▮▮▮▮ .

Use models to show
the number on
Workmat 2.

Write the number.

1. 5 tens 0 ones __50__

2. 2 tens 0 ones __20__

3. 0 tens 4 ones __4__

4. 6 tens 0 ones __60__

5. 1 ten 0 ones __10__

6. 8 tens 0 ones __80__

7. 7 tens 0 ones __70__

8. 4 tens 0 ones __40__

9. 9 tens 0 ones __90__

10. 0 tens 9 ones __9__

11. You show 3.
Your partner shows 30.
Talk about the models you each used.
Tell how the numbers are the same.
Tell how they are different.

Answers will vary.
Each number has a 3 in it.
30 is more than 3; 30 has
3 tens 0 ones, 3 has
0 tens 3 ones.

Macmillan/McGraw-Hill

Chapter 2   Understanding Numbers to 100   fifty-five   **55**

 **PREPARE**   **WARM-UP** To review tens and ones, ask children to add 10 to each of the following numbers. Then have them identify the number of tens and ones in each sum.

    3 [13, 1 ten 3 ones]
    9 [19, 1 ten 9 ones]
    5 [15, 1 ten 5 ones]
    6 [16, 1 ten 6 ones]
    2 [12, 1 ten 2 ones]
    1 [11, 1 ten 1 one]
    0 [10, 1 ten 0 ones]

 TEACH   **MODELING** Have children work in pairs with tens and ones models and Workmat 2. Tell them to model the number 19 on their workmats, and then identify the number of tens and ones. [1 ten 9 ones]

Continue by asking them to add another ones model.

■ **How many tens and ones do you have?** [1 ten 10 ones]
■ **Can you think of another way to show 1 ten 10 ones?** [Exchange the 10 ones for 1 ten to make 2 tens.]

Children should make this exchange and place the ten in the tens column.

■ **Is this still the same number?** [Yes.]

How many? Write the numbers and number words.

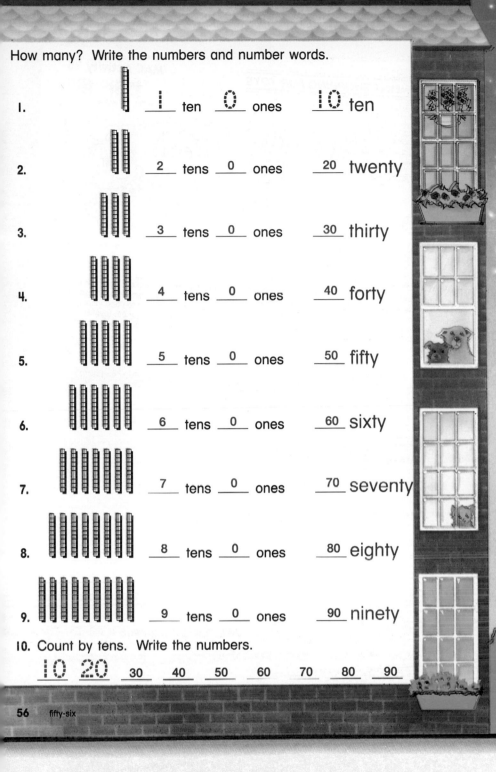

1. __1__ ten __0__ ones __10__ ten

2. __2__ tens __0__ ones __20__ twenty

3. __3__ tens __0__ ones __30__ thirty

4. __4__ tens __0__ ones __40__ forty

5. __5__ tens __0__ ones __50__ fifty

6. __6__ tens __0__ ones __60__ sixty

7. __7__ tens __0__ ones __70__ seventy

8. __8__ tens __0__ ones __80__ eighty

9. __9__ tens __0__ ones __90__ ninety

10. Count by tens. Write the numbers.

__10__ __20__ __30__ __40__ __50__ __60__ __70__ __80__ __90__

 ACTIVITY

Common Error and Remediation

MATERIALS 9 craft sticks, 99 dried beans, glue

Some children may forget to count the tens model as 1 ten. Work individually with each child. Begin by having the child make bean sticks to use as place-value models. Ten dried beans are glued on each craft stick to represent 1 ten. Loose beans represent ones. Then have the child use these bean sticks to do exercises similar to those on page 55.

ONGOING ASSESSMENT

OBSERVATION Determine whether children used models correctly to show the numbers in the activity on p. 55.

INTERVIEW (1) How can you use these models to show the number 14? (2) How can you use these models to show the number 60? (3) What number has 2 tens and 5 ones?

JOURNAL WRITING You may wish to have children record their responses in their math journals.

ALTERNATIVE TEACHING STRATEGY

VISUAL Draw a version of Workmat 2 on the chalkboard and draw models to represent 19.

Draw another ones model and ask children how many tens and ones they see. [1 ten 10 ones]

Review exchanging 10 ones for 1 ten by erasing the ones and drawing a second ten in the tens box. Draw tens to develop 30, 40, ..., 90. Lead the children in counting the tens as ten, twenty, thirty, ..., ninety.

Explain that another name for 2 tens 0 ones is 20. Write 20 on the chalkboard. Then tell children to show another ten on their workmats and count the number of tens and ones. [3 tens 0 ones]

■ **What number does this equal?** [30]

PUPIL'S EDITION pp. 55-56

Page 55 ■ Working Together Have children work in pairs to do the activity. Guide them through ex. 1.

Check for Understanding

■ **What number is shown by 7 tens 0 ones?** [70]

■ **What number is shown by 0 tens 7 ones?** [7]

GUIDED PRACTICE ex. 2–11: For reteaching, use Common Error and Remediation or Alternative Strategy.

Page 56 Point out the number words on the right-hand side of the page. Have children repeat each word after you read it aloud. Have them trace the number.

3 PRACTICE·APPLY **PRACTICE** ex. 1–10: For additional practice with number words, make a set of number cards from 1 to 99 and a set of word cards from one to ninety-nine. Have children match numbers with words and model each number with place-value models.

CLOSE Guide children to summarize the lesson:

■ **What are the next three numbers when you count by tens: 30, 40, 50?** [60, 70, 80]

MATH AND CONSUMERS ■ *SHOPPING FOR TOYS*

MAC Activity 35

On Your Own   Pair and Share   In a Group

70¢   40¢   60¢

Materials newspapers, scissors, envelopes, punchout pennies

Tell children to cut out pictures of toys from newspaper advertisements. Have them price each toy from 10¢ to 90¢, using multiples of ten. Give each child an envelope containing punchout pennies. Each envelope should have a different amount of pennies in multiples of ten. Have each child stack the pennies in piles of ten and identify how many pennies he or she has in all. Then tell children to compare their pennies with the prices of the toys. Have each child identify the toys that cost *less than*, the *same as*, and *more than* the total number of pennies he or she has. Have each child indicate which toys he or she could buy.

▲
MAC Activity 35:
Basic-to-Average

MAC Activity 36:
Average-to-Challenge
▼

MATH AND ART ■ DOT PUZZLES

MAC Activity 36

On Your Own   Pair and Share   In a Group

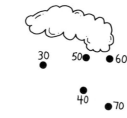

30   50●   ●60

20●   40   ●70

●80

10●   ●90

Materials tracing paper, pictures to trace, acetate, crayons or markers

Tell children they will make a connect-the-dots puzzle. Demonstrate how to trace a simple picture, write consecutively numbered dots around the outline, and then erase the lines in the outline. Have children make their own puzzles, with dots numbered with multiples of ten, from 10 to 90. Display the completed puzzles on a bulletin board. Place a piece of acetate or plastic over each picture. Children should use wipe-off markers or crayons to complete the puzzles.

RETEACHING-17

Name _____

TENS AND ONES

Study

| 🐭 (pencil) | 1 ten 0 ones 10 |
| | 1 ten 1 one 11 |

Check

Ring to make ten.
Write the numbers.

1. 1 ten 2 ones 12

2. 1 ten 3 ones 13

3. 1 ten 4 ones 14

4. 1 ten 5 ones 15

5. 1 ten 6 ones 16

6. 1 ten 7 ones 17

7. 1 ten 8 ones 18

8. 1 ten 9 ones 19

Reteaching-17

Macmillan/McGraw-Hill, MATHEMATICS IN ACTION
Grade 2, Chapter 2, Lesson 2, pages 53–54

PRACTICE-17

Name _____

TENS AND ONES

Write the numbers.

1. 1 ten 6 ones 16 sixteen

2. 1 ten 4 ones 14 fourteen

3. 1 ten 1 one 11 eleven

4. 1 ten 7 ones 17 seventeen

5. 1 ten 3 ones 13 thirteen

6. 1 ten 9 ones 19 nineteen

7. 1 ten 0 ones 10 ten

8. 1 ten 5 ones 15 fifteen

9. 1 ten 8 ones 18 eighteen

10. 1 ten 2 ones 12 twelve

Practice-17

Macmillan/McGraw-Hill, MATHEMATICS IN ACTION
Grade 2, Chapter 2, Lesson 2, pages 53–54

ENRICHMENT-17

On Your Own Pair and Share In a Group

Name _____

TENS AND ONES

READING IN SPACE

Toby is reading a book about space.
She made this chart to show how many
pages she read.

A ☆ equals 10 pages. A ☾ equals 1 page.

Number of Pages Read

Monday ☆☾	Thursday ☆☾☾☾☾☾☾☾☾☾
Tuesday ☾☾☾☾☾☾☾☾☾	Friday ☆☾☾
Wednesday ☆☾☾☾	Saturday ☆☾☾☾☾☾☾

Work with a friend.
Use the chart to answer the questions.

1. How many pages did Toby read on Wednesday? __13__

2. On which day did Toby read 16 pages? __Saturday__

3. On which day did Toby read the most pages? __Thursday__

4. On how many days did Toby read more than 12 pages? __3__

5. Toby read 18 pages on Sunday. How would she show this on her chart? ☆☾☾☾☾☾☾☾☾

Enrichment-17

Macmillan/McGraw-Hill, MATHEMATICS IN ACTION
Grade 2, Chapter 2, Lesson 2, pages 53–54

Problem of the Day

Marta has 2 boxes of crayons with 8 crayons in each box. Can she give a friend 10 crayons and still keep 8 for herself? [No. Children may work it out this way: 8 + 8 = 16; 16 − 10 = 6; 6 < 8.]

AT·A·GLANCE pp. 57-58

LESSON OBJECTIVES
Write how many tens and ones.
Write a number for tens and ones.

ASSIGNMENT GUIDE

COURSE	EXERCISES
Basic	p. 57: 3–10; p. 58: 1–14
Average	p. 57: 3–10; p. 58: 1–14
Challenge	p. 57: 3–10; p. 58: 1–14

MATERIALS
Manipulatives 9 T and 9 O models, 2 spinners for 0–9 (or punchouts), Workmat 2 per pair

Teacher Resources
Reteaching 19
MAC Act. 37, 38
Practice 19
Teacher Aid 11
Enrichment 19

SKILLS TRACE
NUMBERS TO 100

Explore (Concrete)	Develop/Understand (Transitional/Abstract)
52	53–54, 55–56, 57–58, 59, 60, 61–62, 63–64, 71–72, 73–74, 75–76, 77–78
Practice 68, 83, 84, 85–86, 89, 98, 136	**Apply** 65–66, 69–70, 82, 88, 90

See **MANIPULATIVES PLUS 11–12,** pp. 50K–50L.

Name _____

More Tens and Ones

Jack and Mai use spinners to make numbers.

Working Together
Use Workmat 2. Use 9 ▫ ,
9 ▭▭▭ , and 2 ⊛ .

> I spin for ones.

> I spin for tens.

Use models to show the number.
Take turns. Complete.

Tens and Ones	Number	Tens and Ones	Number
1. _6_ tens _3_ ones	63	6. Answers will vary. ____ tens ____ ones	____
2. _0_ tens _5_ ones	5	7. ____ tens ____ ones	____
3. Answers will vary. ____ tens ____ ones	____	8. ____ tens ____ ones	____
4. ____ tens ____ ones	____	9. ____ tens ____ ones	____
5. ____ tens ____ ones	____	10. ____ tens ____ ones	____

Macmillan/McGraw-Hill

---

1 PREPARE **WARM-UP** To review tens, tell children that you will say a number. Have them hold up one finger for each ten in the number. For example, if the number is 30, they should hold up 3 fingers for 3 tens. Say these numbers: 70 [7], 20 [2], 90 [9], 10 [1], 40 [4], 80 [8].

2 TEACH **LISTENING** Tell children that they will play a listening game in which they will be asked to say how many tens or ones. Begin the activity by asking two children to each say a number.

■ **(Child's name), how many tens?** [The child responds by naming a number from 0 to 9.]

■ **(Child's name), how many ones?** [The child responds by naming a number from 0 to 9.]

Then all the children say the number aloud. Continue the activity, by calling on other pairs of children.

PUPIL'S EDITION pp. 57-58

Page 57 ■ Working Together Assign children to work in pairs. Allow them time to practice using the spinners. Guide children through ex. 1 and 2, explaining that these are sample answers.

Check for Understanding
■ **What number would you get if you spin for 4 tens and 6 ones?** [46]

GUIDED PRACTICE ex. 3–10: For reteaching, use Common Error and Remediation or Alternative Strategy.

Page 58 Have the question for ex. 1 read aloud and review how to use a code.

What is the best day to make french fries?

Use the code to find the answer.

19	20	21	23	32	47	58	68	74	85	86	91
d	i	h	n	F	a	b	r	M	y	j	T

1. Write the number, then write the letter.

32 → F   68 → r   20 → i

19 → d   47 → a   85 → y

2. Write the answer. Friday

Complete.

3. 3 tens 9 ones = 39   **4.** 6 tens 4 ones = 64

5. 5 tens 5 ones = 55   **6.** 4 tens 3 ones = 43

7. 7 tens 6 ones = 76   **8.** 6 tens 7 ones = 67

9. 28 = 2 tens 8 ones   **10.** 95 = 9 tens 5 ones

11. 43 = 4 tens 3 ones   **12.** 87 = 8 tens 7 ones

13. 26 = 2 tens 6 ones   **14.** 62 = 6 tens 2 ones

MEETING INDIVIDUAL NEEDS

ACTIVITY ALTERNATIVE TEACHING STRATEGY

MATERIALS 9 T, 9 O models (or punchouts), Workmat 2

VISUAL Display 2 tens 4 ones on Workmat 2 and 4 tens 2 ones on second workmat. Write 24 and 42 on a sheet of paper below each mat. Guide a discussion about the two numbers. Lead children to observe how the numbers are the same and how they are different. Repeat the activity with the numbers 59 and 95, 16 and 61, 83 and 38. Have children write numbers.

For Students Acquiring English (SAE)

Demonstrate the use of a **spinner** and model vocabulary for using it. Encourage pairs to discuss the numbers they make in Working Together. Pair SAE children and non-SAE children to complete page 58.

ACTIVITY Common Error and Remediation

MATERIALS 9 T, 9 O models (or punchouts), Workmat 2, number cards for 0–9

Some children may reverse the tens and ones when writing a number. Work individually with each child. Use a set of exercises, such as:

3 tens 8 ones   1 ten 6 ones   7 tens 1 one   9 tens 3 ones

After modeling the number of tens and ones on Workmat 2, have the child place number cards below the counters and then write the number.

3 PRACTICE•APPLY   PRACTICE   ex. 1–14

CLOSE Guide children to summarize the lesson:
■ **How would you model the number 57?** [5 tens 7 ones]

ESTIMATION ▪ GLASSES OF BEANS

MAC Activity 38

On Your Own   Pair and Share   In a Group

Materials   beans, glasses

Place dried beans or other small objects in nine clear drinking glasses. In one glass put 9 or fewer beans. In the other glasses put from 10 to 19 beans, 20 to 29 beans, and so on. The last glass should contain 90 to 99 beans. Label the glasses randomly with letters A to J for easy identification.

Distribute a lined sheet of paper to each child. Have children list the letters A to J down one side of their papers. Then have them estimate the number of beans in each glass and write that number next to the appropriate letter.

Ask volunteers to arrange the glasses from least to greatest based on their estimates. Then ask the volunteers to dump out the beans from each glass and arrange them into piles of tens and ones. Have each child record the actual number of beans in each glass and compare that number with his or her estimates.

▲ **MAC Activity 38:**
Average-to-Challenge

MATH AND PHYSICAL EDUCATION ▪ *CALLING ALL RABBITS*

MAC Activity 37

On Your Own   Pair and Share   In a Group

Materials   tens cards for 0 tens to 9 tens, ones cards for 0 ones to 9 ones

Take children to a large open space such as the gym or playground to play the game "Calling All Rabbits." Give each child a tens card and a ones card on which 0 to 9 has been written.

   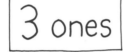

Tell children that you will say a number and name an action, such as, "7, hop." Those children holding either a tens or a ones card with the number 7 on it must hop to an area designated as *The Hutch*. To enter the hutch they must say a number with a 7 in the tens or the ones place, depending on the card they hold.

Continue the game until all the "rabbits" have been admitted to *The Hutch*.

▲ **MAC Activity 37:**
Basic-to-Average

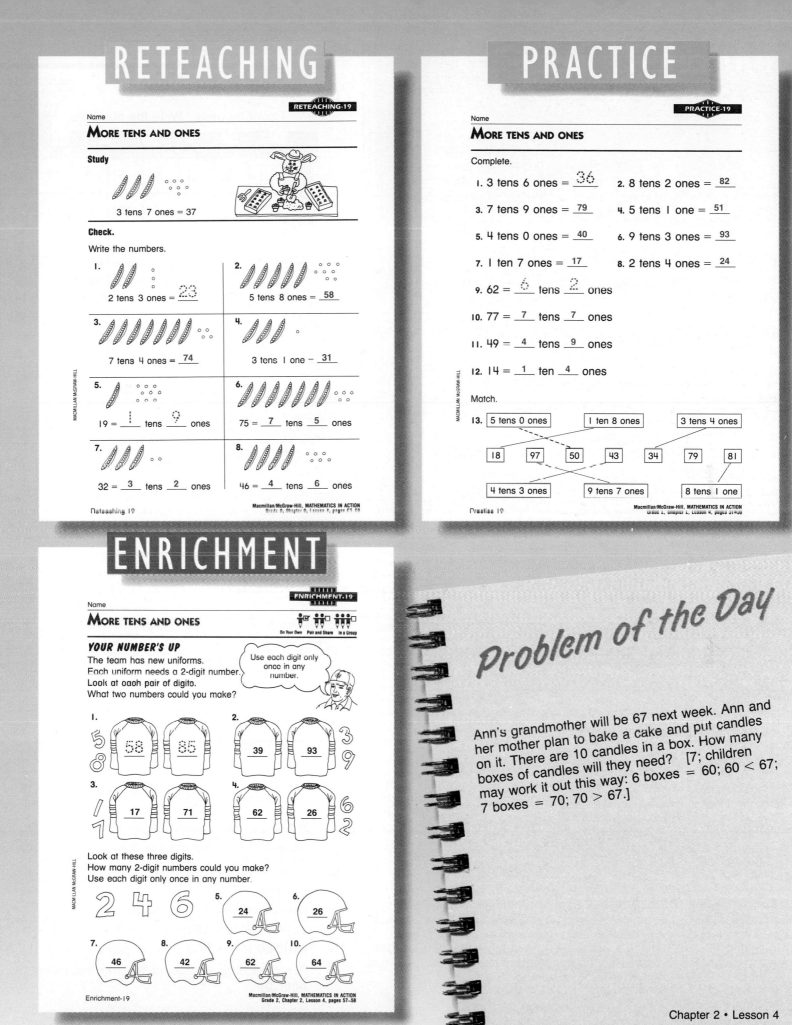

RETEACHING

RETEACHING-19

Name _____

MORE TENS AND ONES

Study

3 tens 7 ones = 37

Check.

Write the numbers.

1. 2 tens 3 ones = 23
2. 5 tens 8 ones = 58
3. 7 tens 4 ones = 74
4. 3 tens 1 one = 31
5. 19 = 1 tens 9 ones
6. 75 = 7 tens 5 ones
7. 32 = 3 tens 2 ones
8. 46 = 4 tens 6 ones

Reteaching-19

Macmillan/McGraw-Hill, MATHEMATICS IN ACTION
Grade 2, Chapter 2, Lesson 4, pages 57-58

PRACTICE

PRACTICE-19

Name _____

MORE TENS AND ONES

Complete.

1. 3 tens 6 ones = 36
2. 8 tens 2 ones = 82
3. 7 tens 9 ones = 79
4. 5 tens 1 one = 51
5. 4 tens 0 ones = 40
6. 9 tens 3 ones = 93
7. 1 ten 7 ones = 17
8. 2 tens 4 ones = 24
9. 62 = 6 tens 2 ones
10. 77 = 7 tens 7 ones
11. 49 = 4 tens 9 ones
12. 14 = 1 ten 4 ones

Match.

13.

| 5 tens 0 ones | 1 ten 8 ones | 3 tens 4 ones |

| 18 | 97 | 50 | 43 | 34 | 79 | 81 |

| 4 tens 3 ones | 9 tens 7 ones | 8 tens 1 one |

Practice-19

Macmillan/McGraw-Hill, MATHEMATICS IN ACTION
Grade 2, Chapter 2, Lesson 4, pages 57-58

ENRICHMENT

ENRICHMENT-19

Name _____

MORE TENS AND ONES

On Your Own   Pair and Share   In a Group

YOUR NUMBER'S UP

The team has new uniforms.
Each uniform needs a 2-digit number.
Look at each pair of digits.
What two numbers could you make?

Use each digit only once in any number.

1. 5 8 — 58   85
2. 3 9 — 39   93
3. 1 7 — 17   71
4. 6 2 — 62   26

Look at these three digits.
How many 2-digit numbers could you make?
Use each digit only once in any number.

2 4 6

5. 24
6. 26
7. 46
8. 42
9. 62
10. 64

Enrichment-19

Macmillan/McGraw-Hill, MATHEMATICS IN ACTION
Grade 2, Chapter 2, Lesson 4, pages 57-58

Problem of the Day

Ann's grandmother will be 67 next week. Ann and her mother plan to bake a cake and put candles on it. There are 10 candles in a box. How many boxes of candles will they need?   [7; children may work it out this way: 6 boxes = 60; 60 < 67; 7 boxes = 70; 70 > 67.]

AT·A·GLANCE p. 59

LESSON OBJECTIVES

Order numbers to 100.
Identify the number just before, just after, and between.

ASSIGNMENT GUIDE

COURSE	EXERCISES
Basic	p. 59: 1–3
Average	p. 59: 1–3
Challenge	p. 59: 1–3
Extra Practice, p. 68	

MATERIALS

Classroom Materials hundred chart*

Teacher Resources
Reteaching 20   Practice 20   Enrichment 20
MAC Act. 39, 40   Teacher Aid 2*

SKILLS TRACE
NUMBERS TO 100

Explore (Concrete)	Develop/Understand (Transitional/Abstract)
52	53–54, 55–56, 57–58, 59, 60, 61–62, 63–64, 71–72, 73–74, 75–76, 77–78
Practice 68, 83, 84, 85–86, 89, 98, 136	**Apply** 65–66, 69–70, 82, 88, 90

See **MANIPULATIVES PLUS 13**, p. 50M.

Name _____

Order to 100

Count by ones. Write the numbers.

1	2	3	4	5	6	7	8	9	10
11	12	13	14	15	16	17	18	19	20
21	22	23	24	25	26	27	28	29	30
31	32	33	34	35	36	37	38	39	40
41	42	43	44	45	46	47	48	49	50
51	52	53	54	55	56	57	58	59	60
61	62	63	64	65	66	67	68	69	70
71	72	73	74	75	76	77	78	79	80
81	82	83	84	85	86	87	88	89	90
91	92	93	94	95	96	97	98	99	100

1. Which number comes just after?

15, __16__

83, __84__

37, __38__

2. Which number comes just before?

__18__, 19

__44__, 45

__59__, 60

3. Which number comes between?

32, __33__, 34

56, __57__, 58

98, __99__, 100

Macmillan/McGraw-Hill

Extra Practice, page 68

PREPARE **WARM-UP** To prepare children for ordering numbers, display a large hundred chart. Point to each of the following numbers. For each, have children say the number that is one more than the number and one less than the number.

24 [25, 23]   78 [79, 77]   50 [51, 49]
86 [87, 85]   63 [64, 62]   31 [32, 30]

TEACH **DISCUSSING** Display a hundred chart. Point to the number 47 and have a volunteer tell which number is **just after** 47. Ask another child to tell which number is **one more** than 47. Help children realize that the number that is **just after** a given number is the same as the number that is **one more** than that number. Repeat the activity with other numbers.

Then point to 52 and ask similar questions, focusing on **just before** and **one less** than that number. Repeat with other numbers.

PUPIL'S EDITION p. 59

Relate the hundred chart on the page to the chart you have been working with. Explain to children that they are to trace the dashed numbers and fill in the blank squares. Do the first row with the children.

Check for Understanding

■ **What three numbers will come after 10?** [11, 12, 13]

GUIDED PRACTICE Have children complete the hundred chart.

For reteaching, use Common Error and Remediation or Alternative Strategy.

ACTIVITY — Common Error and Remediation

MATERIALS 30 ◯ (or punchouts)

Some children may skip numbers in the counting sequence. Work individually with each child. Have the child count aloud to 19 while stacking a set of counters. Next have the child write the numbers 1 to 19. Repeat until the sequence is mastered. Then add 10 more numbers and do the same exercise. Increase the sequence by 10 after each previous sequence has been mastered.

ACTIVITY — ALTERNATIVE TEACHING STRATEGY

MATERIALS adding-machine tape

VISUAL/KINESTHETIC Have children work together in ten groups. Provide each group with a length of adding-machine tape on which you have drawn a number line. Have each group write in the numbers 1 to 0, leaving a space after the 9. Help children tape the ten pieces of paper together. Have children who did the second number line in the series write a number 1, for 1 ten, before each number to show 11 to 19. Ask the next group to write a number 2, and so on to 99. Then have volunteers write 10, 20, 30, and so on to 100.

3 PRACTICE•APPLY **PRACTICE** ex. 1–3

CLOSE Guide children to summarize the lesson:

■ **What numbers come just before and just after 89?** [88, 90]

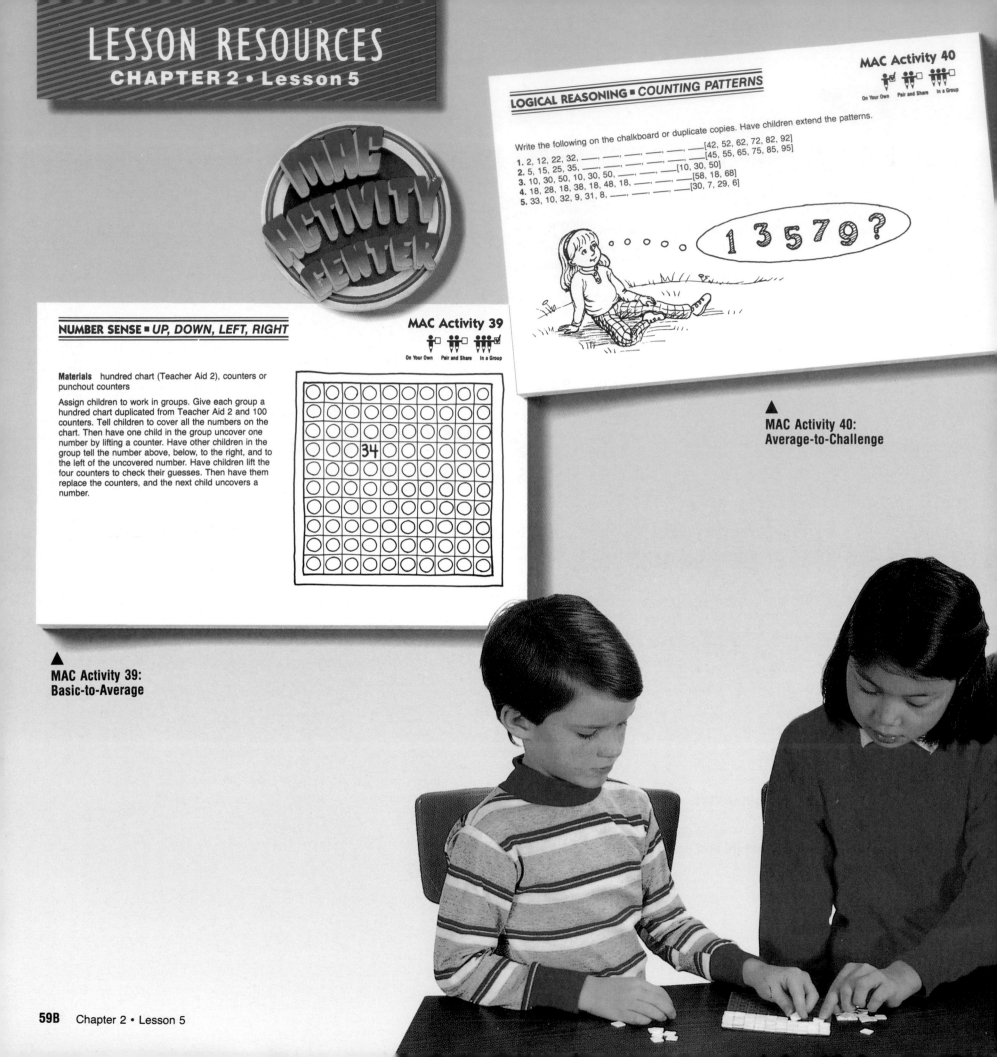

MAC Activity 40

On Your Own Pair and Share In a Group

LOGICAL REASONING ■ COUNTING PATTERNS

Write the following on the chalkboard or duplicate copies. Have children extend the patterns.

1. 2, 12, 22, 32, —— —— —— —— —— —— [42, 52, 62, 72, 82, 92]
2. 5, 15, 25, 35, —— —— —— —— —— —— [45, 55, 65, 75, 85, 95]
3. 10, 30, 50, 10, 30, 50, —— —— —— [10, 30, 50]
4. 18, 28, 18, 38, 18, 48, 18, —— —— —— [58, 18, 68]
5. 33, 10, 32, 9, 31, 8, —— —— —— —— [30, 7, 29, 6]

1 3 5 7 9 ?

▲
MAC Activity 40:
Average-to-Challenge

NUMBER SENSE ■ UP, DOWN, LEFT, RIGHT

MAC Activity 39

On Your Own Pair and Share In a Group

Materials hundred chart (Teacher Aid 2), counters or punchout counters

Assign children to work in groups. Give each group a hundred chart duplicated from Teacher Aid 2 and 100 counters. Tell children to cover all the numbers on the chart. Then have one child in the group uncover one number by lifting a counter. Have other children in the group tell the number above, below, to the right, and to the left of the uncovered number. Have children lift the four counters to check their guesses. Then have them replace the counters, and the next child uncovers a number.

34

▲
MAC Activity 39:
Basic-to-Average

Name _____

ORDER TO 100

Study

(1) (2) (3) (4) (5) (6) (7) (8) (9) (10)

(91) (92) (93) (94) (95) (96) (97) (98) (99) (100)

Check

Write the numbers.

1. 31 32 _33_ 34 _35_ _36_ _37_ 38 _39_ _40_

2. 51 52 _53_ _54_ 55 _56_ _57_ _58_ _59_ 60

3. 71 72 _73_ _74_ _75_ 76 _77_ _78_ _79_ 80

What number comes just after?

4. 14, _15_

29, _30_

60, _61_

85, _86_

What number comes just before?

5. _46_, 47

_89_, 90

_70_, 71

_19_, 20

Macmillan/McGraw-Hill, MATHEMATICS IN ACTION
Grade 2, Chapter 2, Lesson 5, page 59

Reteaching-20

Name _____

ORDER TO 100

Count by ones.

1. 11, 12, 13, _14_ _15_, _16_, _17_, _18_, _19_, _20_

2. 31, 32, 33, _34_, _35_, _36_, _37_, _38_, _39_, _40_

3. 51, 52, 53, _54_, _55_, _56_, _57_, _58_, _59_, _60_

4. 71, 72, 73, _74_, _75_, _76_, _77_, _78_, _79_, _80_

5. 81, 82, 83, _84_, _85_, _86_, _87_, _88_, _89_, _90_

6. 91, 92, 93, _94_, _95_, _96_, _97_, _98_, _99_, _100_

What number comes just after?

7. 89, _90_   55, _56_   37, 38   70, _71_   99, _100_

What number comes just before?

8. _51_, 52   _95_, 96   _19_, 20   _78_, 79   _82_, 83

What number comes between?

9. 77, _78_, 79   45, _46_, 47   29, _30_, 31

Macmillan/McGraw-Hill, MATHEMATICS IN ACTION
Grade 2, Chapter 2, Lesson 5, page 59

Practice-20

Name _____

ORDER TO 100

On Your Own   Pair and Share   In a Group

FISHY NUMBERS

These numbers are mixed up.
You can put them in order.

29, 17, 51, 34   _17_, _29_, _34_, _51_

Try these.

1. 48, 77, 38, 64   _38_, _48_, _64_, _77_

2. 11, 24, 9, 18   _9_, _11_, _18_, _24_

3. 73, 98, 19, 42   _19_, _42_, _73_, _98_

4. 12, 4, 88, 16   _4_, _12_, _16_, _88_

Connect the dots in order.
Some numbers are missing.

Macmillan/McGraw-Hill, MATHEMATICS IN ACTION
Grade 2, Chapter 2, Lesson 5, page 59

Enrichment-20

Problem of the Day

The number fell off Frank's seat. The seat in front of him was number 68. The seat behind him was number 88. What was Frank's seat number?   [78]

Counting On and Counting Back

Write the missing numbers.

1.

Count on by ones.

2. 42, 43, 44, __45__, __46__, __47__, __48__, __49__

3. 55, 56, 57, __58__, __59__, __60__, __61__, __62__

Count back by ones.

4. 9, 8, 7, __6__, __5__, __4__, __3__, __2__

5. 38, 37, 36, __35__, __34__, __33__, __32__, __31__

6. 66, 65, 64, __63__, __62__, __61__, __60__, __59__

Count on by tens.

7.

8. 30, 40, 50, __60__, __70__, __80__, __90__, __100__

Count back by tens.

9. 90, 80, 70, __60__, __50__, __40__, __30__, __20__

Mixed Review

10. $7 + 2 =$ __9__ $10 - 1 =$ __9__ $4 + 6 =$ __10__

11. $9 - 5 =$ __4__ $0 + 8 =$ __8__ $10 - 7 =$ __3__

60   sixty

---

1 PREPARE
WARM-UP To continue work with the hundred chart, call on volunteers to identify patterns they observe on the chart. [Responses will vary, but point out the ones place in each column, the tens place in each column, and various diagonals.]

2 TEACH
PATTERNING Recite four numbers in order; for example, 11, 12, 13, 14. Have children recite the next four numbers in the sequence. Repeat the activity using other number sequences.

Then say four numbers in backward order; for example, 19, 18, 17, 16. Have children give the next four numbers counting backward. Repeat the activity using other sequences.

Display the hundred chart and lead children in **skip counting** forward and backward by tens. Do 10, 20, 30, . . . and 100, 90, 80,. . . . Also include sequences like 12, 22, 32,. . . .

PUPIL'S EDITION p. 60
Do ex. 1 and 7 with the children.

Check for Understanding
■ **What are the next five numbers when you count 45, 46, 47?**
[48, 49, 50, 51, 52]

GUIDED PRACTICE ex. 1 and 7: For reteaching, use Common Error and Remediation or Alternative Strategy.

ACTIVITY
Common Error and Remediation

MATERIALS hundred chart (Teacher Aid 2), small cube

Some children may not be able to count on from a given number. Work individually with each child using a hundred chart duplicated from Teacher Aid 2. Place the chart on the desk and give the child a small cube. Tell the child he or she will toss the cube on to the chart to try to land on a number. Then have the child say the number the cube lands on and count on to the end of the row. Repeat several times.

For Students Acquiring English (SAE)

Fill in some numbers on a large 100s grid; have children tell you more numbers until it is filled. Then have them look for patterns. Circle the patterns and count orally. Then explain the patterns as **skip counting**, **counting on**, or **counting back**.

ACTIVITY
ALTERNATIVE TEACHING STRATEGY

MATERIALS 30 P and 30 D coins (or punchouts)

VISUAL/AUDITORY Place 18 pennies on the desk and have children count in unison as you put down one more penny at a time: 19, 20, 21, ..., 30. Then pick up one penny at a time and have them count back by ones. Repeat the activity with dimes to count on and count back by tens.

3 PRACTICE•APPLY **PRACTICE** ex. 2–6, 8–11

CLOSE Guide children to summarize the lesson:
■ **What are the next five numbers when you count 30, 40, 50?**
[60, 70, 80, 90, 100]

MAC Activity 42

NUMBER SENSE ▪ INVISIBLE NUMBERS

On Your Own   Pair and Share   In a Group

Materials hundred chart (Teacher Aid 2), blank hundred chart (Teacher Aid 3), counters

Procedure Provide groups of children with copies of Teacher Aids 2 and 3. Explain that they are to use the blank hundred chart as a game board and the completed chart as a way to check guesses.

The first player places a counter on a square on the blank chart. The player to his or her right guesses what the number is. If correct, that child gets one point and places another counter on another square. If not correct, the next player takes a turn. Have children use the completed chart to verify numbers.

To Win The first player with 10 points at the end of a round wins the game.

MAC Activity 42:
Average-to-Challenge ▶

MAC Activity 41

MANIPULATIVES ▪ CUBE PATTERNS

On Your Own   Pair and Share   In a Group

Materials connecting cubes

Assign children to work in groups. Give each group a set of connecting cubes. Tell children that you will show a number pattern with cubes. Explain that they are to work together to copy the pattern and then continue it. Show the following patterns.

When children have completed the given patterns, have them create their own patterns.

▲
MAC Activity 41:
Basic-to-Average

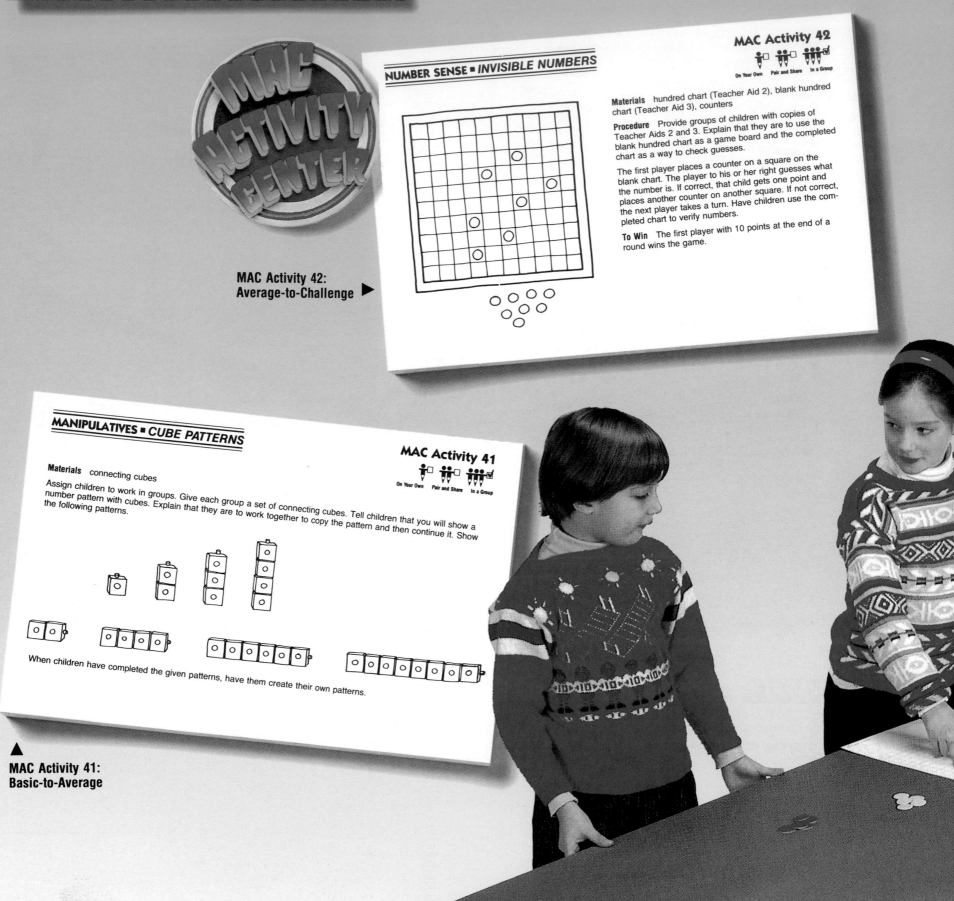

RETEACHING-21

Name

COUNTING ON AND COUNTING BACK

Study

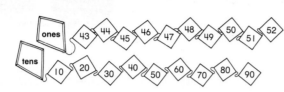

Check

Count on by ones.

1. 8, 9, 10, __11__, __12__, __13__, __14__, __15__, __16__

2. 23, 24, 25, __26__, __27__, __28__, __29__, __30__, __31__

3. 66, 67, 68, __69__, __70__, __71__, __72__, __73__, __74__

4. 90, 91, 92, __93__, __94__, __95__, __96__, __97__, __98__

Count back by ones.

5. 77, 76, 75, __74__, __73__, __72__, __71__, __70__, __69__

Count on by tens.

6. 10, 20, __30__, __40__, __50__, __60__, __70__, __80__, __90__

Reteaching-21

Macmillan/McGraw-Hill, MATHEMATICS IN ACTION
Grade 2, Chapter 2, Lesson 6, page 60

PRACTICE-21

Name

COUNTING ON AND COUNTING BACK

Count on by ones.

1. 36, 37, 38, __39__, __40__, __41__, __42__, __43__

2. 83, 84, 85, __86__, __87__, __88__, __89__, __90__

Count back by ones.

3. 55, 54, 53, __52__, __51__, __50__, __49__, __48__

4. 99, 98, 97, __96__, __95__, __94__, __93__, __92__

Count on by tens.

5. 20, 30, 40, __50__, __60__, __70__, __80__, __90__

6. 5, 15, 25, __35__, __45__, __55__, __65__, __75__

Count back by tens.

7. 90, 80, 70, __60__, __50__, __40__, __30__, __20__

8. 85, 75, 65, __55__, __45__, __35__, __25__, __15__

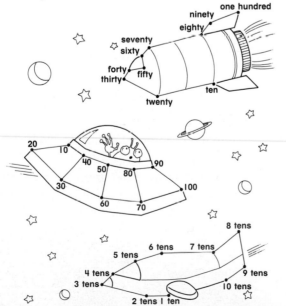

Practice-21

Macmillan/McGraw-Hill, MATHEMATICS IN ACTION
Grade 2, Chapter 2, Lesson 6, page 60

ENRICHMENT-21

Name

COUNTING ON AND COUNTING BACK

On Your Own   Pair and Share   In a Group

OUTER SPACE

Connect the dots.
Count by tens.

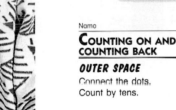

Enrichment-21

Macmillan/McGraw-Hill, MATHEMATICS IN ACTION
Grade 2, Chapter 2, Lesson 6, page 60

Problem of the Day

Ted had 28 baseball cards. He got 6 packs of 10 cards each for his birthday. How many cards does he have now?   [88; children may work it out this way: 38, 48, 58, 68, 78, 88.]

AT·A·GLANCE pp. 61-62

LESSON OBJECTIVE
Count by twos, fives, threes, and fours.

ASSIGNMENT GUIDE

COURSE	EXERCISES
Basic	p. 61: 2, 4–5; p. 62: 2–4, 6
Average	p. 61: 2, 4–5; p. 62: 2–4, 6
Challenge	p. 61: 2, 4–5; p. 62: 2–4, 6
Extra Practice, p. 68	Practice Plus, p. 84

MATERIALS

Calculator
Classroom Materials blue crayons
Manipulatives 1 hundreds chart (Teacher Aid 2) per child

Teacher Resources
Reteaching 22   Practice 22   Enrichment 22
MAC Act. 43, 44   Teacher Aids 2, 11
Math Anthology, pp. 140–142

SKILLS TRACE NUMBERS TO 100	
Explore (Concrete) 52	**Develop/Understand (Transitional/Abstract)** 53–54, 55–56, 57–58, 59, 60, 61–62, 63–64, 71–72, 73–74, 75–76, 77–78
Practice 68, 83, 84, 85–86, 89, 98, 136	**Apply** 65–66, 69–70, 82, 88, 90

Name _____

Skip-Counting Patterns

1. How many shoes?

   __8__ shoes

   ▶ Tell how you found the answer.

2. Count by twos. Write the numbers.

   2, 4, 6, 8, __10__, __12__, __14__, __16__, __18__, **20**

3. How many fingers?

   __20__ fingers

   Tell how you found the answer. counting by ones, by fives, or by twos

4. Count by fives. Color ⬤ blue . Children's answers should be marked in blue

I	2	3	4	5	6	7	8	9	10
11	12	13	14	15	16	17	18	19	20
21	22	23	24	25	26	27	28	29	30
31	32	33	34	35	36	37	38	39	40
41	42	43	44	45	46	47	48	49	50

5. Count by fives. Write the numbers.

   5, 10, 15, **20**, __25__, __30__, __35__, __40__, __45__, __50__

PREPARE **WARM-UP** To prepare children for counting by twos, write the following numbers on the chalkboard. Have children add 2 to each number and say the sums aloud.

0 [2], 2 [4], 4 [6], 6 [8], 8 [10]

Mathematics and Literature CULTURAL CONNECTION

TEACH **DISCUSSING** Have ten children line up in pairs in the front of the room. Discuss how the class can find the total number of children. After the discussion, count the children one at a time. Next count by twos as you point to each pair of children. Then have the children who are lined up count off by twos.

Repeat the activity by having children group themselves by fives; threes; and fours. Have volunteers count the children. Discuss with children why skip counting is faster than counting by ones.

Before reading *A Birthday Basket for Tia* from *Math Anthology* to children, explain that the story comes from Mexico, where people speak Spanish, so they will hear some Spanish words in the story. Then read it to the children. Discuss the story.

■ **How old is Tia?** [90]

■ **In the story, how does Cecilia count to 90?** [by tens]

Have the class skip count by tens. Then have them use the hundred chart to color each number they say when skip counting by tens.

PUPIL'S EDITION pp. 61-62

Page 61 Guide children through ex. 1 and 3. Discuss how they got their answers.

1. How many buttons?

   __12__ buttons

2. Count by threes. Color  red.

1	2	3	4	5	6	7	8	9	10
11	12	13	14	15	16	17	18	19	20
21	22	23	24	25	26	27	28	29	30

3. Count by threes. Write the numbers.

   3, 6, _9_, _12_, _15_, _18_, _21_

4. How many legs? __12__ legs

5. You can use a 🖩 to
   count by fours.
   Press [ON/C] 0 [+] 4 [=].
   Write the number you see.
   Press [=] eight more times.
   Each time write what you see.

   _4_, _8_, _12_, _16_, _20_, _24_, _28_, _32_, _36_

6. Each hat will have 2 🍃.

   How many 🍃 on 5 hats?

   _10_ 🍃

Extra Practice, page 68   *Practice Plus,* page 84

MEETING INDIVIDUAL NEEDS

ALTERNATIVE TEACHING STRATEGY

MATERIALS hundred chart (Teacher Aid 2)

VISUAL Display the hundred chart duplicated from Teacher Aid 2. Explain to children that you want to count by fives. Begin by pointing to each number starting at 1 and count softly until you get to 5, 10, and so on. Say these numbers loudly. Then just point to 5, 10, 15, ..., 50 and have the children count with you in unison.

ONGOING ASSESSMENT 📓 MATH JOURNAL

INTERVIEW (1) How am I counting? 3, 6, 9, 12, 15? (2) Can you count by fours? Start with the number 4 and count to 20. (3) A nickel is worth 5 pennies. How could you find out how many pennies 3 nickels are worth?

JOURNAL WRITING You may wish to have children record their responses in their math journals.

ACTIVITY Common Error and Remediation

MATERIALS 18 🧊, number cards for 1–18 (Teacher Aid 11)

Some children may have difficulty skip counting. Work individually with each child. Have the child place groups of cubes as shown. Ask the child to count cubes, as he or she places a number card below each. Have the child read each top card.

(1,2,3;   4,5,6;   7,8,9)

CLOSE   Guide children to summarize the lesson:
■ **What are the next three numbers in the sequence 8, 10, 12, 14?**
[16, 18, 20]

Check for Understanding
■ **How am I counting: 20, 25, 30, 35, 40?** [by fives]

GUIDED PRACTICE   ex. 1, 5: For reteaching, use Common Error and Remediation or Alternative Strategy.

Page 62   Guide children through ex. 1 and 5. For ex. 5, distribute a calculator to each child. Check that the sequence of key strokes works with the children's calculators. Point out the location of the keys. Have children relate adding by 4 to skip counting.

PRACTICE•APPLY   PRACTICE   ex. 2–4, 6

MAC ACTIVITY CENTER

MAC Activity 43:
Basic-to-Average

MAC Activity 43

On Your Own   Pair and Share   In a Group

MANIPULATIVES ■ SKIP-COUNTING COUNTERS

By Fives

Materials   counters or punchout counters
Have children work in pairs. Distribute about 25 counters to each pair. Tell one child to group the counters in twos, threes, fours, or fives (counters will be left over). Then have the other child skip count to find the number of counters and write the matching number pattern. Have children exchange roles and repeat the activity.

MAC Activity 44:
Average-to-Challenge

MAC Activity 44

On Your Own   Pair and Share   In a Group

CALCULATOR ■ CALCULATOR COUNTING

75   70   65   60   55   50   45

Materials   calculator
Begin by showing children how to skip count on a calculator. Most four-function models will skip count if the following keys are hit: 5 + = = = =. . . . Other models will require hitting 5 + 5 + 5. . . .

Have children use their calculators to skip count by twos, fives, threes, fours, and tens to 100. Allow them to explore other patterns.

Name _____

SKIP-COUNTING PATTERNS

Study

I can jump by twos!

0 1 2 3 4 5 6 7 8 9 10 11 12 13 14 15 16 17 18 19 20

I can jump by fives!

0 1 2 3 4 5 6 7 8 9 10 11 12 13 14 15 16 17 18 19 20 21 22 23 24 25

Check

Count by twos.

1. 2 4 6 8 10 12 14 16

2. 4 6 8 10 12 14 16 18

3. 6 8 10 12 14 16 18 20

Count by fives.

4. 5 10 15 20 25 30 35 40

5. 10 15 20 25 30 35 40 45

6. 15 20 25 30 35 40 45 50

Macmillan/McGraw-Hill, MATHEMATICS IN ACTION
Grade 2, Chapter 2, Lesson 7, pages 61–62   Reteaching-22

Name _____

SKIP-COUNTING PATTERNS

Count by twos.

1. 2 4 6 8 10 12 14 16 18 20

Count by fives.

2. 5 10 15 20 25 30 35 40 45 50

Count by threes.

3. 3 6 9 12 15 18 21 24 27 30

Count by fours.

4. 4 8 12 16 20 24 28 32 36 40

Connect the dots in order.

Macmillan/McGraw-Hill, MATHEMATICS IN ACTION
Grade 2, Chapter 2, Lesson 7, pages 61–62   Practice-22

Name _____

SKIP-COUNTING PATTERNS

On Your Own Pair and Share In a Group

SHAPE-COUNTING PATTERNS

Julia used toothpicks to make a shape pattern.

Have children work in groups of 3.

How many toothpicks did she use to make all the pentagons in her picture? ____ 40

Choose a shape. Your partners also choose a shape. Use 50 toothpicks. Make a row of your shape.

triangle   square   pentagon   hexagon

What shape did you choose? ____ **Answers will vary.**

How many shapes did you make? _____

How many toothpicks do you have left? _____

Complete the chart for your group.

Name	Shape	Number Made

Macmillan/McGraw-Hill, MATHEMATICS IN ACTION
Grade 2, Chapter 2, Lesson 7, pages 61–62   Enrichment-22

Problem of the Day

Mrs. Downing makes 12 hats. She wants to sew 2 bows on each hat. If she buys 25 bows, will she have enough?   [Yes; children may work it out this way: 2, 4, 6, . . . , 24; 24 < 25.]

CHAPTER 2 • Lesson 8

A·T·A·GLANCE pp. 63-64

LESSON OBJECTIVE
Identify even and odd numbers.

ASSIGNMENT GUIDE

COURSE	EXERCISES
Basic	p. 63: 4–10; p. 64: 3–5, Reasoning
Average	p. 63: 4–10; p. 64: 3–5, Reasoning
Challenge	p. 63: 4–10; p. 64: 3–5, Reasoning
Extra Practice, p. 68	

MATERIALS
Manipulatives 10 ▢ (or small square counter punchouts) per pair

Teacher Resources
Reteaching 23
MAC Act. 45, 46
Practice 23
Teacher Aids 1, 4, 11
Enrichment 23
Calculator 2

SKILLS TRACE
NUMBERS TO 100

Explore (Concrete) 52	Develop/Understand (Transitional/Abstract) 53–54, 55–56, 57–58, 59, 60, 61–62, 63–64, 71–72, 73–74, 75–76, 77–78
Practice 68, 83, 84, 85–86, 89, 98, 136	Apply 65–66, 69–70, 82, 88, 90

Name _____

Even and Odd Numbers

Two make a pair.
Who has a pair
of socks?
Don

	Number	How many pairs can you make? Ring each pair.	Number of Pairs	Number of Socks Left Over
1.	1		0	1
2.	2		1	0
3.	3		1	1
4.	4		2	0
5.	5		2	1
6.	6		3	0
7.	7		3	1
8.	8		4	0

9. Talk about the patterns you see.
Possible answers: some numbers make pairs with 1 left over; some numbers make pairs with none left over.

10. How many pairs can you make with 9 socks?

9 socks make 4 pairs with 1 left over.

Chapter 2   Understanding Numbers to 100   sixty-three   **63**

PREPARE

WARM-UP To prepare children for work with odd and even numbers, ask them to identify things that come in pairs, such as socks, shoes, and gloves. List these items on the chalkboard. Some children may name things like a pair of glasses, pants, or scissors. List these items separately. Discuss how the items on the two lists are different.

TEACH

MODELING Assign children to work in pairs, and distribute 10 cubes to each pair. First have each pair of children make a train with 4 cubes. Next ask them to separate the cubes into pairs.

■ **How many pairs do you have?** [2] **How many cubes do you have left over?** [none]

Then tell children to build trains of 10, 8, and 7 cubes and separate them into pairs.

■ **How is making pairs with 7 cubes different from making pairs with 8 or 10 cubes?** [There is one unpaired cube.]

Encourage children to compare the set of 7 to the set of 8. Explain that eight cubes separate evenly into pairs; therefore, 8 is an **even** number. Explain that because 7 does not separate evenly, 7 is called an **odd** number.

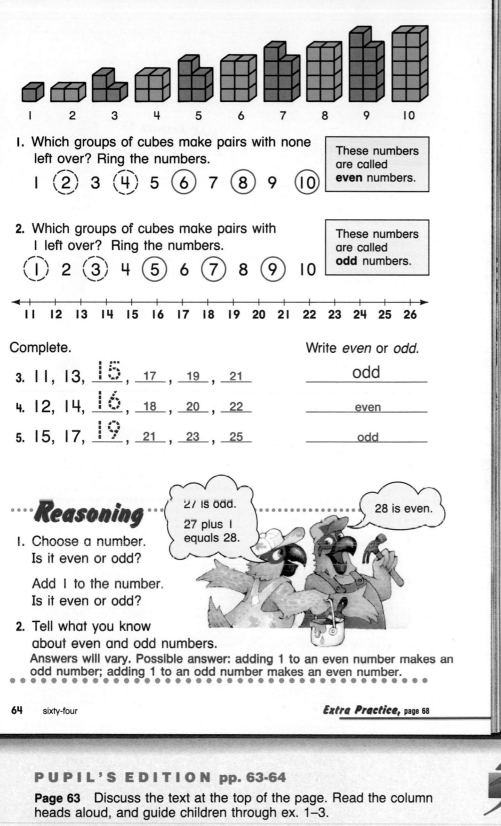

1. Which groups of cubes make pairs with none left over? Ring the numbers.

1 ② 3 ④ 5 ⑥ 7 ⑧ 9 ⑩

> These numbers are called **even** numbers.

2. Which groups of cubes make pairs with 1 left over? Ring the numbers.

① 2 ③ 4 ⑤ 6 ⑦ 8 ⑨ 10

> These numbers are called **odd** numbers.

←—|——|——|——|——|——|——|——|——|——|——|——|——|——|——|——|—→
11 12 13 14 15 16 17 18 19 20 21 22 23 24 25 26

Complete.   Write *even* or *odd.*

3. 11, 13, _15_, _17_, _19_, _21_   odd

4. 12, 14, _16_, _18_, _20_, _22_   even

5. 15, 17, _19_, _21_, _23_, _25_   odd

···· Reasoning ····

> 27 is odd.
> 27 plus 1 equals 28.

> 28 is even.

1. Choose a number. Is it even or odd?

Add 1 to the number. Is it even or odd?

2. Tell what you know about even and odd numbers.
Answers will vary. Possible answer: adding 1 to an even number makes an odd number; adding 1 to an odd number makes an even number.

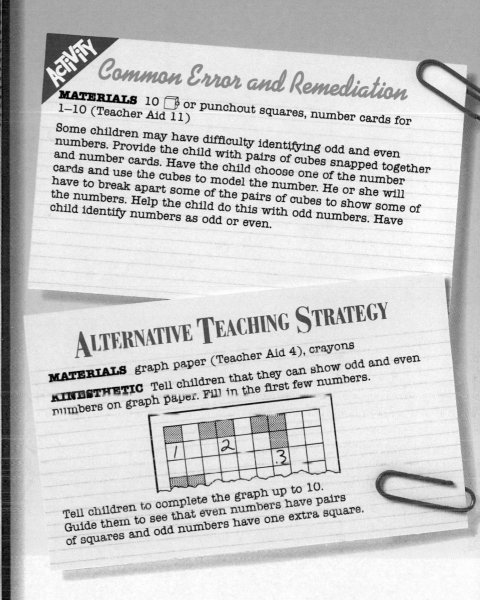

ACTIVITY

Common Error and Remediation

MATERIALS 10 ▭ or punchout squares, number cards for 1–10 (Teacher Aid 11)

Some children may have difficulty identifying odd and even numbers. Provide the child with pairs of cubes snapped together and number cards. Have the child choose one of the number cards and use the cubes to model the number. He or she will have to break apart some of the pairs of cubes to show some of the numbers. Help the child do this with odd numbers. Have child identify numbers as odd or even.

ALTERNATIVE TEACHING STRATEGY

MATERIALS graph paper (Teacher Aid 4), crayons

KINESTHETIC Tell children that they can show odd and even numbers on graph paper. Fill in the first few numbers.

Tell children to complete the graph up to 10. Guide them to see that even numbers have pairs of squares and odd numbers have one extra square.

PUPIL'S EDITION pp. 63-64

Page 63 Discuss the text at the top of the page. Read the column heads aloud, and guide children through ex. 1–3.

Check for Understanding

■ **Can you separate 5 cubes evenly into pairs? What does this tell you?** [No; 5 is an odd number.]

GUIDED PRACTICE ex. 4–10: For reteaching, use Common Error and Remediation or Alternative Strategy.

Page 64 Begin ex. 1 and 2 with the children. Review the words **odd** and **even.**

3 PRACTICE·APPLY   PRACTICE ex. 3–5

REASONING Tell children that the digit in the ones place determines if a number is even or odd.

CLOSE Guide children to summarize the lesson:

■ **Is the number odd or even?**
   17   [odd]
   9   [odd]
   12   [even]

LOGICAL REASONING ▪ ODD AND EVEN GAME

MAC Activity 45

On Your Own   Pair and Share   In a Group

Materials   game board (Teacher Aid 1), game markers, number cube

Procedure   Provide pairs of children with a game board duplicated from Teacher Aid 1, two game markers, and a number cube. You may want to write directions in some spaces on the game board; for example, *Go forward 1 space* and *Go backward 1 space*. Players take turns rolling the number cube. If a child rolls an even number, he or she moves forward two spaces. If a child rolls an odd number, he or she moves forward one space.

To Win   The first child to reach the end of the path wins the round.

MAC Activity 45:
Basic-to-Average ▶

NUMBER SENSE ▪ EVEN AND ODD SUMS

MAC Activity 46

On Your Own   Pair and Share   In a Group

Write the following addition facts on the chalkboard.

$$\frac{4}{+1} \quad \frac{3}{+2} \quad \frac{2}{+2} \quad \frac{4}{+2} \quad \frac{1}{+3} \quad \frac{5}{+4} \quad \frac{1}{+1} \quad \frac{3}{+3}$$

Then have children use the above exercises to complete the following.

$$\frac{\text{even}}{+\text{even}} \quad \frac{\text{odd}}{+\text{odd}} \quad \frac{\text{even}}{+\text{odd}}$$
$$\overline{[\text{even}]} \quad \overline{[\text{even}]} \quad \overline{[\text{odd}]}$$

Have children try other addition facts to see if this is always true.

odd *even*

▲
MAC Activity 46:
Average-to-Challenge

RETEACHING-23

Name

EVEN AND ODD NUMBERS

Study

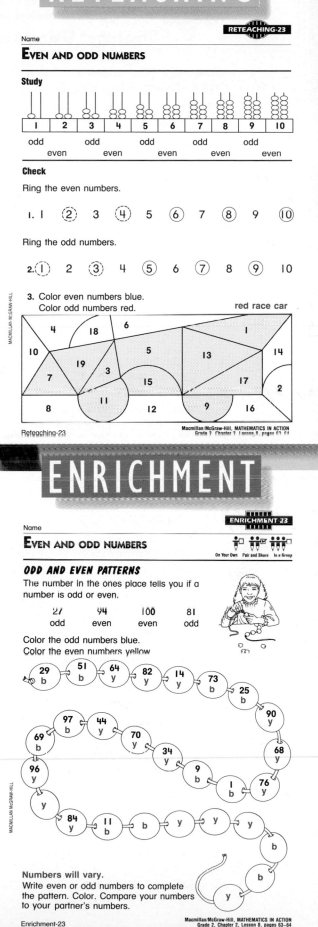

1	2	3	4	5	6	7	8	9	10

odd   odd   odd   odd   odd
  even   even   even   even   even

Check

Ring the even numbers.

1. 1 (2) 3 (4) 5 (6) 7 (8) 9 (10)

Ring the odd numbers.

2. (1) 2 (3) 4 (5) 6 (7) 8 (9) 10

3. Color even numbers blue.
   Color odd numbers red.   red race car

4		18	6			1
10		19	5	13		14
	7	3	15		17	2
8		11	12	9	16	

Reteaching-23

Macmillan/McGraw-Hill, MATHEMATICS IN ACTION
Grade 2, Chapter 2, Lesson 8, pages 63–64

MACMILLAN/McGRAW-HILL

PRACTICE-23

Name

EVEN AND ODD NUMBERS

Ring the even numbers.

1. 1 (2) 3 (4) 5 (6) 7 (8) 9 (10)
   11 (12) 13 (14) 15 (16) 17 (18) 19 (20)

Ring the odd numbers.

2. (1) 2 (3) 4 (5) 6 (7) 8 (9) 10
   (11) 12 (13) 14 (15) 16 (17) 18 (19) 20

Write even or odd.

3. 16 _even_   4. 9 _odd_   5. 18 _even_

    3 _odd_   1 _odd_   11 _odd_

   10 _even_   8 _even_   12 _even_

Connect the odd dots.

Practice-23

Macmillan/McGraw-Hill, MATHEMATICS IN ACTION
Grade 2, Chapter 2, Lesson 8, pages 63–64

MACMILLAN/McGRAW-HILL

ENRICHMENT-23

On Your Own   Pair and Share   In a Group

Name

EVEN AND ODD NUMBERS

ODD AND EVEN PATTERNS

The number in the ones place tells you if a
number is odd or even.

   27   94   100   81
   odd   even   even   odd

Color the odd numbers blue.
Color the even numbers yellow

29 b — 51 b — 64 y — 82 y — 14 y — 73 b — 25 b
97 b — 44 y — 70 y — 90 y
69 b — 34 y — 68 y
96 y — 9 b — 76 y
      1 b
y — 84 y — 11 b — b — y — y — y — b
     b
     y

Numbers will vary.
Write even or odd numbers to complete
the pattern. Color. Compare your numbers
to your partner's numbers.

Enrichment-23

Macmillan/McGraw-Hill, MATHEMATICS IN ACTION
Grade 2, Chapter 2, Lesson 8, pages 63–64

MACMILLAN/McGRAW-HILL

Problem of the Day

There are 5 people on the bus. If they wanted to,
could they all sit in pairs? [No.] Then 3 more
people get on. How many pairs could there now
be? [4]

AT·A·GLANCE pp. 65-66

LESSON OBJECTIVE
Use number sense to solve problems.

ASSIGNMENT GUIDE

COURSE	EXERCISES
Basic	p. 65: 1–2; p. 66: 1–4
Average	p. 65: 1–2; p. 66: 1–4
Challenge	p. 65: 1–2; p. 66: 1–4

MATERIALS
Classroom Materials 2 boxes (or jars, or glasses) of the same size
Manipulatives 34 ○ (or punchouts) for demonstration

Teacher Resources
Reteaching 24   Practice 24   Enrichment 24
Prob. Solv. 6   MAC Act. 47, 48
Math Anthology, p. 143

Name _____

Problem Solving

UNDERSTAND / PLAN / TRY / CHECK / EXTEND

Strategy: Using Number Sense

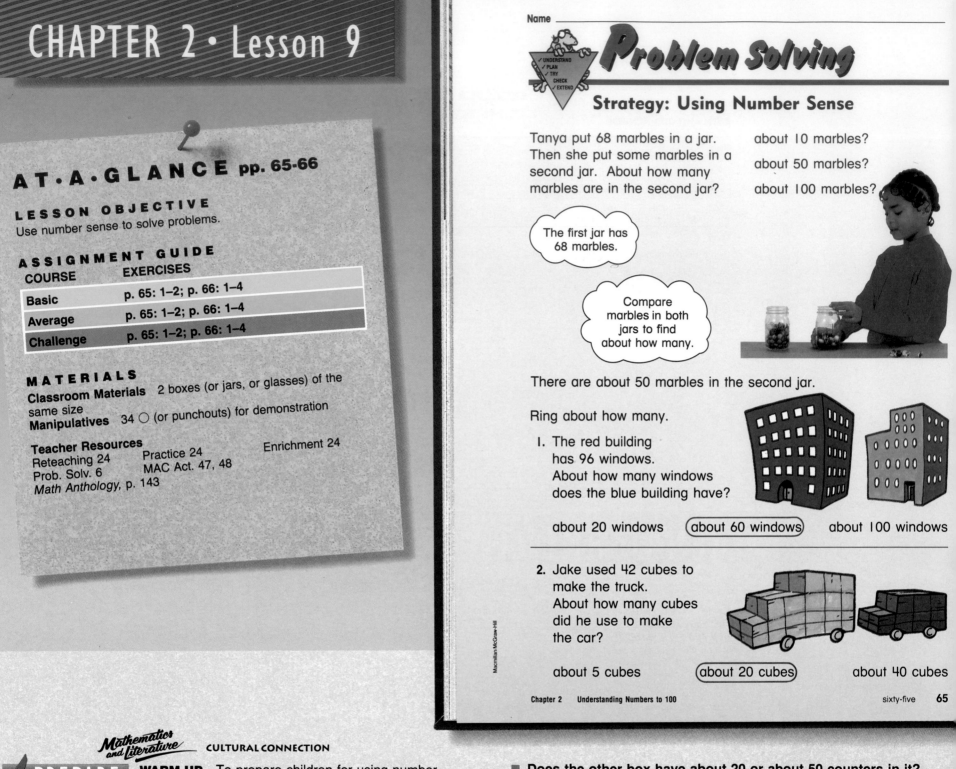

Tanya put 68 marbles in a jar. Then she put some marbles in a second jar. About how many marbles are in the second jar?

about 10 marbles?
about 50 marbles?
about 100 marbles?

The first jar has 68 marbles.

Compare marbles in both jars to find about how many.

There are about 50 marbles in the second jar.

Ring about how many.

1. The red building has 96 windows. About how many windows does the blue building have?

   about 20 windows   (about 60 windows)   about 100 windows

2. Jake used 42 cubes to make the truck. About how many cubes did he use to make the car?

   about 5 cubes   (about 20 cubes)   about 40 cubes

Macmillan McGraw-Hill

Chapter 2   Understanding Numbers to 100   sixty-five   **65**

Mathematics and Literature   **CULTURAL CONNECTION**

1 PREPARE
WARM-UP To prepare children for using number sense to solve problems, sing "Song of the Dragon" found in *Math Anthology* with them, or play the tape. Discuss how many legs there are in the class and compare that number with the number of legs the dragon has.

2 TEACH
QUESTIONING Display two boxes of the same size. Put 7 counters in one box and 21 counters in the other box. Briefly show the boxes to the children. Do not give them time to count the contents.

■ **How do we know which box has more counters?** [Possible response: One box looks fuller than the other.]

■ **Which box has about ten counters?** [the box with 7 counters]

■ **Does the other box have about 20 or about 50 counters in it?** [about 20 counters]

■ **How do we know it has about 20, rather than about 50?** [Possible response: 50 is much more than 20; there does not appear to be that many counters.]

Have a volunteer count the counters in the box to confirm the answer.

PUPIL'S EDITION pp. 65-66

Page 65 Have a volunteer read the problem at the top of the page.

■ **What do you know?** [Tanya put 68 marbles in one jar, and some in a second jar.]

Have volunteers read Tanya's answer to each of these questions:

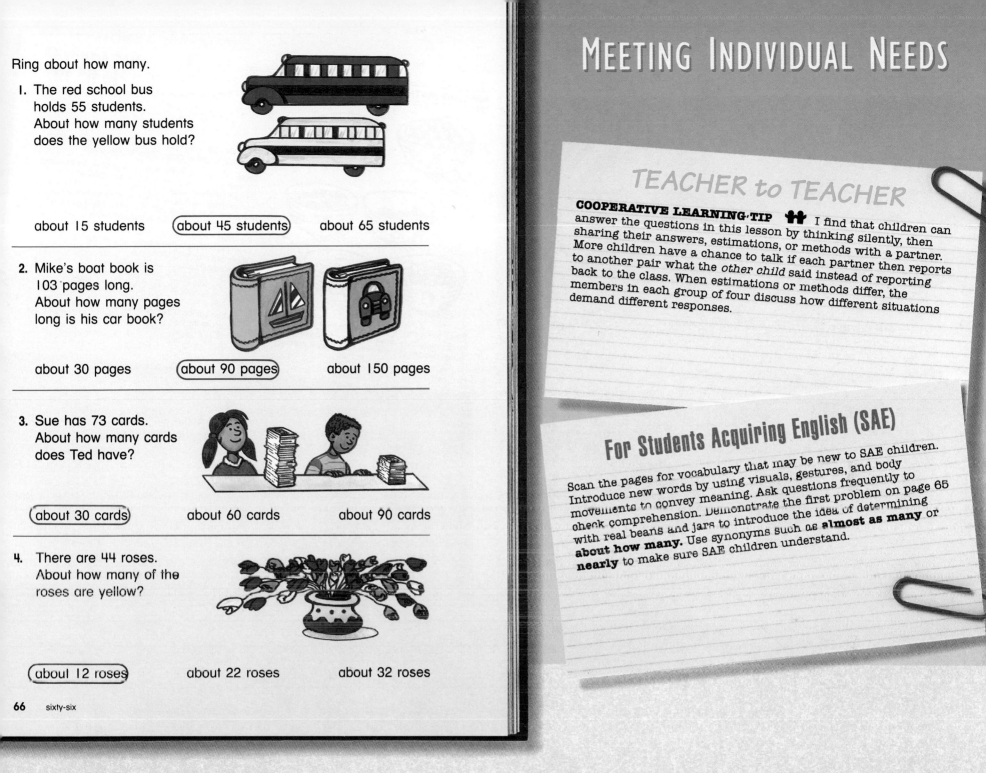

Ring about how many.

1. The red school bus holds 55 students. About how many students does the yellow bus hold?

about 15 students   (about 45 students)   about 65 students

2. Mike's boat book is 103 pages long. About how many pages long is his car book?

about 30 pages   (about 90 pages)   about 150 pages

3. Sue has 73 cards. About how many cards does Ted have?

(about 30 cards)   about 60 cards   about 90 cards

4. There are 44 roses. About how many of the roses are yellow?

(about 12 roses)   about 22 roses   about 32 roses

66   sixty-six

TEACHER to TEACHER

COOPERATIVE LEARNING TIP  I find that children can answer the questions in this lesson by thinking silently, then sharing their answers, estimations, or methods with a partner. More children have a chance to talk if each partner then reports to another pair what the *other child* said instead of reporting back to the class. When estimations or methods differ, the members in each group of four discuss how different situations demand different responses.

For Students Acquiring English (SAE)

Scan the pages for vocabulary that may be new to SAE children. Introduce new words by using visuals, gestures, and body movements to convey meaning. Ask questions frequently to check comprehension. Demonstrate the first problem on page 65 with real beans and jars to introduce the idea of determining **about how many.** Use synonyms such as **almost as many** or **nearly** to make sure SAE children understand.

■ **What does Tanya need to find?** [She needs to find how many are in the second jar.]

■ **How will she find the answer?** [She will compare the marbles in both jars.]

Have children describe what they see when they compare the two jars. Guide them to see that the second jar has a little less in it than the jar with 68 marbles.

■ **Is a "little less" than 68 about 10, about 50 or about 100?** [about 50]

Encourage children to explain other ways to solve this problem.

Check for Understanding

■ **If the second jar had about 100 marbles in it, how would the picture of the second jar change?** [It would look fuller.]

GUIDED PRACTICE   ex. 1–2: Work through problem 1 with the children. Make sure they understand how to solve the problem by using number sense.

Page 66   Help children read the problems as necessary.

3 PRACTICE•APPLY   PRACTICE   ex. 1–4

C L O S E   Guide children to summarize the lesson:

■ **How do you know, just by looking, if one group is larger or smaller than another?** [Possible response: If the group looks smaller, it has less; if it looks larger, it has more.]

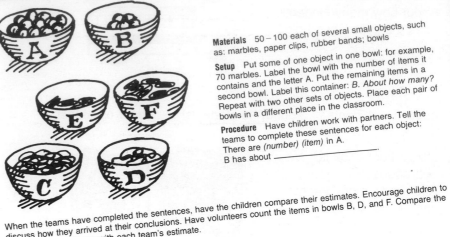

WRITING MATHEMATICS ■ ABOUT TO COUNT

MAC Activity 48

On Your Own Pair and Share In a Group

Materials 50 – 100 each of several small objects, such as: marbles, paper clips, rubber bands; bowls

Setup Put some of one object in one bowl: for example, 70 marbles. Label the bowl with the number of items it contains and the letter A. Put the remaining items in a second bowl. Label this container: *B. About how many?* Repeat with two other sets of objects. Place each pair of bowls in a different place in the classroom.

Procedure Have children work with partners. Tell the teams to complete these sentences for each object:
There are *(number) (item)* in A.
B has about _____

When the teams have completed the sentences, have the children compare their estimates. Encourage children to discuss how they arrived at their conclusions. Have volunteers count the items in bowls B, D, and F. Compare the actual number of items with each team's estimate.

▲
**MAC Activity 48:
Average-to-Challenge**

ESTIMATION ■ BRIEF ENCOUNTERS

MAC Activity 47

On Your Own Pair and Share In a Group

Materials counters or punchout counters, two plates, a cloth or scarf

Prepare groups of counters as indicated and cover them with a cloth. Uncover each display for five to ten seconds for children to see. Then have children answer the questions.

1. Which plate has more? [Plate 2]
2. Plate 1 has 8 counters on it. Does Plate 2 have about 10, about 20, or about 40 counters on it? [about 40]

1. Which plate has fewer counters? [Plate 2]
2. Plate 2 has 20 counters. Does Plate 1 have about 10, about 50, or about 60 counters? [about 50]

Plate 1: 8 counters Plate 2: 35 counters

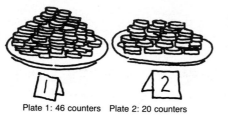

Plate 1: 46 counters Plate 2: 20 counters

Continue the activity with similar problems.

▲
**MAC Activity 47:
Basic-to-Average**

RETEACHING-24

Name

PROBLEM SOLVING STRATEGY: USING NUMBER SENSE

Study

← about 20 balloons

| 12 balloons | more than 12 balloons |

Check

Ring more or fewer.
Then ring about how many.

1.

18 books   more   (fewer)

(about 10 books)
about 20 books

2.

48 pretzels   more   (fewer)

about 10 pretzels
(about 20 pretzels)

3.

5 shirts   (more)   fewer

about 10 shirts
(about 20 shirts)

Macmillan/McGraw-Hill MATHEMATICS IN ACTION
Grade 2, Chapter 2, Lesson 9, pages 65–66   Reteaching-24

PRACTICE-24

Name

PROBLEM SOLVING STRATEGY: USING NUMBER SENSE

Ring about how many.

1. There are 65 bananas in the first bunch. About how many bananas are in the other bunch?

about 15 bananas
(about 30 bananas)
about 55 bananas

2. There are 48 apples on the first tree. About how many apples are on the other tree?

about 30 apples
about 40 apples
(about 90 apples)

3. There are 37 seeds in the first slice. About how many watermelon seeds are in the other slice?

(about 15 seeds)
about 45 seeds
about 60 seeds

4. There are 62 berries on the first bush. About how many are on the other bush?

about 60 berries
(about 80 berries)
about 200 berries

Macmillan/McGraw-Hill, MATHEMATICS IN ACTION
Grade 2, Chapter 2, Lesson 9, pages 65–66   Practice-24

ENRICHMENT-24

Name

PROBLEM SOLVING

On Your Own   Pair and Share   In a Group

A-MAZING DOGS

Color the tee shirts.
Match each child to his or her pet.
Color the dog's dish to match its owner's shirt.
Follow the maze paths to match the children to their pets.

Lines will vary.

My dog weighs 15 pounds.   My dog weighs 15 pounds.   My dog weighs 60 pounds.

Red   Blue   Green

blue   green   red

Macmillan/McGraw-Hill, MATHEMATICS IN ACTION
Grade 2, Chapter 2, Lesson 9, pages 65–66   Enrichment-24

Problem of the Day

Barry is making 10 model cars. He needs 4 wheels for each car. Wheels come in bags of 20, 50, and 100. Which bag or bags should he buy?
[2 bags of 20]

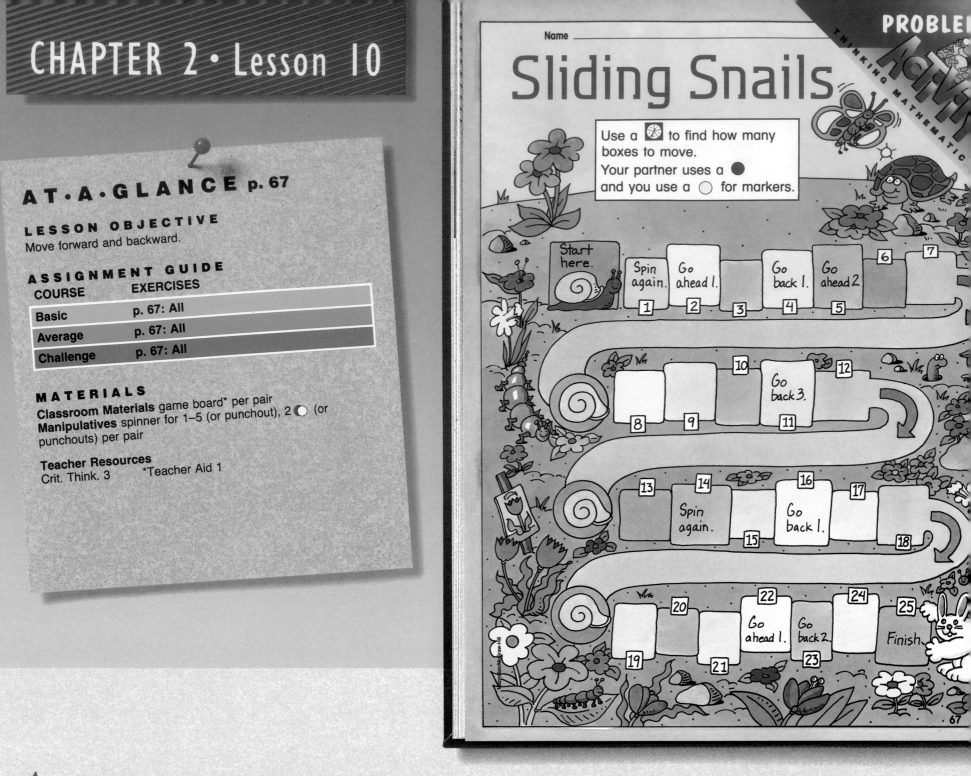

AT·A·GLANCE p. 67

LESSON OBJECTIVE
Move forward and backward.

ASSIGNMENT GUIDE

COURSE	EXERCISES
Basic	p. 67: All
Average	p. 67: All
Challenge	p. 67: All

MATERIALS
Classroom Materials game board* per pair
Manipulatives spinner for 1–5 (or punchout), 2 ⬤ (or punchouts) per pair

Teacher Resources
Crit. Think. 3   *Teacher Aid 1

Sliding Snails

Use a 🕸 to find how many boxes to move.
Your partner uses a ⬤ and you use a ◯ for markers.

PLAN

AIMS AND ATTITUDES This lesson develops number sense through the skill of number recognition. It also develops the skill of following directions through the use of a simple game.

Emphasize the need for cooperation and following rules when playing games with other people.

MANAGEMENT The activity is intended for all children and has been designed for pairs of children. Pairing a child having strong mathematical and language skills with one having weaker skills may be particularly effective.

You may wish to prepare Teacher Aid 1 (Game Board) for use with the activity in the **EXTEND** section of this lesson. Number each box from 1–21 and label some of the boxes with "Spin again," "Go back

2," "Go ahead 2," and so on, as shown on the game board on page 67.

GUIDE

Model the activity before beginning the page. Draw a number line for 0–25 on the chalkboard.

■ **If we start at 0 and move ahead 5, on what number do we end?** [5]

■ **If we move ahead another 5, on what number do we end?** [10]

■ **If we start at 0 and move ahead 3, on what number do we end?** [3]

■ **If we move back 5 from 13, on what number do we end?** [8]

Continue moving ahead or back from 1 to 5 numbers.

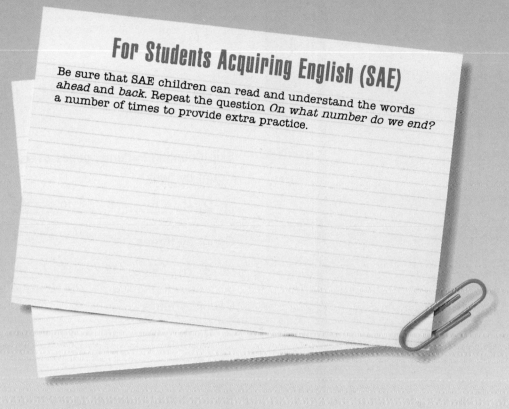

For Students Acquiring English (SAE)

Be sure that SAE children can read and understand the words *ahead* and *back*. Repeat the question *On what number do we end?* a number of times to provide extra practice.

■ **How is moving ahead or back like adding and subtracting?** [Moving ahead is like counting on to add; moving back is like counting back to subtract.]

Read the directions on page 67 with the children. Point out the rebus symbols for the spinner and counters.

■ **How do you know how many boxes to move your counter?** [Spin the spinner and then move the counter the same number of boxes that are shown on the spinner.]

Assign children to work in pairs. Give each pair a spinner and one red and one yellow counter. Remind children to place their counters on the Start box of the game board and then take turns using the spinner.

3 EXTEND Provide pairs of children with a game board (Teacher Aid 1) that you have prepared (see **Management** of the **PLAN** section). It should be similar to the one on page 67. Using the spinner, counters, and the directions on the game board, have pairs play the game again.

EXTRA PRACTICE

Extra Practice items are provided so that children may have an opportunity for further practice.

The *Additional Practice* section also provides practice you may wish to assign.

Extra Practice

Order to 100, page 59

1. What number comes just after?	2. What number comes just before?	3. What number comes between?
17, __18__	__30__, 31	59, __60__, 61
46, __47__	__85__, 86	74, __75__, 76
69, __70__	__99__, 100	88, __89__, 90

Skip Counting Patterns, pages 61–62

Count by twos.

1. 2, 4, __6__, __8__, __10__, __12__, **14**, __16__, __18__, __20__

Count by threes.

2. 3, 6, __9__, __12__, __15__, __18__, **21**, __24__, __27__, __30__

Count by fours.

3. 4, 8, __12__, __16__, __20__, __24__, **28**, __32__, __36__, __40__

Even and Odd Numbers, pages 63–64

Complete.   Write *even* or *odd*.

1. 10, 12, __14__, __16__, __18__, __20__   even

2. 14, 16, __18__, __20__, __22__, __24__   even

3. 13, 15, __17__, __19__, __21__, __23__   odd

68   sixty-eight

ADDITIONAL PRACTICE

p. 59 *Write the number that comes just after.*

1. 19, [20]   41, [42]
   55, [56]   37, [38]
   72, [73]   97, [98]

Write the number that comes just before.

2. [23], 24   [12], 13
   [46], 47   [87], 88

Write the number that comes between.

3. 31, [32], 33   27, [28], 29
   66, [67], 68   42, [43], 44
   94, [95], 96   78, [79], 80
   53, [54], 55   90, [91], 92
   81, [82], 83   60, [61], 62
   15, [16], 17   15, [16], 17

p. 61

Count by twos.

1. 16, 18, 20, [22] , [24] , [26] , [28]

Count by threes.

2. 30, 33, 36, [39] , [42] , [45] , [48]

Count by fours.

3. 40, 44, 48, [52] , [56] , [60] , [64]

p. 63 *Complete. Then write* even *or* odd.

1. 14, 16, 18, [20] , [22] , [24] [even]

2. 1, 3, 5, [7] , [9] , [11] [odd]

3. 35, 37, 39, [41] , [43] , [45] [odd]

4. 48, 50, 52, [54] , [56] , [58] [even]

AT·A·GLANCE pp. 69-70

LESSON OBJECTIVE
Look for patterns to solve problems.

ASSIGNMENT GUIDE

COURSE	EXERCISES
Basic	p. 69: 1–3; p. 70: 1–4
Average	p. 69: 1–3; p. 70: 1–4
Challenge	p. 69: 1–3; p. 70: 1–4
Extra Practice, p. 83	

Teacher Resources
Reteaching 25 Practice 25 Enrichment 25
Prob. Solv. 7 MAC Act. 49, 50

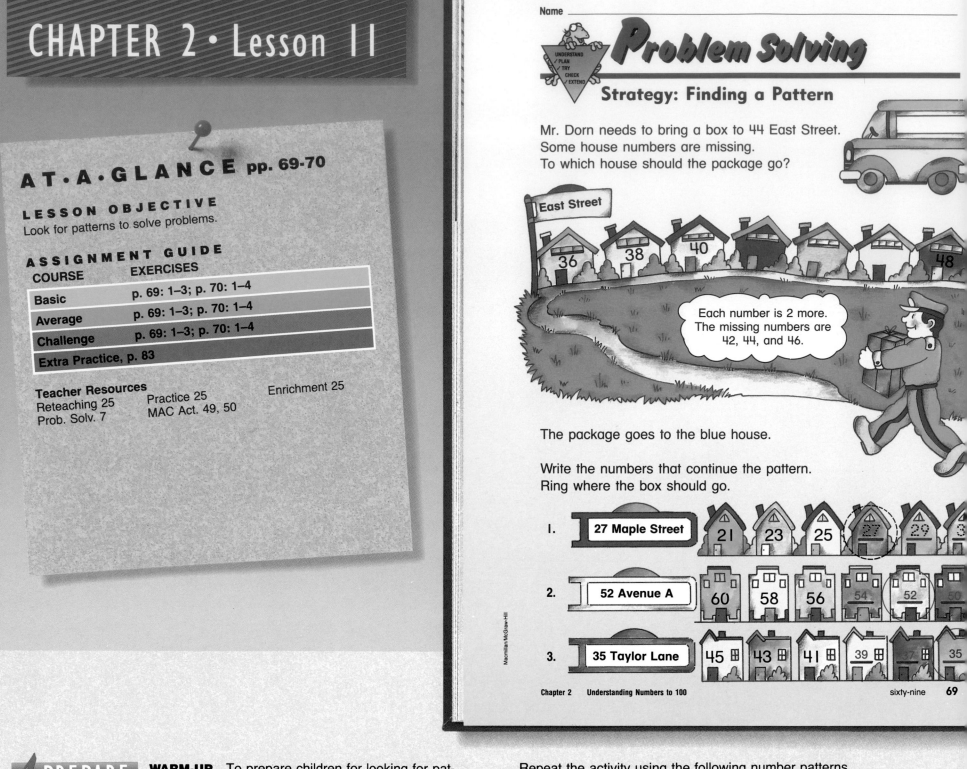

Name _____

Problem Solving

Strategy: Finding a Pattern

Mr. Dorn needs to bring a box to 44 East Street.
Some house numbers are missing.
To which house should the package go?

East Street

36 38 40 48

Each number is 2 more. The missing numbers are 42, 44, and 46.

The package goes to the blue house.

Write the numbers that continue the pattern.
Ring where the box should go.

1. **27 Maple Street**   21 23 25 27 29

2. **52 Avenue A**   60 58 56 54 52 50

3. **35 Taylor Lane**   45 43 41 39 37 35

Chapter 2   Understanding Numbers to 100   sixty-nine **69**

PREPARE **WARM-UP** To prepare children for looking for patterns to solve problems, have them skip-count by twos, fives, threes, and fours from 1 to 30.

TEACH **QUESTIONING** On the chalkboard, write the number **pattern** shown below.

4 6 8 10 [12] [14] 16

Have a volunteer read the numbers aloud.

■ **What do we know about the numbers?** [Each one is 2 more than the one before. They form a pattern.]

■ **How can we figure out the missing numbers?** [Possible response: Count by twos from 10.]

Repeat the activity using the following number patterns.

21 19 17 15 [13] [11]
3 6 9 [12] [15] 18

PUPIL'S EDITION pp. 69-70

Page 69 Have a volunteer read the problem at the top of the page.

■ **What do you need to do?** [Find the house where each package should go.]

Have children look at the numbers on the houses and read them aloud.

■ **What could you do to find the missing numbers?** [Look for a pattern in the given numbers.]

Look for a pattern.
Write the missing numbers.

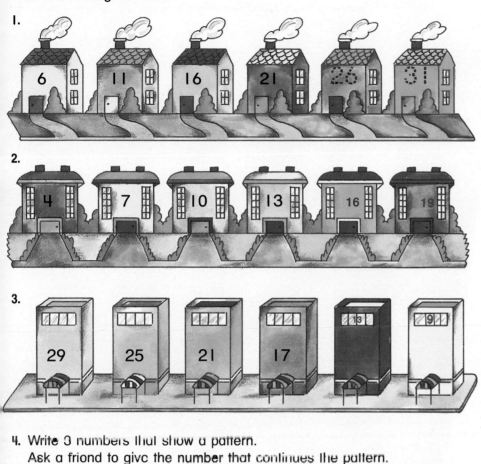

1. 6 11 16 21 26 31

2. 4 7 10 13 16 19

3. 29 25 21 17 13 9

4. Write 3 numbers that show a pattern.
Ask a friend to give the number that continues the pattern.

Answers will vary.

Extra Practice, page 83

Guide children to discover the pattern and figure out the missing numbers. Then read aloud the remaining text to confirm children's responses.

■ **What did you learn?** [Possible response: You can solve a problem by finding a pattern.]

Encourage children to explain other ways to solve this problem.

Check for Understanding

■ **What house number would follow 48?** [50]

GUIDED PRACTICE ex. 1–3: Work through problem 1 with the children. Make sure they understand how to solve the problem by looking for a pattern.

TEACHER to TEACHER

COOPERATIVE LEARNING TIP 👥 When discussing ways of finding patterns, I ask my children to practice the cooperative skills of **attentive listening, restating** what someone else says in their own words, or **encouraging participation.** We talk about the patterns we develop in talking to others and how these need to grow for cooperative work. For the Close segment, I ask students to number off in their groups. Then I roll a number cube to choose a reporter from each group to give the group's conclusions or an example of how someone has used one of the cooperative skills.

For Students Acquiring English (SAE)

As children warm up by skip counting, display a number line and point out the numbers as they say them. Scan the pages for vocabulary that may be new to SAE children. Introduce new words by using visuals, gestures, and body movements to convey meaning. Ask questions frequently to check comprehension.

Page 70 Have a volunteer read the directions at the top of the page. Remind children to be sure they have figured out the pattern before writing the missing numbers. Discuss the problems as necessary.

3 PRACTICE•APPLY PRACTICE ex. 1–4

CLOSE Guide children to summarize the lesson:

■ **How can you find a number pattern?** [Look at the numbers that are given and find the differences between the numbers.]

MAC ACTIVITY CENTER

MAC Activity 49:
Basic-to-Average
▼

MAC Activity 49

On Your Own   Pair and Share   In a Group

MATH AND ART ▪ NUMBERS AND SHAPES

Materials pattern blocks or punchout pattern blocks, crayons, drawing paper, index cards

Setup Write the numbers 2, 3, 4, and 5 on index cards. Make a set for each pair of children.

Procedure Assign children to work in pairs. Provide them with a set of number cards and pattern blocks. Tell children to lay the cards facedown. One partner draws a number and then creates a pattern with the pattern blocks using that number. For example, if the number is 2, the children might place 2 squares, 2 triangles, 2 squares, 2 triangles in a row. The other partner uses pattern blocks to continue the pattern, then guesses the number. The second partner then takes a turn drawing a number and creating a pattern.

Children may continue this activity by copying each pattern they make using crayons.

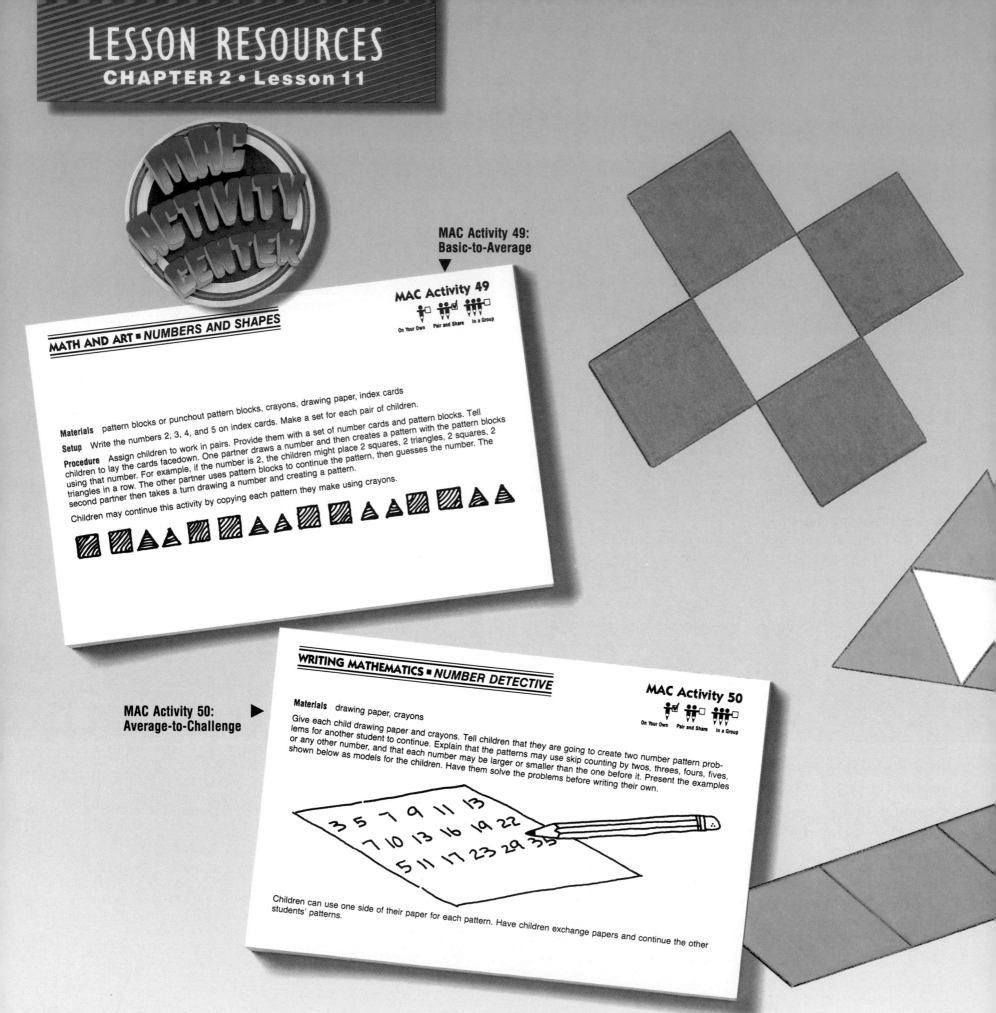

MAC Activity 50:
Average-to-Challenge ▶

MAC Activity 50

On Your Own   Pair and Share   In a Group

WRITING MATHEMATICS ▪ NUMBER DETECTIVE

Materials drawing paper, crayons

Give each child drawing paper and crayons. Tell children that they are going to create two number pattern problems for another student to continue. Explain that the patterns may use skip counting by twos, threes, fours, fives, or any other number, and that each number may be larger or smaller than the one before it. Present the examples shown below as models for the children. Have them solve the problems before writing their own.

Children can use one side of their paper for each pattern. Have children exchange papers and continue the other students' patterns.

RETEACHING

Name

PROBLEM SOLVING STRATEGY: FINDING A PATTERN

Study

Find the missing numbers on the mailboxes.

27 30 33 □ □ 42

Use the number line to help you find a pattern.

27 28 29 30 31 32 33 34 35 36 37 38 39 40 41 42

Each number is 3 more. 36 and 39 are missing.

Check

Write the missing numbers.
Ring the pattern.

1. 25 30 35 40 45 50

(5 more) 5 less

2. 39 35 31 27 23

5 less (4 less)

3. 17 15 13 11 9

(2 less) 0 less

PRACTICE

Name

PROBLEM SOLVING STRATEGY: FINDING A PATTERN

Look for a pattern.
Write the missing numbers.
Ring the house where each person lives.

1. 47 B Lane — 51 49 47 45 43 41

2. 33 C Street — 13 18 23 28 33 38

Continue the pattern.
Write the missing numbers.

3. 60 64 68 72 76 80

4. 38 35 32 29 26 23

5. 53 55 57 59 61 63

ENRICHMENT

Name

PROBLEM SOLVING

On Your Own Pair and Share In a Group

PATHWAYS

Find the way out.
Look for a pattern.
Continue the path with your pencil.
What is the pattern? counting by twos

START

12	14	16	21	29
15	19	18	25	30
11	12	20	22	36
43	45	33	24	39
32	30	28	26	43
34	50	53	31	35
36	38	40	42	44
47	55	51	49	46
56	59	60	63	48

END

Problem of the Day

There are 6 stores on Vine Street. The numbers begin at 39. The number on each store is 2 more than the last number. What is the number of the last store on the street? [49; since there are 6 stores and each number is 2 more, the store numbers are 39, 41, 43, 45, 47, 49.]

LESSON OBJECTIVES

Read tally marks.
Complete a bar graph.
Read and interpret graphs.

ASSIGNMENT GUIDE

COURSE	EXERCISES
Basic	p. 71: 1–4; p. 72: 1–5
Average	p. 71: 1–4; p. 72: 1–5
Challenge	p. 71: 1–4; p. 72: 1–5

MATERIALS

Classroom Materials crayons

Teacher Resources
Reteaching 26   Practice 26   Enrichment 26
MAC Act. 51, 52
Computer Software *Graphs, Stat. and Prob.*: Exploration 1

SKILLS TRACE
NUMBERS TO 100

Explore (Concrete) 52	Develop/Understand (Transitional/Abstract) 53–54, 55–56, 57–58, 59, 60, 61–62, 63–64, 71–72, 73–74, 75–76, 77–78
Practice 68, 83, 84, 85–86, 89, 98, 136	Apply 65–66, 69–70, 82, 88, 90

Name _____

Graphs

These **tallies** tell how many games four soccer teams won.

Tallies
| = 1   ⊮⊬⊬ =5

1. Write the number for each team.

Eagles ⊬⊬⊬ ⊬⊬⊬   **10**

Lions ⊬⊬⊬ ⊬⊬⊬ ⊬⊬⊬ ⊬⊬⊬   20

Bears ⊬⊬⊬ ⊬⊬⊬ ⊬⊬⊬ ⊬⊬⊬ ⊬⊬⊬   25

Tigers ⊬⊬⊬ ⊬⊬⊬ ⊬⊬⊬   15

GAMES WON (bar graph with Games axis 0–40, Teams: Eagles, Lions, Bears, Tigers)

2. Color the **bar graph** to show how many games the teams won.

3. Which bar is the tallest? Why? The Bears Team bar is tallest because 25 is higher on the graph than 20, 15, or 10.

4. Which bar is the shortest? Why? The Eagles Team bar is shortest because 10 is lower on the graph than 15, 20, or 25.

Macmillan/McGraw-Hill

 **PREPARE** **WARM-UP** To prepare children for reading graphs, write the following numbers on the chalkboard.

5 10 15 20 25 30 35 40 45 50
    1   2   3   4   5   6   7   8   9 10

Point to each row and have children count aloud. Ask children to describe how they counted. [by fives and by ones]

TEACH **DISCUSSING** Ask four boys and four girls to form a line in the front of the class. Write the following on the chalkboard.

Boys   Girls

Have that group of children walk past you and then sit down. As each child passes make a tally mark (/) in the appropriate column. Explain that each one of the marks shown on the board is called a tally mark.

■ **How many marks are shown in each column?** [4]

Next call on one more girl and one more boy to walk past you. Show children how to indicate the fifth child by drawing a diagonal line through four lines. Have children read the tally marks as 5.

Discuss with children that tallying is one way to list information.

■ **How could you show the information on the chalkboard another way?** [Help children realize that they could make a graph.]

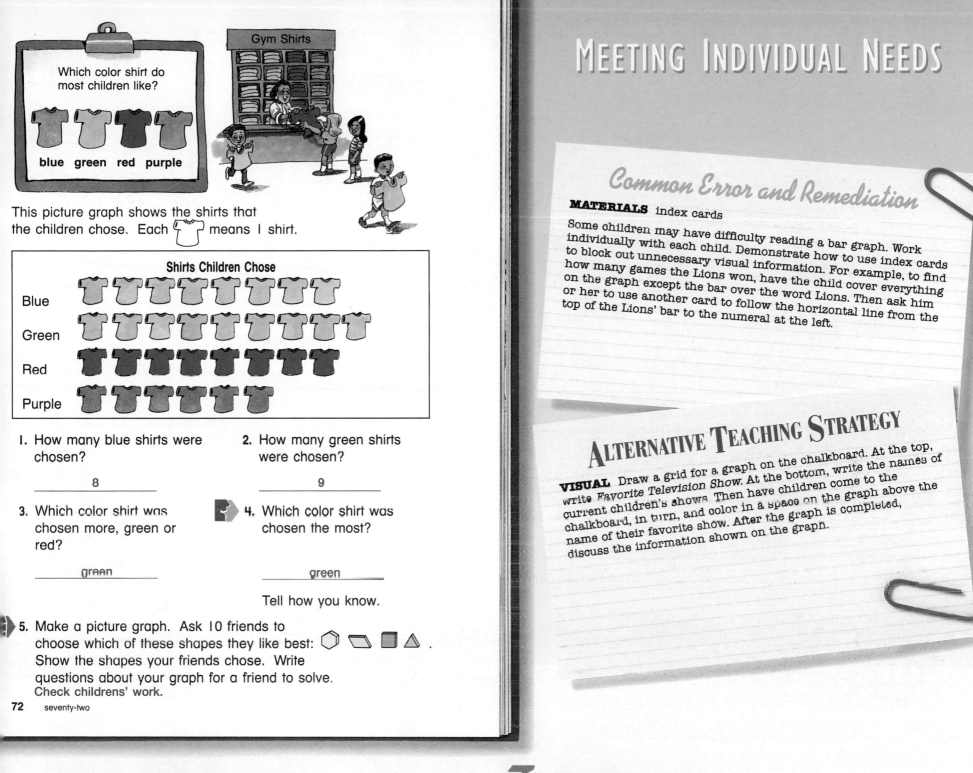

Which color shirt do most children like?

Gym Shirts

blue green red purple

This picture graph shows the shirts that the children chose. Each 👕 means 1 shirt.

Shirts Children Chose

Blue

Green

Red

Purple

1. How many blue shirts were chosen?

_____8_____

2. How many green shirts were chosen?

_____9_____

3. Which color shirt was chosen more, green or red?

_____green_____

4. Which color shirt was chosen the most?

_____green_____

Tell how you know.

5. Make a picture graph. Ask 10 friends to choose which of these shapes they like best: ⬡ ▱ ◻ △ . Show the shapes your friends chose. Write questions about your graph for a friend to solve.
Check childrens' work.

Common Error and Remediation

MATERIALS index cards

Some children may have difficulty reading a bar graph. Work individually with each child. Demonstrate how to use index cards to block out unnecessary visual information. For example, to find how many games the Lions won, have the child cover everything on the graph except the bar over the word Lions. Then ask him or her to use another card to follow the horizontal line from the top of the Lions' bar to the numeral at the left.

ALTERNATIVE TEACHING STRATEGY

VISUAL Draw a grid for a graph on the chalkboard. At the top, write Favorite Television Show. At the bottom, write the names of current children's shows. Then have children come to the chalkboard, in turn, and color in a space on the graph above the name of their favorite show. After the graph is completed, discuss the information shown on the graph.

PUPIL'S EDITION pp. 71-72

Page 71 Discuss the tallies and the graph with the children.

Check for Understanding

■ **Why is the bar for the Eagles colored up to 10?** [because they won 10 games]

GUIDED PRACTICE   ex. 1–4: For reteaching, use Common Error and Remediation or Alternative Strategy.

Page 72 Discuss the picture graph with the children.

■ **Which color shirts are shown on the graph?** [blue, green, red, purple]

3 PRACTICE•APPLY   PRACTICE   ex. 1–5

CLOSE Guide children to summarize the lesson:

■ **Which kind of graphs can you use to show information?** [picture graphs and bar graphs]

MATH AND SCIENCE ▪ SPEEDY ANIMALS

On Your Own   Pair and Share   In a Group

Write the following data on a sheet of paper and dupli-cate a copy for each pair of children.

	Animal	Miles Per Hour
AIR	pigeon	60
	monarch butterfly	20
	honeybee	10
LAND	cheetah	70
	jackrabbit	45
	ostrich	30
WATER	flying fish	40
	dolphin	35
	trout	15

Assign children to work in pairs. Tell children that they are going to find out how fast animals move on land, in water, or in the air, and then record their findings on a bar graph.

Explain that each pair of children will choose one of the categories: land, air, or water. Then each pair will work together to record the data on a bar graph. Encourage children to also write three questions about the information on their graphs for others to answer.

When completed, call on pairs to show and tell about their graphs and ask their questions.

NUMBER SENSE ▪ TAKE A SURVEY

MAC Activity 51

On Your Own   Pair and Share   In a Group

Assign children to work in small groups. Have each group take a survey to learn the different ways their class-mates come to school, such as by bus, bicycle, van, car, walking, or train.

Then have each group decide on how they would like to show their information: picture graph or bar graph. They should decide on the title, labels, pictures, and so on. Have children make their own graphs.

When the graphs are completed, call on each group, in turn, to show and tell about their graph.

▲ MAC Activity 52:
Average-to-Challenge

▲
MAC Activity 51:
Basic-to-Average

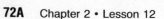

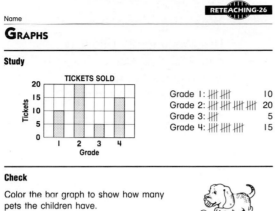

Name _____

GRAPHS

Study

TICKETS SOLD

Grade 1: ⵣⵣ ⵣⵣ	10
Grade 2: ⵣⵣ ⵣⵣ ⵣⵣ ⵣⵣ	20
Grade 3: ⵣⵣ	5
Grade 4: ⵣⵣ ⵣⵣ ⵣⵣ	15

Check

Color the bar graph to show how many pets the children have.

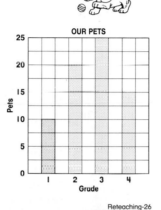

Grade 1
ⵣⵣ ⵣⵣ

Grade 2
ⵣⵣ ⵣⵣ ⵣⵣ ⵣⵣ

Grade 3
ⵣⵣ ⵣⵣ ⵣⵣ

Grade 4
ⵣⵣ ⵣⵣ ⵣⵣ

OUR PETS

Macmillan/McGraw-Hill, MATHEMATICS IN ACTION
Grade 2, Chapter 2, Lesson 12, pages 71–72

Reteaching-26

Name _____

GRAPHS

Color the bar graph to show how many children ride the bus to school.

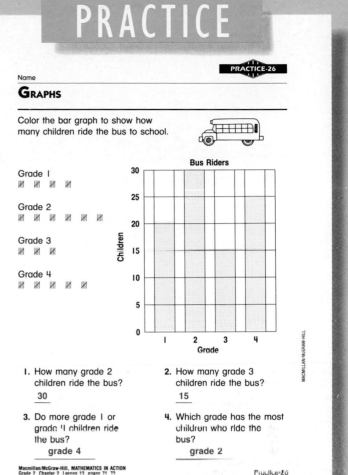

Grade 1
ⵣⵣ ⵣⵣ ⵣⵣ ⵣⵣ

Grade 2
ⵣⵣ ⵣⵣ ⵣⵣ ⵣⵣ ⵣⵣ ⵣⵣ

Grade 3
ⵣⵣ ⵣⵣ ⵣⵣ

Grade 4
ⵣⵣ ⵣⵣ ⵣⵣ ⵣⵣ

Bus Riders

1. How many grade 2 children ride the bus?
   30

2. How many grade 3 children ride the bus?
   15

3. Do more grade 1 or grade 4 children ride the bus?
   grade 4

4. Which grade has the most children who ride the bus?
   grade 2

Macmillan/McGraw-Hill, MATHEMATICS IN ACTION
Grade 2, Chapter 2, Lesson 12, pages 71–72

Practice-26

Name _____

GRAPHS

On Your Own   Pair and Share   In a Group

MAKE MINE JUICE

Ask 20 people which juice they like best.
Make a tally for each person.

apple _____

grape _____

orange _____

pineapple _____

Use the tallies to make a graph.
Let 🧍 = 2 people.
How would you show 1 person? _____

Favorite Juice

apple	Graphs will vary.
grape	
orange	
pineapple	

Macmillan/McGraw-Hill, MATHEMATICS IN ACTION
Grade 2, Chapter 2, Lesson 12, pages 71–72

Enrichment-26

Problem of the Day

Barry was reading a bar graph. It showed that 25 children rode the bus to school. It also showed that 15 children walked to school. Which bar on the graph was shorter, *Bus* or *Walked*? [*Walked*]

AT·A·GLANCE pp. 73-74

LESSON OBJECTIVE
Compare numbers.

ASSIGNMENT GUIDE

COURSE	EXERCISES
Basic	p. 73: 2–6; p. 74: 1–4, Mixed Review
Average	p. 73: 2–6; p. 74: 1–4, Mixed Review
Challenge	p. 73: 2–6; p. 74: 1–4, Mixed Review

MATERIALS

Manipulatives 9 T, 9 O models (or punchouts), Workmat 2 per pair

Teacher Resources
Reteaching 27   Practice 27   Enrichment 27
Prob. Solv. 8   MAC Act. 53, 54

SKILLS TRACE
NUMBERS TO 100

Explore (Concrete)	Develop/Understand (Transitional/Abstract)
52	53–54, 55–56, 57–58, 59, 60, 61–62, 63–64, 71–72, 73–74, 75–76, 77–78
Practice	**Apply**
68, 83, 84, 85–86, 89, 98, 136	65–66, 69–70, 82, 88, 90

See **MANIPULATIVES PLUS 14**, p. 50N.

1 PREPARE **WARM-UP** To prepare children for comparing numbers, read the following numbers aloud, pausing after each. Have volunteers tell the number that is one more. Repeat the activity by having children say the number that is one less.

1. 43 [44] [42]	**2.** 56 [57] [55]	**3.** 70 [71] [69]
4. 91 [92] [90]	**5.** 29 [30] [28]	**6.** 14 [15] [13]

2 TEACH **MODELING** Have children work in pairs with tens and ones models and Workmat 2. Ask them to model 32 on the workmat and then model 25 below the 32. Explain to children that they are going to compare the two numbers to find which

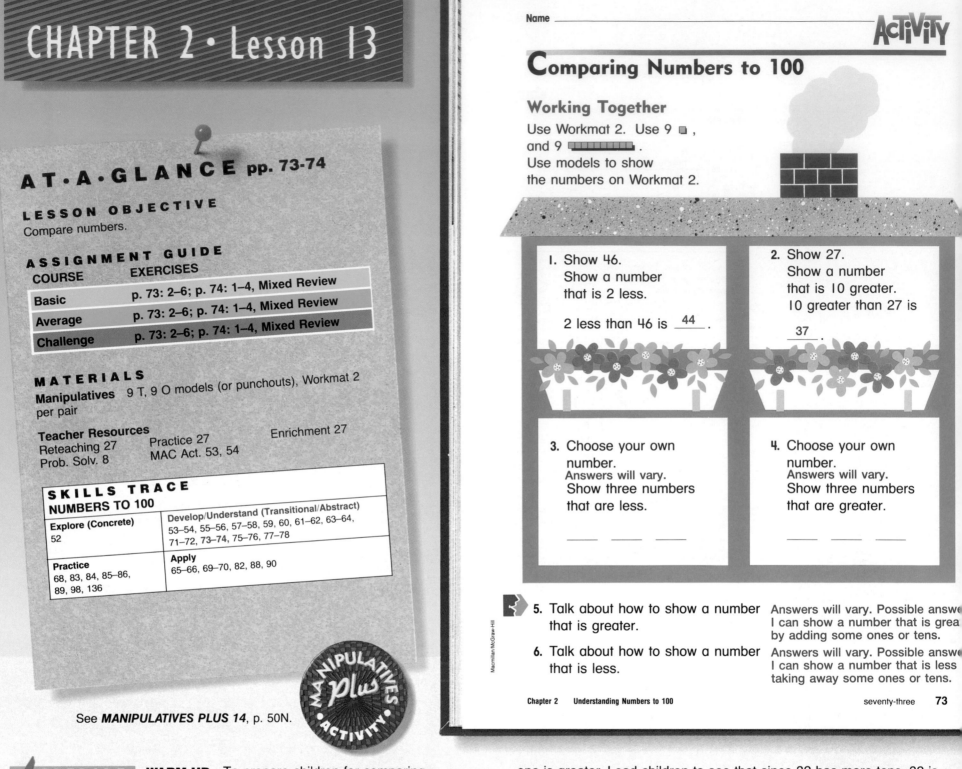

Name _____

ACTIVITY

Comparing Numbers to 100

Working Together

Use Workmat 2. Use 9 ▫ ,
and 9 ▭▭▭▭▭ .
Use models to show
the numbers on Workmat 2.

1. Show 46.
   Show a number
   that is 2 less.

   2 less than 46 is __44__ .

2. Show 27.
   Show a number
   that is 10 greater.
   10 greater than 27 is

   __37__ .

3. Choose your own
   number.
   Answers will vary.
   Show three numbers
   that are less.

   ___ ___ ___

4. Choose your own
   number.
   Answers will vary.
   Show three numbers
   that are greater.

   ___ ___ ___

5. Talk about how to show a number that is greater.

   Answers will vary. Possible answe
   I can show a number that is grea
   by adding some ones or tens.

6. Talk about how to show a number that is less.

   Answers will vary. Possible answe
   I can show a number that is less
   taking away some ones or tens.

Chapter 2   Understanding Numbers to 100   seventy-three   73

Macmillan/McGraw-Hill

one is greater. Lead children to see that since 32 has more tens, 32 is **greater than** 25.

Next compare 48 and 46. After children decide that 46 and 48 have the same number of tens, have them compare the ones to find that 48 is greater than 46.

Repeat the activity to develop the concept of **less than.** Have children compare 19 and 23 and then 32 and 36.

PUPIL'S EDITION pp. 73-74

Page 73 ▪ Working Together Assign children to work in pairs. Guide them through ex. 1. Ask volunteers to explain how they modeled the number that is 2 less than 46.

Yoko and Tony counted the flowers.
Who counted more flowers? **Yoko**
How can you tell? **18 is greater than 16.**

Yoko	Tony
18	16

Ring the number that is greater.
Use models if you need to.   (18)   16

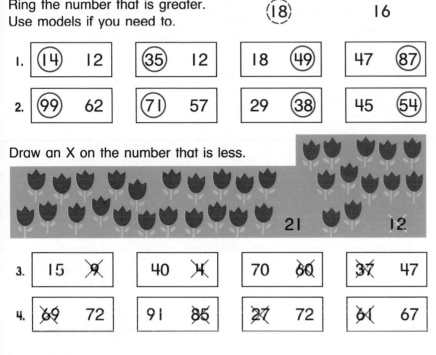

1. (14) 12   (35) 12   18 (49)   47 (87)

2. (99) 62   (71) 57   29 (38)   45 (54)

Draw an X on the number that is less.

21   12

3. | 15 ✗ | | 40 ✗ | | 70 ✗ | | ✗ 47 |

4. | ✗ 72 | | 91 ✗ | | ✗ 72 | | ✗ 67 |

Mixed Review ~~~~~~~~~~~~~~~~~~~~~~~~~~~

5. Complete.   84   9

      8 tens 4 ones   0 tens 9 ones

ACTIVITY Common Error and Remediation

MATERIALS 40

Some children may confuse **less than** and **greater than.** Work individually with each child. Tell the child he or she is going to compare 7 and 12. Have the child make a cube train for each number. Tell the child to compare the two trains and tell you which is shorter, which is longer. Relate this to less than and greater than. Repeat the activity with other numbers.

ONGOING ASSESSMENT

OBSERVATION Determine whether children used models correctly to show the numbers in the activity on p. 73.

INTERVIEW Show 3 T and 5 O models. **(1) What number does the model show? (2) How could you show a number that is 4 less? a number that is 10 more?**

JOURNAL WRITING You may wish to have children record their responses in their math journals.

ALTERNATIVE TEACHING STRATEGY

VISUAL Draw a number line on the chalkboard and write 14 and 23 below it.

Guide children in comparing the two numbers using the number line. Explain that the number that is closer to zero is always less than the other number. Have children compare 18 and 12, 25 and 23, 27 and 34. For the last pair of numbers, help children visualize where 34 would be on the number line.

Check for Understanding
■ **How would you show a number that is 2 more than the number on your workmat?** [Add 2 ones.]

GUIDED PRACTICE ex. 2–6: For reteaching, use Common Error and Remediation or Alternative Strategy.

Page 74 Ask a volunteer to explain how he or she decided which child, Yoko or Tony, has counted more flowers.

3 PRACTICE•APPLY **PRACTICE** ex. 1–4

C L O S E Guide children to summarize the lesson:
■ **Which number is less, 45 or 54?** [45]

MAC Activity 53:
Basic-to-Average
▼

MATH AND CONSUMERS • COMPARING PRICES

MAC Activity 53

On Your Own   Pair and Share   In a Group

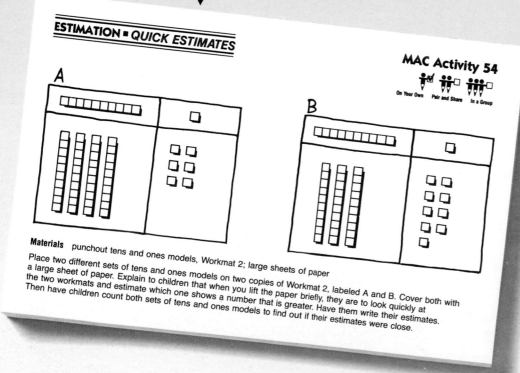

79¢

SOUP

Salad Dressing

59¢

Materials supermarket ads, scissors, paste

Ask children to look through supermarket ads and find two items priced under 99¢. Have them work in pairs to cut out the pictures or words, paste them on a sheet of paper, and write the price below each of them. Then ask children to write a sentence telling about the item whose price is greater.

MAC Activity 54:
Average-to-Challenge
▼

ESTIMATION • QUICK ESTIMATES

MAC Activity 54

On Your Own   Pair and Share   In a Group

A

B

Materials punchout tens and ones models, Workmat 2; large sheets of paper

Place two different sets of tens and ones models on two copies of Workmat 2, labeled A and B. Cover both with a large sheet of paper. Explain to children that when you lift the paper briefly, they are to look quickly at the two workmats and estimate which one shows a number that is greater. Have them write their estimates. Then have children count both sets of tens and ones models to find out if their estimates were close.

RETEACHING-27

Name

COMPARING NUMBERS TO 100

Study

34 is less than 46

46 is greater than 34

Check

Ring the number that is greater.

1. (28) 25

2. 53 (74)

3. | 21 (93) | 74 (76) | (40) 20 | 18 (81) |

Draw an X on the number that is less.

4. 4̶1̶ 51

5. 39 3̶8̶

6. | 75 6̶8̶ | 8̶4̶ 90 | 42 2̶4̶ | 5̶6̶ 66 |

Reteaching 27

Macmillan/McGraw-Hill, MATHEMATICS IN ACTION
Grade 2, Chapter 2, Lesson 13, pages 73–74

PRACTICE-27

Name

COMPARING NUMBERS TO 100

1. Ring the number that is greater.

46 (50)

2. Draw an X on the number that is less.

3̶2̶ 34

Ring the number that is greater.

3. | (17) 9 | 32 (83) | 45 (57) |

4. | (96) 69 | (46) 37 | 29 (65) |

5. | (20) 16 | (99) 88 | 18 (81) |

6. | 56 (57) | 45 (54) | (73) 64 |

Draw an X on the number that is less.

7. | 8̶ 14 | 91 8̶4̶ | 3̶9̶ 56 |

8. | 22 1̶6̶ | 5̶5̶ 66 | 6̶7̶ 83 |

9. | 95 5̶9̶ | 1̶2̶ 13 | 4̶1̶ 96 |

10. | 6̶3̶ 65 | 82 2̶8̶ | 99 9̶8̶ |

Practice 27

Macmillan/McGraw-Hill, MATHEMATICS IN ACTION
Grade 2, Chapter 2, Lesson 13, pages 73–74

ENRICHMENT-27

Name

COMPARING NUMBERS TO 100

On Your Own   Pair and Share   In a Group

WHAT'S THE QUESTION?

| 10 + 4 | 7 tens 3 ones | tens ones | 6 tens 9 ones |
| D | A | H | E |

| tens ones | 10 + 8 | tens ones | tens ones |
| H | M | S | T |

| 6 tens 7 ones | tens ones | 10 + 2 | |
| A | T | W | I |

| tens ones | tens ones | 3 tens 1 one | 5 tens 2 ones |
| N | O | S | E |

Look at the models and words.
Find the number that comes just before and just
after the number below. Write the letter.

W	thirteen	D	T	seventeen	M
H	47	O	H	51	E
A	68	E	I	72	A
T	thirty	S	S	thirty-four	N

Use the letters to write the question.

QUESTION: _____ What does this mean _____ ?

Enrichment-27

Macmillan/McGraw-Hill, MATHEMATICS IN ACTION
Grade 2, Chapter 2, Lesson 13, pages 73–74

Problem of the Day

Sharon scored 37 in her first bowling game. She
scored 20 more pins in her second game than
she did in her first game. Was her score for the
second game greater than or less than 50?
[Greater than; children may work it out this way:
skip count 47, 57; 57 > 50.]

AT·A·GLANCE pp. 75-76

LESSON OBJECTIVE
Compare numbers using the symbols < and >.

ASSIGNMENT GUIDE

COURSE	EXERCISES
Basic	p. 75: 2–6; p. 76: 1–5, Challenge
Average	p. 75: 2–6; p. 76: 1–5, Challenge
Challenge	p. 75: 2–6; p. 76: 1–5, Challenge
Extra Practice, p. 83	Practice Plus, p. 84

MATERIALS
Classroom Materials paste, scissors
Manipulatives stickers for p. 75 per child

Teacher Resources
Reteaching 28   Practice 28   Enrichment 28
MAC Act. 55, 56   Teacher Aid 11

SKILLS TRACE	
NUMBERS TO 100	
Explore (Concrete) 52	**Develop/Understand (Transitional/Abstract)** 53–54, 55–56, 57–58, 59, 60, 61–62, 63–64, 71–72, 73–74, **75–76**, 77–78
Practice 68, 83, 84, 85–86, 89, 98, 136	**Apply** 65–66, 69–70, 82, 88, 90

Name _____

Greater Than and Less Than

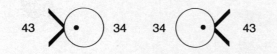

16 is **greater than** 13.
16 > 13

13 is **less than** 16.
13 < 16

Compare. Write > or <.

1. 23 (<) 33

2. 52 (>) 42

3. 35 (>) 28

4. 17 (<) 21

5. 37 (<) 38

6. 41 (<) 43

Macmillan/McGraw-Hill

 **PREPARE** **WARM-UP** Write these number pairs on the chalkboard: 53 and 35, 75 and 80, 46 and 49, and 39 and 41. Have children identify the number that is greater in each pair. [53, 80, 49, 41]

2 TEACH **DISCUSSING** Discuss comparing numbers as you draw the symbols < and > on the chalkboard and make them into duck bills. Tell children that these hungry ducks always eat the greater numbers. Use the following examples to demonstrate.

43 >•< 34   34 <•> 43

■ **Which number is each duck going to eat?** [43, or the greater number]

Write the words **greater than** and **less than** below the appropriate symbol for them. Have children read aloud each number sentence as 43 is greater than 34; 34 is less than 43. Continue with other number pairs.

PUPIL'S EDITION pp. 75-76

Page 75 Point out > and <, noting that these symbols are used when comparing numbers. Discuss the two examples and have the children read the sentences.

Compare. Write > or <.

1. 2 $<$ 9	6 $>$ 4	7 $>$ 3	9 $>$ 8
2. 7 $>$ 1	0 $<$ 3	6 $<$ 7	9 $>$ 4
3. 15 $>$ 5	9 $<$ 30	26 $>$ 8	21 $>$ 8
4. 31 $<$ 45	79 $>$ 66	55 $>$ 43	63 $<$ 88
5. 71 $>$ 68	60 $>$ 47	45 $<$ 54	87 $<$ 89

···· **Challenge** ···

Cut out the puzzle pieces at the bottom.
Decide where each piece belongs.
Then paste the pieces on.

Plan before you paste.

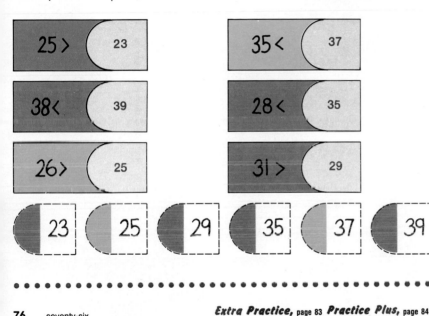

25 >	23
35 <	37
38 <	39
28 <	35
26 >	25
31 >	29

| 23 | 25 | 29 | 35 | 37 | 39 |

Extra Practice, page 83 **Practice Plus,** page 84

ACTIVITY ## ALTERNATIVE TEACHING STRATEGY

MATERIALS 4 T, 7 O models (or punchouts) per child

KINESTHETIC/VISUAL Tell children they are going to compare 27 and 32 as you write the two numbers on the chalkboard. Have children model each number and determine which number is greater. Then write 32 > 27 and 27 < 32. Discuss the meaning of the symbols and have children read the two sentences. Repeat the activity by comparing 46 and 43.

For Students Acquiring English (SAE)

Have children act out the duck story using real objects. For example, a duck could go to the bookcase and "eat" the shelf with the greatest number of books. Have SAE volunteers summarize the story.

ACTIVITY ## Common Error and Remediation

MATERIALS number cards for 1–20 (Teacher Aid 11); construction paper, blunt scissors, crayons

Some children may confuse the symbols < and >. Work individually with each child. Provide the child with, or help the child make, his or her own < or > symbol creature out of construction paper.

Display two number cards between 1 and 20. Have the child place the creature between the two numbers so that it is eating the larger number.

Check for Understanding

■ **Complete the sentences:**
   12 is _____ than 15.   [less]
   18 is _____ than 13.   [greater]

GUIDED PRACTICE   ex. 1–6: For reteaching, use Common Error and Remediation or Alternative Strategy.

Page 76   Remind children that > is always open to the greater number.

 **PRACTICE·APPLY**   PRACTICE   ex. 1–5

CHALLENGE   Explain that since there is more than one right answer for some of the problems, children must place all the puzzle pieces where they think the pieces belong before they paste or use stickers.

CLOSE   Guide children to summarize the lesson:

■ **How do you compare 51 and 49 to find which is greater?** [Possible response: Compare the tens. 51 has more tens than 49, so 51 is greater than 49.]

MAC Activity 55:
Basic-to-Average

MAC Activity 55

On Your Own   Pair and Share   In a Group

MATH AND ART ■ COMPARING CRITTERS

Materials construction paper, crayons, number cards (Teacher Aid 11)

Have children draw their own < or > animal on a sheet of construction paper. They should include the words *less than* or *greater than* in the names they give their animals, for example: *The Less-Than Dragon*. Then have them place number cards on either side of their < or > symbol to demonstrate its use. Display children's artwork, and have volunteers read the number sentences symbolized on each.

MAC Activity 56

On Your Own   Pair and Share   In a Group

MENTAL MATH ■ COMPARING SUMS AND DIFFERENCES

Write the following exercises on the chalkboard. Tell children that they are to compare the number to the addition or to the subtraction, and then write < or > in each circle.

1.	11 O	4 + 6 [>]
2.	9 OOOO	10 − 3 [>]
3.	6 OOOO	2 + 5 [<]
4.	8	5 + 4 [<]
5.	5 O	10 − 8 [>]

▲ MAC Activity 56:
Average-to-Challenge

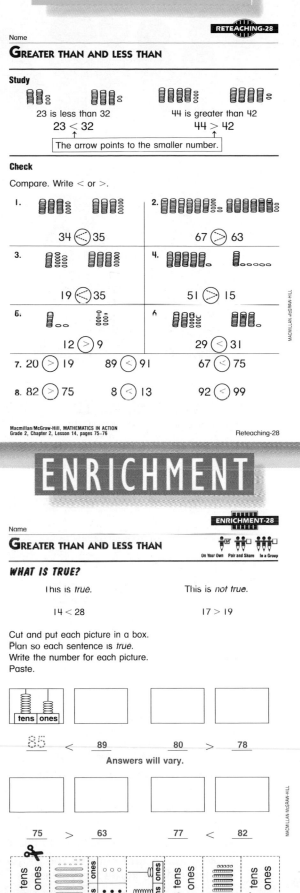

RETEACHING

RETEACHING-28

Name

GREATER THAN AND LESS THAN

Study

23 is less than 32   44 is greater than 42

23 < 32   44 > 42

The arrow points to the smaller number.

Check

Compare. Write < or >.

1. 34 (<) 35   2. 67 (>) 63

3. 19 (<) 35   4. 51 (>) 15

5. 12 (>) 9   6. 29 (<) 31

7. 20 (>) 19   89 (<) 91   67 (<) 75

8. 82 (>) 75   8 (<) 13   92 (<) 99

Macmillan/McGraw-Hill, MATHEMATICS IN ACTION
Grade 2, Chapter 2, Lesson 14, pages 75–76   Reteaching-28

PRACTICE

PRACTICE-28

Name

GREATER THAN AND LESS THAN

Compare. Write > or <.

1. 3 (<) 7   9 (>) 4   2 (<) 5
2. 7 (<) 16   18 (>) 8   21 (>) 7
3. 42 (>) 24   33 (<) 51   65 (<) 66
4. 89 (<) 90   47 (>) 42   38 (<) 83
5. 53 (>) 48   29 (<) 30   14 (<) 21
6. 50 (>) 45   99 (>) 89   75 (>) 57

Color numbers <50 green.
Color numbers >50 yellow.

84	62		80
19	51	75	39
47	82 y	43	
99	10	g 11	52
25	74	12	
42	83	53	41
98	67	72	

Macmillan/McGraw-Hill, MATHEMATICS IN ACTION
Grade 2, Chapter 2, Lesson 14, pages 75–76   Practice-28

ENRICHMENT

ENRICHMENT-28

Name

GREATER THAN AND LESS THAN

On Your Own   Pair and Share   In a Group

WHAT IS TRUE?

This is *true*.   This is *not true*.

14 < 28   17 > 19

Cut and put each picture in a box.
Plan so each sentence is *true*.
Write the number for each picture.
Paste.

tens	ones			

85 < 89   80 > 78

Answers will vary.

75 > 63   77 < 82

✂ | 8 tens 0 ones | tens ones | tens ones | 8 tens 9 ones | | 7 tens 8 ones |

Macmillan/McGraw-Hill, MATHEMATICS IN ACTION
Grade 2, Chapter 2, Lesson 14, pages 75–76   Enrichment-28

Problem of the Day

Rita scored 73, Tom scored 59, and Jeff scored 82 in their bowling game. Whose score was the greatest? [Jeff's] Whose score was the least? [Tom's]

AT·A·GLANCE pp. 77-78

LESSON OBJECTIVES
Identify ordinal position to 20.
Use ordinal numbers.

ASSIGNMENT GUIDE

COURSE	EXERCISES
Basic	p. 77: 1–2; p. 78: 1–4, Reasoning
Average	p. 77: 1–2; p. 78: 1–4, Reasoning
Challenge	p. 77: 1–2; p. 78: 1–4, Reasoning

MATERIALS
Classroom Materials large number cards for 1–10, blunt scissors, paste
Manipulatives stickers for p. 77 per child

Teacher Resources
Reteaching 29   Practice 29   Enrichment 29
MAC Act. 57, 58

SKILLS TRACE
NUMBERS TO 100

Explore (Concrete) 52	Develop/Understand (Transitional/Abstract) 53–54, 55–56, 57–58, 59, 60, 61–62, 63–64, 71–72, 73–74, 75–76, 77–78
Practice 68, 83, 84, 85–86, 89, 98, 136	Apply 65–66, 69–70, 82, 88, 90

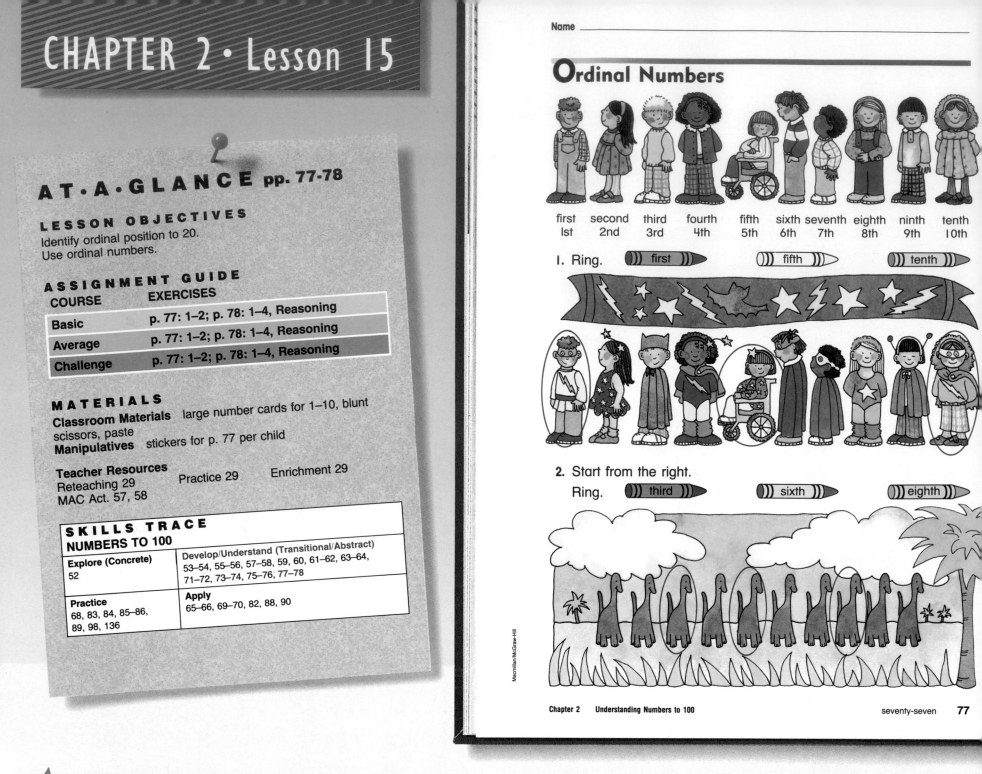

Name _____

Ordinal Numbers

| first 1st | second 2nd | third 3rd | fourth 4th | fifth 5th | sixth 6th | seventh 7th | eighth 8th | ninth 9th | tenth 10th |

I. Ring.   first   fifth   tenth

2. Start from the right.
Ring.   third   sixth   eighth

Chapter 2   Understanding Numbers to 100   seventy-seven   **77**

PREPARE   **WARM-UP**   To prepare children for work with ordinal numbers, place number cards for 1 to 10 in order along the chalkboard ledge. Have children read the numbers as ordered and then tell which number is first and which is last. Mix up the cards and repeat the activity.

TEACH   **DISCUSSING**   Have 5 children line up in the front of the room.

■ **Which child is first? second? third? fourth? fifth?**
Next tell children to face the other direction and repeat the questions. Discuss why the answers are different. Children should recognize that the first child became the last child and that the order of the children is different because the children changed direction. Repeat the activity using 10, 15, and 20 children.

PUPIL'S EDITION pp. 77-78

Page 77   Read the ordinal numbers aloud. Ask children to point to the first, fifth, eighth, and tenth child at the top of the page.

Check for Understanding
■ **How many people are standing in line if the ninth person is last?** [9]

GUIDED PRACTICE   ex. 1–2: For reteaching, use Common Error and Remediation or Alternative Strategy.

Page 78   Point to the picture of children entering the building.

■ **Why is the first child in the picture labeled eleventh?** [The first ten children are inside the building.]

eleventh 11th twelfth 12th thirteenth 13th fourteenth 14th

fifteenth 15th

first ten children are outside.

sixteenth 16th

seventeenth 17th

eighteenth 18th nineteenth 19th twentieth 20th

1. Which child is wearing a cap? **18th**

2. Which child is last in line? **20th**

3. Luis is eleventh in line.
How many children are ahead of him? **10**

4. What grade are you in? **2nd**

Reasoning

Cut and paste to make the totem pole.
The bird is first.
The bear is not second.
The turtle is above the bear.
The wolf is not third.

4th turtle

3rd bear

2nd wolf

1st bird

Extra Practice, page 83

ACTIVITY — Common Error and Remediation

MATERIALS 20 ◯; 20 number cards (Teacher Aid 11), ordinal-number cards through twentieth made from index cards

Some children may confuse the ordinal positions. Work individually with each child, using number cards, ordinal-number cards, and counters. Place 5 counters in a row. Have the child count and place a number card under each counter. Then ask the child to place the corresponding ordinal-number card under each counting number card. Repeat the activity using ordinal numbers to tenth, fifteenth, and twentieth.

ACTIVITY — ALTERNATIVE TEACHING STRATEGY

MATERIALS large ordinal-number/number-word cards for first to twentieth

VISUAL Stand ordinal-number cards for first to tenth on the chalkboard ledge in order. Have children read the numbers in unison. Then have them close their eyes while you remove a card. Have a volunteer tell which card is missing. Repeat the activity several times. Then place the cards for eleventh to twentieth one at a time on the ledge, as you read each number aloud. Have children read these numbers in unison. Repeat the activity of removing a card and having a volunteer tell which card is missing.

---

3 PRACTICE•APPLY PRACTICE ex. 1–4

REASONING Encourage children to plan how they will arrange their totem pole before doing any pasting or using stickers.

C L O S E Guide children to summarize the lesson:

■ **There are 20 children in line. Joe is sixth. How many people are in front of him?** [5] **How many people are behind him?** [14]

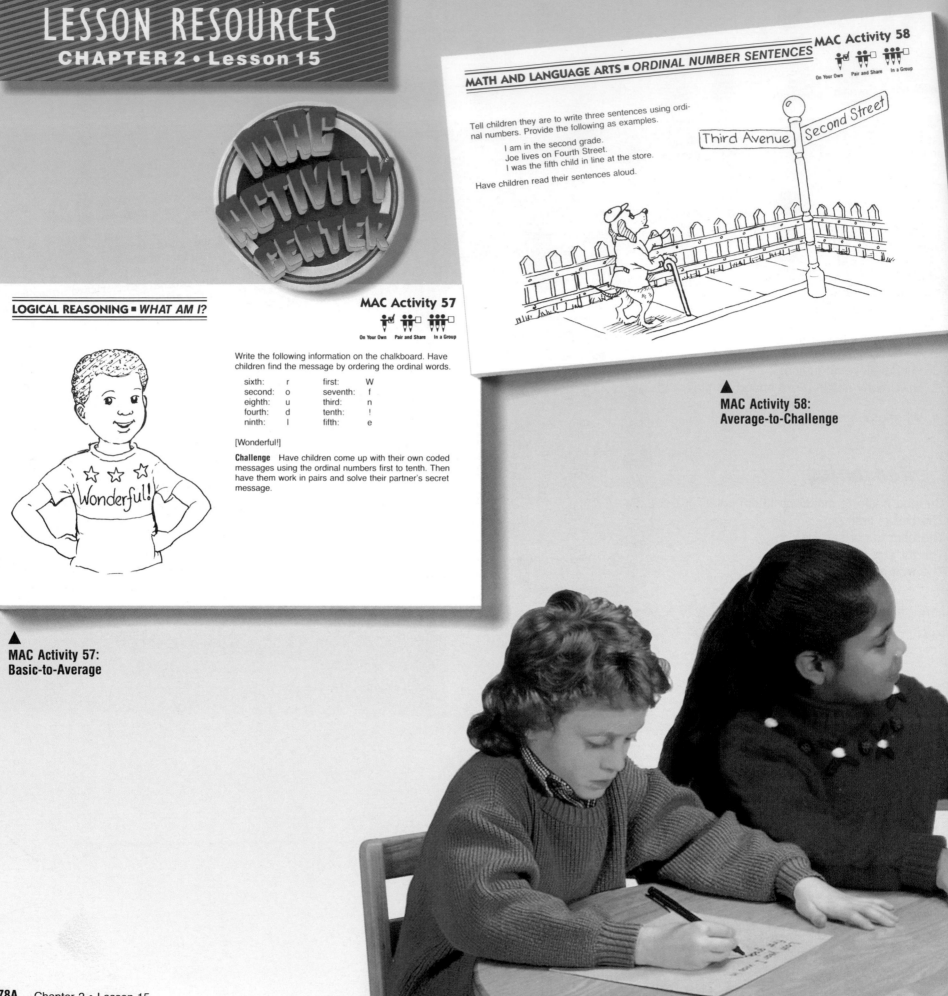

MAC Activity 58
MATH AND LANGUAGE ARTS ▪ ORDINAL NUMBER SENTENCES

On Your Own   Pair and Share   In a Group

Tell children they are to write three sentences using ordinal numbers. Provide the following as examples.

I am in the second grade.
Joe lives on Fourth Street.
I was the fifth child in line at the store.

Have children read their sentences aloud.

Third Avenue   Second Street

▲
MAC Activity 58:
Average-to-Challenge

LOGICAL REASONING ▪ WHAT AM I?

MAC Activity 57

On Your Own   Pair and Share   In a Group

Write the following information on the chalkboard. Have children find the message by ordering the ordinal words.

sixth:	r	first:	W
second:	o	seventh:	f
eighth:	u	third:	n
fourth:	d	tenth:	!
ninth:	l	fifth:	e

[Wonderful!]

Challenge Have children come up with their own coded messages using the ordinal numbers first to tenth. Then have them work in pairs and solve their partner's secret message.

Wonderful!

▲
MAC Activity 57:
Basic-to-Average

RETEACHING

Name

ORDINAL NUMBERS

Study

A	B	C	D	E	F	G	H	I	J
1st first	2nd second	3rd third	4th fourth	5th fifth	6th sixth	7th seventh	8th eighth	9th ninth	10th tenth

T	S	R	Q	P	O	N	M	L	K
20th twentieth	19th nineteenth	18th eighteenth	17th seventeenth	16th sixteenth	15th fifteenth	14th fourteenth	13th thirteenth	12th twelfth	11th eleventh

Check

Ring the letters.

1. Ring. first ⟩⟩ red ⟩⟩   ninth ⟩⟩ blue ⟩⟩   eleventh ⟩⟩ green ⟩⟩

Ⓐ B C D E F G H Ⓘ J Ⓚ L

2. Ring. 3rd ⟩⟩ yellow ⟩⟩   6th ⟩⟩ orange ⟩⟩   12th ⟩⟩ purple ⟩⟩

A B Ⓒ D E Ⓕ G H I J K Ⓛ

3. Which letter of the alphabet is seventeenth? __Q__

4. Which letter of the alphabet is twentieth? __T__

5. G is the __seventh__ letter.

6. P is the __sixteenth__ letter.

Macmillan/McGraw-Hill, MATHEMATICS IN ACTION
Grade 2, Chapter 2, Lesson 15, pages 77–78

PRACTICE

Name

ORDINAL NUMBERS

1. Which lion has a ⬯ ? __13th__

2. Is the twelfth lion last? __no__

3. Linda Lion is fifteenth in line.
How many lions are ahead of her? __14__

4. Leo Lion is eighteenth in line.
How many lions are ahead of him? __17__

5. Which lion is last in line? __20th__

6. What is the sixteenth letter
of the alphabet? __P__

7. What is the sixth letter of
the alphabet? __F__

8. Color the seventeenth lion yellow.

Macmillan/McGraw-Hill, MATHEMATICS IN ACTION
Grade 2, Chapter 2, Lesson 15, pages 77–78

ENRICHMENT

Name

ORDINAL NUMBERS

On Your Own   Pair and Share   In a Group

TAKE ME OUT TO THE BALLGAME

There are 20 people on line. Three people are inside Gate 5.
You can't see the two people behind the popcorn stand.

Write the ordinal words to complete what people
are saying.

Three people are ahead of me.
I am __fourth__ on the line.

You are __seventh__
I am __eighth__

The two people ahead of me are __ninth__ and __tenth__ on line.

You can say I am last or __twentieth__ on line.

This is a long line. I am __fourteenth__

Macmillan/McGraw-Hill, MATHEMATICS IN ACTION
Grade 2, Chapter 2, Lesson 15, pages 77–78

Problem of the Day

Shawn was in the nineteenth row at the dog show.
Then he moved up 10 rows. Is he now closer to
the tenth row or the fifth row?   [tenth]

AT·A·GLANCE pp. 79-80

LESSON OBJECTIVE
Make a list to solve problems.

ASSIGNMENT GUIDE

COURSE	EXERCISES
Basic	p. 79: All; p. 80: 1–3
Average	p. 79: All; p. 80: 1–3
Challenge	p. 79: All; p. 80: 1–3

MATERIALS
Classroom Materials colored chalk, paper cutouts of orange circles, green circles, blue squares, red squares

Teacher Resources
Reteaching 30   Practice 30   Enrichment 30
Prob. Solv. 9   MAC Act. 59, 60

Name _____

Problem Solving

UNDERSTAND
PLAN
TRY
CHECK
EXTEND

Strategy: Making a List

Dad wanted to buy a tablecloth and some napkins.

The store had white tablecloths and yellow tablecloths.

It had checkered napkins and flowered napkins.

A list can show all the choices.

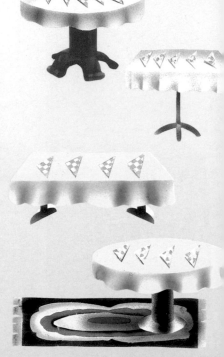

Tablecloths	Napkins
white	checkered
white	flowered
yellow	checkered
yellow	flowered

There are __4__ choices.

Macmillan/McGraw-Hill

---

1 PREPARE **WARM-UP** To prepare children for making a list to solve problems, call on volunteers to write their names in a list on the chalkboard. Make several lists on the chalkboard, each with five names.

2 TEACH **MODELING** Assign children to work in pairs. Give each pair a precut orange circle, a green circle, a blue square, and a red square. Display the same shapes along the chalkboard ledge. Then tell children to use their shapes to find different combinations for the pairs of shapes.

■ **What is one way you could record your choices?** [List the color and shape combinations as they are made.]

List children's combinations on the chalkboard. You may wish to suggest that children start with the orange circle and find all the combina-

tions they can make with it before using the green circle. Review the list with the children when it is completed.

circles	squares
orange	blue
orange	red
green	blue
green	red

PUPIL'S EDITION pp. 79-80

Page 79 Have a volunteer read the problem at the top of the page. Discuss the picture with the children.

■ **What do you need to do?** [Make a list to show all the choices.]

■ **Why is a list helpful?** [Possible response: It helps you figure out the choices and keeps you from repeating the same ones.]

Make a list to show all the choices.

1. Maro was dressing for the picnic. She could wear her gray sweater or her red sweater. She could wear her black pants or her blue pants.

   There are __4__ choices.

Sweaters	Pants
gray	black
gray	blue
red	black
red	blue

2. There were sports and contests at the picnic. You could play baseball or soccer. You could be in a ring toss or a horseshoe contest.

   There are __4__ choices.

Sports	Contests
baseball	ring toss
baseball	horseshoe
soccer	ring toss
soccer	horseshoe

3. Later fruit and punch were served. There were apples, oranges, and pears. There was cherry punch and lemon punch.

   There are __6__ choices.

Fruits	Punches
apple	cherry
apple	lemon
orange	cherry
orange	lemon
pear	cherry
pear	lemon

TEACHER to TEACHER

MANIPULATIVES TIP My children were better able to see possible combinations of things after using concrete objects.

For Students Acquiring English (SAE)

Scan the pages for vocabulary that may be new to SAE children. Introduce new words by using visuals, gestures, and body movements to convey meaning. Ask questions frequently to check comprehension.

Have a volunteer read the information in the lists. Review the completed lists with the children.

■ **How many choices of tablecloths and napkins are there?** [4 choices]

■ **Are all of the possible choices listed?** [Yes.]

Guide children to see that the list shows all the possible choices with the white tablecloths before showing the possible choices with the yellow tablecloths.

■ **What have you learned?** [Possible response: A list can help you figure out different choices to solve a problem.]

Encourage children to explain other ways to solve this problem.

Check for Understanding

■ **What if there were only white tablecloths? How many choices would there be?** [2 choices]

GUIDED PRACTICE ex. All: Work through the problem with the children. Make sure they understand how to solve the problem by making a list.

Page 80 Have a volunteer read the directions at the top of the page. Have the labels above each list identified. Help children read the problems as necessary.

PRACTICE•APPLY

CLOSE Guide children to summarize the lesson:

■ **How can a list help you to solve a problem?** [Possible response: A list can help you figure out the different choices you have in solving the problem.]

MAC ACTIVITY CENTER

MAC Activity 59:
Basic-to-Average

MAC Activity 59

On Your Own   Pair and Share   In a Group

MATH AND ART ■ SETTING THE TABLE

Materials red, yellow, and white construction paper; crayons

Setup Create a blank list form with two columns. Use the heading "Place Mats" for the left column and "Napkins" for the right column. Make one copy for each pair of children.

Procedure Assign children to work in pairs. Give each pair a blank list form, crayons, 2 red sheets, 2 yellow sheets of construction paper, and 4 half-sheets of white construction paper. Explain that the large red and yellow sheets are place mats and the smaller white sheets are napkins. Have one child in each pair decorate two of the napkins with polka dots and the other child decorate two of the napkins with flowers. Tell children they are to figure out the different choices for setting a table with a place mat and napkin and then to list those choices.

When the lists are completed, have children compare their lists. Have volunteers show their choices using the place mats and decorated napkins. The finished list should be similar to the one shown.

Place Mats	Napkins
red	dots
red	flowers
yellow	dots
yellow	flowers

MAC Activity 60:
Average-to-Challenge ▶

WRITING MATHEMATICS ■ SOLVE IT

MAC Activity 60

On Your Own   Pair and Share   In a Group

Materials index cards

Separate the class into four groups. Assign two categories to each group; for example, *sandwiches/fruit; clothing tops/clothing bottoms; shapes/colors;* and *boats/bodies of water.* Then give each group 5 index cards.

Explain to children that they are going to create a problem for another group to solve by making a list. Have each group write or draw an item on each index card that fits their assigned categories. Three items should be identified for the first category and two items for the second. Then have groups exchange cards, figure out the choices, and list them on the form. Here are suggested lists:

Sandwiches/Fruit
tuna   apple
cheese   banana
peanut butter

Shapes/Colors
circle   red
square   blue
triangle

Clothing
Tops/Clothing
Bottoms
blouse   pants
sweater   shorts
T-shirt

Boats/Bodies of Water
rowboat   river
sailboat lake
canoe

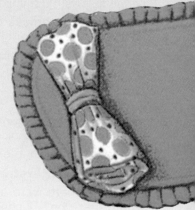

RETEACHING-30

Name

PROBLEM SOLVING STRATEGY: MAKING A LIST

Study

You have pants with dots.
You have pants with stripes.
You have a shirt with dots.
You have a shirt with stripes.
How many different outfits
can you make?

Make a list to
show your choices.

Pants	Shirts
dots	dots
dots	stripes
stripes	stripes
stripes	dots

Check

Make a list to show all the choices.

1. There was vegetables
and meat for supper.
You could have carrots
or beans.
You could have ham
or fish.

Vegetables	Meat
carrots	ham
carrots	fish
beans	ham
beans	fish

2. The baseball team
needed shoes and socks.
They could have black
shoes or white shoes.
They could have white
socks or black socks.

Shoes	Socks
black	white
black	black
white	white
white	black

Macmillan/McGraw-Hill, MATHEMATICS IN ACTION
Grade 2, Chapter 2, Lesson 16, pages 79–80

Reteaching-30

PRACTICE-30

Name

PROBLEM SOLVING STRATEGY: MAKING A LIST

Make a list to show all the choices.

1. Sam wanted to
play in the snow.
He could wear gloves
or mittens on his hands.
He could wear a hat
or earmuffs on his head.

Hands	Head
gloves	hat
gloves	earmuffs
mittens	hat
mittens	earmuffs

2. There were breads and
drinks for breakfast.
There were muffins,
pancakes, and toast.
There was milk and juice.

Breads	Drinks
muffins	milk
pancakes	milk
toast	milk
muffins	juice
pancakes	juice
toast	juice

3. The band was choosing
their uniforms.
There were red, blue,
or green jackets.
There were tan or
black pants.

Jackets	Pants
red	tan
blue	tan
green	tan
red	black
blue	black
green	black

Macmillan/McGraw-Hill, MATHEMATICS IN ACTION
Grade 2, Chapter 2, Lesson 16, pages 79–80

Practice-30

ENRICHMENT-30

Name

PROBLEM SOLVING

On Your Own   Pair and Share   In a Group

WHAT'S FOR LUNCH?

How many different pizzas can you make?
Put 2 toppings on each pizza.

Toppings	
tomato **T**	meatball **M**
onion **O**	green pepper **G**
pineapple **P**	

Complete the chart.
Use the letters **T**, **O**, **M**, **G** and **P**.
Start with **T**. Put **T** with each of the other letters.
Then go on to **O**.
Make sure each set of letters is different.

T	O	M	G
T-O	O-M	M-G	G-P
T-M	O-G	M-P	
T-G	O-P		
T-P			

Count the sets of letters.

I can make __10__ different pizzas.

Macmillan/McGraw-Hill, MATHEMATICS IN ACTION
Grade 2, Chapter 2, Lesson 16, pages 79–80

Enrichment-30

Problem of the Day

Linda has a blue winter hat, a red winter hat, and a white winter hat. She has a red scarf and a white scarf. How many ways can she wear scarves and hats together?
[6; blue hat—red scarf; blue hat—white scarf; red hat—red scarf; red hat—white scarf; white hat—red scarf; white hat—white scarf]

AT·A·GLANCE p. 81

LESSON OBJECTIVE
Make decisions using information.

ASSIGNMENT GUIDE

COURSE	EXERCISES
Basic	p. 81: 1–5
Average	p. 81: 1–5
Challenge	p. 81: 1–5

MATERIALS
Classroom Materials game board*, game markers, index cards, crayons
Manipulatives 1 spinner for 1–5*, play bills (or punchout bills) per group

Teacher Resources
Prob. Solv. 10   *Teacher Aids 1, 16   Crit. Think. 4

Name _____

Decision Making

Problem Solving: Planning a Game

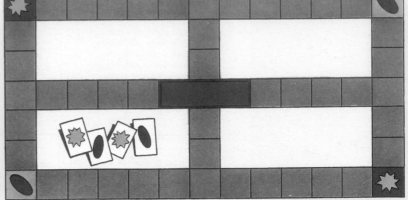

Make a game.
What things do you need to think
about to plan your game? Answers will vary.

1. How many players do you need? _____

2. What do you do with each game part? _____

_____

3. How do you play? _____

_____

_____

4. Play your game with friends.

5. Talk about things you might change to make the game more fun.

Chapter 2   Understanding Numbers to 100   eighty-one   **81**

Macmillan/McGraw-Hill

PREPARE   **WARM-UP**   To review numbers to 100, write the following on the chalkboard. Have children supply the numbers that come before and after each number.

___ 67 ___ [66, 68]
___ 26 ___ [25, 27]
___ 11 ___ [10, 12]
___ 99 ___ [98, 100]
___ 43 ___ [42, 44]
___ 70 ___ [69, 71]

TEACH   **DISCUSSING**   Have children name some of the games they like to play and explain why. List children's responses on the chalkboard. Then help children categorize the games by where they are played, the equipment or materials needed, number of players, and so on.

PUPIL'S EDITION p. 81

Have children look at the game board and game pieces at the top of the page. Have them think about a game they could make that uses these materials.

Check for Understanding
■ **What are you going to plan?** [a game]
■ **What game pieces are needed to play your game?** [Answers will vary.]

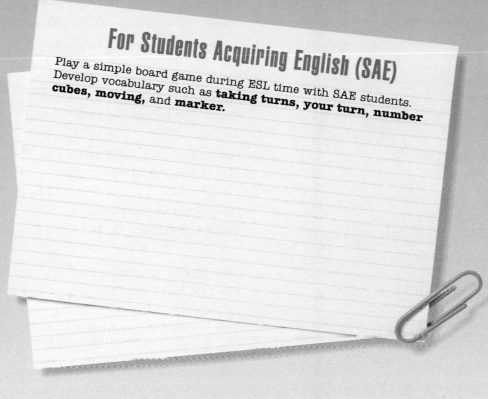

For Students Acquiring English (SAE)

Play a simple board game during ESL time with SAE students. Develop vocabulary such as **taking turns, your turn, number cubes, moving,** and **marker.**

---

3 PRACTICE•APPLY

Have children complete ex. 1–5. Call on volunteers to tell about the games they made and how their games are played. Encourage them to tell how they would make the items needed to play their games.

CLOSE Guide children to summarize the lesson:

■ **What should you do before playing a game?** [Decide what game to play, and plan the things needed to make and to play the game.]

CLASS PROJECT

Materials construction paper, cardboard, index cards, play money, game markers, crayons, paste, paper fasteners

Gather the items shown on page 81. Provide children with a variety of materials that can be used to make game pieces and game boards. Then have children make the game that they described on the page.

When children have completed the project, call on volunteers to show and tell about their games.

Allow time for children to play their games with other students.

AT·A·GLANCE p. 82

OBJECTIVE
Understand, read, and write numbers using the Japanese numeration system.

MULTICULTURAL OUTCOME
Familiarize children with the Japanese number system and number characters.

MATERIALS
Classroom Materials water color paints, brushes, and paper

Curriculum Connection

Math and Writing

Japanese children learn to write numbers like these.
Some numbers have lines that connect.
Some numbers have lines that almost touch each other.

一 二 三 四 五 六 七 八 九 十
one two three four five six seven eight nine ten

Toshi Mori is 12 years old.
She writes her age like this: 十二

Her brother, Aki, is 17 years old.
This is how he writes his age: 十七   **10 plus 7**

How would you write the
Japanese number for 16? 十六   **10 plus 6**

Mrs. Mori is 38 years old.
Her age looks like this: 三十八

This number shows 3 tens
plus 8 more. Do you see how?
3 over the 10 means 3 tens;
that written above the 8 means 3 tens + 8, or 38.

Working Together

Use Japanese numbers.
Write the ages of two people you know.
Trade papers.
Can you read each other's numbers?

Use your own paper.

82 eighty-two

---

1 PREPARE

WARM-UP Review some of the number words children may recall from other languages such as Ashanti or Cheyenne.

Tell children that many people who speak languages other than English write the numbers using the same digits we do. But in other parts of the world, such as Japan and China, people not only speak a different language, but they also use a different form of writing.

2 TEACH

DISCUSSING Have children examine the chart of Japanese number characters. Encourage them to describe and discuss the characters and look for ways to understand their formation. Ask:

■ **What do you notice about the Japanese numbers for 1, 2, and 3?** [Children may say that they look like 1, 2, and 3 lines, almost like tallies sideways.]

Guide children to analyze the numbers greater than 10 that are used to describe the ages of the Mori family. Ask:

■ **What numbers appear in Toshi's age?** [10 and 2]

■ **In what pattern?** [10 over the 2]

■ **Does the same pattern work for Aki's age? Explain.** [Yes; 17 has a 10 over a 7.]

For Question 1, encourage children to explain how they would write 16 using Japanese characters. For Question 2, help them understand how to show greater numbers, such as 38. Ask:

■ **How much is 3 tens?** [30]

CULTURAL DIVERSITY

JAPANESE NUMBER CHARACTERS

Written Japanese employs two sets of characters, *kanji* (kahn-jee) and *kana* (kah-nah). *Kanji* (the characters shown on the pupil's page) is made up of characters taken unchanged from written Chinese and represents whole words. *Kana* is used to represent syllabic sounds.

Greater numbers are formed using principles of addition (for example, 13 = 10 + 3), multiplication (for example, 40 = 4 × 10), and a combination of both operations (for example, 56 = [5 × 10] + 6).

■ **How is this shown in Japanese numbers?** [3 over 10]

■ **How is that different from 13?** [13 is 10 over a 3.]

3 PRACTICE•APPLY

Explain that Japanese characters are often written with special ink and brushes, like painting, so the children will be using paint to make Japanese numbers. Tell them that when painting Japanese characters, the strokes are made in a definite order. Certain strokes must come before others. As a general rule, strokes are painted from top to bottom and from left to right.

Provide time for the children to practice making the characters. Assign the rest of the page. Help children who may have difficulty making the characters plan their strokes to make the formation of characters more predictable.

WORKING TOGETHER Divide the children into pairs. Encourage partners to talk about how Japanese numbers are combined so they can correctly write the ages of family or friends.

CLOSE Guide children to summarize the lesson:

■ **How did you know what numbers to use to write people's ages in Japanese?** [Accept all reasonable answers.]

CHAPTER 2

Name _____

Extra Practice

Problem Solving: Looking for a Pattern, pages 69–70 . . . .

Write the numbers to continue the pattern.

1. 42 46 50 54 58 62

Greater Than and Less Than, pages 75–76 . . . .

Write > or <.

1. 6 (<) 9   14 (>) 11   29 (<) 30   56 (<) 65

2. 77 (>) 67   48 (<) 84   95 (>) 89   99 (>) 98

Ordinal Numbers, pages 77–78 . . . .

Start at the left.

1. Ring the (third) , (seventh) , (tenth) .

ADDITIONAL PRACTICE

p. 69 *Write the numbers to continue the pattern.*

1. 52 56 60 [64] [68] [72]
2. 19 22 25 [28] [31] [34]
3. 56 51 46 [41] [36] [31]
4. 82 71 60 [49] [38] [27]

p. 75 *Write < or >.*

1. 10 [>] 8   24 [<] 36   63 [>] 61
2. 25 [>] 22   19 [>] 17   50 [<] 51
3. 91 [>] 88   13 [<] 31   36 [>] 33

p. 77 *Ring the second fish. Draw a line under the eighth fish.*

Practice Plus

PRACTICE PLUS

Practice Plus is provided to supply additional practice for the two key skills in this chapter.

Key Skills
  Page 62: Skip-Counting Patterns
  Page 76: Greater Than and Less Than

The *Additional Practice* also provides practice you may wish to assign for key skills in this chapter.

Key Skill: Skip-Counting Patterns, page 62 . . . .

1. Count by twos.

   84 , 86 , 88 , 90 , 92 , 94 , 96 , 98

2. Count by fives.

   55 , 60 , 65 , 70 , 75 , 80 , 85 , 90

3. Count by threes.

   32 , 35 , 38 , 41 , 44 , 47 , 50 , 53

4. Count by fours.

   66 , 70 , 74 , 78 , 82 , 86 , 90 , 94

Key Skill: Greater Than and Less Than, page 76 . . . .

Compare. Write > or <.

1. 25 ⟩ 21	66 ⟨ 68	30 ⟨ 39	89 ⟩ 86
2. 60 ⟩ 40	40 ⟩ 39	48 ⟨ 84	91 ⟩ 53
3. 77 ⟨ 86	32 ⟩ 28	98 ⟨ 99	55 ⟨ 66
4. 42 ⟩ 37	88 ⟨ 91	29 ⟨ 92	64 ⟩ 54
5. 19 ⟨ 91	77 ⟩ 49	38 ⟩ 37	40 ⟩ 36

ADDITIONAL PRACTICE

p. 62 *Count by twos.*
1. 36 , 38 , [40] , [42] , [44] , [46]

Count by fives.
2. 25 , 30 , [35] , [40] , [45] , [50]

Count by threes.
3. 45 , 48 , [51] , [54] , [57] , [60]

Count by fours.
4. 72 , 76 , [80] , [84] , [88] , [92]

p. 76 *Compare. Write > or <.*

1. 61 [>] 46   32 [<] 46   81 [>] 62
2. 20 [>] 12   90 [>] 81   14 [<] 41
3. 78 [<] 87   51 [>] 41   25 [<] 52
4. 37 [>] 27   59 [>] 58   43 [>] 41

5. 83 [>] 73   27 [<] 30   20 [<] 25
6. 67 [<] 76   32 [>] 23   16 [>] 14
7. 91 [>] 89   79 [<] 81   39 [>] 30
8. 14 [<] 41   48 [>] 46   99 [>] 89

AT·A·GLANCE pp. 85-86

OBJECTIVE
Review/test the concepts and skills presented in Chapter 2.

2A. Read, write, and order numbers to 100.
2B. Skip-count by twos, threes, fours, fives, and tens.
2C. Identify odd and even numbers.
2D. Compare numbers through 100.
2E. Identify and use ordinal numbers to twentieth.
2F. Solve problems including those that involve finding a pattern.

Teacher Resources
Testing Program, pp. 13–24

Name _____

Chapter Review/Test

Language and Mathematics
Choose the correct words.

1. 2, 4, 6, 8, and 10 are called

_____even_____ numbers.

2. 1, 3, 5, 7, and 9 are called

_____odd_____ numbers.

odd
greater than
even

3. The sign > means ___greater than___ .

Concepts and Skills
Complete.

4. 4 tens 8 ones = __48__   5. 5 tens 3 ones = __53__

6. 26 = __2__ tens __6__ ones   7. 63 = __6__ tens __3__ ones

8. Which number comes just after?	9. Which number comes just before?	10. Which number comes between?
19, __20__	__69__, 70	48, __49__, 50
56, __57__	__98__, 99	79, __80__, 81
80, __81__	__14__, 15	25, __26__, 27

11. Count by fours. Write the numbers.

60, 64, __68__, __72__, __76__, __80__, __84__, __88__, __92__

12. Count by threes. Write the numbers.

21, 24, __27__, __30__, __33__, __36__, __39__, __42__, __45__

Macmillan/McGraw-Hill

USING THE CHAPTER REVIEW/TEST

The Chapter Review/Test may be used as a review to survey children's knowledge and understanding of the chapter material. Or it may be used as a test to formally assess children's understanding of the concepts and skills taught in the chapter. If used as a test, you may wish to assign one or more of the resources listed in *Reinforcement and Remediation* on p. 86 after reviewing children's test results.

If the Chapter Review/Test is used as a review, you may wish to have children work in pairs to complete it. Have them talk about different ways models can be used to show the number 75. Then, you can use the Chapter Tests—Forms A, B, and C—provided in the *Testing Program Blackline Master and Teacher's Manual* for testing purposes. Any of these forms may be used for pretesting, posttesting, or retesting.

A performance assessment activity for the key concept in this chapter is provided on page 87.

13. Ring the number that is greater.

49 (51)

14. Ring the number that is less.

(68) 80

Write > or <.

15. 27 (<) 41   68 (>) 38   90 (>) 89

16. Match.

third   tenth   eighteenth

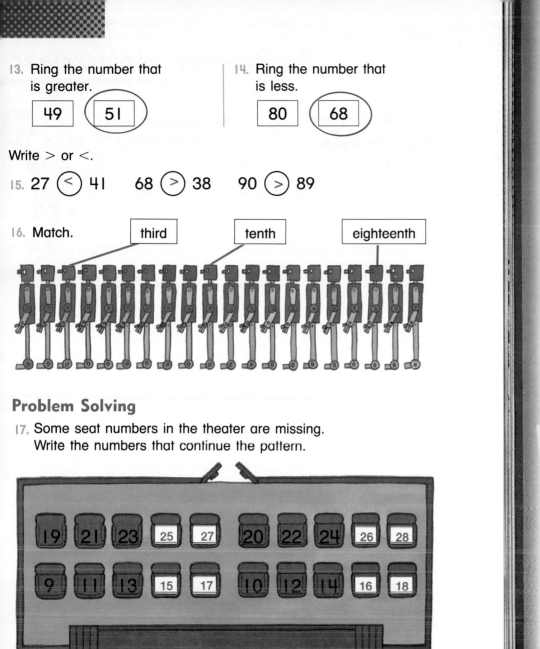

Problem Solving

17. Some seat numbers in the theater are missing. Write the numbers that continue the pattern.

19 21 23 25 27   20 22 24 26 28

9 11 13 15 17   10 12 14 16 18

Reinforcement and Remediation

CHAP. OBJ.	TEST ITEMS	PUPIL'S EDITION pp.			TEACHER'S EDITION pp.	TEACHER RESOURCES	
		Lesson	Extra Practice	Practice Plus	Alt. Teaching Strategy	Reteaching	Practice
2A	4–10	53–59	68				
2B	11–12	60–62	68		54, 56, 58, 59A	17, 18, 19, 20	17, 18, 19, 20
2C	1–2	63–64	68	84	60A, 62	21, 22	21, 22
2D	3, 13–15	73–76	83		64	23	23
2E	16	77–78	83	84	74, 76	27, 28	27, 28
2F	17	69–70	83		78	29	29
						25	25

For Students Acquiring English (SAE)

Before beginning the Chapter Review/Test with SAE children, scan the pages for any unfamiliar vocabulary that should be pretaught. You may wish to pair or group SAE children with non-SAE children. You may also wish to repeat some of the activities and techniques for SAE children that were suggested earlier in this chapter.

AT·A·GLANCE p. 87

OBJECTIVE
Assess whether children understand place value and ordering numbers to 100.

MATERIALS
Classroom Materials number cards for 0–9 and > and < signs*

Teacher Resources
Performance Assessment booklet, pp. 12–15, *Teacher Aid 11

For Students Acquiring English (SAE)

Before beginning the performance assessment with SAE children, scan the page for any unfamiliar vocabulary that should be pretaught. You may wish to pair or group SAE children with non-SAE children. You may also wish to repeat some of the activities and techniques for SAE children that were suggested earlier in this chapter.

Performance Assessment

Work with a partner.

Use number cards to make 2 numbers.
Then use a > or < sign to make a sentence with the numbers.

Make a number with tens and ones each time.

Write your sentence in the box.
Make 3 more sentences in the same way.

You may put this page in your Portfolio

Macmillan/McGraw-Hill

USING PERFORMANCE ASSESSMENT
The Performance Assessment activity may be used to informally assess children's understanding of the key concept(s) of the chapter. Additional assessment activities and Math Journal Options are provided in the *Performance Assessment* booklet.

Performing the Activity
Assign children to work in pairs. Give each pair > and < signs and 2 sets of number cards for 0–9. Then have children use number cards to create 2-digit number sentences with < and >. Children should then write each sentence in the box individually. You may want to ask children to read their sentences to you (for example, "35 is greater than 17").

Evaluation Guidelines
Use these criteria to help determine the holistic score for each child.

The holistic scoring scale can be found in the Teacher's Reference Section.

- Can children compare 2-digit numbers?
- Do children understand place value?
- Can children write number sentences comparing two numbers?

[Example Response: Sentences might include: 95 > 72; 34 < 86.]

If children do not have a full understanding of the key concept(s), you may wish to use the Alternative Teaching Strategies or the MAC Activities within the chapter.

You may wish to have children put their final revised work in their portfolios.

A formal assessment of the concepts and skills taught in this chapter is provided on pages 85–86.

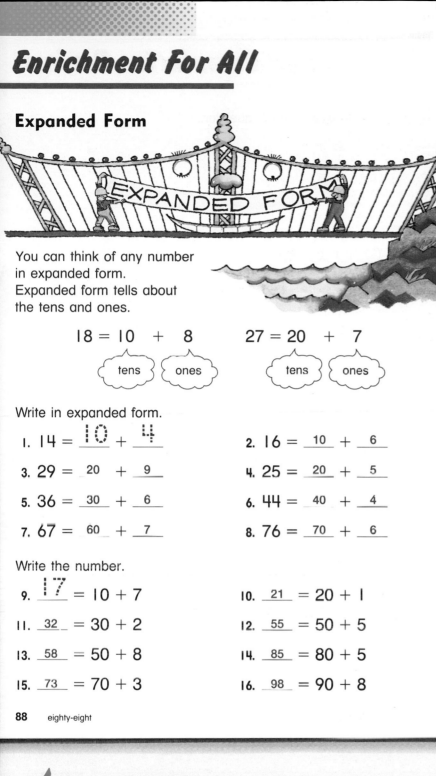

Enrichment For All

Expanded Form

You can think of any number in expanded form. Expanded form tells about the tens and ones.

$$18 = 10 + 8 \qquad 27 = 20 + 7$$

tens   ones   tens   ones

Write in expanded form.

1. $14 = \underline{10} + \underline{4}$
2. $16 = \underline{10} + \underline{6}$
3. $29 = \underline{20} + \underline{9}$
4. $25 = \underline{20} + \underline{5}$
5. $36 = \underline{30} + \underline{6}$
6. $44 = \underline{40} + \underline{4}$
7. $67 = \underline{60} + \underline{7}$
8. $76 = \underline{70} + \underline{6}$

Write the number.

9. $\underline{17} = 10 + 7$
10. $\underline{21} = 20 + 1$
11. $\underline{32} = 30 + 2$
12. $\underline{55} = 50 + 5$
13. $\underline{58} = 50 + 8$
14. $\underline{85} = 80 + 5$
15. $\underline{73} = 70 + 3$
16. $\underline{98} = 90 + 8$

CHAPTER 2

AT·A·GLANCE p. 88

OBJECTIVE
Identify and write numbers in expanded form.

ASSIGNMENT GUIDE

COURSE	EXERCISES
Basic	p. 88: 1–16
Average	p. 88: 1–16
Challenge	p. 88: 1–16

MATERIALS

Manipulatives   9 T, 9 O models (or punchouts), Workmat 2* per pair

Teacher Resources
*Teacher Aid 8

For Students Acquiring English (SAE)

Read the page aloud to SAE children, explaining and demonstrating key vocabulary. Model the phrase **expanded form** and assist them to pronounce it. Use visuals, gestures, and body movements to convey meaning. Have children point to aspects of the visuals in the textbook as you explain concepts presented. To check comprehension of the directions, ask SAE children to restate them. Pair SAE and non-SAE children to complete ex. 1–16 together.

PREPARE   **WARM-UP**   To review numbers in expanded form, have children tell how many tens and ones are in each of the following.

1. 23 [2 tens 3 ones]
2. 12 [1 ten 2 ones]
3. 66 [6 tens 6 ones]
4. 56 [5 tens 6 ones]
5. 34 [3 tens 4 ones]
6. 47 [4 tens 7 ones]

TEACH   **MODELING**   Have children study the numbers written in expanded form at the top of the page. Explain that a number written in *expanded form* shows the tens and the ones that make up that number.

Distribute tens and ones models and Workmat 2 to each pair of children. Have them model 18 and 27 on Workmat 2.

■ **How many tens did you show for 18?** [1] **How many ones?** [8]
■ **How many tens did you show for 27?** [2] **How many ones?** [7]

PRACTICE·APPLY   Have children complete ex. 1–16.

CLOSE   Guide children to summarize the lesson:

■ **How is 93 written in expanded form? How is the number for 40 + 9 written?** [93 = 90 + 3; 40 + 9 = 49]

AT·A·GLANCE p. 89

OBJECTIVE
Review and maintain previously learned concepts and skills.

Name _____

Cumulative Review

Fill in the ◯ to answer each question.

1.

$6 + 4 =$ _?_

2	8	9	10
◯	◯	◯	●

2.

$$\begin{array}{r} 3 \\ + 3 \\ \hline \end{array}$$

8	6	5	0
◯	●	◯	◯

3.

$9 - 4 =$ _?_

13	6	5	4
◯	◯	●	◯

4.

$10 - 3 =$ _?_

10	9	8	7
◯	◯	◯	●

5. Which number is
4 tens 3 ones?

43	34	7	1
●	◯	◯	◯

6. Complete.

$10, 20, 30, 40,$ _?_

42	43	45	50
◯	◯	◯	●

7. Which number sentence solves the problem?
6 kittens were playing.
1 more kitten came to play.
How many kittens played in all?

● $6 + 1 = 7$
◯ $6 - 1 = 5$

Macmillan/McGraw-Hill

USING THE CUMULATIVE REVIEW

The Cumulative Review is presented in a multiple-choice format to provide practice in taking a standardized test. It gives children an opportunity to review previously learned skills. An answer sheet, similar to those used when taking standardized tests, can be found in the *Testing Program Blackline Masters and Teacher's Manual.*

The table that follows correlates the review items to the lesson pages on which the skills are taught.

Review Items	Text Pages		Review Items	Text Pages
1	35		5	55
2	30		6	56, 60
3	33		7	39–40
4	35			

Testing Program Blackline Masters
In addition to the Cumulative Review in the Pupil's Edition, there are quarterly Cumulative Tests and an End-Year Test. These tests are multiple choice and provide additional opportunities for children to practice taking standardized tests.

Cumulative Tests measure children's performance on major skills and concepts taught during the previous quarters. The **End-Year Test** measures children's performance on major skills and concepts taught throughout the year.

Home Activity

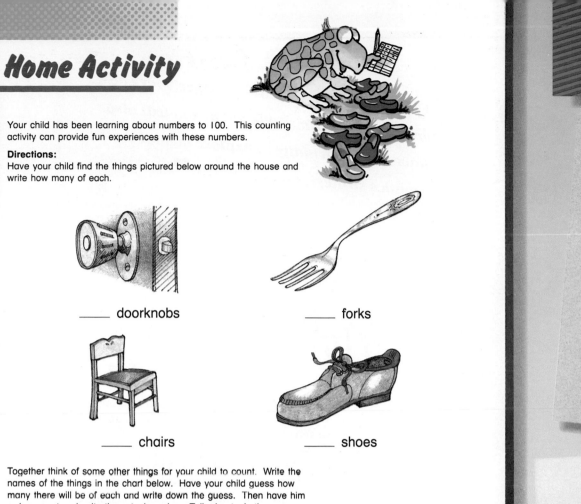

Your child has been learning about numbers to 100. This counting activity can provide fun experiences with these numbers.

Directions:
Have your child find the things pictured below around the house and write how many of each.

_____ doorknobs

_____ forks

_____ chairs

_____ shoes

Together think of some other things for your child to count. Write the names of the things in the chart below. Have your child guess how many there will be of each and write down the guess. Then have him or her count and write the actual number. Talk about whether your child's guess was too many or too few.

Things to Count	Guess	Actual Number

A T · A · G L A N C E p. 90

OBJECTIVE
Give family members an opportunity to share in their child's mathematics learning.

For Students Acquiring English (SAE)

Before assigning this Home Activity to SAE children, find out if someone at home will be able to work with them in English. If not, prepare them to complete the activity independently at home. Explain the directions of the activity and ask SAE children to restate them so you can check comprehension. Scan the page and preteach any difficult vocabulary or phrases that they may not know. If you feel that an SAE child will need extra help with the activity, you might assign that student a non-SAE partner and arrange a time for them to work on the activity in or out of school.

USING THE ACTIVITY

Have children look at the page. Explain that the page has an activity that an adult in the family can help them complete. Read the page with the children, making sure that they understand what needs to be done. Tell children that they will do this page at home.

Previewing
CHAPTER 3

ADDING and SUBTRACTING FACTS to 18

> *IN CHAPTER 3, you will introduce your children to subtracting facts to 18. You will also have the opportunity to explore mental mathematics strategies and patterns.*

Notes
FROM THE AUTHOR

Here are some notes on the concepts presented in this chapter and how your children can apply them to solve problems.

ADDITION and SUBTRACTION

As you introduce the harder facts, encourage children by letting them know that they have already learned 64 basic addition facts and 64 basic subtraction facts. Help them use their understanding of relationship and of fact families to learn new basic facts.

As children work with manipulatives to show facts that equal from 11–18, encourage them to model *basic facts*—facts with addends, number subtracted, or difference with numbers 0–9. Facts such as 10 + 1 or 12 − 1 are not basic facts and do not need to be memorized.

Steve Leinwand

+	0	1	2	3	4	5	6	7	8	9
0	0	1	2	3	4	5	6	7	8	9
1	1	2	3	4	5	6	7	8	9	10
2	2	3	4	5	6	7	8	9	10	11
3	3	4	5	6	7	8	9	10	11	12
4	4	5	6	7	8	9	10	11	12	13
5	5	6	7	8	9	10	11	12	13	14
6	6	7	8	9	10	11	12	13	14	15
7	7	8	9	10	11	12	13	14	15	16
8	8	9	10	11	12	13	14	15	16	17
9	9	10	11	12	13	14	15	16	17	18

MENTAL MATHEMATICS

Introduce mental math strategies by having your children look for tens in computation. For example, they think of a factor for ten when they add 7 + 5. They add 5 + 5 or 7 + 3, and then add 2 to find the sum of 12.

A number line enables children to visualize the strategy of counting on with the larger number. Children easily see that counting on 9 + 3 is faster than counting on 3 + 9.

```
+--+--+--+--+--+--+--+--+--+--+--+--+
0  1  2  3  4  5  6  7  8  9  10 11 12
           3 + 9

+--+--+--+--+--+--+--+--+--+--+--+--+
0  1  2  3  4  5  6  7  8  9  10 11 12
           9 + 3
```

A third strategy your children use is relating an addition fact to find a difference for a subtraction fact. For example, to find 16 - 7, children think, "7 + ? = 16," to determine that the difference is 9.

PATTERNS

Children examine ordered addition or subtraction facts to find a pattern. They learn the facts by repeating them in order. Patterns also help children use a "neighboring fact" to complete a harder fact. Children use patterns such as the following to find that when the first addend stays the same, and the second addend increases by one, the sum also increases by one.

7	7	7	7	7	7	7
+ 3	+ 4	+ 5	+ 6	+ 7	+ 8	+ 9
10	11	12	13	14	15	16

PROBLEM SOLVING

In **Problem Solving** your children (1) solve problems by choosing the operation and (2) use data from a bar graph to solve problems.

In **Thinking Mathematically** children use number sense to write addition and subtraction facts to create game cards. Children will enjoy playing Crazy Cards with their partners.

In **Decision Making** children read and use information to decide how to choose a classroom pet.

Mathematics and Literature

To use literature in the application of mathematics.

■ Children are introduced to two poems in the K–2 *Math Anthology* on pages 144 and 148. By reading *Homework Machine* and *Don't Ask Me,* children build their concepts of addition and subtraction facts.

CHAPTER PLANNING GUIDE

CHAPTER OBJECTIVES
WITH STANDARDIZED TEST CORRELATIONS

A. Add, facts to 18	MAT, CAT, SAT, ITBS, CTBS
B. Subtract, facts to 18	MAT, CAT, SAT, ITBS, CTBS
C. Add three or more 1-digit numbers	MAT, CAT, SAT, ITBS, CTBS
D. Solve problems including those that involve choosing the operation and using data from a bar graph	MAT, CAT, SAT, ITBS, CTBS

SUGGESTED PACING-14 DAYS

LESSONS	NCTM STANDARDS	ASSIGNMENTS Basic/Average/Challenge	STUDENT EDITION Extra Practice/ Practice Plus	Manip. Plus	Reteach	Practice	Enrich	MAC Activities
Chapter Opener: "Homework Machine" page 91	1, 2, 3, 4, 8	p. 91: All						
✔ 1 Adding and Subtracting Facts to 18 page 92	1, 2, 3, 7, 8	p. 92: 1–3						
✔ 2 Facts to 11 pages 93–94	1, 2, 3, 7, 8	p. 93: 2–8; p. 94: 1–6		15	31	31	31	61, 62
✔ 3 Facts to 12 pages 95–96	1, 2, 3, 8	p. 95: 2–7; p. 96: 1–5, Mental Math		16	32	32	32	63, 64
4 Mental Math Strategies pages 97–98	1, 2, 3, 4, 8	p. 97: 1–4; p. 98: 1–6		17	33	33	33	65, 66
✔ 5 Facts to 13 pages 99–100	1, 2, 3, 8	p. 99: 2–6; p. 100: 1–3, Reasoning			34	34	34	67, 68
✔ 6 Facts to 14 and 15 pages 101–102	1, 2, 3, 8	p. 101: 1–5; p. 102: 1–10	p. 106		35	35	35	69, 70
7 PS: Choosing the Operation pages 103–104	1, 2, 3, 7, 8	p. 103: 1–2; p. 104: 1–5	p. 106		36	36	36	71, 72
✔ 8 PS: Thinking Mathematically page 105	1, 2, 3, 8	p. 105: All						
✔ 9 Facts to 16, 17, and 18 pages 107–108	1, 2, 3, 8	p. 107: 1–6; p. 108: 1–7, Estimation	pp. 117, 118		37	37	37	73, 74
10 Informal Algebra: Addition and Subtraction Patterns pages 109–110	1, 2, 3, 8, 13	p. 109: All; p. 110: 1–7		18	38	38	38	75, 76
11 Three or More Addends page 111	1, 2, 3, 8	p. 111: 1–3	pp. 117, 118		39	39	39	77, 78
12 Adding and Subtracting Money page 112	1, 2, 3, 8	p. 112: 1–3			40	40	40	79, 80
13 PS: Using Data from a Bar Graph pages 113–114	1, 2, 3, 11	p. 113: 1–4; p. 114: 1–7	p. 117		41	41	41	81, 82
14 PS: Decision Making page 115	1, 2, 3, 6, 8	p. 115: 1–4						

Technology: Computer page 116

Chapter Review/Test pages 119, 120

Performance Assessment page 121

Cumulative Review page 123

Enrichment for All/Home Activity pages 122, 124

NATIONAL COUNCIL OF TEACHERS OF MATHEMATICS Grades K–4

1. Problem Solving
2. Communication
3. Reasoning
4. Connections
5. Estimation
6. Number Sense and Numeration
7. Concepts of Whole Number Operations
8. Whole Number Computation
9. Geometry and Spatial Sense
10. Measurement
11. Statistics and Probability
12. Fractions and Decimals
13. Patterns and Relationships

✔ Activity   ᛒᛒ Cooperative Learning

MEETING the NCTM STANDARDS

Problem Solving

Strategies and Skills	• choosing the operation pp. 103–104 • using data from a bar graph pp. 113–114
Applications	• **Decision Making** lesson p. 115 • **Problem of the Day** TE pp. 92, 94B, 96B, 98B, 100B, 102B, 104B, 108B, 110B, 111C, 112C, 114B
Mathematical Investigations	• **Thinking Mathematically** lesson p. 105

Communication

Language	• using the language of mathematics TE pp. 93–94, 116
Oral/Written	• using cooperative learning activities pp. 92, 95, 105, 115; TE pp. 90I–90L • **Journal Writing** opportunities TE pp. 92, 98, 100, 104, 108, 110, 111A, 114

Reasoning

Critical Thinking	• answering questions that analyze and extend concepts pp. 91, 97, 114, 115, 116, 122

Connections

To other subject areas	• Literature p. 91; Literature TE pp. 91–92, 95

Concept Development

Whole Number Computation	• adding facts to 18 pp. 92, 93–94, 95–96, 97–98, 99–100, 101–102, 107–108; TE pp. 90I–90K • adding three or more 1-digit numbers p. 111 • subtracting facts to 18 pp. 92, 93–94, 95–96, 97–98, 99–100, 101–102, 107–108 • adding and subtracting money amounts p. 112
Patterns and Relationships	• finding patterns in addition and subtraction pp. 109–110; TE p. 90L

ASSESSMENT OPTIONS

PERFORMANCE ASSESSMENT

Preassessment Activity

Before beginning Chapter 3, have each child write five subtraction examples using numbers less than 10 and find the differences. Then have them recopy each example, replacing each minus sign (–) with a plus sign (+). Challenge children to find those sums.

Ongoing Assessment

The Ongoing Assessment cards under MEETING INDIVIDUAL NEEDS on TE pp. 100 and 108 provide criteria and questions for assessing children's understanding of the key mathematical concepts developed in the chapter.

Journal Writing opportunities encourage children to write about mathematics. Their responses can be recorded either pictorially or in words. The journal writing opportunities on the Ongoing Assessment cards also allow you to assess children's understanding of the lessons.

In addition to the Ongoing Assessment cards, other assessment and journal writing opportunities in this chapter include:

• **CLOSE** TE pp. 92, 98, 100, 104, 110, 111A, 114

Performance Assessment Activity

The Performance Assessment activity on p. 121 provides an alternative to formal assessment. This activity assesses children's understanding of the key concepts of the chapter.

For performance assessment activities that are keyed to individual chapter objectives, see the *Performance Assessment* booklet.

BUILDING A PORTFOLIO

Children should be encouraged to keep a selection of their best work in portfolios. The portfolios provide a way of documenting children's growth in understanding mathematical concepts. Portfolio opportunities in this chapter include:

• **Performance Assessment** p. 121
• **Class Project** TE p. 115A

If you wish to provide additional opportunities for portfolio work, you may choose to use:

• **MAC Activities** 64, 66, 67, 73, 81

You may also wish to have children include their journal writing from the Ongoing Assessment on TE pp. 100 and 108 in their portfolio.

Formal Assessment

The **Chapter Review/Test** assesses children's understanding of the concepts and skills developed in the chapter. The **Cumulative Review** assesses children's understanding of the concepts and skills developed from the beginning of the year.

You can use **Form A** or **Form B** of the **Chapter Test** found in the *Testing Program Blackline Masters and Teacher's Manual* if you wish to use a multiple-choice

format to assess children's understanding of the chapter concepts and skills. You can use **Form C** if you wish to use a free-response format. Any of the forms may be used as a pretest, posttest, or for retesting.

The **COMPUTER MANAGEMENT SYSTEM**, or **CMS**, enables you to score **Forms A** and **B** of the **Chapter Test** quickly and automatically. It also prescribes learning activities based on children's test results.

For more information about Assessment, see the *Professional Handbook*.

Common Error and Remediation

The Teacher's Edition notes for each Develop/Understand (Transitional/Abstract) lesson provide a common error analysis and a remediation activity. Some errors defy quick analysis and can only be identified by interviewing the child.

ALTERNATIVE TEACHING STRATEGY

Alternative Teaching Strategies appear frequently in the chapter. These strategies provide other presentations of the lessons for children who might benefit from instruction in different learning modalities: kinesthetic, visual, and/or auditory.

For Students Acquiring English (SAE)

Multiple-meaning words are difficult for SAE children and should be pretaught and practiced. During the chapter, pre-teach **table** as a math graphic versus a piece of furniture. Explain the difference between a **fact family** and a family of people. Use visuals (magazine pictures, family photos, and so on) to illustrate and compare.

SAE notes appear periodically in the chapter. These notes provide suggestions for how to work with children to improve comprehension and build vocabulary.

MANIPULATIVES WORKSHOP

Two-color counters are used in this chapter to examine number facts to 18. They provide concrete representations of the relationships within fact families.

USING MANIPULATIVES

Here a child models a fact family for 12.

The child starts with 12 counters, all one color.

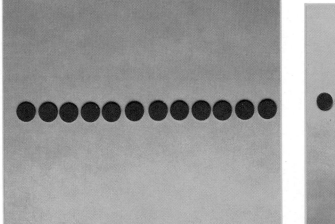

The child turns 5 counters to the yellow side. The model shows that $12 - 5 = 7$ and $12 - 7 = 5$. It also shows that $7 + 5 = 12$ and $5 + 7 = 12$.

The child explores other fact families with the same 12 counters.

The child rearranges the counters.

Now the model shows that $3 + 9 = 12$, $9 + 3 = 12$, $12 - 3 = 9$, and $12 - 9 = 3$.

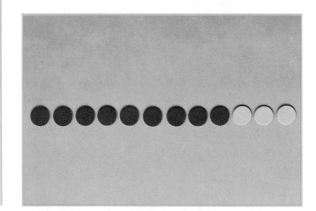

MAKING MANIPULATIVES See the Manipulatives section of the *Professional Handbook* for materials that can be used as a substitute for two-color counters.

COOPERATIVE LEARNING WORKSHOP

GETTING STARTED

Winning Together: By adapting your MAC Activity time, you can continue group building by playing cooperative rather than competitive games. Try some simple community-building structures such as **line-ups** (in which children line up based on common preferences or opinions) or **cluster activities** (in which children group by categories). For pairs or small groups, use structures such as **round robin** (taking turns sharing around the table) or **partner interview** on the topic being studied.

Competitive games in the MAC Activities can be modified to become cooperative community-builders or team-builders by labeling the winning outcome as a score for "the class community" or "our group." Groups can compete against previous scoring records or try to achieve new records. All children should become winners.

IDEAS TO TRY

Cooperative Skills: Children need to practice the skills of **attentive listening, taking turns, restating,** and **explaining.** A class **silence signal** can bring all groups to one focus of attention, and a **volume check** signal can remind the community that group work needs to be carried on with **"inside voices"** (loud enough for group work, but low enough as to not disturb other groups). Signals can be auditory, visual, or kinesthetic. Their common characteristic is that they must be repeated by everyone until the goal of silence or reduced volume is achieved.

You can apply the above cooperative skills in these lessons:
3-1 *Adding and Subtracting Facts to 18* p. 92
3-3 *Facts to 12* pp. 95–96
3-5 *Facts to 13* pp. 99–100
3-6 *Facts to 14 and 15* pp. 101–102

Coaching One Another: Children enjoy coaching one another, taking turns showing each other how to use the addition table and find patterns, or explaining and using the addition strategies. Partners first work individually and then check their methods as well as their answers with one another.

Ask each partner to express appreciation of the other's work each time they check a problem. One way to teach the cooperative skill of **appreciation** is by having children volunteer expressions that would make them feel good about doing a first-rate job. Write their suggestions on the chalkboard so that they can refer to them when they want to show appreciation of their partners' work.

You can apply the above cooperative skills in these lessons:
3-10 *Informal Algebra: Addition and Subtraction Patterns* pp. 109–110
3-11 *Three or More Addends* p. 111

SEE ALSO

Cooperative Learning Tip for lessons 3-7 Problem Solving p. 104; 3-8 Thinking Mathematically p. 105A; 3-13 Problem Solving p. 114

The Cooperative Learning section of the *Professional Handbook* for additional information

---

INTERACTIVE BULLETIN BOARD

SETUP Using an enlargement of the barn pattern as shown on the illustration, cut out barn patterns on sheets of red construction paper. Write a number from 10 through 18 on each barn.

PROCEDURE Assign children to small groups. Give each group a red barn, black felt-tipped pens, drawing paper, scissors, and crayons. Have children work together to write two addition facts and two subtraction facts for the number on the barn. Then encourage children to draw and cut out pictures of farm animals, farm machinery, farm crops, and so on, to decorate the board. Call on groups, in turn, to fasten their farms and pictures to the board.

For use before LESSON 3.2, pp. 93-94

15

ACTING OUT PROBLEMS

OBJECTIVE
Solve oral addition and subtraction problems.

MATERIALS
Classroom Materials
index cards (EXTENDING THE ACTIVITY only)

WHOLE GROUP ACTIVITY ⏱

Tell children that they are going to act out addition and subtraction problems. First have them listen as you read this problem aloud:

■ **6 children were painting a mural together. 4 children went home. How many children were still painting together?**

Call on six children to act out the word problem as you read it again. Then write the subtraction sentence for the problem on the chalkboard: 6 − 4 = 2. Have a volunteer give the answer to the problem. [2 children]

Continue in the same way for these problems.

■ **5 children were building a sand castle. 4 more children came to help them. How many children in all were building the sand castle?**
[5 + 4 = 9; 9 children]

■ **8 children were watching a movie. 2 children went to buy popcorn. How many children were still watching the movie?**
[8 − 2 = 6; 6 children]

■ **8 birds were eating seeds. 3 flew away. How many birds were still eating seeds?**
[8 − 3 = 5; 5 birds]

■ **7 horses were in the barn. 3 more horses came in from the field. Now how many horses are in the barn?** [7 + 3 = 10; 10 horses]

■ **10 rabbits were sleeping near a lake. 6 rabbits woke up and hopped away. How many rabbits were still sleeping?**
[10 − 6 = 4; 4 rabbits]

EXTENDING THE ACTIVITY

Write addition and subtraction facts on separate index cards. Assign groups of children to come up with their own skits to act out the problems. After each skit is presented, have a volunteer from the rest of the class tell the story that they saw and say the addition or subtraction sentence.

ONGOING ASSESSMENT

✔ Are children able to appropriately model the addition and subtraction in the stories?

MANIPULATIVES plus ACTIVITY

For use before LESSON 3.3, pp. 95-96

16

USES OF SUBTRACTION

OBJECTIVE
To solve word problems using subtraction to compare and to equalize.

MATERIALS
Classroom Materials
pencils

WHOLE GROUP ACTIVITY

Call on two children to come to the front of the room. Give one child 6 pencils and the other child 3 pencils.

■ **(Child's name) has 6 pencils. (Child's name) has 3 pencils. Who has more pencils?** [the child with 6 pencils]

■ **How could we find how many more pencils (the first child) has?** [Possible responses: subtract 3 from 6; count on from 3 to 6; match up the pencils, then count the pencils left over]

Demonstrate each of the strategies for children. Have a volunteer write the subtraction sentence that solves the problem. [6 − 3 = 3]

Continue in the same way with other problems involving number of objects in two groups, such as 10 crayons and 4 books, 11 Team A members and 9 Team B members, 5 pieces of chalk and 11 pieces of chalk.

EXTENDING THE ACTIVITY

Have children write how they solved each of the above problems. Have volunteers share their strategies for solving each problem.

ONGOING ASSESSMENT

✔ Are children able to compare the number of objects in two groups and describe the comparison using numbers?

17

MENTAL MATH
READINESS

OBJECTIVE
Identify sets of ten objects.

MATERIALS
Classroom Materials
1 large cardboard box
Manipulatives 50 🗂

WHOLE GROUP ACTIVITY ⬍

Obtain a large cardboard box and cut out a hole in one of the sides large enough for a child's hand to go through. Tape around the edge of the hole.

Snap together connecting cubes to make varying lengths of cube trains, from 2 to 5 cubes per train. Place the trains into the box.

Explain to children that they will each have a turn to place their hand into the box and try to pull out two or more cube trains that equal 10 cubes in all. After they pull out the trains, have them determine if they have 10 cubes in all. If a child's trains do not equal 10 cubes, have her or him tell how many more or less cubes would make 10.

EXTENDING THE ACTIVITY

Allow each child another chance to choose cube trains. This time, challenge children to say the number of cubes in the train they choose before they pull the train out of the box. Then, before choosing the next trains, have them say aloud the number that they need in order to make 10 cubes in all.

ONGOING ASSESSMENT

✔ Are children able to combine sets of objects to make 10 in all, and are they beginning to use mental math to determine the total?

For use before LESSON 3.10, pp. 109-110

18

ADDITION AND SUBTRACTION PATTERNS

OBJECTIVE
Recognize addition and subtraction patterns.

MATERIALS
Classroom Materials
graph paper*, red and blue crayons
Manipulatives 28
and 28 per pair
Teacher Resources
*Teacher Aid 5

WHOLE GROUP ACTIVITY ⏱

Seat children in pairs, and provide each pair with 28 red and 28 blue connecting cubes. Provide the following directions for making cube trains to the children as a whole group.

Have pairs work together to make the cube trains. Tell children to make a cube train with 1 red cube and 7 blue cubes. Then have them make trains with 2 red, 6 blue and 3 red, 5 blue cubes. Then have them place the three trains in a row. Have pairs work to continue the pattern until they have a 7 red and 1 blue cube train.

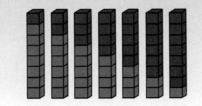

■ **What pattern do you see?** [Possible response: The red increased by 1 as the blue decreased by 1.]

Have volunteers write the addition facts for the cube trains on the chalkboard.

1	2	3	4	5	6	7
+7	+6	+5	+4	+3	+2	+1

■ **What pattern do you see?** [In their own words, children may note that as one addend increases, the other decreases.]

PAIRS ACTIVITY ⏱ 👥

Provide each pair with graph paper and crayons for recording. Have pairs work together to develop other cube train patterns and addition fact patterns. Children may record by showing the color patterns developed with the cube trains. Have them write the fact below each model on the paper.

EXTENDING THE ACTIVITY

Have children explore patterns beyond the basic facts to 18.

ONGOING ASSESSMENT

✔ Are children beginning to recognize the relationship between addends when working with facts with the same sum?

Mathematics and Literature

Listening and Speaking

The Read-Aloud selection can be used with the Chapter 3 Opener and Lesson 3-1 on pages 91-92.

Homework Machine

FROM *A LIGHT IN THE ATTIC*, BY SHEL SILVERSTEIN

The Homework Machine, oh the Homework Machine,
Most perfect contraption that's ever been seen.
Just put in your homework, then drop in a dime,
Snap on the switch, and in ten seconds' time,
Your homework comes out, quick and clean as can be.
Here it is—"nine plus four?" and the answer is "three."
Three?
Oh me . . .
I guess it's not as perfect
As I thought it would be.

AT·A·GLANCE pp. 91-92

LESSON OBJECTIVES
Explore mathematical concepts through literature.
Explore the concept of addition and subtraction.

ASSIGNMENT GUIDE

COURSE	EXERCISES
Basic	p. 91: All; p. 92: 1–3
Average	p. 91: All; p. 92: 1–3
Challenge	p. 91: All; p. 92: 1–3

MATERIALS

Classroom Materials shoebox
Manipulatives 18 ○ (or punchouts)

Teacher Resources
Math Anthology, p. 144

SKILLS TRACE
FACTS TO 18

Explore (Concrete) 92	Develop/Understand (Transitional/Abstract) 93–94, 95–96, 97–98, 99–100, 101–102, 107–108, 109–110, 111, 112
Practice 106, 117, 118, 119–120, 123, 138, 168	Apply 103–104, 105, 113–114, 116, 122

CHAPTER 3

Adding and Subtracting Facts to 18

READ ALOUD

A LIGHT IN THE ATTIC By Shel Silverstein

👂 Listen to the poem <u>Homework Machine</u>.

🗨 Tell how the Homework Machine's answer **is wrong.** Children may note that three is smaller than 9 and 4; you need to add to get the correct answer.

91

Mathematics and Literature

PREPARE **WARM-UP** To review addition and subtraction facts to 10, write the following fact families on the chalkboard. Have children give the sums and differences.

3 + 4 = __[7]	2 + 6 = __[8]	3 + 6 = __[9]
4 + 3 = __[7]	6 + 2 = __[8]	6 + 3 = __[9]
7 − 4 = __[3]	8 − 2 = __[6]	9 − 3 = __[6]
7 − 3 = __[4]	8 − 6 = __[2]	9 − 6 = __[3]

TEACH **DISCUSSING** Before reading the poem "Homework Machine," have children discuss the advantages and disadvantages of such a machine.

PUPIL'S EDITION pp. 91-92

Page 91 Read *Homework Machine* found on page 90M or in *Math Anthology* to children.

■ **If the machine could do homework for only one subject, which would you have it do?** [Accept all reasonable responses.]

Discuss the directive on the page. Guide children to find the answer to 9 + 4 by counting on from 9.

Page 92 ■ Working Together Assign each child a partner. Give each pair 18 counters and a shoebox. Explain that by following the directions, they can make their own number machine.

Check for Understanding

■ **What do you need to make a number machine?** [shoebox, 18 counters]

ACTIVITY

Adding and Subtracting Facts to 18

Working Together

Use a shoebox and 18 ⬤.

Make a number machine.
Each of you takes some counters.
Do not show your counters to each other.
Guess how many counters in all.

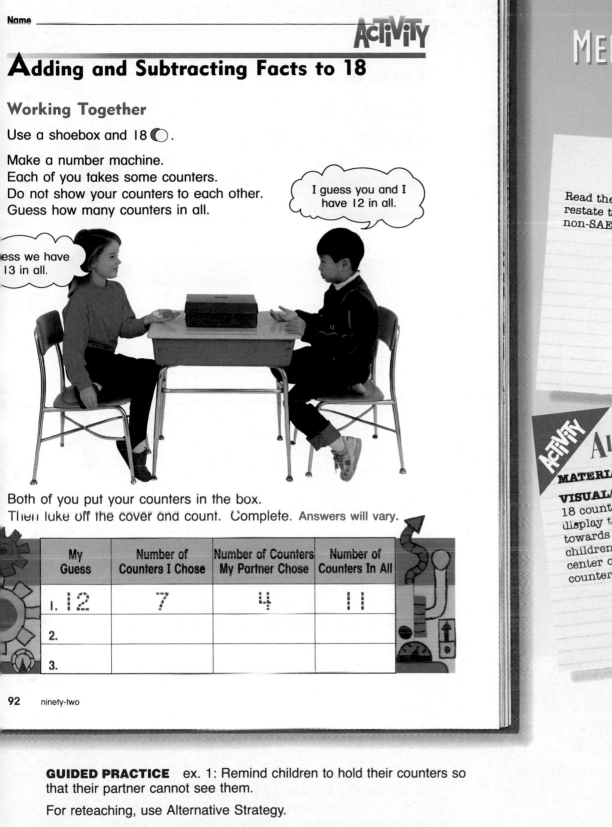

I guess you and I have 12 in all.

...ess we have ...13 in all.

Both of you put your counters in the box.
Then take off the cover and count. Complete. Answers will vary.

My Guess	Number of Counters I Chose	Number of Counters My Partner Chose	Number of Counters In All
1. 12	7	4	11
2.			
3.			

GUIDED PRACTICE ex. 1: Remind children to hold their counters so that their partner cannot see them.

For reteaching, use Alternative Strategy.

3 PRACTICE·APPLY **PRACTICE** ex. 2–3: Have children complete the page. Remind them to remember how many counters they put in the box so they can complete the table.

C L O S E Guide children to summarize the lesson:

■ **What two numbers must equal the total number of counters in the box?** [the number of counters put in by each person]

MEETING INDIVIDUAL NEEDS

For Students Acquiring English (SAE)

Read the directions on page 92 aloud and have SAE children restate them so you can check comprehension. Pair SAE and non-SAE children to work together.

ACTIVITY

ALTERNATIVE TEACHING STRATEGY

MATERIALS 18 ○ (or punchouts), paper bag

VISUAL/KINESTHETICS Gather children around a table. Place 18 counters in a bag. Have two volunteers remove counters, display the counters in front of them, and push each counter towards the center of the table as they count aloud. Then have all children count with you to find the number of counters in the center of the table. Repeat by having other children remove counters from the bag.

Problem of the Day

Nick put 8 counters in the number machine. Betty put 7 counters in the machine. How many counters were inside the number machine? [15 counters]

CHAPTER 3 • Lesson 2

AT·A·GLANCE pp. 93-94

LESSON OBJECTIVE
Add and subtract facts to 11.

ASSIGNMENT GUIDE

COURSE	EXERCISES
Basic	p. 93: 2–8; p. 94: 1–6
Average	p. 93: 2–8; p. 94: 1–6
Challenge	p. 93: 2–8; p. 94: 1–6

MATERIALS
Classroom Materials red and blue crayons
Manipulatives 9 ▥, 9 ▤ (or square counter punchouts) per child

Teacher Resources
Reteaching 31   Practice 31   Enrichment 31
MAC Act. 61, 62

SKILLS TRACE
FACTS TO 18

Explore (Concrete) 92	Develop/Understand (Transitional/Abstract) 93–94, 95–96, 97–98, 99–100, 101–102, 107–108, 109–110, 111, 112
Practice 106, 117, 118, 119–120, 123, 138, 168	Apply 103–104, 105, 113–114, 116, 122

See **MANIPULATIVES PLUS 15**, p. 90l.

---

1 PREPARE **WARM-UP** To review facts to 10, ask children to give each sum or difference orally.

4 + 3 [7]	8 − 2 [6]	0 + 9 [9]
9 − 5 [4]	3 + 7 [10]	9 − 7 [2]
5 + 5 [10]	10 − 6 [4]	6 + 3 [9]

2 TEACH **MODELING** Give each child 9 red and 9 blue connecting cubes. Tell children to use 5 cubes of each color to make a train.

■ **How many red cubes do you have in your train?** [5]
■ **How many blue cubes do you have?** [5]

Write 5 + 5 = 10 on the chalkboard and read the addition sentence aloud.

Facts to 11

Use 9 ▥, 9 ▤,

a ▭ red ▭ , and a ▭ blue ▭ .

Build a train to show the fact.
Color to show the train. Complete.

Write the sum.   Write the difference.

1. $9 + 2 = 11$ $11 - 2 = 9$

2. $8 + 3 = 11$ $11 - 3 = 8$

r	r	r	r	r	r	r	r	b	b	b

3. $7 + 4 = 11$ $11 - 4 = 7$

r	r	r	r	r	r	r	b	b	b	b

4. $6 + 5 = 11$ $11 - 5 = 6$

r	r	r	r	r	r	b	b	b	b	b

5. $5 + 6 = 11$ $11 - 6 = 5$

r	r	r	r	r	b	b	b	b	b	b

6. $4 + 7 = 11$ $11 - 7 = 4$

r	r	r	r	b	b	b	b	b	b	b

7. $3 + 8 = 11$ $11 - 8 = 3$

r	r	r	b	b	b	b	b	b	b	b

8. $2 + 9 = 11$ $11 - 9 = 2$

r	r	b	b	b	b	b	b	b	b	b

Chapter 3   Adding and Subtracting Facts to 18   ninety-three   **93**

Next have children snap on 1 more cube of either color.
■ **What addition fact can you make up for your train?**
[6 + 5 = 11 or 5 + 6 = 11]

Write the sentences on the chalkboard. Then tell children to make a train of 11 cubes and break off 5 cubes. Have children explain what they did. Write 11 − 5 = 6 and have the subtraction sentence read aloud.

PUPIL'S EDITION pp. 93-94

Page 93 Guide children as they work through ex. 1.

Check for Understanding

■ **How would you model 8 + 3 and 11 − 3?** [8 red cubes and 3 blue cubes or 8 blue cubes and 3 red cubes]

Write the fact family.

1.  $8 + 3 = 11$ $11 - 3 = 8$

    $3 + 8 = 11$ $11 - 8 = 3$

2. $4 + 7 = 11$ $11 - 7 = 4$

    $7 + 4 = 11$ $11 - 4 = 7$

Add or subtract.

3.
$$\begin{array}{c} 4 \\ +5 \\ \hline 9 \end{array} \quad \begin{array}{c} 8 \\ +3 \\ \hline 11 \end{array} \quad \begin{array}{c} 2 \\ +9 \\ \hline 11 \end{array} \quad \begin{array}{c} 4 \\ +6 \\ \hline 10 \end{array} \quad \begin{array}{c} 6 \\ +5 \\ \hline 11 \end{array} \quad \begin{array}{c} 5 \\ +2 \\ \hline 7 \end{array}$$

4.
$$\begin{array}{c} 9 \\ -7 \\ \hline 2 \end{array} \quad \begin{array}{c} 11 \\ -4 \\ \hline 7 \end{array} \quad \begin{array}{c} 7 \\ -4 \\ \hline 3 \end{array} \quad \begin{array}{c} 8 \\ -6 \\ \hline 2 \end{array} \quad \begin{array}{c} 11 \\ -7 \\ \hline 4 \end{array} \quad \begin{array}{c} 10 \\ -2 \\ \hline 8 \end{array}$$

5.
$$\begin{array}{c} 11 \\ -2 \\ \hline 9 \end{array} \quad \begin{array}{c} 8 \\ -0 \\ \hline 8 \end{array} \quad \begin{array}{c} 9 \\ -4 \\ \hline 5 \end{array} \quad \begin{array}{c} 7 \\ -7 \\ \hline 0 \end{array} \quad \begin{array}{c} 9 \\ -3 \\ \hline 6 \end{array} \quad \begin{array}{c} 10 \\ -7 \\ \hline 3 \end{array}$$

I use the double $3 + 3$ to find $3 + 4$.

$3 + 3 = 6$
$6 + 1 = 7$

6. What double can you use to find $5 + 6$? _____ $5 + 5 = 10$

ACTIVITY — Common Error and Remediation

MATERIALS 18 ○ (or punchout counters)

Some children may guess instead of using strategies for finding sums and differences which they do not know. Work individually with each child. Use a set of counters to work through each fact that he or she wrote incorrectly. Have the child model the first addend with counters, the second addend with counters, and then count on from the first addend to find the sum. Have the child find differences by counting back by ones, removing 1 counter at a time.

ALTERNATIVE TEACHING STRATEGY

VISUAL Write the following addition and subtraction facts on the chalkboard. Draw a set of 5 and a set of 6 dots to represent the addends.

$5 + 6 = 11$ $6 + 5 = 11$ $11 - 6 = 5$ $11 - 5 = 6$

Then discuss the addition, noting that these are related facts. Use a sheet of paper to cover 6 dots and discuss the first subtraction. Then cover 5 dots and discuss the second subtraction.

GUIDED PRACTICE ex. 2–8: For reteaching, use Common Error and Remediation or Alternative Strategy.

Page 94 Review the meaning of the terms **fact family** and **related facts**.

3 PRACTICE•APPLY

PRACTICE ex. 1–6: Call on volunteers to explain their answers to ex. 6.

CLOSE Guide children to summarize the lesson:

■ **Can you say an addition and subtraction fact for 11?** [Possible responses: $8 + 3 = 11$ and $11 - 3 = 8$, $4 + 7 = 11$ and $11 - 7 = 4$]

Chapter 3 • Lesson 2 **94**

MAC ACTIVITY CENTER

ESTIMATION ▪ WHITE SNEAKERS

MAC Activity 62

On Your Own   Pair and Share   In a Group

Ask children to look around the room very quickly to decide whether more than or fewer than 11 of their classmates are wearing white sneakers. Then call on children to give their estimates. Have children count the actual number of children wearing white sneakers and compare that number with their estimates. Repeat the activity with other kinds of clothing or different objects, like books on a desk.

▲
MAC Activity 62:
Average-to-Challenge

CALCULATOR ▪ *KEY IT!*

MAC Activity 61

On Your Own   Pair and Share   In a Group

Materials calculators, counters or punchout counters

Have children work in pairs. Explain that one child says an addition or subtraction fact, like 9 + 2, and enters it into the calculator. The other child gives the answer orally, using counters to find the sum or difference if needed. Then the first child presses the = key. Both children check the calculator to see if the oral response was correct.

▲
MAC Activity 61:
Basic-to-Average

white sneakers 4
books on desk 6
yellow pencils

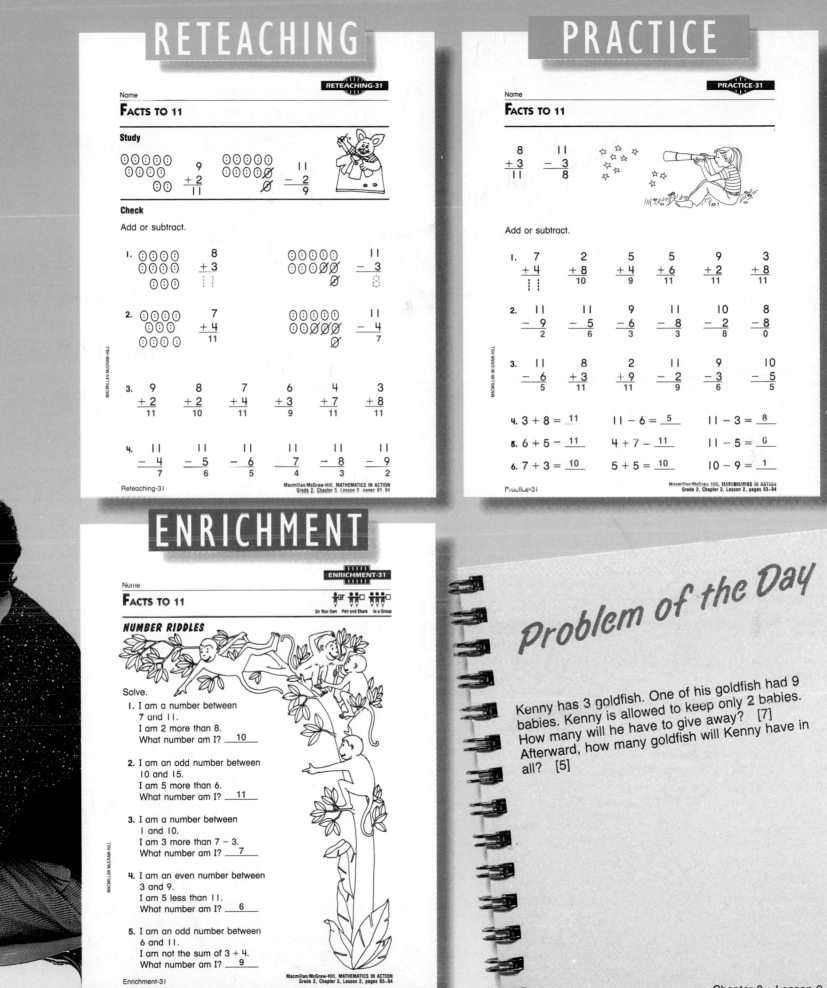

Study

9
+2
11

11
− 2
9

Check

Add or subtract.

1.
8
+3
11

11
− 3
8

2.
7
+4
11

11
− 4
7

3.
9
+2
11

8
+2
10

7
+4
11

6
+3
9

4
+7
11

3
+8
11

4.
11
− 4
7

11
− 5
6

11
− 6
5

11
− 7
4

11
− 8
3

11
− 9
2

Reteaching-31

Macmillan/McGraw-Hill, MATHEMATICS IN ACTION
Grade 2, Chapter 3, Lesson 2, pages 93–94

8
+3
11

11
− 3
8

Add or subtract.

1.
7
+4
11

2
+8
10

5
+4
9

5
+6
11

9
+2
11

3
+8
11

2.
11
− 9
2

11
− 5
6

9
− 6
3

11
− 8
3

10
− 2
8

8
− 8
0

3.
11
− 6
5

8
+3
11

2
+9
11

11
− 2
9

9
− 3
6

10
− 5
5

4. 3 + 8 = __11__   11 − 6 = __5__   11 − 3 = __8__

5. 6 + 5 = __11__   4 + 7 = __11__   11 − 5 = __6__

6. 7 + 3 = __10__   5 + 5 = __10__   10 − 9 = __1__

Practice-31

Macmillan/McGraw-Hill, MATHEMATICS IN ACTION
Grade 2, Chapter 3, Lesson 2, pages 93–94

NUMBER RIDDLES

Solve.

1. I am a number between
   7 and 11.
   I am 2 more than 8.
   What number am I? __10__

2. I am an odd number between
   10 and 15.
   I am 5 more than 6.
   What number am I? __11__

3. I am a number between
   1 and 10.
   I am 3 more than 7 − 3.
   What number am I? __7__

4. I am an even number between
   3 and 9.
   I am 5 less than 11.
   What number am I? __6__

5. I am an odd number between
   6 and 11.
   I am not the sum of 3 + 4.
   What number am I? __9__

Enrichment-31

Macmillan/McGraw-Hill, MATHEMATICS IN ACTION
Grade 2, Chapter 3, Lesson 2, pages 93–94

Problem of the Day

Kenny has 3 goldfish. One of his goldfish had 9 babies. Kenny is allowed to keep only 2 babies. How many will he have to give away? [7] Afterward, how many goldfish will Kenny have in all? [5]

AT·A·GLANCE pp. 95-96

LESSON OBJECTIVE
Add and subtract facts to 12.

ASSIGNMENT GUIDE

COURSE	EXERCISES
Basic	p. 95: 2–7; p. 96: 1–5, Mental Math
Average	p. 95: 2–7; p. 96: 1–5, Mental Math
Challenge	p. 95: 2–7; p. 96: 1–5, Mental Math

MATERIALS
Classroom Materials red and yellow crayons
Manipulatives 12 ◯ (or punchouts) per child

Teacher Resources
Reteaching 32   Practice 32   Enrichment 32
MAC Act. 63, 64
Math Anthology, p. 148

SKILLS TRACE
FACTS TO 18

Explore (Concrete) 92	Develop/Understand (Transitional/Abstract) 93–94, 95–96, 97–98, 99–100, 101–102, 107–108, 109–110, 111, 112
Practice 106, 117, 118, 119–120, 123, 138, 168	Apply 103–104, 105, 113–114, 116, 122

See **MANIPULATIVES PLUS 16**, p. 90J.

---

1 PREPARE **WARM-UP** To review addition and subtraction facts, write these pairs of sentences on the chalkboard.

3 + 8 = 11	11 − 8 = 3
[8 + 3 = 11]	[11 − 3 = 8]
5 + 6 = 11	11 − 6 = 5
[6 + 5 = 11]	[11 − 5 = 6]
4 + 6 = 10	10 − 6 = 4
[6 + 4 = 10]	[10 − 4 = 6]

Have children give the two related number sentences that complete each fact family.

Facts to 12

Working Together
Use 12 ◯, a ✏ red ▷, and a ✏ yellow ▷.

Take 12 ◯.   Shake.   Drop.

Color to show them.
Write two facts for each drop.
Order of answers will vary.

Try to color a new fact each time.

1.	3 + 9 = 12	12 − 9 = 3
2.	4 + 8 = 12	12 − 8 = 4
3.	5 + 7 = 12	12 − 7 = 5
4.	6 + 6 = 12	12 − 6 = 6
5.	7 + 5 = 12	12 − 5 = 7
6.	8 + 4 = 12	12 − 4 = 8
7.	9 + 3 = 12	12 − 3 = 9

Macmillan/McGraw-Hill

Chapter 3   Adding and Subtracting Facts to 18   ninety-five   **95**

---

2 TEACH **MODELING** Have each child display a red and a yellow counter to show 1 + 1. Next have each child put down another red and another yellow counter.

■ **What is the name of the addition fact for this new model?** [2 + 2]

Continue the activity until the children have shown 3 + 3, 4 + 4, 5 + 5, and 6 + 6.

After children have displayed 6 + 6, have them turn over one yellow counter.

■ **What is the name of the addition fact for this model?** [7 + 5 = 12 or 5 + 7 = 12, depending upon the order of their colors]

Write a number sentence on the chalkboard for each model.

Add or subtract.

1.
$$9 + 2 = 11$$ $$2 + 9 = 11$$ $$7 + 5 = 12$$ $$5 + 7 = 12$$ $$8 + 2 = 10$$ $$2 + 8 = 10$$

2.
$$7 - 5 = 2$$ $$7 - 2 = 5$$ $$11 - 3 = 8$$ $$11 - 8 = 3$$ $$12 - 9 = 3$$ $$12 - 3 = 9$$

3.
$$6 + 5 = 11$$ $$5 + 6 = 11$$ $$8 + 4 = 12$$ $$4 + 8 = 12$$ $$4 + 7 = 11$$ $$7 + 4 = 11$$

Solve.

4. Rita gave 3 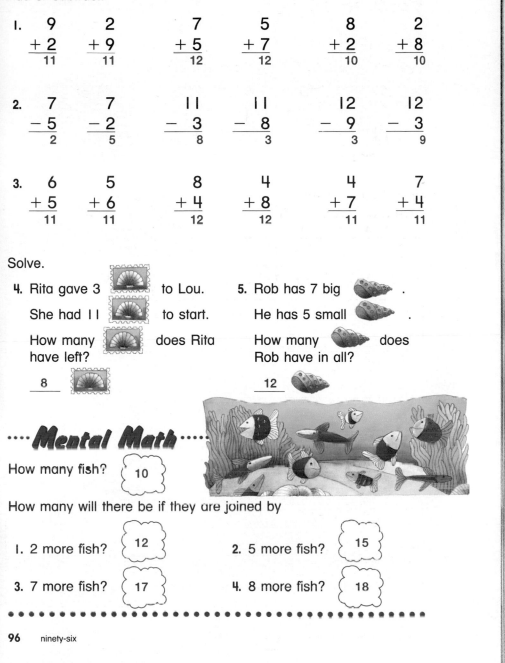 to Lou.
She had 11 to start.
How many does Rita have left?

   8

5. Rob has 7 big .
He has 5 small .
How many does Rob have in all?

   12

···· *Mental Math* ····

How many fish? (10)

How many will there be if they are joined by

1. 2 more fish? (12)   2. 5 more fish? (15)

3. 7 more fish? (17)   4. 8 more fish? (18)

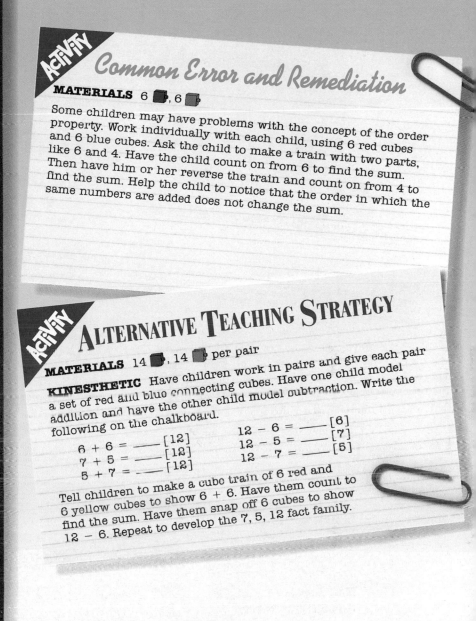

ACTIVITY *Common Error and Remediation*

MATERIALS 6 ■, 6 ■

Some children may have problems with the concept of the order property. Work individually with each child, using 6 red cubes and 6 blue cubes. Ask the child to make a train with two parts, like 6 and 4. Have the child count on from 6 to find the sum. Then have him or her reverse the train and count on from 4 to find the sum. Help the child to notice that the order in which the same numbers are added does not change the sum.

ACTIVITY ALTERNATIVE TEACHING STRATEGY

MATERIALS 14 ■, 14 ■ per pair

KINESTHETIC Have children work in pairs and give each pair a set of red and blue connecting cubes. Have one child model addition and have the other child model subtraction. Write the following on the chalkboard.

$$6 + 6 = \underline{\quad} [12]$$ $$12 - 6 = \underline{\quad} [6]$$
$$7 + 5 = \underline{\quad} [12]$$ $$12 - 5 = \underline{\quad} [7]$$
$$5 + 7 = \underline{\quad} [12]$$ $$12 - 7 = \underline{\quad} [5]$$

Tell children to make a cube train of 6 red and 6 yellow cubes to show 6 + 6. Have them count to find the sum. Have them snap off 6 cubes to show 12 − 6. Repeat to develop the 7, 5, 12 fact family.

PUPIL'S EDITION pp. 95-96

Page 95 ■ Working Together Have children work in pairs to do the activity. Guide them through ex. 1.

Check for Understanding

■ **How would you model 8 + 4 and 12 − 4?** [8 red counters and 4 yellow counters or 8 yellow counters and 4 red counters]

GUIDED PRACTICE ex. 2–7: For reteaching, use Common Error and Remediation or Alternative Strategy.

Page 96 Remind children that addition and subtraction facts can be written horizontally or vertically.

Mathematics and Literature

PRACTICE·APPLY **PRACTICE** ex. 1–5: Read ex. 4–5 aloud before children complete them.

MENTAL MATH Allow children who are having difficulty doing the activity mentally to work with counters.

Read the poem "Don't Ask Me" found in *Math Anthology*. Invite children to share their reactions to the poem. Then reread the poem, pausing at each number fact so children can model it with counters or find the answer using mental math.

CLOSE Guide children to summarize the lesson:

■ **What addition fact is related to 12 − 5 = 7?** [7 + 5 = 12 or 5 + 7 = 12]

Chapter 3 • Lesson 3   **96**

MAC ACTIVITY CENTER

MAC Activity 63:
Basic-to-Average ▼

MAC Activity 63

On Your Own   Pair and Share   In a Group

SPEAKING MATHEMATICALLY ▪ MODEL FACTS

Materials   connecting cubes

Have children work in pairs, taking turns modeling and saying number facts for 12. One child uses connecting cubes to model an addition or a subtraction fact. The second child says the fact for that model and the three related facts that complete the fact family. Have children exchange roles and repeat the activity.

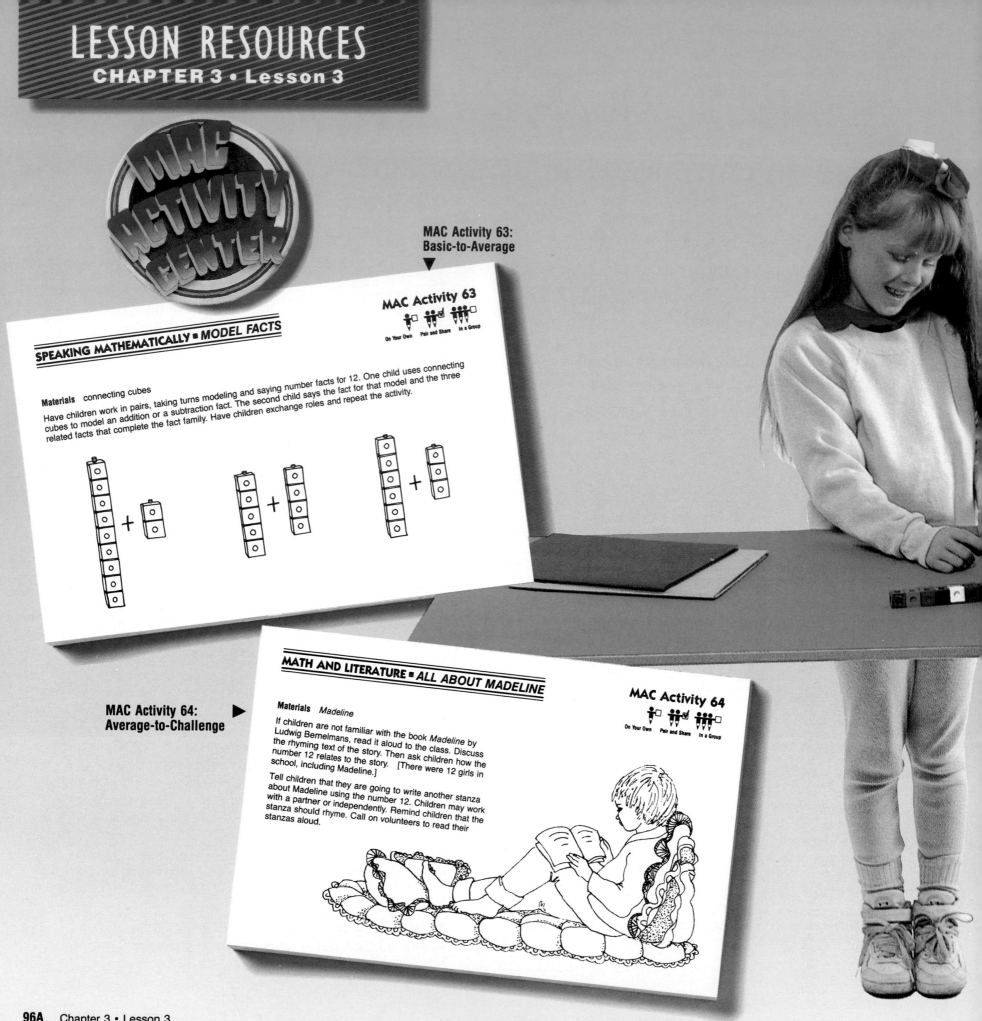

MAC Activity 64:
Average-to-Challenge ▶

MAC Activity 64

On Your Own   Pair and Share   In a Group

MATH AND LITERATURE ▪ ALL ABOUT MADELINE

Materials   *Madeline*

If children are not familiar with the book *Madeline* by Ludwig Bemelmans, read it aloud to the class. Discuss the rhyming text of the story. Then ask children how the number 12 relates to the story.   [There were 12 girls in school, including Madeline.]

Tell children that they are going to write another stanza about Madeline using the number 12. Children may work with a partner or independently. Remind children that the stanza should rhyme. Call on volunteers to read their stanzas aloud.

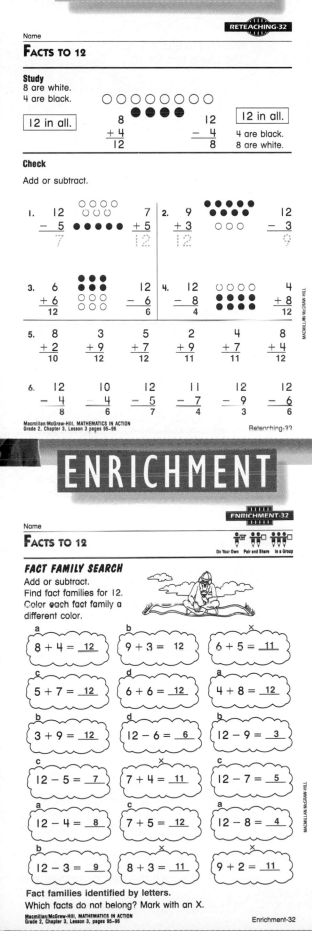

Reteaching

Name

FACTS TO 12

RETEACHING-32

Study
8 are white.
4 are black.

○○○○○○○○ ●●●●

12 in all.

$\begin{array}{r} 8 \\ +4 \\ \hline 12 \end{array}$ $\begin{array}{r} 12 \\ -4 \\ \hline 8 \end{array}$

12 in all.

4 are black.
8 are white.

Check

Add or subtract.

1. $\begin{array}{r} 12 \\ -5 \\ \hline 7 \end{array}$ 2. $\begin{array}{r} 9 \\ +3 \\ \hline 12 \end{array}$

$\begin{array}{r} 7 \\ +5 \\ \hline 12 \end{array}$ $\begin{array}{r} 12 \\ -3 \\ \hline 9 \end{array}$

3. $\begin{array}{r} 6 \\ +6 \\ \hline 12 \end{array}$ 4. $\begin{array}{r} 12 \\ -8 \\ \hline 4 \end{array}$

$\begin{array}{r} 12 \\ -6 \\ \hline 6 \end{array}$ $\begin{array}{r} 4 \\ +8 \\ \hline 12 \end{array}$

5. $\begin{array}{r} 8 \\ +2 \\ \hline 10 \end{array}$ $\begin{array}{r} 3 \\ +9 \\ \hline 12 \end{array}$ $\begin{array}{r} 5 \\ +7 \\ \hline 12 \end{array}$ $\begin{array}{r} 2 \\ +9 \\ \hline 11 \end{array}$ $\begin{array}{r} 4 \\ +7 \\ \hline 11 \end{array}$ $\begin{array}{r} 8 \\ +4 \\ \hline 12 \end{array}$

6. $\begin{array}{r} 12 \\ -4 \\ \hline 8 \end{array}$ $\begin{array}{r} 10 \\ -4 \\ \hline 6 \end{array}$ $\begin{array}{r} 12 \\ -5 \\ \hline 7 \end{array}$ $\begin{array}{r} 11 \\ -7 \\ \hline 4 \end{array}$ $\begin{array}{r} 12 \\ -9 \\ \hline 3 \end{array}$ $\begin{array}{r} 12 \\ -6 \\ \hline 6 \end{array}$

Macmillan/McGraw-Hill, MATHEMATICS IN ACTION
Grade 2, Chapter 3, Lesson 3 pages 95–96

Reteaching-32

Practice

Name

FACTS TO 12

PRACTICE-32

Write the fact family for the picture.

1. $\begin{array}{r} 4 + 8 = 12 \\ 8 + 4 = 12 \end{array}$ $\begin{array}{r} 12 - 8 = 4 \\ 12 - 4 = 8 \end{array}$

2. $\begin{array}{r} 7 + 5 = 12 \\ 5 + 7 = 12 \end{array}$ $\begin{array}{r} 12 - 5 = 7 \\ 12 - 7 = 5 \end{array}$

Add or subtract.

3. $\begin{array}{r} 6 \\ +6 \\ \hline 12 \end{array}$ $\begin{array}{r} 9 \\ +3 \\ \hline 12 \end{array}$ $\begin{array}{r} 4 \\ +6 \\ \hline 10 \end{array}$ $\begin{array}{r} 5 \\ +7 \\ \hline 12 \end{array}$ $\begin{array}{r} 8 \\ +4 \\ \hline 12 \end{array}$ $\begin{array}{r} 2 \\ +9 \\ \hline 11 \end{array}$

4. $\begin{array}{r} 12 \\ -3 \\ \hline 9 \end{array}$ $\begin{array}{r} 10 \\ -3 \\ \hline 7 \end{array}$ $\begin{array}{r} 12 \\ -6 \\ \hline 6 \end{array}$ $\begin{array}{r} 11 \\ -2 \\ \hline 9 \end{array}$ $\begin{array}{r} 12 \\ -7 \\ \hline 5 \end{array}$ $\begin{array}{r} 12 \\ -9 \\ \hline 3 \end{array}$

5. $\begin{array}{r} 12 \\ -8 \\ \hline 4 \end{array}$ $\begin{array}{r} 7 \\ +5 \\ \hline 12 \end{array}$ $\begin{array}{r} 3 \\ +8 \\ \hline 11 \end{array}$ $\begin{array}{r} 11 \\ -7 \\ \hline 4 \end{array}$ $\begin{array}{r} 4 \\ +8 \\ \hline 12 \end{array}$ $\begin{array}{r} 12 \\ -5 \\ \hline 7 \end{array}$

Macmillan/McGraw-Hill, MATHEMATICS IN ACTION
Grade 2, Chapter 3, Lesson 3, pages 95–96

Practice-32

Enrichment

Name

FACTS TO 12

ENRICHMENT-32

On Your Own   Pair and Share   In a Group

FACT FAMILY SEARCH
Add or subtract.
Find fact families for 12.
Color each fact family a
different color.

a
8 + 4 = __12__

b
9 + 3 = 12

x
6 + 5 = __11__

c
5 + 7 = __12__

d
6 + 6 = __12__

a
4 + 8 = __12__

b
3 + 9 = __12__

d
12 − 6 = __6__

b
12 − 9 = __3__

c
12 − 5 = __7__

x
7 + 4 = __11__

c
12 − 7 = __5__

a
12 − 4 = __8__

c
7 + 5 = __12__

a
12 − 8 = __4__

b
12 − 3 = __9__

x
8 + 3 = __11__

x
9 + 2 = __11__

Fact families identified by letters.
Which facts do not belong? Mark with an X.

Macmillan/McGraw-Hill, MATHEMATICS IN ACTION
Grade 2, Chapter 3, Lesson 3, pages 95–96

Enrichment-32

Problem of the Day

On Monday Yolanda found 3 shells; on Tuesday she found 3 more shells. Today she did not find any shells. Yolanda needs 12 shells to make a necklace. How many more shells does she need to find?   [6; children may work it out this way: 3 + 3 + 0 = 6; 12 − 6 = 6.]

AT·A·GLANCE pp. 97-98

LESSON OBJECTIVE
Use computation strategies to find sums and differences.

ASSIGNMENT GUIDE

COURSE	EXERCISES
Basic	p. 97: 1–4; p. 98: 1–6
Average	p. 97: 1–4; p. 98: 1–6
Challenge	p. 97: 1–4; p. 98: 1–6

Teacher Resources
Reteaching 33   Practice 33   Enrichment 33
MAC Act. 65, 66

SKILLS TRACE
FACTS TO 18

Explore (Concrete)	Develop/Understand (Transitional/Abstract)
92	93–94, 95–96, 97–98, 99–100, 101–102, 107–108, 109–110, 111, 112
Practice 106, 117, 118, 119–120, 123, 138, 168	**Apply** 103–104, 105, 113–114, 116, 122

See **MANIPULATIVES PLUS 17**, p. 90K.

MANIPULATIVES *plus* ACTIVITY

PREPARE **WARM-UP** To review addition and subtraction strategies, write the following on the chalkboard.

10 = 9 + __ [1]   10 = 1 + __ [9]
10 = 7 + __ [3]   10 = 5 + __ [5]
10 = 3 + __ [7]   10 = 4 + __ [6]

Have children give each missing addend.

TEACH **DISCUSSING** Copy the following addition fact and model on the chalkboard.

o o o o o o o o o o o
5 + 6 = 11

Name _____

Mental Math Strategies

We want to find 7 + 5.
We use a fact for 10.

7 + 3 = 10
10 + 2 = 12

Find the sum. Use a fact for 10 to help.

1. 8 + 4 = _12_   5 + 7 = _12_   7 + 4 = _11_

2. 8 + 3 = _11_   5 + 6 = _11_   6 + 5 = _11_

Ann and Dan like to begin with the larger number when they add.

We want to find 3 + 8.
We think 8 + 3.

Start with 8.
Count on to add 3.

3. Tell why it is easier to begin with the larger number. Answers will va[...]
Possible answer: you count on less if you begin with the larger number fi[...]

Try these.

4. 4 + 8 = _12_   3 + 9 = _12_   4 + 7 = _11_

Macmillan/McGraw-Hill

Chapter 3   Adding and Subtracting Facts to 18   ninety-seven   **97**

Explain to children that finding a fact for 10 and then counting on is a way to find sums. Have a volunteer fill in 5 of the circles to show the first addend.

■ **How many more circles must be filled in to make 10?** [5]

Have the child fill in 5 more circles. Guide children to find the sum by counting on the remaining circle. Repeat with other facts.

Explain that another way to find sums is to count on from the greater addend. Have children count on for each of these facts: 2 + 9 = __ and 9 + 2 = __. Establish that it is easier to find 9 + 2 than 2 + 9.

PUPIL'S EDITION pp. 97-98

Page 97 Discuss the two examples with the children.

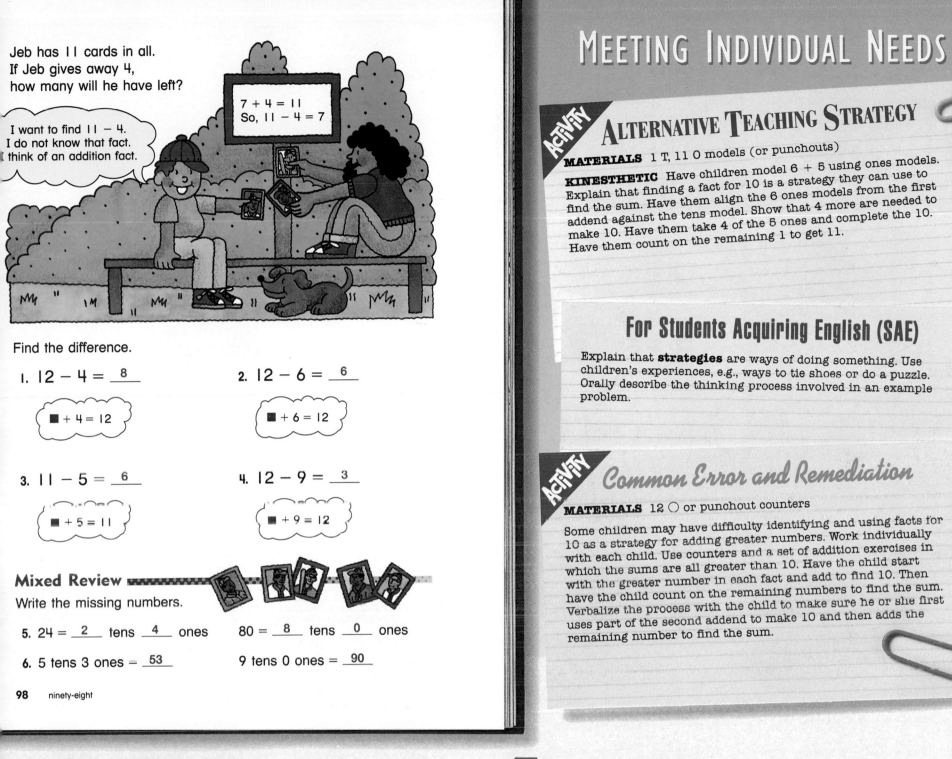

Jeb has 11 cards in all.
If Jeb gives away 4,
how many will he have left?

I want to find 11 − 4.
I do not know that fact.
I think of an addition fact.

7 + 4 = 11
So, 11 − 4 = 7

Find the difference.

1. 12 − 4 = __8__

   ■ + 4 = 12

2. 12 − 6 = __6__

   ■ + 6 = 12

3. 11 − 5 = __6__

   ■ + 5 = 11

4. 12 − 9 = __3__

   ■ + 9 = 12

Mixed Review

Write the missing numbers.

5. 24 = __2__ tens __4__ ones   80 = __8__ tens __0__ ones

6. 5 tens 3 ones = __53__   9 tens 0 ones = __90__

ACTIVITY ALTERNATIVE TEACHING STRATEGY

MATERIALS 1 T, 11 O models (or punchouts)

KINESTHETIC Have children model 6 + 5 using ones models. Explain that finding a fact for 10 is a strategy they can use to find the sum. Have them align the 6 ones models from the first addend against the tens model. Show that 4 more are needed to make 10. Have them take 4 of the 5 ones and complete the 10. Have them count on the remaining 1 to get 11.

For Students Acquiring English (SAE)

Explain that **strategies** are ways of doing something. Use children's experiences, e.g., ways to tie shoes or do a puzzle. Orally describe the thinking process involved in an example problem.

ACTIVITY Common Error and Remediation

MATERIALS 12 ○ or punchout counters

Some children may have difficulty identifying and using facts for 10 as a strategy for adding greater numbers. Work individually with each child. Use counters and a set of addition exercises in which the sums are all greater than 10. Have the child start with the greater number in each fact and add to find 10. Then have the child count on the remaining numbers to find the sum. Verbalize the process with the child to make sure he or she first uses part of the second addend to make 10 and then adds the remaining number to find the sum.

Check for Understanding

■ **How can you find the sum of 4 + 7?** [Possible response: Find a fact for 10 and count on 1.]

GUIDED PRACTICE ex. 1–4: For reteaching, use Common Error and Remediation or Alternative Strategy.

Page 98 Review with children the strategy of using a related addition fact to find the difference.

3 PRACTICE•APPLY   PRACTICE ex. 1–6

CLOSE Guide children to summarize the lesson:

■ **What strategy could you use to find the sum of two numbers?** [Possible response: Begin with the greater number and count on.]

■ **What strategy could you use to find the difference between two numbers?** [Possible response: Think of a related addition fact.]

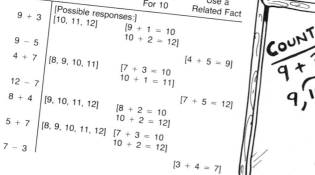

**MAC Activity 65:
Basic-to-Average**
▼

MENTAL MATH ▪ MATH DETECTIVE

MAC Activity 65

On Your Own Pair and Share In a Group

$$3 + \boxed{7} = 10$$

Materials number cards from 0–9 (Teacher Aid 11)

Procedure Form two teams. Say or display a number card from 0 to 9, such as 3, to the first player from each team. Explain that the number is one addend in an addition fact for 10. Have the player tell the other addend. The first child to say the missing addend, 7, becomes a detective and scores 1 point for his or her team.

To Win The team that scores the most points by the end of the game wins.

**MAC Activity 66:
Average-to-Challenge**
▼

NUMBER SENSE ▪ FACT TO FACT

MAC Activity 66

On Your Own Pair and Share In a Group

Write the following addition and subtraction facts in a chart on the chalkboard. Have children fill in the chart to show which strategies they used and how they used them.

	Count On	Use a Fact For 10	Use a Related Fact
	[Possible responses:]		
9 + 3	[10, 11, 12]	[9 + 1 = 10 10 + 2 = 12]	
9 − 5			
4 + 7	[8, 9, 10, 11]	[7 + 3 = 10 10 + 1 = 11]	[4 + 5 = 9]
12 − 7			
8 + 4	[9, 10, 11, 12]	[8 + 2 = 10 10 + 2 = 12]	[7 + 5 = 12]
5 + 7	[8, 9, 10, 11, 12]	[7 + 3 = 10 10 + 2 = 12]	
7 − 3			[3 + 4 = 7]

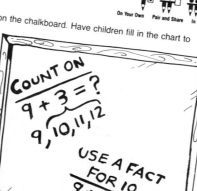

COUNT ON
9 + 3 = ?
9, 10, 11, 12

USE A FACT
FOR 10
9 + 1 = 10
10 + 2 = 12

Fact | Use a Related Fact

0
12

4 + 5 = 9

10
11

0
12

7 + 5 = 12

3 + 4 = 7

RETEACHING-33

Name

MENTAL MATH STRATEGIES

Study

$2 + 7 = \boxed{?}$ Count on from the greater number. **7, 8, 9** $2 + 7 = 9$

$11 - 8 = \boxed{?}$ Use an addition fact. $8 + \boxed{?} = 11$ $11 - 8 = 3$
$8 + \mathbf{3} = 11$

Check

Find the sum.

1. $4 + 7 = \underline{11}$ (7, 8, 9, 10, 11)
2. $2 + 6 = \underline{8}$ (6, 7, 8)
3. $1 + 9 = \underline{10}$
4. $7 + 5 = \underline{12}$
5. $3 + 9 = \underline{12}$
6. $2 + 8 = \underline{10}$
7. $3 + 7 = \underline{10}$

Find the difference.

8. $12 - 9 = \underline{3}$ ($9 + \boxed{3} = 12$)
9. $11 - 6 = \underline{5}$ ($6 + \boxed{5} = 11$)
10. $12 - 5 = \underline{7}$
11. $11 - 4 = \underline{7}$
12. $10 - 8 = \underline{2}$
13. $12 - 7 = \underline{5}$
14. $11 - 5 = \underline{6}$

Reteaching-33

Macmillan/McGraw-Hill, MATHEMATICS IN ACTION
Grade 2, Chapter 3, Lesson 4, pages 97–98

PRACTICE-33

Name

MENTAL MATH STRATEGIES

$7 + 4 = \underline{\quad}$ I think of a fact for 10.

$3 + 9 = \underline{\quad}$ I count on from the greater number.

$12 - 5 = \underline{\quad}$ I think of an addition fact.

Use strategies to find the sums and differences.

1. $7 + 5 = \underline{12}$ $3 + 9 = \underline{12}$ $4 + 7 = \underline{11}$
2. $8 + 4 = \underline{12}$ $5 + 7 = \underline{12}$ $2 + 6 = \underline{8}$
3. $2 + 7 = \underline{9}$ $9 + 2 = \underline{11}$ $3 + 9 = \underline{12}$
4. $3 + 8 = \underline{11}$ $5 + 6 = \underline{11}$ $4 + 8 = \underline{12}$

5. $9 - 7 = \underline{2}$ $10 - 9 = \underline{1}$ $12 - 7 = \underline{5}$
6. $11 - 8 = \underline{3}$ $12 - 9 = \underline{3}$ $10 - 6 = \underline{4}$
7. $12 - 8 = \underline{4}$ $10 - 3 = \underline{7}$ $11 - 9 = \underline{2}$
8. $12 - 5 = \underline{7}$ $9 - 6 = \underline{3}$ $11 - 7 = \underline{4}$

Practice 33

Macmillan/McGraw-Hill, MATHEMATICS IN ACTION
Grade 2, Chapter 3, Lesson 4, pages 97–98

ENRICHMENT-33

Name

MENTAL MATH STRATEGIES

On Your Own   Pair and Share   In a Group

CODED SENTENCES

Sam writes number sentences in code. This is his code.

0	1	2	3	4	5	6	7	8	9	10	11	12
A	B	C	D	E	F	G	H	I	J	BA	BB	BC

Complete each sentence.

1. $BC - D = \underline{J}$ $J + B = \underline{BA}$
2. $E + I = \underline{BC}$ $H - C = \underline{F}$
3. $BB - F = \underline{G}$ $D + H = \underline{BA}$
4. $G + A = \underline{G}$ $I - B = \underline{H}$

Write the missing letters.

5. $D + \underline{G} = J$ $BA - \underline{F} = F$
6. $J - \underline{A} = J$ $G + \underline{G} = BC$
7. $I + \underline{C} = BA$ $BB - \underline{D} = I$
8. $\underline{F} + C = H$ $\underline{G} + F = BB$

Enrichment-33

Macmillan/McGraw-Hill, MATHEMATICS IN ACTION
Grade 2, Chapter 3, Lesson 4, pages 97–98

Problem of the Day

3 children and 9 adults want to take an automobile trip. They have 2 cars, each of which can hold 5 passengers. They also have a van that can hold 13 people. Which will they take, the cars or the van? [The van. Children may work it out this way: $3 + 9 = 12$; $5 + 5 = 10$; $12 > 10$]

AT·A·GLANCE pp. 99-100

LESSON OBJECTIVE
Add and subtract, facts to 13.

ASSIGNMENT GUIDE

COURSE	EXERCISES
Basic	p. 99: 2–6; p. 100: 1–3, Reasoning
Average	p. 99: 2–6; p. 100: 1–3, Reasoning
Challenge	p. 99: 2–6; p. 100: 1–3, Reasoning

MATERIALS
Classroom Materials red and yellow crayons
Manipulatives 13 ◖ (or punchouts) per child

Teacher Resources
Reteaching 34   Practice 34   Enrichment 34
MAC Act. 67, 68   Teacher Aid 18

SKILLS TRACE
FACTS TO 18

Explore (Concrete) 92	Develop/Understand (Transitional/Abstract) 93–94, 95–96, 97–98, 99–100, 101–102, 107–108, 109–110, 111, 112
Practice 106, 117, 118, 119–120, 123, 138, 168	Apply 103–104, 105, 113–114, 116, 122

Facts to 13

13 children answered this question.
Show 1 red counter for each child.

● ● ● ● ● ● ● ● ●
● ● ● ●

Do you collect comic books?
Yes 👤👤👤👤👤👤👤👤👤
No 👤👤👤👤

How can you show how many children answered no?
Turn over 4 counters.
Think of an addition sentence and a subtraction sentence that tells about this graph.

$9 + 4 = 13; 13 - 4 = 9$ or $13 - 9 = 4$

Use 13 ◖ to show facts for 13. Order of answers will vary.

1. $9 + 4 = 13$ $13 - 4 = 9$
2. $8 + 5 = 13$ $13 - 5 = 8$
3. $7 + 6 = 13$ $13 - 6 = 7$
4. $6 + 7 = 13$ $13 - 7 = 6$
5. $5 + 8 = 13$ $13 - 8 = 5$
6. $4 + 9 = 13$ $13 - 9 = 4$

Macmillan/McGraw-Hill

 **PREPARE**

WARM-UP To review addition facts, write the following on the chalkboard. Have children find each sum and then give a related subtraction fact for each addition fact.

$7 + 5 =$ ___ [12; 12 − 5 = 7]
$4 + 7 =$ ___ [11; 11 − 7 = 4]
$6 + 6 =$ ___ [12; 12 − 6 = 6]
$7 + 0 =$ ___ [7; 7 − 0 = 7]

2 TEACH

MODELING Read the following problem to the class.

7 children were in the playground. 6 more children joined them. How many children are now in the playground?

Have children work in pairs. Tell them to use two-color counters to model the numbers in the story. Write $7 + 6$ on the chalkboard. Have children relate each number to the problem and tell how to find the sum. [13] Repeat the activity using a subtraction problem.

PUPIL'S EDITION pp. 99-100

Page 99 Discuss the pictograph at the top of the page with the children. Work through the example with them. Have the directions read aloud. Tell children to start with 13 counters each time. Remind them to turn over 4 or more counters, but not more than 9.

■ **What addition sentence tells about the graph?** [Possible responses: 9 + 4 = 13, 4 + 9 = 13]

Add or subtract.

1.	7 +5 — 12	7 +4 — 11	9 +3 — 12	8 +5 — 13	7 +3 — 10	4 +9 — 13
2.	3 +8 — 11	6 +7 — 13	8 +0 — 8	9 +4 — 13	6 +4 — 10	2 +9 — 11
3.	13 −9 — 4	12 −8 — 4	11 −7 — 4	10 −6 — 4	9 −5 — 4	8 −4 — 4

Reasoning

Each child collects something different.
Draw a line to show what each child collects.

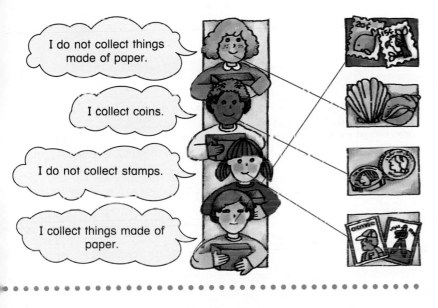

I do not collect things made of paper.

I collect coins.

I do not collect stamps.

I collect things made of paper.

ACTIVITY Common Error and Remediation

MATERIALS pack of index cards

Some children may continue to have problems finding sums and differences. Work individually with each child. Prepare a set of addition and subtraction flash cards. Make two sets of cards for facts to 13; one set of fact cards should not have answers and the other set should have only answers. Provide opportunities for matching facts to answers by playing the game "Concentration."

ONGOING ASSESSMENT MATH JOURNAL

INTERVIEW (1) Imagine you have 6 seashells, and your friend has 7 seashells. Tell an addition story about the seashells. **(2)** Imagine you have 12 pieces of pizza, and your friend has none. Tell a subtraction story about the pizza.

JOURNAL WRITING You may wish to have children record their responses in their math journals.

ACTIVITY ALTERNATIVE TEACHING STRATEGY

MATERIALS 13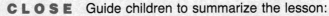

VISUAL Display a cube train with 13 cubes and write 13 on the chalkboard. Have a volunteer pick a number between 4 and 9, such as 6. Snap 6 cubes off the train and write 13 − 6 = _____ on the chalkboard. Have the same volunteer count the remaining cubes to find the difference. [7] Then place the 6-cube part next to the 7-cube part. Write 6 + 7 = _____ on the chalkboard. Snap the cubes together and write the sum. [13] Repeat the activity with other facts to 13.

■ **What subtraction sentence tells about the graph?** [Possible responses: 13 − 4 = 9, 13 − 9 = 4]

GUIDED PRACTICE ex. 2–6. Have children use red and yellow crayons to record facts. For reteaching, use Common Error and Remediation or Alternative Strategy.

Page 100 Remind children that addition and subtraction facts can be written horizontally or vertically.

³PRACTICE•APPLY PRACTICE ex. 1–3

REASONING Ask children if anyone has a collection. Call on those children to tell what they collect and why. After children have completed the activity, have them explain their answers.

C L O S E Guide children to summarize the lesson:
■ **Why are 7 + 6 = 13, 6 + 7 = 13, 13 − 7 = 6, and 13 − 6 = 7 a fact family?** [They are related facts with the same three numbers.]

MAC Activity 67

On Your Own   Pair and Share   In a Group

NUMBER SENSE ■ SUM WHEELS

Materials   worksheets with blank computation wheels
(Teacher Aid 18)

Have children work in pairs and provide each pair with a copy of the wheel. Tell children to write 13 in the center circle and explain that this is a sum. Then one child writes a number less than 13 inside a space in the inner or outer section of the wheel. The other child writes the missing addend in the appropriate space. Then that child writes a number less than 13 in a space. The activity continues until all spaces are filled.

MAC Activity 67:
Basic-to-Average ▶

LOGICAL REASONING ■ MYSTERY NUMBER

MAC Activity 68

On Your Own   Pair and Share   In a Group

...a 1 digit number which is two less than 6+5...

8....?   ?   9..?

Procedure   Begin the game by reading the following riddles.

I am thinking of a number.
It has 1 digit.
It is two less than the sum of 6 + 5. [9]

I am thinking of a number.
It has 2 digits.
It is one less than the sum of 8 + 5. [12]

I am thinking of a number.
It has 1 digit.
It is two more than the difference for 13 − 7. [8]

The child who figures out the mystery number first scores 1 point. Continue with similar riddles.

To Win   The child with the most points at the end of the game is the winner.

Children could also play "Mystery Number" in small groups. Have them prepare, and possibly write, clues for two or three mystery numbers before they begin playing.

▲
MAC Activity 68:
Average-to-Challenge

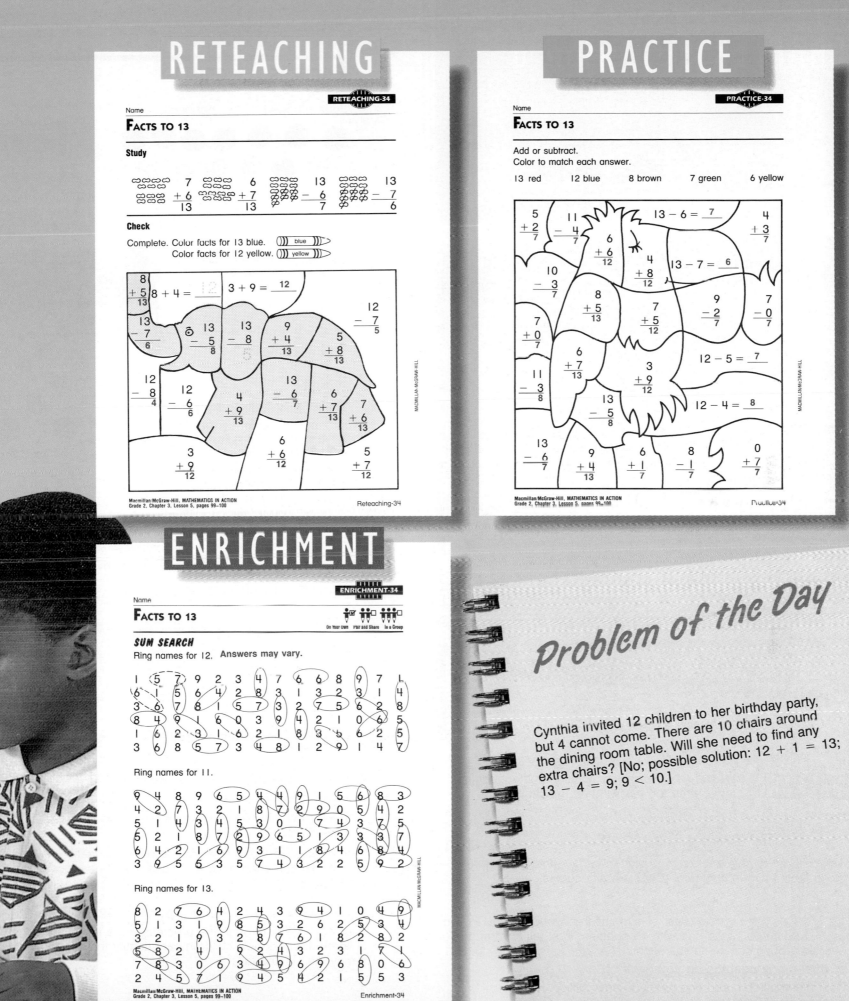

RETEACHING

Name

FACTS TO 13

Study

$$\begin{array}{r} 7 \\ +\ 6 \\ \hline 13 \end{array} \qquad \begin{array}{r} 6 \\ +\ 7 \\ \hline 13 \end{array} \qquad \begin{array}{r} 13 \\ -\ 6 \\ \hline 7 \end{array} \qquad \begin{array}{r} 13 \\ -\ 7 \\ \hline 6 \end{array}$$

Check

Complete. Color facts for 13 blue.   blue
Color facts for 12 yellow.   yellow

$$\begin{array}{r} 8 \\ +\ 5 \\ \hline 13 \end{array} \quad 8+4=\underline{12} \quad 3+9=\underline{12}$$

$$\begin{array}{r} 13 \\ -\ 7 \\ \hline 6 \end{array} \quad \begin{array}{r} 13 \\ -\ 5 \\ \hline 8 \end{array} \quad \begin{array}{r} 13 \\ -\ 8 \\ \hline 5 \end{array} \quad \begin{array}{r} 9 \\ +\ 4 \\ \hline 13 \end{array} \quad \begin{array}{r} 5 \\ +\ 8 \\ \hline 13 \end{array}$$

$$\begin{array}{r} 12 \\ -\ 7 \\ \hline 5 \end{array}$$

$$\begin{array}{r} 12 \\ -\ 8 \\ \hline 4 \end{array} \quad \begin{array}{r} 12 \\ -\ 6 \\ \hline 6 \end{array} \quad \begin{array}{r} 4 \\ +\ 9 \\ \hline 13 \end{array} \quad \begin{array}{r} 13 \\ -\ 6 \\ \hline 7 \end{array} \quad \begin{array}{r} 6 \\ +\ 7 \\ \hline 13 \end{array} \quad \begin{array}{r} 7 \\ +\ 6 \\ \hline 13 \end{array}$$

$$\begin{array}{r} 3 \\ +\ 9 \\ \hline 12 \end{array} \quad \begin{array}{r} 6 \\ +\ 6 \\ \hline 12 \end{array} \quad \begin{array}{r} 5 \\ +\ 7 \\ \hline 12 \end{array}$$

Macmillan/McGraw-Hill, MATHEMATICS IN ACTION
Grade 2, Chapter 3, Lesson 5, pages 99–100

Reteaching-34

PRACTICE

Name

FACTS TO 13

Add or subtract.
Color to match each answer.

13 red   12 blue   8 brown   7 green   6 yellow

$$\begin{array}{r} 5 \\ +\ 2 \\ \hline 7 \end{array} \quad \begin{array}{r} 11 \\ -\ 4 \\ \hline 7 \end{array} \qquad 13-6=\underline{7} \qquad \begin{array}{r} 4 \\ +\ 3 \\ \hline 7 \end{array}$$

$$\begin{array}{r} 6 \\ +\ 6 \\ \hline 12 \end{array} \quad \begin{array}{r} 4 \\ +\ 8 \\ \hline 12 \end{array} \quad 13-7=\underline{6}$$

$$\begin{array}{r} 10 \\ -\ 3 \\ \hline 7 \end{array} \quad \begin{array}{r} 8 \\ +\ 5 \\ \hline 13 \end{array} \quad \begin{array}{r} 7 \\ +\ 5 \\ \hline 12 \end{array} \quad \begin{array}{r} 9 \\ -\ 2 \\ \hline 7 \end{array} \quad \begin{array}{r} 7 \\ -\ 0 \\ \hline 7 \end{array}$$

$$\begin{array}{r} 7 \\ +\ 0 \\ \hline 7 \end{array} \quad \begin{array}{r} 6 \\ +\ 7 \\ \hline 13 \end{array} \qquad 12-5=\underline{}$$

$$\begin{array}{r} 11 \\ -\ 3 \\ \hline 8 \end{array} \quad \begin{array}{r} 3 \\ +\ 9 \\ \hline 12 \end{array}$$

$$\begin{array}{r} 13 \\ -\ 5 \\ \hline 8 \end{array} \qquad 12-4=\underline{8}$$

$$\begin{array}{r} 13 \\ -\ 6 \\ \hline 7 \end{array} \quad \begin{array}{r} 9 \\ +\ 4 \\ \hline 13 \end{array} \quad \begin{array}{r} 6 \\ +\ 1 \\ \hline 7 \end{array} \quad \begin{array}{r} 8 \\ -\ 1 \\ \hline 7 \end{array} \quad \begin{array}{r} 0 \\ +\ 7 \\ \hline 7 \end{array}$$

Macmillan/McGraw-Hill, MATHEMATICS IN ACTION
Grade 2, Chapter 3, Lesson 5, pages 99–100

Practice-34

ENRICHMENT

On Your Own   Pair and Share   In a Group

Name

FACTS TO 13

SUM SEARCH

Ring names for 12.   **Answers may vary.**

Ring names for 11.

Ring names for 13.

Macmillan/McGraw-Hill, MATHEMATICS IN ACTION
Grade 2, Chapter 3, Lesson 5, pages 99–100

Enrichment-34

Problem of the Day

Cynthia invited 12 children to her birthday party, but 4 cannot come. There are 10 chairs around the dining room table. Will she need to find any extra chairs? [No; possible solution: 12 + 1 = 13; 13 − 4 = 9; 9 < 10.]

CHAPTER 3 • Lesson 6

AT·A·GLANCE pp. 101-102

LESSON OBJECTIVE
Add and subtract facts for 14 and 15.

ASSIGNMENT GUIDE

COURSE	EXERCISES
Basic	p. 101: 1–5; p. 102: 1–8, Mixed Review
Average	p. 101: 1–5; p. 102: 1–8, Mixed Review
Challenge	p. 101: 1–5; p. 102: 1–8, Mixed Review
Extra Practice, p. 106	

MATERIALS
Manipulatives 15 P coins (or punchouts) per child

Teacher Resources
Reteaching 35   Practice 35   Enrichment 35
MAC Act. 69, 70

SKILLS TRACE
FACTS TO 18

Explore (Concrete) 92	Develop/Understand (Transitional/Abstract) 93–94, 95–96, 97–98, 99–100, 101–102, 107–108, 109–110, 111, 112
Practice 106, 117, 118, 119–120, 123, 138, 168	Apply 103–104, 105, 113–114, 116, 122

ACTIVITY

Facts to 14 and 15

June dropped all her pennies!

How many heads? __9__

How many tails? __5__

Think of an addition sentence and a subtraction sentence that tells about this.
$9 + 5 = 14, 14 - 5 = 9$.
Find facts for 14.
Use 14 pennies. Show all heads.
Turn over 5 to 9 pennies.

	Addition Facts	Subtraction Facts
1.	$9 + 5 = 14$	$14 - 5 = 9$
	Order of answers will vary.	
2.	$8 + 6 = 14$	$14 - 6 = 8$
3.	$7 + 7 = 14$	$14 - 7 = 7$
4.	$6 + 8 = 14$	$14 - 8 = 6$
5.	$5 + 9 = 14$	$14 - 9 = 5$

Chapter 3   Adding and Subtracting Facts to 18   one hundred one **101**

Macmillan·McGraw-Hill

PREPARE **WARM-UP** To review addition and subtraction facts, write the following on the chalkboard.

$1 + 1$ [2] $2 + 2$ [4]
$3 + 3$ [6] $4 + 4$ [8]
$5 + 5$ [10] $6 + 6$ [12]

Ask children to give each sum orally. Then have them tell what all these facts have in common. [They are all doubles.]

TEACH **MODELING** Have children work in pairs. Provide each pair with 15 pennies. First tell children to count out two groups of six pennies each.

■ **How many pennies do you have?** [12]
Next have children add one penny to each group.

■ **What new doubles fact did you make?** [$7 + 7 = 14$]
Have children move one penny from one group to the other.

■ **What new fact for 14 did you make?** [$6 + 8 = 14$ or $8 + 6 = 14$]

Give children an opportunity to discover subtraction facts for 14 in a similar manner. Then have them use the same procedure to develop facts for 15.

PUPIL'S EDITION pp. 101-102

Page 101 Work through the problem at the top of the page with the children. Discuss how children can identify the different sides of a penny: heads and tails.

Find facts for 15.
Use 15 pennies. Show all heads.
Turn over 6 to 9 pennies.

1. $6 + 9 = 15$ $15 - 9 = 6$

Order of answers will vary.

2. ___ $7 + 8 = 15$ ___   ___ $15 - 8 = 7$ ___

3. ___ $8 + 7 = 15$ ___   ___ $15 - 7 = 8$ ___

4. ___ $9 + 6 = 15$ ___   ___ $15 - 6 = 9$ ___

Write the fact family for the picture.

5. ___ $9 + 5 = 14$ ___   ___ $14 - 5 = 9$ ___

   ___ $5 + 9 = 14$ ___   ___ $14 - 9 = 5$ ___

6. ___ $7 + 8 = 15$ ___   ___ $15 - 8 = 7$ ___

   ___ $8 + 7 = 15$ ___   ___ $15 - 7 = 8$ ___

7. ___ $9 + 6 = 15$ ___   ___ $15 - 6 = 9$ ___

   ___ $6 + 9 = 15$ ___   ___ $15 - 9 = 6$ ___

8. ___ $6 + 8 = 14$ ___   ___ $14 - 8 = 6$ ___

   ___ $8 + 6 = 14$ ___   ___ $14 - 6 = 8$ ___

Mixed Review

Add or subtract.

9. $8 - 6 = \underline{2}$ $5 + 5 = \underline{10}$ $6 - 2 = \underline{4}$

10. $9 - 4 = \underline{5}$ $3 + 7 = \underline{10}$ $10 - 5 = \underline{5}$

Extra Practice, page 106

ACTIVITY Common Error and Remediation

MATERIALS 4 fact cards for each of three fact families

Some children may not recognize the relationships between facts and fact families. Work individually with each child by playing a game with fact cards. Provide four fact cards for each of three fact families. Mix up the cards and place them facedown in a pile. Begin the game by having the child take four cards. Then you take four cards. Tell the child to take the next card. If it is in the same fact family as any of the cards he or she is already holding, the child keeps the card and discards one not needed.

ACTIVITY ALTERNATIVE TEACHING STRATEGY

MATERIALS tape recorder, blank tape

AUDITORY Write facts for 14 on the chalkboard.

$$\begin{array}{ccccc} 9 & 8 & 7 & 6 & 5 \\ +5 & +6 & +7 & +8 & +9 \\ \hline 14 & 14 & 14 & 14 & 14 \end{array} \qquad \begin{array}{ccccc} 14 & 14 & 14 & 14 & 14 \\ -5 & -6 & -7 & -8 & -9 \\ \hline 9 & 8 & 7 & 6 & 5 \end{array}$$

Have children take turns reading a fact as you record them on the tape. Play back the tape and have children read along with it. Repeat the activity with facts for 15.

$$\begin{array}{cccc} 9 & 8 & 7 & 6 \\ +6 & +7 & +8 & +9 \\ \hline 15 & 15 & 15 & 15 \end{array} \qquad \begin{array}{cccc} 15 & 15 & 15 & 15 \\ -6 & -7 & -8 & -9 \\ \hline 9 & 8 & 7 & 6 \end{array}$$

Check for Understanding

■ **What addition sentence tells about 8 heads and 6 tails?**
[$8 + 6 = 14$]

GUIDED PRACTICE ex. 1–5: For reteaching, use Common Error and Remediation or Alternative Strategy.

Page 102 Remind children to use their punchout coins.

PRACTICE•APPLY   PRACTICE ex. 1–8

CLOSE Guide children to summarize the lesson:
■ **What is an addition and subtraction fact for 14?** [Possible response: $8 + 6 = 14$; $14 - 6 = 8$]

■ **What is an addition and subtraction fact for 15?** [Possible response: $6 + 9 = 15$; $15 - 9 = 6$]

MANIPULATIVES ▪ ZERO COUNTDOWN

MAC Activity 70

On Your Own   Pair and Share   In a Group

Materials   counters or punchout counters, number cards for 1–9 (Teacher Aid 11)

Procedure   Assign children to play in pairs. Give each pair counters and a set of number cards for 1 to 9. Have each pair begin the game by displaying 15 counters. Then have children, in turn, pick a card, remove the same number of counters as the number indicated on the card, and return the card to the pile. Explain that the object of the game is to reach 0 exactly. For example, if 3 counters are left and a child draws the number 4, he or she loses a turn. On the other hand, a child who picks the number 3 wins.

To Win   The child who removes the last counter wins the round.

MATH AND LANGUAGE ARTS ▪ *WHAT'S YOUR STORY?*

MAC Activity 69

On Your Own   Pair and Share   In a Group

Have a volunteer say a number sentence for 14 or 15, such as 9 + 5 = 14. Call on another volunteer to make up an addition or subtraction story for that sentence, as in the example below.

My friend and I rode on a Ferris wheel. We went around 9 times before the wheel stopped. Then we went around 5 more times. We went around 14 times in all.

Continue the activity with other volunteers.

▲
MAC Activity 69:
Basic-to-Average

▲
MAC Activity 70:
Average-to-Challenge

RETEACHING

Name

FACTS TO 14 AND 15

Study

$$\begin{array}{r} 9 \\ +6 \\ \hline 15 \end{array} \quad \begin{array}{r} 15 \\ -6 \\ \hline 9 \end{array} \qquad \begin{array}{r} 6 \\ +9 \\ \hline 15 \end{array} \quad \begin{array}{r} 15 \\ -9 \\ \hline 6 \end{array}$$

Check

Write a fact family for the picture.

1. $8 + 6 = 14 \qquad 14 - 6 = 8$
   $6 + 8 = 14 \qquad 14 - 8 = 6$

2. $7 + 8 = 15 \qquad 15 - 8 = 7$
   $8 + 7 = 15 \qquad 15 - 7 = 8$

Add or subtract.

3. $\begin{array}{r} 8 \\ +7 \\ \hline 15 \end{array} \quad \begin{array}{r} 6 \\ +9 \\ \hline 15 \end{array} \quad \begin{array}{r} 7 \\ +7 \\ \hline 14 \end{array} \quad \begin{array}{r} 6 \\ +8 \\ \hline 14 \end{array} \quad \begin{array}{r} 8 \\ +5 \\ \hline 13 \end{array} \quad \begin{array}{r} 5 \\ +9 \\ \hline 14 \end{array}$

4. $\begin{array}{r} 15 \\ -7 \\ \hline 8 \end{array} \quad \begin{array}{r} 14 \\ -5 \\ \hline 9 \end{array} \quad \begin{array}{r} 15 \\ -9 \\ \hline 6 \end{array} \quad \begin{array}{r} 14 \\ -6 \\ \hline 8 \end{array} \quad \begin{array}{r} 13 \\ -9 \\ \hline 4 \end{array} \quad \begin{array}{r} 14 \\ -7 \\ \hline 7 \end{array}$

Reteaching-35

PRACTICE

Name

FACTS TO 14 AND 15

Add or subtract.

1. $\begin{array}{r} 5 \\ +9 \\ \hline 14 \end{array} \quad \begin{array}{r} 7 \\ +7 \\ \hline 14 \end{array} \quad \begin{array}{r} 8 \\ +7 \\ \hline 15 \end{array} \quad \begin{array}{r} 9 \\ +6 \\ \hline 15 \end{array} \quad \begin{array}{r} 5 \\ +8 \\ \hline 13 \end{array} \quad \begin{array}{r} 7 \\ +5 \\ \hline 12 \end{array}$

2. $\begin{array}{r} 15 \\ -6 \\ \hline 9 \end{array} \quad \begin{array}{r} 14 \\ -7 \\ \hline 7 \end{array} \quad \begin{array}{r} 13 \\ -9 \\ \hline 4 \end{array} \quad \begin{array}{r} 15 \\ -9 \\ \hline 6 \end{array} \quad \begin{array}{r} 14 \\ -5 \\ \hline 9 \end{array} \quad \begin{array}{r} 15 \\ -8 \\ \hline 7 \end{array}$

3. $\begin{array}{r} 7 \\ +8 \\ \hline 15 \end{array} \quad \begin{array}{r} 8 \\ +5 \\ \hline 13 \end{array} \quad \begin{array}{r} 9 \\ +5 \\ \hline 14 \end{array} \quad \begin{array}{r} 6 \\ +5 \\ \hline 11 \end{array} \quad \begin{array}{r} 5 \\ +7 \\ \hline 12 \end{array} \quad \begin{array}{r} 6 \\ +9 \\ \hline 15 \end{array}$

4. $\begin{array}{r} 14 \\ -6 \\ \hline 8 \end{array} \quad \begin{array}{r} 15 \\ -7 \\ \hline 8 \end{array} \quad \begin{array}{r} 14 \\ -9 \\ \hline 5 \end{array} \quad \begin{array}{r} 13 \\ -7 \\ \hline 6 \end{array} \quad \begin{array}{r} 14 \\ -8 \\ \hline 6 \end{array} \quad \begin{array}{r} 12 \\ -8 \\ \hline 4 \end{array}$

Complete the subtraction wheels.

5.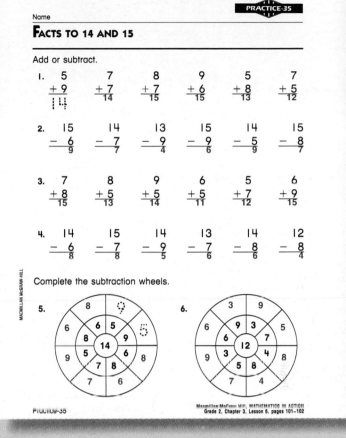
6.

Practice-35

ENRICHMENT

Name

FACTS TO 14 AND 15

AT THE FAIR

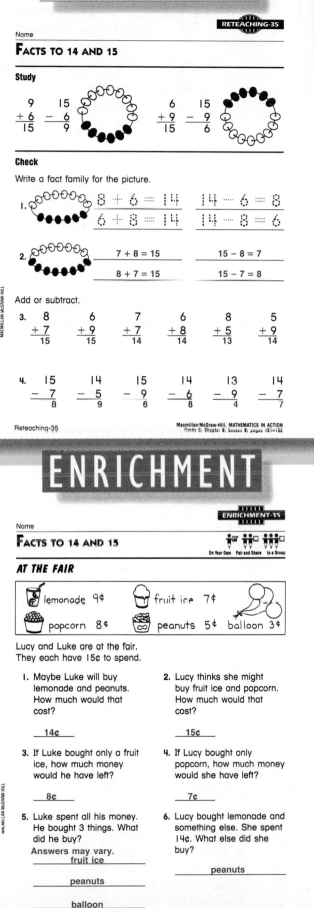

lemonade 9¢   fruit ice 7¢
popcorn 8¢   peanuts 5¢   balloon 3¢

Lucy and Luke are at the fair.
They each have 15¢ to spend.

1. Maybe Luke will buy lemonade and peanuts. How much would that cost?

   14¢

2. Lucy thinks she might buy fruit ice and popcorn. How much would that cost?

   15¢

3. If Luke bought only a fruit ice, how much money would he have left?

   8¢

4. If Lucy bought only popcorn, how much money would she have left?

   7¢

5. Luke spent all his money. He bought 3 things. What did he buy?
   Answers may vary.
   fruit ice

   peanuts

   balloon

6. Lucy bought lemonade and something else. She spent 14¢. What else did she buy?

   peanuts

Enrichment-35

Problem of the Day

Aaron had 14 pennies. He gave Myra 5. Myra added them to the 3 pennies that she already had in her bag. Now who has more pennies, Aaron or Myra? [Aaron. Children may work it out this way: $14 - 5 = 9$; $5 + 3 = 8$; $9 > 8$.]

AT·A·GLANCE pp. 103-104

LESSON OBJECTIVE
Choose the operation to solve problems.

ASSIGNMENT GUIDE

COURSE	EXERCISES
Basic	p. 103: 1–2; p. 104: 1–5
Average	p. 103: 1–2; p. 104: 1–5
Challenge	p. 103: 1–2; p. 104: 1–5
Extra Practice, p. 106	

MATERIALS
Manipulatives 16 ○ (or punchouts) per child

Teacher Resources
Reteaching 36
Prob. Solv. 11
Practice 36
MAC Act. 71, 72
Enrichment 36

Name _____

Problem Solving

Strategy: Choosing the Operation

Decide if you should add or subtract.

Kay has 6 red beads.
She has 8 blue beads.
How many beads does
she have in all?

Phil has 14 trains.
He gives 8 to Sue.
How many trains
does Phil have left?

I need to join the groups. I can add.

Part of the group is taken away. I subtract.

$$\begin{array}{r} 6 \\ + 8 \\ \hline 14 \end{array}$$ 14 beads in all

$$\begin{array}{r} 14 \\ - 8 \\ \hline 6 \end{array}$$ 6 trains left

Ring the example that solves the problem.
Use ○ or mental math to solve.

1. Rick has 9 toy cars.
   He sells 6 toy cars at the fair.
   How many toy cars are left?

   $$\begin{array}{r} 9 \\ + 6 \\ \hline \end{array}$$ $$\begin{array}{r} 9 \\ - 6 \\ \hline 3 \end{array}$$

2. Nora has 4 fair tickets.
   Her mother buys Nora 4 more tickets.
   How many tickets does Nora have?

   $$\begin{array}{r} 4 \\ + 4 \\ \hline 8 \end{array}$$ $$\begin{array}{r} 4 \\ - 4 \\ \hline \end{array}$$

Chapter 3   Adding and Subtracting Facts to 18   one hundred three   **103**

Macmillan/McGraw-Hill

---

1 PREPARE **WARM-UP** To prepare children for choosing the operation to solve problems, have them give the following sums and differences:

8 + 7 [15]   13 − 9 [4]   9 + 3 [12]   7 − 6 [1]

2 TEACH **MODELING** Tell children to use counters to model the numbers in the following problem:

Walter had 12 crackers.
His sister ate 7 of his crackers.
How many crackers did Walter have left?

■ **What do we know?** [Walter had 12 crackers. His sister ate 7 crackers.]

■ **How many counters did you put down?** [12]

■ **What do we need to find out?** [how many crackers are left]

■ **How can we show how many crackers Walter has left?** [Take away 7 counters, or subtract, 12 − 7 = 5.]

PUPIL'S EDITION pp. 103-104

Page 103 Read the directions and the first problem at the top of the page.

■ **What do you know?** [Kay has 6 red beads and 8 blue beads.]

■ **What do you need to find out?** [how many beads in all]

■ **What can you do to find out how many in all?** [Add the two groups.]

Have children find the addition exercise and trace the answer. Read the second problem at the top of the page.

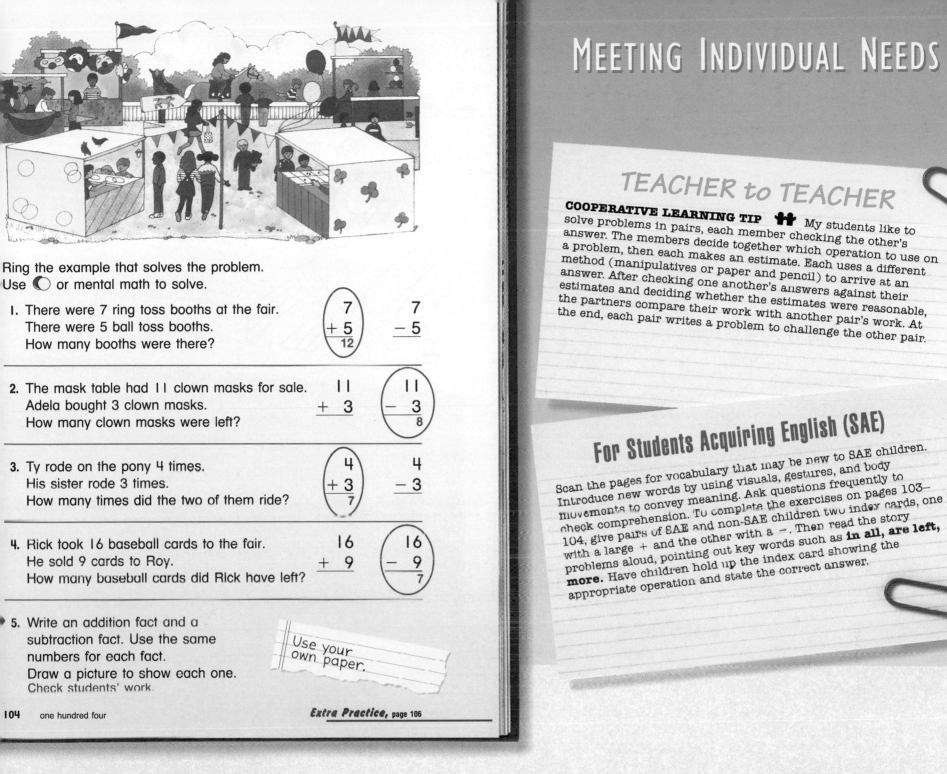

Ring the example that solves the problem.
Use ◐ or mental math to solve.

1. There were 7 ring toss booths at the fair.
   There were 5 ball toss booths.
   How many booths were there?

   $$\begin{array}{r} 7 \\ + 5 \\ \hline 12 \end{array}$$ $$\begin{array}{r} 7 \\ - 5 \\ \hline \end{array}$$

2. The mask table had 11 clown masks for sale.
   Adela bought 3 clown masks.
   How many clown masks were left?

   $$\begin{array}{r} 11 \\ + 3 \\ \hline \end{array}$$ $$\begin{array}{r} 11 \\ - 3 \\ \hline 8 \end{array}$$

3. Ty rode on the pony 4 times.
   His sister rode 3 times.
   How many times did the two of them ride?

   $$\begin{array}{r} 4 \\ + 3 \\ \hline 7 \end{array}$$ $$\begin{array}{r} 4 \\ - 3 \\ \hline \end{array}$$

4. Rick took 16 baseball cards to the fair.
   He sold 9 cards to Roy.
   How many baseball cards did Rick have left?

   $$\begin{array}{r} 16 \\ + 9 \\ \hline \end{array}$$ $$\begin{array}{r} 16 \\ - 9 \\ \hline 7 \end{array}$$

5. Write an addition fact and a subtraction fact. Use the same numbers for each fact.
   Draw a picture to show each one.
   Check students' work.

   Use your own paper.

Extra Practice, page 106

- **What do you know?** [Phil has 14 trains. He gives 8 trains to Sue.]
- **What do you need to find out?** [how many trains Phil has left]
- **What can you do to find out how many are left?** [Subtract some trains.]

Have children find the subtraction exercise and trace the answer.

- **What did you learn?** [Possible response: choosing the correct operation to solve a problem.]

Check for Understanding

- **What if Phil gave 3 more trains to Sue? Would you add or subtract to find out how many he had left?** [Subtract.]

GUIDED PRACTICE ex. 1–2: Work through problem 1 with the children. Make sure they understand how to solve the problem by choosing the correct operation.

Page 104 Read the directions at the top of the page. Make sure children understand that they should decide whether to add or subtract and then find the example that shows the correct operation.

3 PRACTICE·APPLY   **PRACTICE** ex. 1–5: Check children's work.

CLOSE Guide children to summarize the lesson:

- **How do you decide if you should add or subtract?** [Add to find how many in all and subtract to find how many are left.]

MAC Activity 72
On Your Own **Pair and Share** **In a Group**

SPEAKING MATHEMATICALLY ■ TROUBLE IN SPACE

Materials   index cards, large empty carton (optional)

Setup   Use the index cards to prepare number cards 1 to 15. If a large empty carton is available, have children color, paint, or decorate it to create a spaceship as a background prop for the game they will play.

Procedure   Separate the children into 2 teams. Have one member of each team come forward and sit in a chair facing the opposing team. Explain to children that the players in the chairs are the pilots of a spaceship. To make the trip safely, the pilots must keep the ship at the number 10. Each team takes a turn flashing a number to the pilot of the opposing team; for example, a pilot might be shown the number 8. Then he or she calls out "add 2" within 10 seconds. If the pilot is correct, he or she gets a point. If the pilot is incorrect, a point is lost. You may wish to time the responses on a watch with a second hand. Have two new pilots sit in the chairs for each round.

To Win   After every child has been a pilot, the team with more points wins.

▲
MAC Activity 72:
Average-to-Challenge

CAREER—CATERER ■ *THE BUSINESS OF FOOD*

MAC Activity 71
On Your Own **Pair and Share** **In a Group**

Materials   counters or punchout counters

Provide each child with 15 counters. Tell children that in many jobs people use addition and subtraction. Explain that a caterer is someone who is hired by people to prepare food for parties and dinners. Tell them you will read some problems about a caterer. Explain that they are to decide whether to add or subtract, then use their counters to model the numbers in the problems. Have children give the answers to the problems and explain what they did.

1. Anna is a caterer who is working on a dinner for 12 people. She has 7 plates on the table. What does she need to do? [She has to add 5 more plates to make 12.]
2. Anna puts 12 chicken dinners on the table. Then she finds out at the last minute that 2 people will not be at the dinner. What does she need to do? [She has to take away, or subtract 2 dinners, to leave 10 dinners.]

Continue the activity with similar problems.

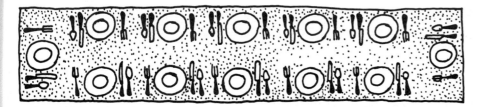

▲
MAC Activity 71:
Basic-to-Average

RETEACHING-36

Name _____

PROBLEM SOLVING STRATEGY: CHOOSING THE OPERATION

Study

Pat has 8 pencils.

Add to find how many in all.

She finds 5 more pencils.
How many pencils does
she have in all?

$$\begin{array}{r} 8 \\ + 5 \\ \hline 13 \end{array}$$ in all

Pat gives 4 pencils to Dan.

Subtract to find how many are left.

How many pencils.
are left?

$$\begin{array}{r} 13 \\ - 4 \\ \hline 9 \end{array}$$ are left

Check

Ring the exercise that solves the problem.

1. Lenny has 11 paint brushes.
He gives 5 brushes to Liu.
How many brushes are left?

$$\begin{array}{r} 11 \\ + 5 \\ \hline 16 \end{array}$$ $$\boxed{\begin{array}{r} 11 \\ - 5 \\ \hline 6 \end{array}}$$

2. Joy picks up 9 crayons.
Donna picks up 6 more crayons.
How many crayons do they have?

$$\boxed{\begin{array}{r} 9 \\ + 6 \\ \hline 15 \end{array}}$$ $$\begin{array}{r} 9 \\ - 6 \\ \hline 3 \end{array}$$

3. There are 9 books on the shelf.
Bill brought 5 more books.
How many books are
on the shelf?

$$\boxed{\begin{array}{r} 9 \\ + 5 \\ \hline 14 \end{array}}$$ $$\begin{array}{r} 9 \\ - 5 \\ \hline 4 \end{array}$$

PRACTICE-36

Name _____

PROBLEM SOLVING STRATEGY: CHOOSING THE OPERATION

Complete the exercise that
solves the problem.
Ring it.

1. Fran saw 8 crows by the road.
Her sister saw 6 turkeys.
How many birds did they see?

$$\boxed{\begin{array}{r} 8 \\ + 6 \\ \hline 14 \end{array}}$$ $$\begin{array}{r} 8 \\ - 6 \end{array}$$

2. Tom counted 12 swans on the lake.
He watched 5 swans fly away.
How many swans were left?

$$\begin{array}{r} 12 \\ + 5 \end{array}$$ $$\boxed{\begin{array}{r} 12 \\ - 5 \\ \hline 7 \end{array}}$$

3. 7 deer played in a field.
6 more deer joined them.
How many deer were there?

$$\boxed{\begin{array}{r} 7 \\ + 6 \\ \hline 13 \end{array}}$$ $$\begin{array}{r} 7 \\ - 6 \end{array}$$

4. Marcia picked up 9 rocks.
She lost 4 rocks on the way home.
How many rocks did she have?

$$\begin{array}{r} 9 \\ + 4 \end{array}$$ $$\boxed{\begin{array}{r} 9 \\ - 4 \\ \hline 5 \end{array}}$$

5. 11 children walked down the trail.
7 children sat down to rest.
How many children kept walking?

$$\begin{array}{r} 11 \\ + 7 \end{array}$$ $$\boxed{\begin{array}{r} 11 \\ - 7 \\ \hline 4 \end{array}}$$

ENRICHMENT-36

Name _____

PROBLEM SOLVING

On Your Own   Pair and Share   In a Group

PLAY BALL

A baseball team has 9 players.
Look at the teams.

Jets   Suns

1. Write a number sentence to show what each team
should do to get 9 players.

Jets   12 − 3 = 9

Suns   5 + 4 = 9

2. The Jets make 4 points.
They make 7 more points.
The Suns make 6 points.
Then they make 3 more points.
Is the scoreboard correct? no
Write number sentences to show the points.

Jets	Suns
9	11

Jets   4 + 7 = 11

Suns   6 + 3 = 9

Ring the winner.   （Jets）   Suns

Problem of the Day

Barry had 15 pennies on Monday. On Tuesday he
had 9 pennies. Did he spend or save money? [He
spent money. 9 pennies are less than 15 pennies.
If he saved money, he would have more than 15
pennies.]

AT·A·GLANCE p. 105

LESSON OBJECTIVE
Write facts for given numbers.

ASSIGNMENT GUIDE

COURSE	EXERCISES
Basic	p. 105: All
Average	p. 105: All
Challenge	p. 105: All

MATERIALS
Classroom Materials index cards
Manipulatives 18 ◯ (or punchouts) per child

Teacher Resources
Crit. Think. 5

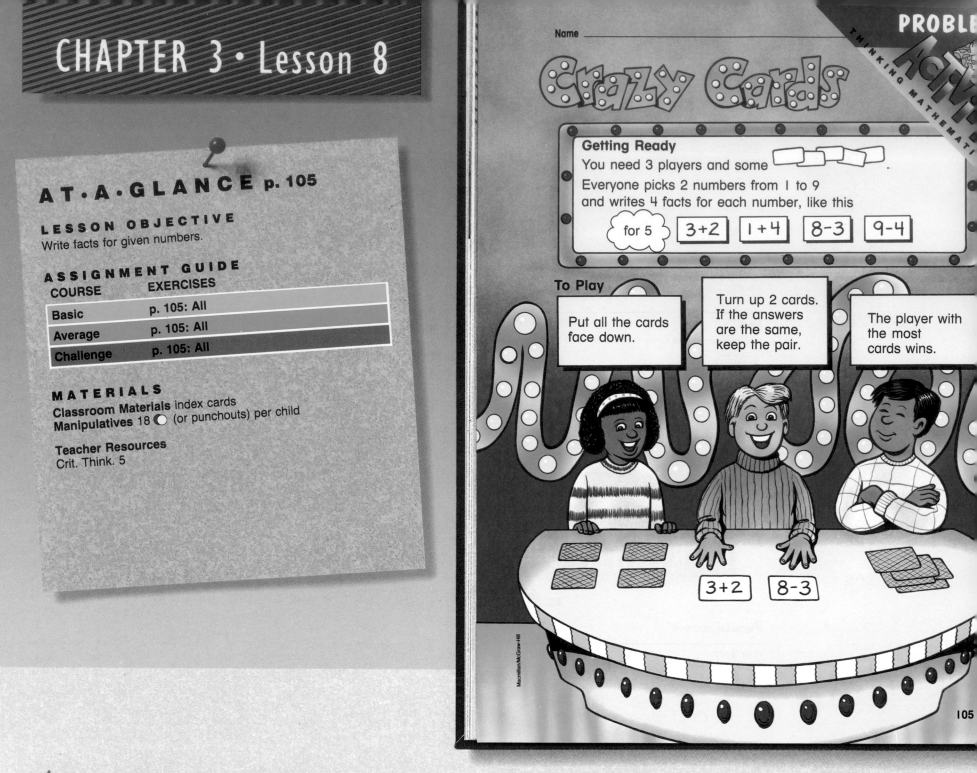

PROBLE

Crazy Cards

Getting Ready

You need 3 players and some [index cards]

Everyone picks 2 numbers from 1 to 9
and writes 4 facts for each number, like this

for 5 | 3+2 | 1+4 | 8-3 | 9-4 |

To Play

Put all the cards face down.

Turn up 2 cards. If the answers are the same, keep the pair.

The player with the most cards wins.

3+2   8-3

Macmillan/McGraw-Hill

105

---

1 PLAN

AIMS AND ATTITUDES This lesson develops number sense through the skills of addition and subtraction facts. The skills are reviewed in a gamelike manner. Encourage children who may have difficulty remembering their facts to use counters.

MANAGEMENT The activity is intended for all children and has been designed for groups of three. It is also appropriate for pairs of children or larger groups.

To make sure that there are no duplicate facts within a group, you may wish to check that each child has chosen two numbers that are different from those of the other members of the group.

2 GUIDE Distribute 18 counters to each child. Write the number 7 on the chalkboard.

■ **What addition fact can you show with your counters that has 7 as the answer?** [Possible responses: 3 + 4; 5 + 2; 6 + 1]

■ **What subtraction fact can you show with counters that has 7 as the answer?** [Possible responses: 9 − 2; 10 − 3; 13 − 6]

Repeat the activity with the numbers 3, 9, 8, 6, and 4.

Read the directions for page 105 with children. Point out the rebus symbol for index cards. Assign children to work in groups of 3. Give each group 24 index cards. Remind children to write 4 facts for each of the numbers that they chose. Then have them play the game according to the directions.

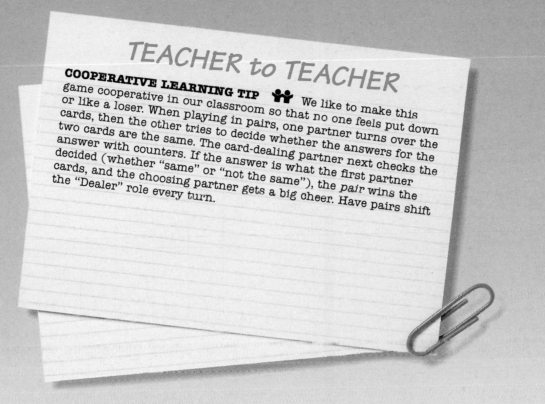

TEACHER to TEACHER

COOPERATIVE LEARNING TIP  We like to make this game cooperative in our classroom so that no one feels put down or like a loser. When playing in pairs, one partner turns over the cards, then the other tries to decide whether the answers for the two cards are the same. The card-dealing partner next checks the answer with counters. If the answer is what the first partner decided (whether "same" or "not the same"), the *pair* wins the cards, and the choosing partner gets a big cheer. Have pairs shift the "Dealer" role every turn.

3 EXTEND Have each group switch their index cards with another group's and play the game again. Although there may be some of the same facts that children saw in the previous game, there will probably be some new addition and subtraction facts. In any case, the outcome of the game will not be affected.

CHAPTER 3

EXTRA PRACTICE

Extra Practice items are provided so that children may have an opportunity for further practice.

The *Additional Practice* section also provides practice you may wish to assign.

Extra Practice

Facts to 14 and 15, pages 101–102 ....

Write the fact family for each picture.

1. $8 + 6 = 14$ $14 - 8 = 6$

   $6 + 8 = 14$ $14 - 6 = 8$

2. $9 + 6 = 15$ $15 - 9 = 6$

   $6 + 9 = 15$ $15 - 6 = 9$

Complete the chart. Add or subtract.

3.

+	8
3	11
6	14
7	15

+	7
7	14
5	12
4	11

−	8
12	4
15	7
13	5

−	7
15	8
12	5
13	6

Problem Solving: Choosing the Operation, pages 103–104 ....

Complete the example that solves the problem. Ring it.

1. Wilma has 7 balloons. Seth gives her 8 more. How many balloons does Wilma have in all?

ADDITIONAL PRACTICE

p. 101 *Write the fact family for the picture.*

1.

[8 + 7 = 15]   [15 − 7 = 8]

[7 + 8 = 15]   [15 − 8 = 7]

2.

[9 + 5 = 14]   [14 − 5 = 9]

[5 + 9 = 14]   [14 − 9 = 5]

3. *Complete the charts. Add or subtract.*

+	6
3	[9]
6	[12]
9	[15]

−	9
15	[6]
14	[5]
13	[4]

p. 103 *Complete the exercise that solves the problem. Ring it.*

1. Brian has 5 books. Sara gave him 9 more. How many books does Brian have in all?

$$\begin{array}{cc} 9 & 5 \\ -5 & +9 \\ \hline & [14] \end{array}$$

Complete the exercise that solves the problem. Ring it.

2. Larry made 15 belts. He sold 6. How many belts does Larry have left?

$$\begin{array}{cc} 15 & 15 \\ -\ 6 & +\ 6 \\ \hline [9] & \end{array}$$

AT·A·GLANCE pp. 107-108

LESSON OBJECTIVE
Add and subtract facts to 18.

ASSIGNMENT GUIDE

COURSE	EXERCISES
Basic	p. 107: 1–6; p. 108: 1–7, Estimation
Average	p. 107: 1–6; p. 108: 1–7, Estimation
Challenge	p. 107: 1–6; p. 108: 1–7, Estimation
Extra Practice, p. 117	Practice Plus, p. 118

MATERIALS
Manipulatives 18 ⬤ (or punchouts) per child

Teacher Resources
Reteaching 37   Practice 37   Enrichment 37
MAC Act. 73, 74
Computer Software *Mathematics Skills:* Disk 2 Act. 2, 3;
    Disk 3 Act. 2, 3

SKILLS TRACE

FACTS TO 18

Explore (Concrete) 92	Develop/Understand (Transitional/Abstract) 93–94, 95–96, 97–98, 99–100, 101–102, 107–108, 109–110, 111, 112
Practice 106, 117, 118, 119–120, 123, 138, 168	Apply 103–104, 105, 113–114, 116, 122

ACTIVITY

Facts to 16, 17, and 18

Use 16 ◖ to show facts for 16.

Show 16 red. Turn over 7, 8, or 9.

Write the facts.

Addition Facts	Subtraction Facts
1. $9 + 7 = 16$	$16 - 7 = 9$

Order of answers will vary.

| 2. $8 + 8 = 16$ | $16 - 8 = 8$ |
| 3. $7 + 9 = 16$ | $16 - 9 = 7$ |

Use 17 ◖ to show facts for 17.

Show 17 red. Turn over 8 or 9.

Write the facts.

Addition Facts	Subtraction Facts
4. $9 + 8 = 17$	$17 - 8 = 9$
5. $8 + 9 = 17$	$17 - 9 = 8$

Use 18 ◖ to show facts for 18.

Show 18 red. Turn over 9.

Write the facts.

Addition Fact	Subtraction Fact
6. $9 + 9 = 18$	$18 - 9 = 9$

Macmillan/McGraw-Hill

Chapter 3   Adding and Subtracting Facts to 18   one hundred seven **107**

**PREPARE**   **WARM-UP**   To prepare children to add and subtract facts to 18, draw the following on the chalkboard.

Ask a volunteer to name a fact for 14 and write it in the top left-hand box. Call on other children to complete the fact family to which that fact belongs.

**TEACH**   **MODELING**   Provide pairs of children with 18 two-color counters. Ask them to show an equal number of each color.

■ **What addition and subtraction facts are modeled by your counters?** [$9 + 9 = 18$ and $18 - 9 = 9$]
Next have children remove 1 counter.
■ **What is the addition fact for this model?** [$9 + 8 = 17$, or $8 + 9 = 17$]
■ **What is the subtraction fact for this model?** [$17 - 9 = 8$, or $17 - 8 = 9$]
Continue the activity with the facts $8 + 8 = 16$ and $16 - 8 = 8$.

PUPIL'S EDITION pp. 107-108

Page 107   Make sure children understand that they should lay out a row of two-color counters with 1 color showing. Explain that they will turn over 7, 8, or 9 counters to develop facts for 16, 17, and 18.

Complete the chart.

1.

+	9
3	12
7	16
9	18
8	17

2.

+	8
9	17
5	13
8	16
4	12

3.

−	6
9	3
14	8
12	6
13	7

4.

−	7
15	8
12	5
13	6
16	9

Add or subtract.

5.

15	16	11	17	15	13
− 9	− 8	− 6	− 9	− 8	− 4
6	8	5	8	7	9

6.

14	12	13	14	15	16
− 6	− 7	− 9	− 5	− 7	− 8
8	5	4	9	8	8

7.

8	8	6	6	7	7
+ 8	+ 9	+ 6	+ 7	+ 7	+ 8
16	17	12	13	14	15

···· Estimation ····

Which box has more jacks? Ring the box that shows the greater sum.

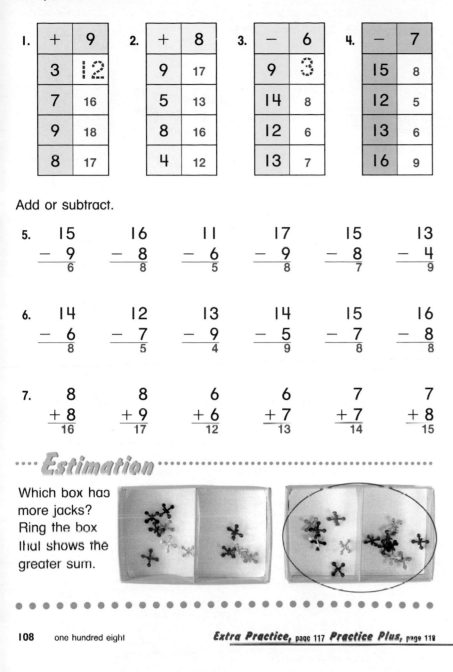

Extra Practice, page 117 *Practice Plus,* page 118

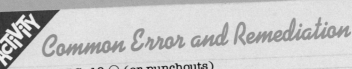

MEETING INDIVIDUAL NEEDS

ACTIVITY Common Error and Remediation

MATERIALS 18 ○ (or punchouts)

Some children may not be using strategies to find the sums of harder facts. Work individually with each child, using a set of exercises in which the top addend is less than the bottom addend. Have the child restate the exercise with the greater addend first and then count on from the greater addend to find the sum. Have the child use counters to check each sum.

ONGOING ASSESSMENT MATH JOURNAL

INTERVIEW (1) 9 + 8 = 17. What subtraction sentence can you make with these numbers? (2) 18 − 9 = 9. What addition sentence can you make with these numbers? (3) You have 16 hats. How can you put the hats into two groups to make a total of 16?

JOURNAL WRITING You may wish to have children record their responses in their math journals.

ACTIVITY ALTERNATIVE TEACHING STRATEGY

MATERIALS 9 ■, 9 ■ (or red and blue square punchout counters) per pair

KINESTHETIC Read the following problem to the class.

8 children were at the beach.
8 more children joined them.
How many children are now at the beach?

Have children work in pairs. Tell them to use connecting cubes to model the numbers in the story. Write 8 + 8 = _____ on the chalkboard. Have children relate each number to the problem and tell how to find the sum. [16] Repeat the activity using different addition and subtraction facts for 16, 17, and 18.

Check for Understanding

■ **What subtraction fact is related to 8 + 8 = 16?** [16 − 8 = 8]

GUIDED PRACTICE ex. 1–6: For reteaching, use Common Error and Remediation or Alternative Strategy.

Page 108 Review with children how to complete the charts. Remind them to look carefully at the operation signs.

3 PRACTICE•APPLY **PRACTICE** ex. 1–7: Children may note the patterns of doubles and doubles plus one in ex. 7.

ESTIMATION Call on a volunteer to explain how he or she quickly guessed which box had more. [by estimating]

CLOSE Guide children to summarize the lesson:

■ **What is the subtraction fact for 18?** [18 − 9 = 9]

Chapter 3 • Lesson 9 **108**

MAC Activity 73

On Your Own   Pair and Share   In a Group

MATH AND CONSUMERS ■ AT THE MARKET

Write the following list of items and prices on the chalkboard.

	Jumbo Mart	Shoprich
onion	7¢	13¢
cucumber	17¢	9¢
juice	10¢	15¢
box of raisins	15¢	12¢
bag of nuts	18¢	18¢
pad	11¢	14¢
pencil	10¢	6¢

Read the list aloud with the children. Then call on volunteers to answer questions such as the following:

■ **Which store charges less for pads?** [Jumbo Mart]
■ **At which store would you pay more for raisins?** [Jumbo Mart]
■ **How much do raisins cost at Jumbo Mart?** [15¢]

After children have answered 4 or 5 questions, give them an opportunity to ask and answer their own questions about the list.

MAC Activity 73:
Basic-to-Average ▶

NUMBER SENSE ■ WHAT'S MISSING?

MAC Activity 74

On Your Own   Pair and Share   In a Group

Explain to children that you will read number sentences aloud. Each sentence will have a missing part which they are to provide. You may want to read each missing part as "blank;" for example, 9 "blank" 5 = 14.

9 — 5 = 14   [+]
8 — 2 = 6   [−]
7 — 8 = 15   [+]
18 — 9 = 9   [−]
17 — _ = 8   [9]
7 + _ = 12   [5]

▲ **MAC Activity 74:**
Average-to-Challenge

RETEACHING

RETEACHING-37

Name

FACTS TO 16, 17, AND 18

Study

$9 + 7 = 16$ $\quad$ $16 - 9 = 7$

$9 + 8 = 17$ $\quad$ $17 - 9 = 8$

$9 + 9 = 18$ $\quad$ $18 - 9 = 9$

Check

Add or subtract.

1. $7 + 9 = \underline{16}$ $\quad$ $16 - 7 = \underline{9}$

2. $8 + 9 = \underline{17}$ $\quad$ $17 - 8 = \underline{9}$

3.
$\begin{array}{r} 8 \\ +8 \\ \hline 16 \end{array}$
$\begin{array}{r} 9 \\ +5 \\ \hline 14 \end{array}$
$\begin{array}{r} 9 \\ +8 \\ \hline 17 \end{array}$
$\begin{array}{r} 9 \\ +9 \\ \hline 18 \end{array}$
$\begin{array}{r} 7 \\ +9 \\ \hline 16 \end{array}$
$\begin{array}{r} 6 \\ +9 \\ \hline 15 \end{array}$

4.
$\begin{array}{r} 17 \\ -8 \\ \hline 9 \end{array}$
$\begin{array}{r} 18 \\ -9 \\ \hline 9 \end{array}$
$\begin{array}{r} 16 \\ -7 \\ \hline 9 \end{array}$
$\begin{array}{r} 17 \\ -9 \\ \hline 8 \end{array}$
$\begin{array}{r} 16 \\ -9 \\ \hline 7 \end{array}$
$\begin{array}{r} 16 \\ -8 \\ \hline 8 \end{array}$

5.
$\begin{array}{r} 8 \\ +5 \\ \hline 13 \end{array}$
$\begin{array}{r} 16 \\ -9 \\ \hline 7 \end{array}$
$\begin{array}{r} 15 \\ -9 \\ \hline 6 \end{array}$
$\begin{array}{r} 8 \\ +9 \\ \hline 17 \end{array}$
$\begin{array}{r} 14 \\ -7 \\ \hline 7 \end{array}$
$\begin{array}{r} 18 \\ -9 \\ \hline 9 \end{array}$

Reteaching-37

Macmillan/McGraw-Hill, MATHEMATICS IN ACTION
Grade 2, Chapter 3, Lesson 9, pages 107–108

PRACTICE

PRACTICE-37

Name

FACTS TO 16, 17, AND 18

Add or subtract.

1.
$\begin{array}{r} 7 \\ +9 \\ \hline 16 \end{array}$
$\begin{array}{r} 9 \\ +9 \\ \hline 18 \end{array}$
$\begin{array}{r} 6 \\ +9 \\ \hline 15 \end{array}$
$\begin{array}{r} 9 \\ +8 \\ \hline 17 \end{array}$
$\begin{array}{r} 8 \\ +8 \\ \hline 16 \end{array}$
$\begin{array}{r} 9 \\ +5 \\ \hline 14 \end{array}$

2.
$\begin{array}{r} 16 \\ -8 \\ \hline 8 \end{array}$
$\begin{array}{r} 16 \\ -9 \\ \hline 7 \end{array}$
$\begin{array}{r} 17 \\ -9 \\ \hline 8 \end{array}$
$\begin{array}{r} 16 \\ -7 \\ \hline 9 \end{array}$
$\begin{array}{r} 18 \\ -9 \\ \hline 9 \end{array}$
$\begin{array}{r} 17 \\ -8 \\ \hline 9 \end{array}$

3.
$\begin{array}{r} 18 \\ -9 \\ \hline 9 \end{array}$
$\begin{array}{r} 14 \\ -7 \\ \hline 7 \end{array}$
$\begin{array}{r} 16 \\ -8 \\ \hline 8 \end{array}$
$\begin{array}{r} 9 \\ +8 \\ \hline 17 \end{array}$
$\begin{array}{r} 8 \\ +5 \\ \hline 13 \end{array}$
$\begin{array}{r} 6 \\ +9 \\ \hline 15 \end{array}$

Complete.

4.

+	7
5	12
6	13
7	14
8	15

−	8
14	6
15	7
16	8
17	9

+	9
9	18
8	17
7	16
6	15

−	6
15	9
14	8
13	7
12	6

Practice-37

Macmillan/McGraw-Hill, MATHEMATICS IN ACTION
Grade 2, Chapter 3, Lesson 9, pages 107–108

ENRICHMENT

ENRICHMENT-37

Name

FACTS TO 16, 17, AND 18

On Your Own Pair and Share In a Group

TOADVILLE

This is a map of Toadville.
It shows where the Toad family lives.

Use the map to solve.

1. Tony Toad is at school.
   How many jumps is he
   from the pond?

   11 jumps

2. Tessa Toad is at the pond.
   How many jumps is the
   shortest path home?

   14 jumps

3. Tina Toad went from
   school to Cattail Corner.
   She took 16 jumps. Use a
   crayon to show the path
   she took.

4. Teddy Toad is at the pond.
   Is he closer to home or
   Patsy's Store?

   Patsy's Store

5. Write another map problem.
   Have your partner solve it.

   Check student's problems.

Enrichment-37

Macmillan/McGraw-Hill, MATHEMATICS IN ACTION
Grade 2, Chapter 3, Lesson 9, pages 107–108

Problem of the Day

Brian had 9 cherries in his lunch bag. He ate 3
and traded 4 to Sherry for 4 grapes. How many
cherries did Brian have left in his lunch bag?
[2; children may work it out this way: $9 - 3 = 6$;
$6 - 4 = 2$.]

AT·A·GLANCE pp. 109-110

LESSON OBJECTIVES
Complete addition and subtraction tables.
Recognize addition and subtraction patterns.

ASSIGNMENT GUIDE

COURSE	EXERCISES
Basic	p. 109: All; p. 110: 1–7
Average	p. 109: All; p. 110: 1–7
Challenge	p. 109: All; p. 110: 1–7

Teacher Resources
Reteaching 38   Practice 38   Enrichment 38
Prob. Solv. 12   MAC Act. 75, 76

SKILLS TRACE
FACTS TO 18

Explore (Concrete)	Develop/Understand (Transitional/Abstract)
92	93–94, 95–96, 97–98, 99–100, 101–102, 107–108, 109–110, 111, 112
Practice 106, 117, 118, 119–120, 123, 138, 168	**Apply** 103–104, 105, 113–114, 116, 122

See **MANIPULATIVES PLUS 18**, p. 90L

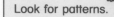

Name _____

Informal Algebra: Addition and Subtraction Patterns

Look for patterns.

1. Complete the addition table.

+	0	1	2	3	4	5	6	7	8	9
0	0	1	2	3	4	5	6	7	8	9
1	1	2	3	4	5	6	7	8	9	10
2	2	3	4	5	6	7	8	9	10	11
3	3	4	5	6	7	8	9	10	11	12
4	4	5	6	7	8	9	10	11	12	13
5	5	6	7	8	9	10	11	12	13	14
6	6	7	8	9	10	11	12	13	14	15
7	7	8	9	10	11	12	13	14	15	16
8	8	9	10	11	12	13	14	15	16	17
9	9	10	11	12	13	14	15	16	17	18

2. Make your own table on another piece of paper.
   Choose your own numbers from 0 to 9 to add.
   Does your completed table make a pattern?
   Answers will vary.

PREPARE   **WARM-UP**   To prepare children to complete addition and subtraction patterns, write the following on the chalkboard. Have children give each sum and difference orally.

6 + 6 = ___ [12]	12 − 6 = ___ [6]
7 + 7 = ___ [14]	14 − 7 = ___ [7]
8 + 8 = ___ [16]	16 − 8 = ___ [8]
9 + 9 = ___ [18]	18 − 9 = ___ [9]

TEACH   **QUESTIONING**   Draw the following table on the chalkboard.

+	0	1	2
0	0	1	2
1	1	2	3
2	2	3	4

Explain to children that this is part of an addition table that can help them to find sums. Demonstrate by showing how to find 0 + 0. Describe the process as you point to each 0. Then move your finger down and across and read the sum in that box. [0] Repeat for 1 + 1.

■ **What is the sum?** [2]

Call on a volunteer to show how he or she would find the sum of 2 + 2.

Complete each subtraction table. Look for patterns.

1.

−	1	2	3	4	5	6	7	8	9
10	9	8	7	6	5	4	3	2	1

2.

−	5	6	7	8	9
11	6	5	4	3	2
12	7	6	5	4	3
13	8	7	6	5	4
14	9	8	7	6	5

3.

−	9	8	7	6
15	6	7	8	9
16	7	8	9	
17	8	9		
18	9			

Tara writes three subtraction facts in a row.
Write two more facts that belong in the row.

4.

$$\begin{array}{ccc} 7 & 9 & 6 \\ -0 & -0 & -0 \\ \hline 7 & 9 & 6 \end{array}$$

Answers will vary.
Accept answers such as

$$\begin{array}{ccc} 4 & 12 & 10 \\ -0, & -0, & -0, \\ \hline 4 & 12 & 10 \end{array}$$

5.

$$\begin{array}{ccc} 8 & 9 & 5 \\ -8 & -9 & -5 \\ \hline 0 & 0 & 0 \end{array}$$

Answers will vary.
Possible answer:

$$\begin{array}{ccc} 6 & 11 & 13 \\ -6, & -11, & -13, \\ \hline 0 & 0 & 0 \end{array}$$

6.

$$\begin{array}{ccc} 14 & 8 & 12 \\ -7 & -4 & -6 \\ \hline 7 & 4 & 6 \end{array}$$

Answers will vary.
Possible answer:

$$\begin{array}{ccc} 4 & 10 & 16 \\ -2, & -5, & -8, \\ \hline 2 & 5 & 8 \end{array}$$

7. Make up a row of your own. Answers will vary.

110 one hundred ten

ACTIVITY

Common Error and Remediation

MATERIALS acetate strips in two different colors

Some children may have problems using the addition table to find sums. Work individually with each child, using addition exercises and acetate strips of two colors. Use the table on page 109, and have the child find sums for the exercises by placing the two acetate strips over the appropriate row and column. Explain that the number in the box where the strips cross is the sum.

ALTERNATIVE TEACHING STRATEGY

VISUAL Write the addition facts with 0 on the chalkboard.

$$\begin{array}{ccccc} 0 & 0 & 0 & 0 & 0 \\ +0 & +1 & +2 & +3 & \cdots & +9 \\ \hline 0 & 1 & 2 & 0 & 9 \end{array}$$

Explain to children that an addition table is an easier way to organize facts. Draw the first rows of the table on the chalkboard. Then write in the facts with 1 and with 2. Extend the table a row at a time.

+	0	1	2	3	4	5	6	7	8	9
0	0	1	2	3	4	5	6	7	8	9
1	1	2	3	4						

PUPIL'S EDITION pp. 109–110

Page 109 Explain that this addition table, when complete, will contain all the facts to 18. Help children discover the vertical, horizontal, and diagonal patterns of sums. For example, each sum increases by 1 vertically, and different addends have the same sum diagonally.

Point out that when the numbers in the outside boxes are in mixed order, there is no longer a pattern formed inside the table.

Check for Understanding

■ **How could you find the sum of 4 + 3 on an addition table?**
[Possible response: Find the number 4 in the side column. Then move across that row to the 3 column.]

GUIDED PRACTICE All: For reteaching, use Common Error and Remediation or Alternative Strategy.

Page 110 Point out that to find the difference between two numbers on a subtraction table, children must begin with the number in the left-hand column.

3 PRACTICE•APPLY **PRACTICE** ex. 1–7

CLOSE Guide children to summarize the lesson:

■ **What pattern do you see when you read sums across in the addition table?** [Each sum increases by 1.]

■ **What pattern do you see when you read the differences across in the subtraction table?** [Each difference decreases or increases by 1.]

MENTAL MATH ▪ SUBTRACTION ACTION

MAC Activity 75

On Your Own   Pair and Share   In a Group

Materials   number cards for 1–18 (Teacher Aid 11)

Procedure   Children play the game in small groups. Give each group two sets of number cards for 1 to 8 and 9 to 18. Tell children to mix each set of cards and place them facedown in two stacks. Have each player, in turn, turn over two cards at once and then mentally subtract the lesser number from the greater number. If a child says the correct difference, he or she scores 1 point.

To Win   The player with the most points at the end of the game is the winner.

▲ **MAC Activity 75:**
Basic-to-Average

MAC Activity 76:
Average-to-Challenge
▼

CALCULATOR ▪ FUN WITH FACTS

MAC Activity 76

On Your Own   Pair and Share   In a Group

Materials   calculators

Write the following exercises on the chalkboard. Have children use their calculators to find the answers.

1. $16 - 9 + 3 + 4 = $ ___   [14]
2. $6 + 9 - 2 - 5 = $ ___   [8]
3. $18 - 9 - 4 + 8 = $ ___   [13]
4. $15 - 6 + 4 - 9 = $ ___   [4]
5. $7 + 3 - 6 + 6 = $ ___   [10]

RETEACHING-38

Name _____

ADDITION AND SUBTRACTION PATTERNS

Study

+	3	4
4	7	8
5	8	9

4 + 3 = **7**
4 + 4 = **8**
5 + 3 = **8**
5 + 4 = **9**

−	3	4
8	5	4
9	6	5

8 − 3 = **5**
8 − 4 = **4**
9 − 3 = **6**
9 − 4 = **5**

Check

Complete the tables.

1.

+	0	1	2	3	4	5	6	7	8	9
3	3	4	5	6	7	8	9	10	11	12

2.

−	0	1	2	3	4	5	6	7	8	9
9	9	8	7	6	5	4	3	2	1	0

Complete the patterns.

3.

4	5	6	7	8	9
+1	+1	+1	+1	+1	+1
5	6	7	8	9	10

4.

9	8	7	6	5	4
−2	−2	−2	−2	−2	−2
7	6	5	4	3	2

Macmillan/McGraw-Hill, MATHEMATICS IN ACTION
Grade 2, Chapter 3, Lesson 10, pages 109–110

MACMILLAN/McGRAW-HILL

Reteaching-38

PRACTICE-38

Name _____

ADDITION AND SUBTRACTION PATTERNS

Complete the tables.

1.

+	0	1	2	3	4	5	6	7	8	9
5	5	6	7	8	9	10	11	12	13	14
6	6	7	8	9	10	11	12	13	14	15

2.

−	0	1	2	3	4	5
5	5	4	3	2	1	0
6	6	5	4	3	2	1

3.

−	9	8	7
15	6	7	8
14	5	6	7

Continue each pattern.

4.

1	2	3	4	5	6
+1	+2	+3	+4	+5	+6
2	4	6	8	10	12

5.

15	14	13	12	11	10
−9	−9	−9	−9	−9	−9
6	5	4	3	2	1

6.

1	2	3	4	5	6
+9	+8	+7	+6	+5	+4
10	10	10	10	10	10

Macmillan/McGraw-Hill, MATHEMATICS IN ACTION
Grade 2, Chapter 3, Lesson 10, pages 109–110

MACMILLAN/McGRAW-HILL

Practice-38

ENRICHMENT-38

Name _____

ADDITION AND SUBTRACTION PATTERNS

MISSING SIGNS AND NUMBERS

On Your Own   Pair and Share   In a Group

Write the missing signs and numbers.

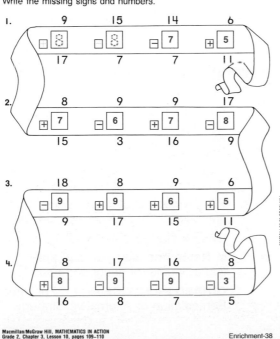

1.
9	15	14	6
+ 8	− 8	− 7	+ 5
17	7	7	11

2.
8	9	9	17
+ 7	− 6	+ 7	− 8
15	3	16	9

3.
18	8	9	6
− 9	+ 9	+ 6	+ 5
9	17	15	11

4.
8	17	16	8
+ 8	− 9	− 9	− 3
16	8	7	5

Macmillan/McGraw-Hill, MATHEMATICS IN ACTION
Grade 2, Chapter 3, Lesson 10, pages 109–110

MACMILLAN/McGRAW-HILL

Enrichment-38

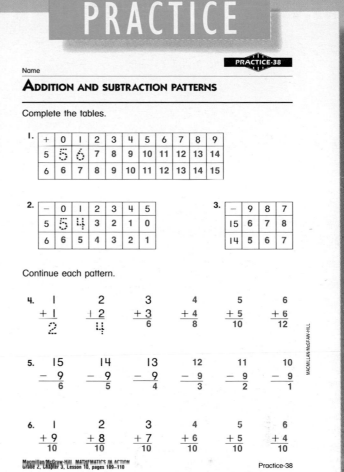

Problem of the Day

Paul returned 7 books to the library. He decided to take 3 of the books out again. Then Paul found 9 more that he wanted to take out. He was only allowed to borrow 8 books. How many books did Paul have to leave for next time? [4. Children may work it out this way: 3 + 9 = 12; 12 − 8 = 4.]

AT·A·GLANCE p. 111

LESSON OBJECTIVE
Add three or more 1-digit numbers.

ASSIGNMENT GUIDE

COURSE	EXERCISES
Basic	p. 111: 1–3
Average	p. 111: 1–3
Challenge	p. 111: 1–3
Extra Practice, page 117	Practice Plus, page 118

Teacher Resources
Reteaching 39
MAC Act. 77, 78
Practice 39
Calculator 3
Enrichment 39
Teacher Aid 17

SKILLS TRACE
FACTS TO 18

Explore (Concrete) 92	Develop/Understand (Transitional/Abstract) 93–94, 95–96, 97–98, 99–100, 101–102, 107–108, 109–110, 111, 112
Practice 106, 117, 118, 119–120, 123, 138, 168	Apply 103–104, 105, 113–114, 116, 122

Name _____

Three or More Addends

When you add 3 or more numbers, you can add
in different ways. Look for facts you know.

$$\begin{array}{r} 4 \\ 6 \\ +2 \end{array} \rangle 10 \qquad \begin{array}{r} 4 \\ 6 \\ +2 \end{array} \rangle 6 \quad 6 \qquad \begin{array}{r} 4 \\ 6 \\ +2 \end{array} \rangle 10$$

Look for a 10.   Find a double.   Count on to add.

$10 + 2 = 12$ $6 + 6 = 12$ $10 \!-\! 11 \!-\! 12$

Add.

1.
3	4	8	6	2	4
6	3	2	4	7	5
+3	+4	+4	+3	+2	+1
12	11	14	13	11	10

2.
1	2	1	1	6	3
0	1	4	7	1	2
3	4	3	1	2	5
+6	+4	+6	+8	+8	+5
10	11	14	17	17	15

Solve.

3. How many sticks are on each side?
How many sticks in all?

4

3 _____   _____ 5

_____12_____ in all

Macmillan/McGraw-Hill

Extra Practice, page 117 **Practice Plus,** page 118   one hundred eleven   **111**

PREPARE

WARM-UP To prepare children to add three or
more numbers, read each of the following pairs of
exercises aloud. Have children give the sums.

5 + 4 [9]	9 + 3 [12]
5 + 3 [8]	8 + 4 [12]
6 + 2 [8]	8 + 7 [15]
8 + 1 [9]	9 + 9 [18]
2 + 6 [8]	8 + 7 [15]
2 + 7 [9]	9 + 6 [15]

TEACH

DISCUSSING Call on ten children to come up to
the front of the classroom and form groups of 2, 5,
and 3. Describe the three groups of children in terms of addition as
2 + 5 + 3. Write the addition vertically on the chalkboard. Ask chil-

dren to suggest different ways in which they might add the numbers to
find the sum. Help children realize that by adding 2 + 3 first, they will
get 5, and 5 + 5 is a double. Repeat the activity, using 4 groups of
children.

PUPIL'S EDITION p. 111
Review each strategy shown for finding the sum. Work through the
steps for each strategy with the children.

Check for Understanding

■ **Name one way you can add 3 or more numbers.** [Look for a 10,
find a double, or count on to add.]

GUIDED PRACTICE ex. 1: For reteaching, use Common Error and
Remediation or Alternative Strategy.

ACTIVITY

Common Error and Remediation

MATERIALS fact cards

Some children may not think to use strategies when they do not know an addition fact. Work individually with each child. First have the child work with addition cards that show facts that are near doubles, like 7 + 8. Have the child say the lesser of the two numbers.

■ **What is the double that has a 7 in it?** [7 + 7 = 14]

■ **What is one more than 14?** [15]

ALTERNATIVE TEACHING STRATEGY

MATERIALS 3 pieces of colored chalk

VISUAL Draw a row of 2 circles on the chalkboard. Use a different color of chalk to draw a second row of 5 circles. Use a different color of chalk to draw a third row of 3 circles.

OO	[2]
OOOOO	[5]
OOO	[3]

Call on children to count the circles in each row and write the number next to each row. Then ask children to find the sum of the three numbers. [10]
Repeat with other shapes and other numbers.

PRACTICE•APPLY **PRACTICE** ex. 2–3: Have children count the number of sticks on each side of the figure and then add to find the total.

CLOSE Guide children to summarize the lesson:

■ **What do you know about adding 3 or more numbers?** [Possible response: You can add in different ways.]

MAC Activity 77

On Your Own   Pair and Share   In a Group

CALCULATOR ▪ SUM RACE

Materials   calculators, index cards

Review with children how to enter an addition exercise into the calculator and find the sum. Prepare exercise cards by writing three or more addends on each index card. Assign children to work in groups of four. Give each group four cards and a calculator. Tell children to place the cards facedown. Then have them turn over one card and play a race-type game involving one child using a calculator and the others who are not. Those without calculators try to write the answer to the addition exercise before the other child can show the answer on the calculator. Children take turns using the calculator.

MAC Activity 77:
Basic-to-Average ▶

MENTAL MATH ▪ THREE CUBES

MAC Activity 78

On Your Own   Pair and Share   In a Group

Materials   3 number cubes for 1–6 (Teacher Aid 17)

Procedure   Assign children to play in pairs. Give each pair three number cubes for 1 to 6. Have one of the children in each group toss their three cubes. Tell those children to mentally add the three numbers showing on the cubes. Remind them that they can group the numbers in any order to add. Then have the other child in each pair take a turn. Players score one point for each correct sum.

To Win   The player with the most points at the end of the fourth round wins the game.

▲
MAC Activity 78:
Average-to-Challenge

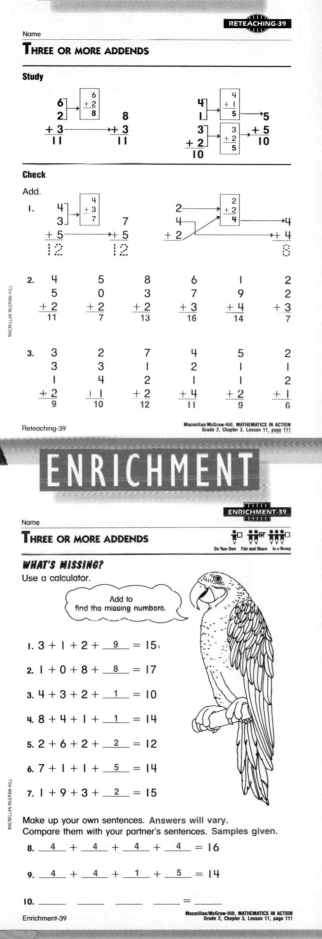

RETEACHING

Name _____

THREE OR MORE ADDENDS

Study

$$\begin{array}{c}6\\2\\+3\\\hline 11\end{array} \rightarrow \begin{array}{c}6\\+2\\\hline 8\end{array} \quad \begin{array}{c}8\\+3\\\hline 11\end{array}$$

$$\begin{array}{c}4\\1\\3\\+2\\\hline 10\end{array} \rightarrow \begin{array}{c}4\\+1\\\hline 5\end{array} \rightarrow 5 \quad \begin{array}{c}3\\+2\\\hline 5\end{array} \rightarrow \begin{array}{c}5\\+5\\\hline 10\end{array}$$

Check

Add.

1.
$$\begin{array}{c}4\\3\\+5\\\hline 12\end{array} \rightarrow \begin{array}{c}4\\+3\\\hline 7\end{array} \rightarrow \begin{array}{c}7\\+5\\\hline 12\end{array}$$

$$\begin{array}{c}2\\4\\+2\\\hline 8\end{array} \rightarrow \begin{array}{c}2\\+2\\\hline 4\end{array} \rightarrow \begin{array}{c}4\\+4\\\hline 8\end{array}$$

2.
4	5	8	6	1	2
5	0	3	7	9	2
+2	+2	+2	+3	+4	+3
11	7	13	16	14	7

3.
3	2	7	4	5	2
3	3	1	2	1	1
1	4	2	1	1	2
+2	+1	+2	+4	+2	+1
9	10	12	11	9	6

Reteaching-39

Macmillan/McGraw-Hill, MATHEMATICS IN ACTION
Grade 2, Chapter 3, Lesson 11, page 111

PRACTICE

Name _____

THREE OR MORE ADDENDS

Add.

1.
4	1	2	6	3	6
4	1	5	4	7	9
+1	+7	+2	+1	+4	+1
9	9	9	11	14	16

2.
1	2	5	1	3	7
4	6	2	7	6	4
+3	+2	+3	+3	+3	+3
8	10	10	11	12	14

3.
1	2	3	4	5	1
6	7	2	9	3	4
+3	+2	+8	+1	+2	+5
10	11	13	14	10	10

4.
9	1	4	2	3	4
1	3	3	8	2	6
2	5	1	1	3	3
+3	+7	+2	+3	+2	+1
15	16	10	14	10	14

Solve.

5. Ben has 6 fish. He has 2 dogs and 1 bird. How many pets does Ben have? __9__

Practice-39

Macmillan/McGraw-Hill, MATHEMATICS IN ACTION
Grade 2, Chapter 3, Lesson 11, page 111

ENRICHMENT

Name _____

THREE OR MORE ADDENDS

Do Your Own   Pair and Share   In a Group

WHAT'S MISSING?

Use a calculator.

> Add to find the missing numbers.

1. $3 + 1 + 2 + \underline{9} = 15$

2. $1 + 0 + 8 + \underline{8} = 17$

3. $4 + 3 + 2 + \underline{1} = 10$

4. $8 + 4 + 1 + \underline{1} = 14$

5. $2 + 6 + 2 + \underline{2} = 12$

6. $7 + 1 + 1 + \underline{5} = 14$

7. $1 + 9 + 3 + \underline{2} = 15$

Make up your own sentences. Answers will vary.
Compare them with your partner's sentences. Samples given.

8. $\underline{4} + \underline{4} + \underline{4} + \underline{4} = 16$

9. $\underline{4} + \underline{4} + \underline{1} + \underline{5} = 14$

10. ____ ____ ____ = ____

Enrichment-39

Macmillan/McGraw-Hill, MATHEMATICS IN ACTION
Grade 2, Chapter 3, Lesson 11, page 111

Problem of the Day

There were 4 children making a dog house. There were 3 children making a bird house and 2 children making a bird feeder. How many children were making houses? [7]

AT·A·GLANCE p. 112

LESSON OBJECTIVE
Add and subtract money amounts.

ASSIGNMENT GUIDE

COURSE	EXERCISES
Basic	p. 112: 1–3
Average	p. 112: 1–3
Challenge	p. 112: 1–3

MATERIALS
Classroom Materials scissors, paste
Manipulatives 10 P coins (or punchouts) per pair; stickers for p. 112 per child

Teacher Resources
Reteaching 40
Problem Solv. 13
Practice 40
MAC Act. 79, 80
Enrichment 40

SKILLS TRACE
FACTS TO 18

Explore (Concrete) 92	Develop/Understand (Transitional/Abstract) 93–94, 95–96, 97–98, 99–100, 101–102, 107–108, 109–110, 111, 112
Practice 106, 117, 118, 119–120, 123, 138, 168	**Apply** 103–104, 105, 113–114, 116, 122

Name _____

Adding and Subtracting Money

Add or subtract. Then break the code.

1.
7¢ + 4¢	11¢ − 9¢	14¢ − 8¢	16¢ − 9¢	15¢ − 6¢
11¢	2¢	6¢	7¢	9¢
Where	can	you	always	find

2.
16¢ − 8¢	11¢ − 7¢	9¢ + 7¢	7¢ − 7¢	9¢ − 6¢
8¢	4¢	16¢	0¢	3¢
money?	You	can	always	find

3.
8¢ 1¢ + 9¢	4¢ 4¢ + 6¢	5¢ 3¢ + 7¢	8¢ 0¢ + 9¢	3¢ 1¢ + 9¢	6¢ 3¢ + 3¢
18¢	14¢	15¢	17¢	13¢	12¢
money	in	a	dictionary	under	m!

0¢ always	2¢ can	3¢ find	4¢ You	5¢ just	6¢ you
7¢ always	8¢ money?	9¢ find	11¢ Where	12¢ m!	13¢ under
14¢ in	15¢ a	16¢ can	17¢ dictionary	18¢ money	20¢ for

112   one hundred twelve

---

① PREPARE   **WARM-UP**   To prepare children to work with money amounts, distribute 10 punchout pennies to each pair of children. Say the following amounts aloud, one at a time.

8¢   10¢   6¢   4¢

Have children show each amount with their pennies.

② TEACH   **MODELING**   Read the following story aloud. Have children use their pennies to model the two numbers in the story.

Emily and June go to the store to buy muffins. Emily has 8¢. June has 5¢. Each muffin costs 11¢.

■ **How much money do the girls have altogether?** [13¢]
■ **How many muffins can the girls buy?** [1]

Write the addition in vertical form on the chalkboard, and point out the sign. Then ask children to remove the pennies the girls will have to spend.

■ **How much money is left?** [2¢]

Write the subtraction in vertical form on the chalkboard.

PUPIL'S EDITION p. 112

Explain to children that they must first complete the addition and subtraction exercises. Then they are to cut out the boxes and paste each one over the matching answer to find the riddle and the answer, or use stickers.

Common Error and Remediation

Some children may be careless in reading operation signs when doing mixed exercises. Work individually with each child to review checking strategies. Remind children that when they add the sum it is always greater than either of the two addends. When they subtract, the difference is always less than the first number in the exercise. Provide several exercises and have the child check to see if the rules are always true.

For Students Acquiring English (SAE)

Together do an additional example of **break the code** on the chalkboard to practice using the phrase.

ALTERNATIVE TEACHING STRATEGY

VISUAL Write the following on the chalkboard. Have children tell if they have to add or subtract. Have volunteers write the sum or difference for each.

11¢	8¢	3¢	7¢	9¢	14¢
−8¢	−3¢	+8¢	+4¢	−2¢	−6¢
[subtract]	[subtract]	[add]	[add]	[subtract]	[subtract]
[3¢]	[5¢]	[11¢]	[11¢]	[7¢]	[8¢]

Check for Understanding

■ **What is 7¢ + 4¢?** [11¢]

■ **What word would you paste under the first exercise?** [Where]

GUIDED PRACTICE   ex. 1: For reteaching, use Common Error and Remediation or Alternative Strategy.

 **PRACTICE•APPLY**   **PRACTICE**   ex. 2–3: Call on volunteers to read the completed riddle and answer to the class.

CLOSE   Guide children to summarize the lesson:

■ **Why do you have to write a cent sign after the sum of 9¢ + 7¢?** [because it is a money amount]

MAC Activity 80

MATH AND CONSUMERS ■ YARD SALE

On Your Own   Pair and Share   In a Group

Write the following on the chalkboard.

Yard Sale
Small books   1¢ each
Big books   3¢ each
Toys   5¢ each

Read the chart with the children. Then have them answer these questions.

1. Pat bought 2 big books and 1 toy. How much did she spend?   [11¢]
2. Jose bought 1 toy, 2 small books, and 1 big book. How much did he spend?   [10¢]
3. Dan bought 2 toys, 2 big books, and 1 small book. How much did he spend?   [17¢]

Continue the activity with your own problems or have children make up problems to be solved by classmates.

▲
MAC Activity 80:
Average-to-Challenge

MANIPULATIVES ■ *BLUE, RED AND GREEN*

MAC Activity 79

On Your Own   Pair and Share   In a Group

Materials   punchout pennies

Have children work in groups of three and give each group 20 punchout pennies. Assign the three children in each group the names *Blue*, *Red*, and *Green*. Explain that when they hear their "name" in a problem they should take that number of pennies from the group's pile of coins. Then they are to combine their pennies to find how much money in all.

1. Blue has 4¢.
   Red has 2¢.
   Green has 3¢.
   How much do they
   have in all?   [9¢]

2. Blue has 1¢.
   Red has 3¢.
   Green has 4¢.
   How much do they
   have in all?   [8¢]

3. Blue has 2¢.
   Red has 6¢.
   Green has 5¢.
   How much do they
   have in all?   [13¢]

4. Blue has 3¢.
   Red has 5¢.
   Green has 2¢.
   How much do they
   have in all?   [10¢]

▲
MAC Activity 79:
Basic-to-Average

RETEACHING

RETEACHING-40

Name

ADDING AND SUBTRACTING MONEY

Study

Remember the cent sign.

3	3¢	8	8¢		
+ 2	+ 2¢	2	2¢	6	6¢
5	5¢	+ 1	+ 1¢	− 3	− 3¢
		11	11¢	3	3¢

Check

Add or subtract.

1.
4¢	5¢	8¢	9¢	12¢
+ 2¢	− 2¢	+ 1¢	+ 9¢	− 7¢
6¢	3¢	9¢	18¢	5¢

2.
16¢	9¢	5¢	13¢	18¢
− 7¢	+ 8¢	+ 7¢	− 4¢	− 9¢
9¢	17¢	12¢	9¢	9¢

3.
8¢	15¢	16¢	7¢	4¢
+ 8¢	− 7¢	− 9¢	− 6¢	+ 9¢
16¢	8¢	7¢	1¢	13¢

4.
2¢	7¢	3¢	8¢	7¢
9¢	3¢	1¢	0¢	2¢
+ 2¢	+ 5¢	+ 8¢	+ 9¢	+ 3¢
13¢	15¢	12¢	17¢	12¢

Macmillan/McGraw-Hill, MATHEMATICS IN ACTION
Grade 2, Chapter 3, Lesson 12, page 112

Reteaching-40

PRACTICE

PRACTICE-40

Name

ADDING AND SUBTRACTING MONEY

Add or subtract.

1.
6¢	9¢	2¢	8¢	7¢	16¢
+ 2¢	− 4¢	+ 9¢	− 5¢	+ 9¢	− 8¢
8¢	5¢	11¢	3¢	16¢	8¢

2.
12¢	13¢	5¢	17¢	14¢	3¢
− 8¢	− 5¢	+ 7¢	− 9¢	− 7¢	+ 8¢
4¢	8¢	12¢	8¢	7¢	11¢

3.
8¢	18¢	4¢	16¢	15¢	11¢
+ 7¢	− 9¢	+ 7¢	− 7¢	− 8¢	− 4¢
15¢	9¢	11¢	9¢	7¢	7¢

4.
4¢		5¢	2¢		
2¢	2¢	1¢	5¢	3¢	1¢
1¢	1¢	1¢	2¢	5¢	1¢
+ 6¢	+ 8¢	+ 3¢	+ 1¢	+ 4¢	+ 9¢
13¢	11¢	10¢	10¢	12¢	11¢

Macmillan/McGraw-Hill, MATHEMATICS IN ACTION
Grade 2, Chapter 3, Lesson 12, page 112

Practice-40

ENRICHMENT

ENRICHMENT-40

Name

ADDING AND SUBTRACTING MONEY

On Your Own   Pair and Share   In a Group

BIG SALE

Ken buys one of each.
Draw a line to the price he paid.

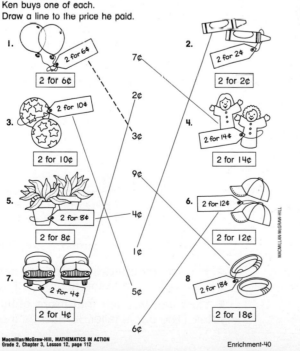

1. 2 for 6¢ (2 for 6¢)
2. 2 for 2¢ (2 for 2¢)
3. 2 for 10¢ (2 for 10¢)
4. 2 for 14¢ (2 for 14¢)
5. 2 for 8¢ (2 for 8¢)
6. 2 for 12¢ (2 for 12¢)
7. 2 for 4¢ (2 for 4¢)
8. 2 for 18¢ (2 for 18¢)

7¢   2¢   3¢   9¢   1¢   4¢   5¢   6¢

Macmillan/McGraw-Hill, MATHEMATICS IN ACTION
Grade 2, Chapter 3, Lesson 12, page 112

Enrichment-40

Problem of the Day

Karen had 17¢. If she spent 9¢ on a sticker, could she still buy cough drops for 10¢? [No. Children may work it out this way: 17¢ − 9¢ = 8¢; 8¢ < 10¢.]

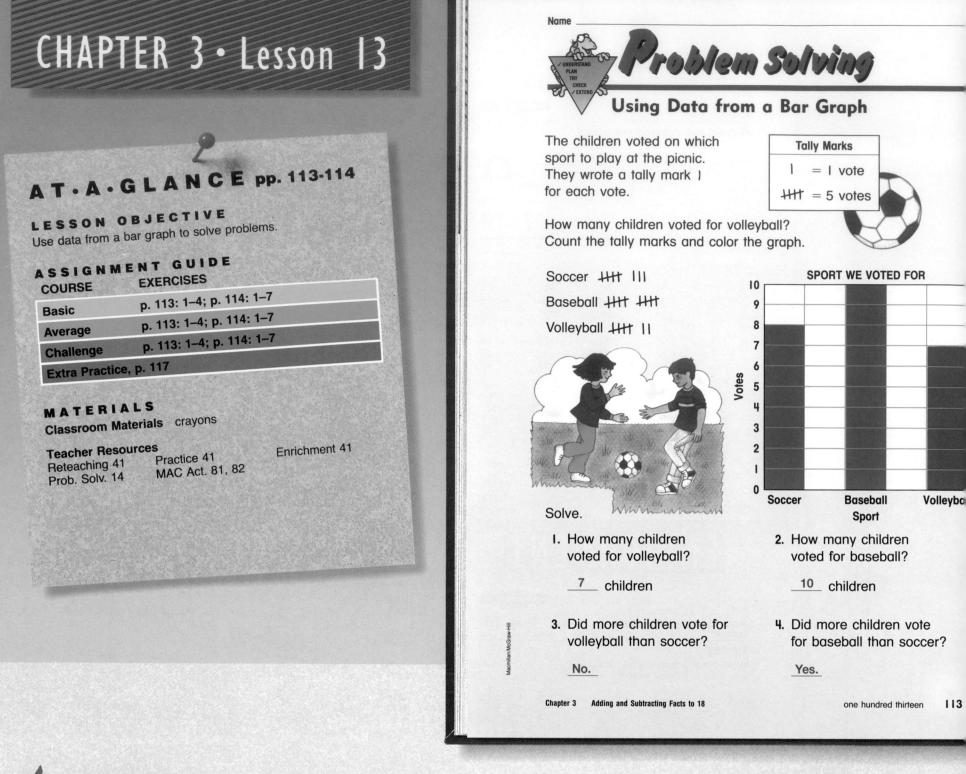

AT·A·GLANCE pp. 113-114

LESSON OBJECTIVE
Use data from a bar graph to solve problems.

ASSIGNMENT GUIDE

COURSE	EXERCISES
Basic	p. 113: 1–4; p. 114: 1–7
Average	p. 113: 1–4; p. 114: 1–7
Challenge	p. 113: 1–4; p. 114: 1–7
Extra Practice, p. 117	

MATERIALS
Classroom Materials crayons

Teacher Resources
Reteaching 41   Practice 41   Enrichment 41
Prob. Solv. 14   MAC Act. 81, 82

Name _____

Problem Solving

UNDERSTAND
PLAN
TRY
CHECK
EXTEND

Using Data from a Bar Graph

The children voted on which sport to play at the picnic. They wrote a tally mark | for each vote.

Tally Marks	
		= 1 vote
|||||	= 5 votes

How many children voted for volleyball? Count the tally marks and color the graph.

Soccer ||||| |||

Baseball ||||| |||||

Volleyball ||||| ||

SPORT WE VOTED FOR

(Bar graph: Votes 0–10; Soccer = 8, Baseball = 10, Volleyball = 7)

Votes
Sport

Solve.

1. How many children voted for volleyball?

   __7__ children

2. How many children voted for baseball?

   __10__ children

3. Did more children vote for volleyball than soccer?

   __No.__

4. Did more children vote for baseball than soccer?

   __Yes.__

Macmillan/McGraw-Hill

---

1 PREPARE   **WARM-UP** To prepare children for using data from a bar graph to solve a problem, draw 3 rows of squares on the chalkboard. Vary the number of squares in each row. Have children count and tell how many squares are in each row.

2 TEACH   **ORGANIZING** Write the words *carrots, raisins,* and *apples* on the chalkboard. Review the use of tally marks. Read aloud the story below:

The children voted on whether to snack on carrots, raisins, or apples. They used tally marks to keep track of the votes.

Mark the following: Carrots—4; Raisins—5; Apples—7.

Create the following bar graph:

SNACK WE VOTED FOR

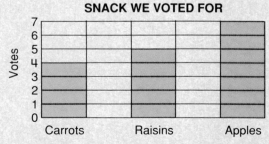

(Bar graph: Votes 0–7; Carrots = 4, Raisins = 5, Apples = 7)

Votes
Carrots   Raisins   Apples

■ **How many children voted for carrots? How do you know?** [4; the bar is filled in to the number 4.]

■ **How can you tell that more children voted for raisins than carrots?** [The bar is taller. It reaches the number 5.]

Use the graph to solve the problems.

The Book Club voted for a president.

VOTES FOR PRESIDENT

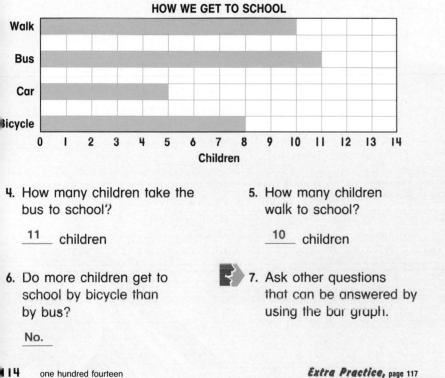

1. How many club members voted

   for Yumi? __5__ members

2. How many members voted

   for Peg? __2__ members

3. Who got the most votes? ___Tad___

The children in the Book Club made a bar graph to show how they get to school.

HOW WE GET TO SCHOOL

4. How many children take the bus to school?

   ___11___ children

5. How many children walk to school?

   ___10___ children

6. Do more children get to school by bicycle than by bus?

   No.

7. Ask other questions that can be answered by using the bar graph.

114   one hundred fourteen

Extra Practice, page 117

MEETING INDIVIDUAL NEEDS

TEACHER to TEACHER

COOPERATIVE LEARNING TIP 🎬 A class survey helped our community decide which cooperative sports and games we wanted to play at our picnic. We put up large sheets of graph paper with the names of several different games on each sheet. Each family group took turns filling in the squares for the games the group preferred. Each group member made her or his entry in the group's color. When all graphs were filled in, each small group wrote mathematical statements, such as "More children in our group wanted to play cooperative volleyball than soccer." We played the games with the most votes.

For Students Acquiring English (SAE)

Make sure SAE children have experience with constructing and interpreting a graph based on their own experience. Use the example of carrots, raisins, and apples to have class members complete a graph showing their own preferences.

■ **Which snack got the most votes? How do you know?** [Apples; that bar is the tallest. It reaches the number 7.]

PUPIL'S EDITION pp. 113-114

Page 113 Have a volunteer read the problem at the top of the page.

■ **What do you need to do?** [Count the tally marks and color the graph.]

■ **How do you know which sport got the most votes?** [Find the tallest bar.]

■ **What did you learn?** [to use data on a graph to solve problems]

Check for Understanding

■ **What if 9 children had voted for volleyball? How many more squares would be filled in on the graph?** [2]

GUIDED PRACTICE ex. 1–4: Work through ex. 1 with the children. Make sure they understand how to solve the problem using the data from the bar graph.

Page 114 Read the problems aloud and discuss the graphs with children as necessary.

PRACTICE•APPLY PRACTICE ex. 1–7

CLOSE Guide children to summarize the lesson:

■ **How do you use data on a bar graph to solve problems?** [Possible response: Decide what you need to know and find where that data is on the bar graph. Then use that data to solve the problem.]

Chapter 3 • Lesson 13   **114**

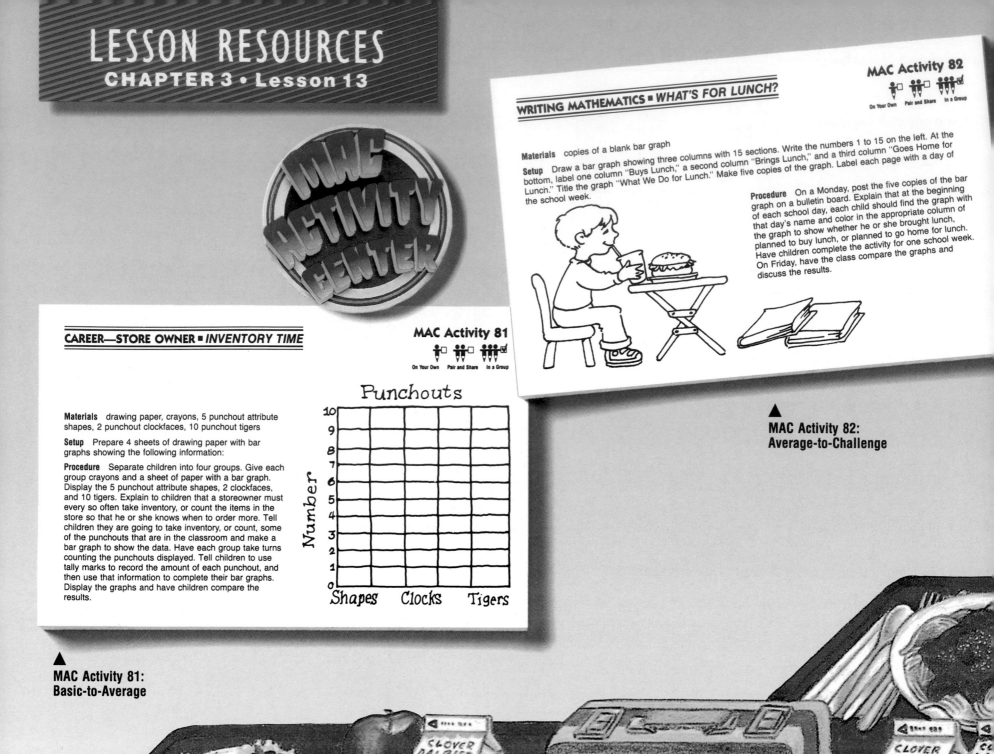

MAC Activity 82

On Your Own Pair and Share In a Group

WRITING MATHEMATICS ■ WHAT'S FOR LUNCH?

Materials copies of a blank bar graph

Setup Draw a bar graph showing three columns with 15 sections. Write the numbers 1 to 15 on the left. At the bottom, label one column "Buys Lunch," a second column "Brings Lunch," and a third column "Goes Home for Lunch." Title the graph "What We Do for Lunch." Make five copies of the graph. Label each page with a day of the school week.

Procedure On a Monday, post the five copies of the bar graph on a bulletin board. Explain that at the beginning of each school day, each child should find the graph with that day's name and color in the appropriate column of the graph to show whether he or she brought lunch, planned to buy lunch, or planned to go home for lunch. Have children complete the activity for one school week. On Friday, have the class compare the graphs and discuss the results.

▲ **MAC Activity 82:**
Average-to-Challenge

CAREER—STORE OWNER ■ INVENTORY TIME

MAC Activity 81

On Your Own Pair and Share In a Group

Materials drawing paper, crayons, 5 punchout attribute shapes, 2 punchout clockfaces, 10 punchout tigers

Setup Prepare 4 sheets of drawing paper with bar graphs showing the following information:

Procedure Separate children into four groups. Give each group crayons and a sheet of paper with a bar graph. Display the 5 punchout attribute shapes, 2 clockfaces, and 10 tigers. Explain to children that a storeowner must every so often take inventory, or count the items in the store so that he or she knows when to order more. Tell children they are going to take inventory, or count, some of the punchouts that are in the classroom and make a bar graph to show the data. Have each group take turns counting the punchouts displayed. Tell children to use tally marks to record the amount of each punchout, and then use that information to complete their bar graphs. Display the graphs and have children compare the results.

Punchouts

	Shapes	Clocks	Tigers
10			
9			
8			
7			
6			
5			
4			
3			
2			
1			
0			

Number

▲ **MAC Activity 81:**
Basic-to-Average

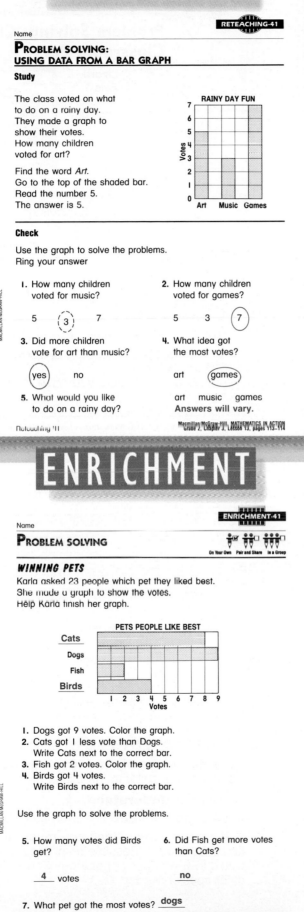

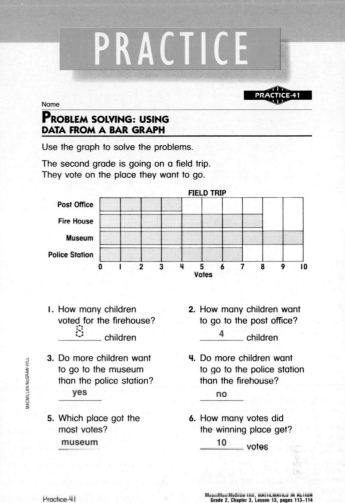

RETEACHING-41

Name _____

PROBLEM SOLVING: USING DATA FROM A BAR GRAPH

Study

The class voted on what to do on a rainy day. They made a graph to show their votes. How many children voted for art?

Find the word *Art*.
Go to the top of the shaded bar.
Read the number 5.
The answer is 5.

RAINY DAY FUN
(Votes — Art, Music, Games)

Check

Use the graph to solve the problems.
Ring your answer

1. How many children voted for music?

   5   (3)   7

2. How many children voted for games?

   5   3   (7)

3. Did more children vote for art than music?

   (yes)   no

4. What idea got the most votes?

   art   (games)

5. What would you like to do on a rainy day?
   art   music   games
   Answers will vary.

Reteaching-41

Macmillan/McGraw-Hill, MATHEMATICS IN ACTION
Grade 2, Chapter 3, Lesson 13, pages 113–114

PRACTICE-41

Name _____

PROBLEM SOLVING: USING DATA FROM A BAR GRAPH

Use the graph to solve the problems.

The second grade is going on a field trip.
They vote on the place they want to go.

FIELD TRIP
(Post Office, Fire House, Museum, Police Station — Votes 0–10)

1. How many children voted for the firehouse?
   ___8___ children

2. How many children want to go to the post office?
   ___4___ children

3. Do more children want to go to the museum than the police station?
   yes

4. Do more children want to go to the police station than the firehouse?
   no

5. Which place got the most votes?
   museum

6. How many votes did the winning place get?
   ___10___ votes

Practice-41

Macmillan/McGraw-Hill, MATHEMATICS IN ACTION
Grade 2, Chapter 3, Lesson 13, pages 113–114

ENRICHMENT-41

Name _____

PROBLEM SOLVING

On Your Own   Pair and Share   In a Group

WINNING PETS

Karla asked 23 people which pet they liked best.
She made a graph to show the votes.
Help Karla finish her graph.

PETS PEOPLE LIKE BEST
(Cats, Dogs, Fish, Birds — Votes 1–9)

1. Dogs got 9 votes. Color the graph.
2. Cats got 1 less vote than Dogs. Write Cats next to the correct bar.
3. Fish got 2 votes. Color the graph.
4. Birds got 4 votes. Write Birds next to the correct bar.

Use the graph to solve the problems.

5. How many votes did Birds get?
   ___4___ votes

6. Did Fish get more votes than Cats?
   no

7. What pet got the most votes? **dogs**

Enrichment-41

Macmillan/McGraw-Hill, MATHEMATICS IN ACTION
Grade 2, Chapter 3, Lesson 13, pages 113–114

Problem of the Day

Milly looked at a graph showing the children's votes on what game to play at recess. The bar for Hide-and-Seek was the shortest. The bar for Tag was the longest. Did more students vote for Hide-and-Seek or for Tag? [Tag; because Tag had the longest bar, the graph showed that more children voted for Tag than for Hide-and-Seek.]

AT·A·GLANCE p. 115

LESSON OBJECTIVE
Make decisions using information.

ASSIGNMENT GUIDE

COURSE	EXERCISES
Basic	p. 115: 1–4
Average	p. 115: 1–4
Challenge	p. 115: 1–4

Teacher Resources
Crit. Think. 6   Prob. Solv. 15

Name _____

Decision Making

Problem Solving: Choosing a Classroom Pet

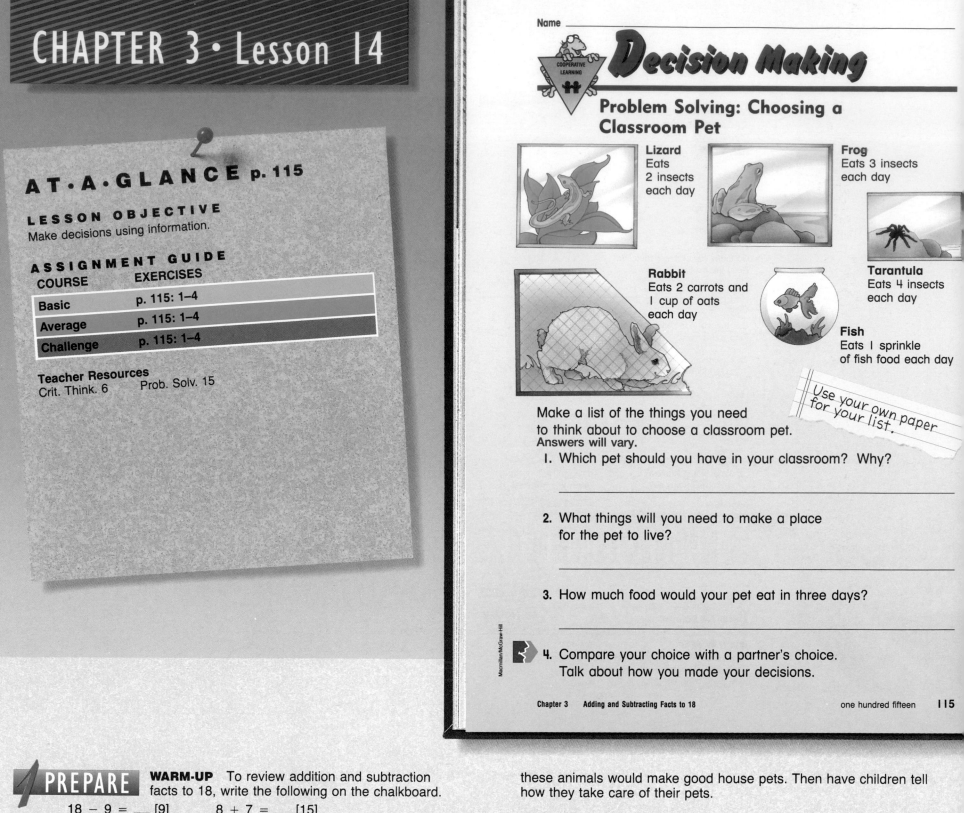

Lizard
Eats
2 insects
each day

Frog
Eats 3 insects
each day

Tarantula
Eats 4 insects
each day

Rabbit
Eats 2 carrots and
1 cup of oats
each day

Fish
Eats 1 sprinkle
of fish food each day

Make a list of the things you need
to think about to choose a classroom pet.
Answers will vary.

Use your own paper for your list.

1. Which pet should you have in your classroom? Why?

_____

2. What things will you need to make a place
for the pet to live?

_____

3. How much food would your pet eat in three days?

_____

4. Compare your choice with a partner's choice.
Talk about how you made your decisions.

Chapter 3   Adding and Subtracting Facts to 18   one hundred fifteen **115**

Macmillan/McGraw-Hill

PREPARE   **WARM-UP** To review addition and subtraction
facts to 18, write the following on the chalkboard.

18 − 9 = __ [9]	8 + 7 = __ [15]
17 − 9 = __ [8]	15 − 7 = __ [8]
6 + 5 = __ [11]	7 + 7 = __ [14]
8 + 9 = __ [17]	13 − 9 = __ [4]

Have children complete the number sentences.

TEACH   **DISCUSSING** Explain to children that pets are
tame animals that are kept for fun. Have children
name the kinds of pets they have at home or would like to have. List
children's responses on the chalkboard. Guide them to suggest why

these animals would make good house pets. Then have children tell
how they take care of their pets.

PUPIL'S EDITION p. 115
Have children identify the animals pictured at the top of the page.
Read with the children the things each pet eats in one day.

Check for Understanding

■ **What does a lizard eat each day?** [2 insects]

■ **What are some things you must think about before choosing a
classroom pet?** [Possible responses: the size of the animal, where it
would live, whether or not the pet could be harmful, what it eats, and
other special needs]

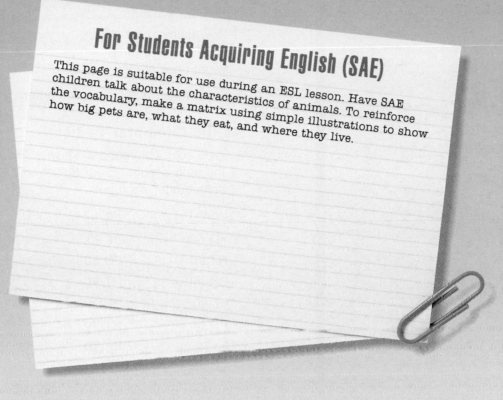

For Students Acquiring English (SAE)

This page is suitable for use during an ESL lesson. Have SAE children talk about the characteristics of animals. To reinforce the vocabulary, make a matrix using simple illustrations to show how big pets are, what they eat, and where they live.

3 PRACTICE•APPLY

Have children complete ex. 1–4. Call on volunteers to name the pet they would like to have in the classroom and have them explain their choices. Encourage children to tell about the things that are needed to make a home for their pet.

CLOSE Guide children to summarize the lesson:

■ **What should you do before choosing a classroom pet?** [Decide on the needs of the pet and on the things required to take good care of the pet.]

CLASS PROJECT

Materials drawing paper, crayons, tongue depressors, scissors, paste, oval shapes of cardboard

Give each child crayons, one-half sheet of drawing paper, paste, and a tongue depressor. Tell children that they are going to make stick puppets. Have them draw the pet they chose on page 115, then cut out and paste the picture onto an oval shape of cardboard. Then have them slip a tongue depressor between the picture and the cardboard.

When children have completed the project, have them work in small groups to plan a puppet show using their pet puppets.

OBJECTIVE
Use directional terms to draw paths on a computer.

MATERIALS
Computer
Classroom Materials crayons, dried beans or other small objects, Logo language disk

Teacher Resources
Teacher Aid 5

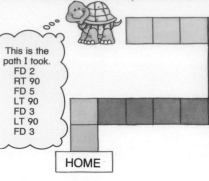

Technology

Computer: Logo Paths

Look at the path the turtle took.
It has right and left turns.
Each part can be
measured in steps.

> This is the
> path I took.
> FD 2
> RT 90
> FD 5
> LT 90
> FD 3
> LT 90
> FD 3

1. How many steps would
   it take for the turtle
   to get back home? __13__

HOME

You can make paths on a computer.

At the Computer

2. Type each command to show
   the turtle's path. Clear the
   screen after each path.

Path 1	Path 2
FD 60	LT 90
RT 90	FD 50
BK 40	RT 90
LT 90	BK 70
FD 50	RT 90
	BK 70

> Can you guess how
> the turtle will move
> in Path 2 before
> you put in
> the commands?

3. Talk about how the turtle moved when you put
   in each command. Children should use directional terms, such as
   forward, backward, left, right, to describe the turtle's movement.

4. You write commands and show a path. Your
   partner turns the turtle around and tries to get
   it home. Take turns.

5. Talk about what you need to know to draw
   paths on a computer. Possible answer: To draw paths on a computer,
   I need to know how to write commands for turning right and left, moving
   forward and backward, and taking different numbers of steps.

116   one hundred sixteen

PREPARE

WARM-UP To prepare children to use directional
terms to draw paths, review the terms *forward,
backward, left,* and *right* by playing a game of Simon Says. Use directions such as "Simon says, make a left turn." Make sure children remain in place as they turn.

TEACH

MODELING Give each child a copy of Teacher
Aid 5, a dried bean, and crayons. Tell children to
color the center square red, and identify it as *home.* Have children
mark their bean to indicate a "head," and identify the bean as a *turtle.*
Write the following program on the chalkboard:

FD 4   [forward 4 steps]
RT 90   [right turn]
FD 5   [forward 5 steps]

LT 90   [left turn]
BK 3   [backward 3 steps]

Tell children to put their turtle in the home square with its head facing
the top of the sheet. Explain that the *commands* on the chalkboard
show the direction the turtle will walk away from home. Have a volunteer act out the turtle's path as you read each command. Others will
work with the bean and grid. Explain that the number 90 after the
turns means how much to turn. Model it. Guide children to keep the
turtle in place as they turn it. Also model moving backward. Then
guide children through the program using opposites to get the turtle
home.

For Students Acquiring English (SAE)

As the story at the top of the page is read aloud, have a child or children model the turtle's walk. Children may enjoy making up similar stories of their own and presenting them to the class. As they do, make sure to emphasize directional words. Then relate these special words to the computer commands by saying that FD stands for "forward," RT for "right turn," etc.

PRACTICE • APPLY

Read the story at the top of the page and discuss the picture.

AT THE COMPUTER Before children begin working in pairs at the computer, load the Logo language disk and identify the figure as a turtle. Be sure children understand that they must type in the commands exactly as shown, with a space between the letters and the numbers. Tell them that they should press RETURN after each number. Discuss how to correct mistakes before pressing RETURN (check your Logo documentation) and how to clear the screen and return home (Apple: CLEAR-SCREEN or CS; Krell or Terrapin: DRAW; LogoWriter: CG). Remind them to clear the screen after each path.

Allow children to explore Logo by making their own paths in ex. 4. They may find it helpful to record their commands and to draw the resulting paths. Guide children to turn the turtle around by making two right or left turns. Children may find that when they input a large number for forward or backward, the turtle may move off the screen and reappear at the opposite side. Have them clear the screen and begin again using a smaller number.

C L O S E Guide children to summarize the lesson:

■ **What should you type into the computer to move forward 40 steps?** [FD 40]

■ **What direction does the turtle turn when you type RT?** [right]

CHAPTER 3

EXTRA PRACTICE

Extra Practice items are provided so that children may have an opportunity for further practice.

The *Additional Practice* section also provides practice you may wish to assign.

Extra Practice

Facts to 16, 17, and 18, pages 107–108 ....

Add or subtract.

1.
$$\begin{array}{r} 8 \\ +8 \\ \hline 16 \end{array} \qquad \begin{array}{r} 9 \\ +7 \\ \hline 16 \end{array} \qquad \begin{array}{r} 8 \\ +9 \\ \hline 17 \end{array} \qquad \begin{array}{r} 9 \\ +9 \\ \hline 18 \end{array} \qquad \begin{array}{r} 9 \\ +8 \\ \hline 17 \end{array} \qquad \begin{array}{r} 7 \\ +8 \\ \hline 15 \end{array}$$

2.
$$\begin{array}{r} 18 \\ -9 \\ \hline 9 \end{array} \qquad \begin{array}{r} 17 \\ -8 \\ \hline 9 \end{array} \qquad \begin{array}{r} 16 \\ -7 \\ \hline 9 \end{array} \qquad \begin{array}{r} 16 \\ -8 \\ \hline 8 \end{array} \qquad \begin{array}{r} 16 \\ -9 \\ \hline 7 \end{array} \qquad \begin{array}{r} 17 \\ -9 \\ \hline 8 \end{array}$$

Three or More Addends, page 111 ....

Add.

1.
$$\begin{array}{r} 3 \\ 5 \\ +9 \\ \hline 17 \end{array} \qquad \begin{array}{r} 8 \\ 1 \\ +9 \\ \hline 18 \end{array} \qquad \begin{array}{r} 7 \\ 2 \\ +7 \\ \hline 16 \end{array} \qquad \begin{array}{r} 3 \\ 4 \\ 4 \\ +6 \\ \hline 17 \end{array} \qquad \begin{array}{r} 5 \\ 3 \\ 3 \\ +7 \\ \hline 18 \end{array} \qquad \begin{array}{r} 6 \\ 2 \\ 2 \\ +8 \\ \hline 18 \end{array}$$

Problem Solving: Using Data from a Bar Graph, pages 113–114 ......

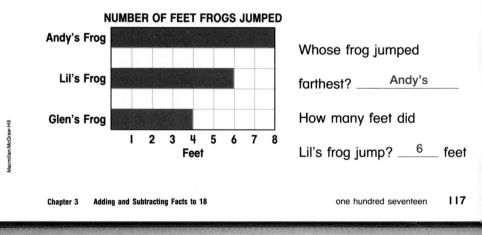

NUMBER OF FEET FROGS JUMPED

Whose frog jumped farthest? _____Andy's_____

How many feet did Lil's frog jump? __6__ feet

Chapter 3   Adding and Subtracting Facts to 18   one hundred seventeen   117

ADDITIONAL PRACTICE

p. 107 *Add or subtract.*

1.
$$\begin{array}{r} 8 \\ +7 \\ \hline [15] \end{array} \quad \begin{array}{r} 9 \\ +8 \\ \hline [17] \end{array} \quad \begin{array}{r} 8 \\ +8 \\ \hline [16] \end{array} \quad \begin{array}{r} 7 \\ +7 \\ \hline [14] \end{array} \quad \begin{array}{r} 9 \\ +9 \\ \hline [18] \end{array} \quad \begin{array}{r} 7 \\ +9 \\ \hline [16] \end{array}$$

2.
$$\begin{array}{r} 15 \\ -8 \\ \hline [7] \end{array} \quad \begin{array}{r} 14 \\ -7 \\ \hline [7] \end{array} \quad \begin{array}{r} 16 \\ -8 \\ \hline [8] \end{array} \quad \begin{array}{r} 17 \\ -9 \\ \hline [8] \end{array} \quad \begin{array}{r} 17 \\ -8 \\ \hline [9] \end{array} \quad \begin{array}{r} 16 \\ -9 \\ \hline [7] \end{array}$$

p. 111 *Add.*

1.
$$\begin{array}{r} 4 \\ 9 \\ +3 \\ \hline [16] \end{array} \qquad \begin{array}{r} 8 \\ 4 \\ +5 \\ \hline [17] \end{array} \qquad \begin{array}{r} 6 \\ 3 \\ +9 \\ \hline [18] \end{array} \qquad \begin{array}{r} 7 \\ 2 \\ +7 \\ \hline [16] \end{array}$$

2.
$$\begin{array}{r} 6 \\ 4 \\ +6 \\ \hline [16] \end{array} \qquad \begin{array}{r} 5 \\ 2 \\ 4 \\ +6 \\ \hline [17] \end{array} \qquad \begin{array}{r} 6 \\ 0 \\ 5 \\ +7 \\ \hline [18] \end{array} \qquad \begin{array}{r} 1 \\ 8 \\ 7 \\ +2 \\ \hline [18] \end{array}$$

p. 113 *Solve.*

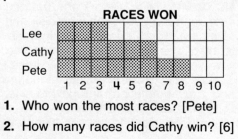

RACES WON

Lee
Cathy
Pete

1 2 3 4 5 6 7 8 9 10

1. Who won the most races? [Pete]

2. How many races did Cathy win? [6]

Practice Plus

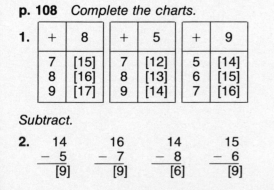
My sticker book.

Key Skill: Facts to 18, page 108 ....

Complete the chart.

1.

+	8
3	11
5	13
7	15

+	7
7	14
8	15
5	12

+	6
9	15
4	10
7	13

+	9
8	17
5	14
9	18

Subtract.

2.
$$\begin{array}{r} 15 \\ -\ 8 \\ \hline 7 \end{array} \quad \begin{array}{r} 18 \\ -\ 9 \\ \hline 9 \end{array} \quad \begin{array}{r} 16 \\ -\ 8 \\ \hline 8 \end{array} \quad \begin{array}{r} 17 \\ -\ 9 \\ \hline 8 \end{array} \quad \begin{array}{r} 16 \\ -\ 7 \\ \hline 9 \end{array} \quad \begin{array}{r} 13 \\ -\ 8 \\ \hline 5 \end{array}$$

Key Skill: Three or More Addends, page 111 ....

Add.

1.
$$\begin{array}{r} 8 \\ 2 \\ +7 \\ \hline 17 \end{array} \quad \begin{array}{r} 6 \\ 1 \\ +8 \\ \hline 15 \end{array} \quad \begin{array}{r} 4 \\ 2 \\ +9 \\ \hline 15 \end{array} \quad \begin{array}{r} 5 \\ 4 \\ +9 \\ \hline 18 \end{array} \quad \begin{array}{r} 7 \\ 7 \\ +2 \\ \hline 16 \end{array} \quad \begin{array}{r} 3 \\ 4 \\ +5 \\ \hline 12 \end{array}$$

2.
$$\begin{array}{r} 2 \\ 5 \\ +8 \\ \hline 15 \end{array} \quad \begin{array}{r} 2 \\ 3 \\ +6 \\ \hline 11 \end{array} \quad \begin{array}{r} 4 \\ 3 \\ +7 \\ \hline 14 \end{array} \quad \begin{array}{r} 6 \\ 1 \\ +9 \\ \hline 16 \end{array} \quad \begin{array}{r} 5 \\ 2 \\ 1 \\ +8 \\ \hline 16 \end{array} \quad \begin{array}{r} 7 \\ 2 \\ 3 \\ +6 \\ \hline 18 \end{array}$$

ADDITIONAL PRACTICE

p. 108 *Complete the charts.*

1.

+	8
7	[15]
8	[16]
9	[17]

+	5
7	[12]
8	[13]
9	[14]

+	9
5	[14]
6	[15]
7	[16]

Subtract.

2.
$$\begin{array}{r} 14 \\ -\ 5 \\ \hline [9] \end{array} \quad \begin{array}{r} 16 \\ -\ 7 \\ \hline [9] \end{array} \quad \begin{array}{r} 14 \\ -\ 8 \\ \hline [6] \end{array} \quad \begin{array}{r} 15 \\ -\ 6 \\ \hline [9] \end{array}$$

Complete the charts.

3.

+	7
4	[11]
9	[16]
6	[13]

+	6
8	[14]
7	[13]
6	[12]

+	9
4	[13]
9	[18]
6	[15]

Subtract.

4.
$$\begin{array}{r} 13 \\ -\ 9 \\ \hline [4] \end{array} \quad \begin{array}{r} 18 \\ -\ 9 \\ \hline [9] \end{array} \quad \begin{array}{r} 16 \\ -\ 9 \\ \hline [7] \end{array} \quad \begin{array}{r} 12 \\ -\ 6 \\ \hline [6] \end{array}$$

p. 111 *Add.*

1.
$$\begin{array}{r} 8 \\ 8 \\ +1 \\ \hline [17] \end{array} \quad \begin{array}{r} 3 \\ 9 \\ +4 \\ \hline [16] \end{array} \quad \begin{array}{r} 3 \\ 7 \\ +5 \\ \hline [15] \end{array} \quad \begin{array}{r} 7 \\ 7 \\ +4 \\ \hline [18] \end{array}$$

2.
$$\begin{array}{r} 3 \\ 3 \\ 3 \\ +5 \\ \hline [14] \end{array} \quad \begin{array}{r} 8 \\ 1 \\ 4 \\ +2 \\ \hline [15] \end{array} \quad \begin{array}{r} 6 \\ 4 \\ 2 \\ +2 \\ \hline [14] \end{array} \quad \begin{array}{r} 9 \\ 0 \\ +7 \\ \hline [16] \end{array}$$

PRACTICE *PLUS*

Practice Plus is provided to supply additional practice for the two key skills in this chapter.

Key Skills
Page 108: Facts to 16, 17, and 18
Page 111: Three or More Addends

The *Additional Practice* also provides practice you may wish to assign for key skills in this chapter.

AT·A·GLANCE 119-120

OBJECTIVE
Review/test the concepts and skills presented in Chapter 3.

3A. Add, facts to 18.
3B. Subtract, facts to 18.
3C. Add three or more 1-digit numbers.
3D. Solve problems including those that involve choosing the operation and using data from a bar graph.

Teacher Resources
Testing Program, pp. 25–36

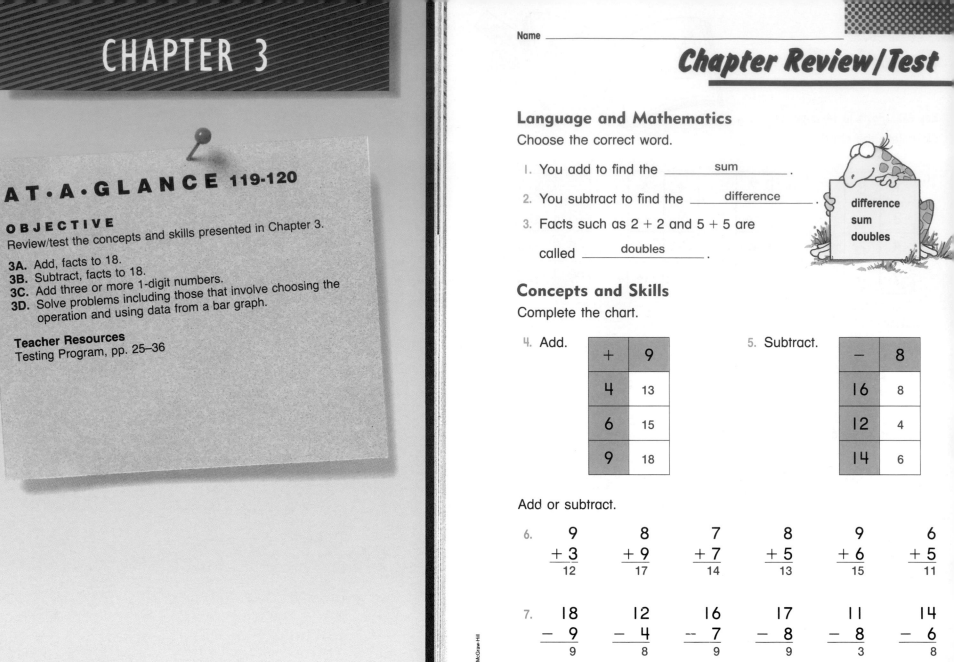

Chapter Review/Test

Name _____

Language and Mathematics
Choose the correct word.

1. You add to find the _____sum_____ .

2. You subtract to find the ____difference____ .

3. Facts such as 2 + 2 and 5 + 5 are

   called ____doubles____ .

> difference
> sum
> doubles

Concepts and Skills
Complete the chart.

4. Add.

+	9
4	13
6	15
9	18

5. Subtract.

−	8
16	8
12	4
14	6

Add or subtract.

6.
9	8	7	8	9	6
+3	+9	+7	+5	+6	+5
12	17	14	13	15	11

7.
18	12	16	17	11	14
−9	−4	−7	−8	−8	−6
9	8	9	9	3	8

Chapter 3   Adding and Subtracting Facts to 18   one hundred nineteen   119

USING THE CHAPTER REVIEW/TEST

The Chapter Review/Test may be used as a review to survey children's knowledge and understanding of the chapter material. Or it may be used as a test to formally assess children's understanding of the concepts and skills taught in the chapter. If used as a test, you may wish to assign one or more of the resources listed in *Reinforcement and Remediation* on p. 120 after reviewing children's test results.

If the Chapter Review/Test is used as a review, you may wish to have children work in pairs to complete it. Have them talk about how doubles can be used to find the sum of 6 + 1 + 7. Then, you can use the Chapter Tests—Forms A, B, and C—provided in the *Testing Program Blackline Master and Teacher's Manual* for testing purposes. Any of these forms may be used for pretesting, posttesting, or retesting.

A performance assessment activity for the key concept in this chapter is provided on page 121.

Add.

8.

3	7	6	2	5	3
6	1	2	6	1	4
+7	+8	+5	2	0	2
16	16	13	+6	+9	+8
			16	15	17

Problem Solving

Complete the example that solves the problem.
Ring it.

9. Neil had 8 toy cars.
   Mona had 5 toy trucks.
   How many toy cars and trucks
   did they have altogether?

$$\left(\begin{array}{r} 8 \\ +5 \\ \hline 13 \end{array}\right) \qquad \begin{array}{r} 8 \\ -5 \\ \hline \end{array}$$

Solve.

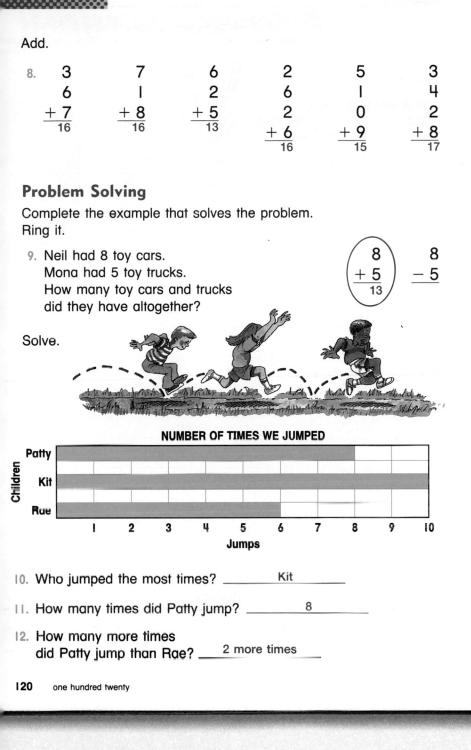

NUMBER OF TIMES WE JUMPED

Children

Patty

Kit

Rae

| Jumps | 1 | 2 | 3 | 4 | 5 | 6 | 7 | 8 | 9 | 10 |

10. Who jumped the most times? _____Kit_____

11. How many times did Patty jump? _____8_____

12. How many more times
    did Patty jump than Rae? ___2 more times___

Reinforcement and Remediation

CHAP. OBJ.	TEST ITEMS	PUPIL'S EDITION pp.			TEACHER'S EDITION pp.	TEACHER RESOURCES	
		Lesson	Extra Practice	Practice Plus	Alt. Teaching Strategy	Reteaching	Practice
3A	1, 3–4, 6	93–102, 107–110	106, 117	118	94, 96, 98, 100, 102, 108, 110	31–35, 37–38	31–35, 37–38
3B	2, 5, 7	93–102, 107–110	106, 117	118	94, 96, 100, 102, 108	31–35, 37–38	31–35, 37–38
3C	8	111	117		111A	39	39
3D	9–12	103–104, 113–114	106, 117	118		36, 41	36, 41

For Students Acquiring English (SAE)

Before beginning the Chapter Review/Test with SAE children, scan the pages for any unfamiliar vocabulary that should be pretaught. You may wish to pair or group SAE children with non-SAE children. You may also wish to repeat some of the activities and techniques for SAE children that were suggested earlier in this chapter.

CHAPTER 3

Performance Assessment

Work with a partner.

Use a bag and 9 ◯.
Place the counters in the bag.
Shake the bag and empty it.
Count the ● and the ◯.

Fill in the table.
Repeat the activity.

	●	◯
1st Try		
2nd Try		

Then write a problem using
the numbers in the table.

_____

_____

_____

Solve your problem.
Write the number sentence.

_____

You may put this page in your Portfolio

Macmillan/McGraw-Hill

AT·A·GLANCE p. 121

OBJECTIVE
Assess whether children can add and subtract facts to 18.

MATERIALS
Classroom Materials paper bags
Manipulatives 9 ◯ per pair

Teacher Resources
Performance Assessment booklet, pp. 16–19

For Students Acquiring English (SAE)

Before beginning the performance assessment with SAE children, scan the page for any unfamiliar vocabulary that should be pretaught. You may wish to pair or group SAE children with non-SAE children. You may also wish to repeat some of the activities and techniques for SAE children that were suggested earlier in this chapter.

USING PERFORMANCE ASSESSMENT
The Performance Assessment activity may be used to informally assess children's understanding of the key concept(s) of the chapter. Additional assessment activities and Math Journal Options are provided in the *Performance Assessment* booklet.

Performing the Activity
Assign children to work in pairs. Have them work together to make up a problem involving addition or subtraction of the numbers shown in the table. Then have them write the problem individually, including a number sentence showing how to solve the problem.

Evaluation Guidelines
Use these criteria to help determine the holistic score for each child. The holistic scoring scale can be found in the Teacher's Reference Section.

- Do children use the numbers in the table in an addition or subtraction problem?
- Can the child write a number sentence showing how to solve the addition or subtraction problem?

[Example Response: A story problem might be: 7 counters were red in the first try and 4 counters were red in the second try. How many counters were red in all? 7 + 4 = 11 red counters]

If children do not have a full understanding of the key concept(s), you may wish to use the Alternative Teaching Strategies or the MAC Activities within the chapter.

You may wish to have children put their final revised work in their portfolios.

A formal assessment of the concepts and skills taught in this chapter is provided on pages 119–120.

Enrichment For All

Missing Signs

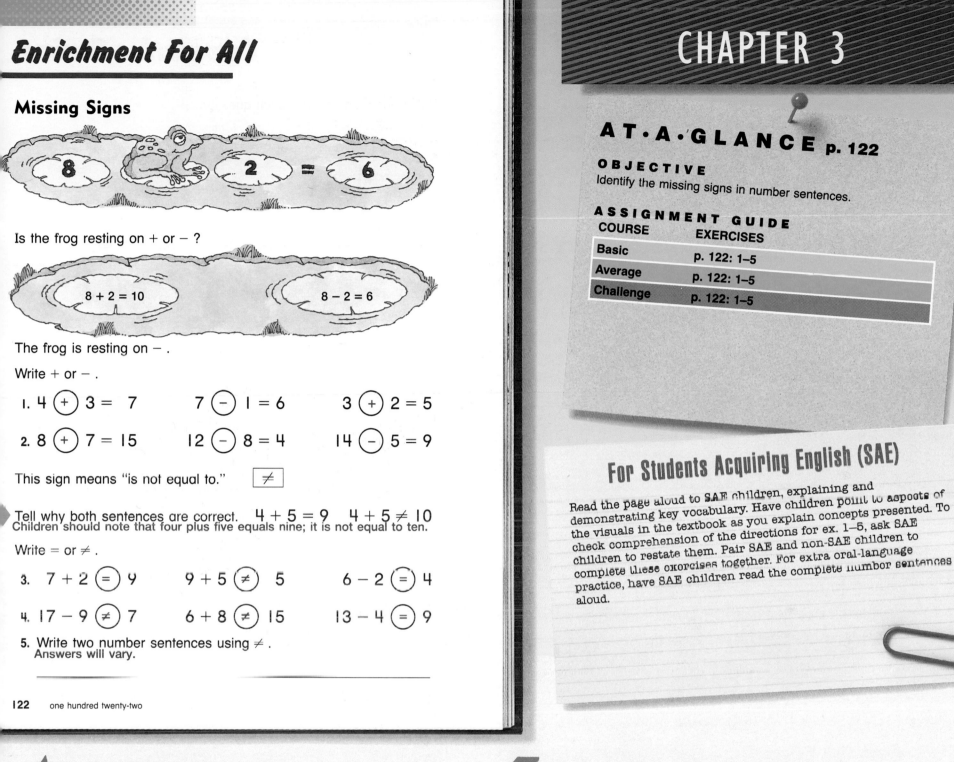

Is the frog resting on + or − ?

$$8 + 2 = 10 \qquad 8 - 2 = 6$$

The frog is resting on − .

Write + or − .

1. $4 \; \oplus \; 3 = 7$ $7 \; \ominus \; 1 = 6$ $3 \; \oplus \; 2 = 5$

2. $8 \; \oplus \; 7 = 15$ $12 \; \ominus \; 8 = 4$ $14 \; \ominus \; 5 = 9$

This sign means "is not equal to." $\boxed{\neq}$

Tell why both sentences are correct. $4 + 5 = 9 \qquad 4 + 5 \neq 10$
Children should note that four plus five equals nine; it is not equal to ten.

Write = or ≠ .

3. $7 + 2 \; \textcircled{=} \; 9$ $9 + 5 \; \textcircled{\neq} \; 5$ $6 - 2 \; \textcircled{=} \; 4$

4. $17 - 9 \; \textcircled{\neq} \; 7$ $6 + 8 \; \textcircled{\neq} \; 15$ $13 - 4 \; \textcircled{=} \; 9$

5. Write two number sentences using ≠ .
   Answers will vary.

CHAPTER 3

AT·A·GLANCE p. 122

OBJECTIVE
Identify the missing signs in number sentences.

ASSIGNMENT GUIDE

COURSE	EXERCISES
Basic	p. 122: 1–5
Average	p. 122: 1–5
Challenge	p. 122: 1–5

For Students Acquiring English (SAE)

Read the page aloud to SAE children, explaining and demonstrating key vocabulary. Have children point to aspects of the visuals in the textbook as you explain concepts presented. To check comprehension of the directions for ex. 1–5, ask SAE children to restate them. Pair SAE and non-SAE children to complete these exercises together. For extra oral-language practice, have SAE children read the complete number sentences aloud.

 **PREPARE**   **WARM-UP** To prepare children to complete number sentences, write the following on the chalkboard.

1. $4 + 2 = \underline{\hphantom{0}}$ [6]   4. $13 - 5 = \underline{\hphantom{0}}$ [8]
2. $6 + 8 = \underline{\hphantom{0}}$ [14]   5. $9 + 4 = \underline{\hphantom{0}}$ [13]
3. $18 - 8 = \underline{\hphantom{0}}$ [10]   6. $14 - 7 = \underline{\hphantom{0}}$ [7]

Have children write the answers and then tell whether they added or subtracted to find the answers.

TEACH   **DISCUSSING** Have children study the illustration at the very top of the page. Explain that the frog is covering up the sign, so they have to decide if it is a plus or minus sign. Have children add and subtract and then choose the correct sign. [minus sign]

PRACTICE·APPLY Have children complete ex. 1–5. For ex. 5, call on volunteers to write their sentences on the chalkboard and have others evaluate if the sentences are correct. Children should explain their answers.

CLOSE Guide children to summarize the lesson:

Write the following on the chalkboard.

$$8 \quad 6 = 14 \qquad 8 \quad 6 = 2$$

■ **Which sentence requires a minus sign?** [8   6 = 2]

CHAPTER 3

OBJECTIVE
Review and maintain previously learned concepts and skills.

Teacher Resources
Computer Software *Mathematics Skills: Disk 2 Final Checkup;*
Disk 3 Final Checkup

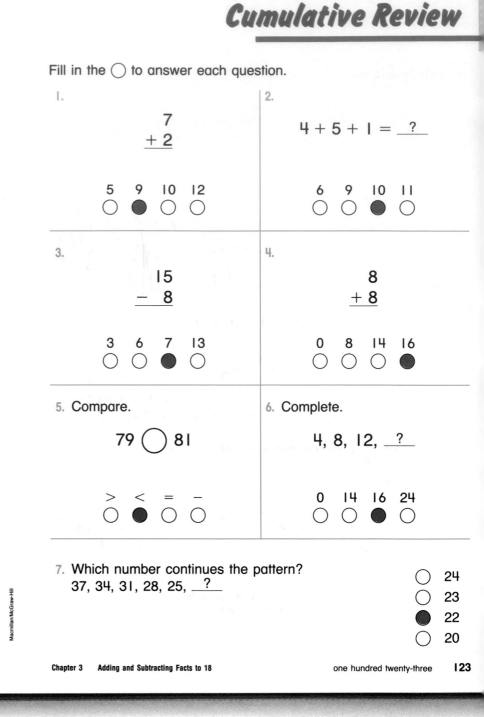

Cumulative Review

Name _____

Fill in the ◯ to answer each question.

1.

$$7 + 2$$

5	9	10	12
◯	●	◯	◯

2.

$4 + 5 + 1 = \underline{\ ?\ }$

6	9	10	11
◯	◯	●	◯

3.

$$15 - 8$$

3	6	7	13
◯	◯	●	◯

4.

$$8 + 8$$

0	8	14	16
◯	◯	◯	●

5. Compare.

$79 \bigcirc 81$

>	<	=	−
◯	●	◯	◯

6. Complete.

$4, 8, 12, \underline{\ ?\ }$

0	14	16	24
◯	◯	●	◯

7. Which number continues the pattern?
37, 34, 31, 28, 25, __?__

- ◯ 24
- ◯ 23
- ● 22
- ◯ 20

Macmillan/McGraw-Hill

Chapter 3   Adding and Subtracting Facts to 18   one hundred twenty-three   **123**

USING THE CUMULATIVE REVIEW

The Cumulative Review is presented in a multiple-choice format to provide practice in taking a standardized test. It gives children an opportunity to review previously learned skills. An answer sheet, similar to those used when taking standardized tests, can be found in the *Testing Program Blackline Masters and Teacher's Manual.*

The table that follows correlates the review items to the lesson pages on which the skills are taught.

Review Items	Text Pages	Review Items	Text Pages
1	34	5	75–76
2	31	6	62
3	108	7	69–70
4	108		

Testing Program Blackline Masters

In addition to the Cumulative Review in the Pupil's Edition, there are quarterly Cumulative Tests and an End-Year Test. These tests are multiple choice and provide additional opportunities for children to practice taking standardized tests.

Cumulative Tests measure children's performance on major skills and concepts taught during the previous quarters. The **End-Year Test** measures children's performance on major skills and concepts taught throughout the year.

Home Activity

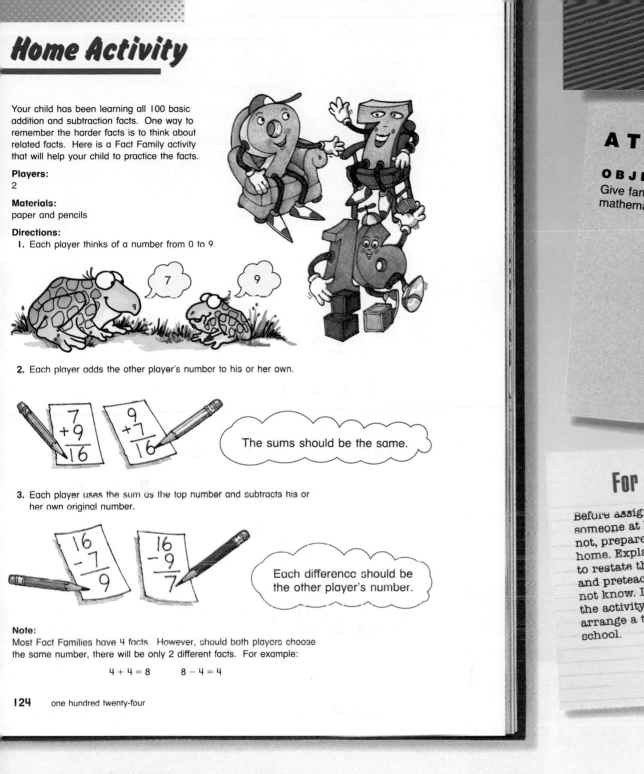

Your child has been learning all 100 basic addition and subtraction facts. One way to remember the harder facts is to think about related facts. Here is a Fact Family activity that will help your child to practice the facts.

Players:
2

Materials:
paper and pencils

Directions:

1. Each player thinks of a number from 0 to 9.

7   9

2. Each player adds the other player's number to his or her own.

$$\begin{array}{r} 7 \\ +9 \\ \hline 16 \end{array} \qquad \begin{array}{r} 9 \\ +7 \\ \hline 16 \end{array}$$

The sums should be the same.

3. Each player uses the sum as the top number and subtracts his or her own original number.

$$\begin{array}{r} 16 \\ -7 \\ \hline 9 \end{array} \qquad \begin{array}{r} 16 \\ -9 \\ \hline 7 \end{array}$$

Each difference should be the other player's number.

Note:
Most Fact Families have 4 facts. However, should both players choose the same number, there will be only 2 different facts. For example:

$$4 + 4 = 8 \qquad 8 - 4 = 4$$

124   one hundred twenty-four

AT·A·GLANCE p. 124

OBJECTIVE
Give family members an opportunity to share in their child's mathematics learning.

For Students Acquiring English (SAE)

Before assigning this Home Activity to SAE children, find out if someone at home will be able to work with them in English. If not, prepare them to complete the activity independently at home. Explain the directions of the activity and ask SAE children to restate them so you can check comprehension. Scan the page and preteach any difficult vocabulary or phrases that they may not know. If you feel that an SAE child will need extra help with the activity, you might assign that child a non-SAE partner and arrange a time for them to work on the activity in or out of school.

USING THE ACTIVITY

Have children look at the page. Explain that the page has an activity that an adult in the family can help them complete. Read the page with the children, making sure that they understand what needs to be done. Tell children that they will do this page at home.

Previewing
CHAPTER 4

Notes
FROM THE AUTHOR

Here are some notes on the concepts presented in this chapter and how your children can apply them to solve problems.

THE VALUE of COINS

Encourage your children to understand informally the main idea of the cent as the basic unit of measurement of value. As children review the value of different coins, help them use the penny, worth 1¢, as the coin of unit value.

COUNTING MONEY

Your children have already explored the second main idea—counting money. For example, children find the total value of a set of pennies by counting by ones. They count by fives to find the value of a set of nickels.

Gary Musser

MONEY

Help children understand how to count to find the total value of a mixed set of coins. As shown in the example, children begin counting with the largest denomination and count by tens, then fives, then ones.

10	10	10	5	5	5	1	1
10¢	20¢	30¢	35¢	40¢	45¢	46¢	47¢

Children memorize counting by 25 to count the value of quarters. To count sets of mixed coins including quarters, they start with the largest denomination and begin counting by 25.

25	25	10	5	5	1
25¢	50¢	60¢	65¢	70¢	71¢

DOLLAR

Your children learn that a dollar is 100 cents and is written as $1.00. While children are already familiar with a dollar bill, they should have many experiences using money punchouts to explore counting sets of mixed coins and bills. Children gain experience in counting money by taking part in activities such as classroom stores and other "buying" activities.

PROBLEM SOLVING

In **Problem Solving** your children use (1) data from a picture to solve problems involving money and (2) guess and test to solve problems involving money.

In **Thinking Mathematically** children use number sense to solve problems. Your children use punchout coins to determine which coins are placed in the Piggy Bank.

In **Decision Making** children use information to plan what purchases to include in a card collection, given 18 dollars.

Mathematics and Literature

To use literature in the application of mathematics.

■ Children are introduced to a story in the K–2 Math Anthology on page 149. By reading Penelope Gets Wheels, children build their concept of money.

CHAPTER PLANNING GUIDE

A. Give the value of a group of coins — MAT, CAT, SAT, ITBS
B. Give the value of a group of bills and coins — MAT, CAT, SAT, ITBS
C. Solve problems including those that involve using data from a picture — MAT, CAT, SAT, ITBS, CTBS

SUGGESTED PACING-9 DAYS

LESSONS	NCTM STANDARDS	ASSIGNMENTS Basic/Average/Challenge	STUDENT EDITION Extra Practice/ Practice Plus	Manip. Plus	Reteach	Practice	Enrich	MAC Activities
Chapter Opener: *Penelope Gets Wheels* page 125	1, 2, 3, 4	p. 125: All						
✔ 1 Money page 126	1, 2, 3, 6, 7	p. 126: All						
✔ 2 Pennies, Nickels, and Dimes pages 127–128	1, 2, 3, 6, 7	p. 127: 1–4; p. 128: 1–4		19	42	42	42	83, 84
✔ 3 Quarters pages 129–130	1, 2, 3, 6, 7	p. 129: 2–4; p. 130: 1–3, Challenge	pp. 134, 144	20	43	43	43	85, 86
4 PS: Using Data from a Picture pages 131–132	1, 2, 3, 11	p. 131: 1–5; p. 132: 1–5	p. 134		44	44	44	87, 88
✔ 5 PS: Thinking Mathematically page 133	1, 2, 3, 6, 7	p.133: All						
✔ 6 Dollars and Cents pages 135–136	1, 2, 3, 6, 7	p. 135: 1–4; p. 136: 1–6	p. 143		45	45	45	89, 90
✔ 7 More Dollars and Cents pages 137–138	1, 2, 3, 6, 7	p. 137: 1–3; p. 138: 1–6	pp. 143, 144	21	46	46	46	91, 92
8 PS: Guess and Test pages 139–140	1, 2, 3, 8	p. 139: 1–2; p. 140: 1–6		22	47	47	47	93, 94
9 PS: Decision Making page 141	1, 2, 3, 6, 7	p. 141: 1–3						

Technology: Computer page 142

Chapter Review/Test pages 145–146

Performance Assessment page 147

Cumulative Review page 149

Enrichment for All/Home Activity pages 148, 150

NATIONAL COUNCIL OF TEACHERS OF MATHEMATICS Grades K–4

1. Problem Solving
2. Communication
3. Reasoning
4. Connections
5. Estimation
6. Number Sense and Numeration
7. Concepts of Whole Number Operations
8. Whole Number Computation
9. Geometry and Spatial Sense
10. Measurement
11. Statistics and Probability
12. Fractions and Decimals
13. Patterns and Relationships

✔ Activity 🧑‍🤝‍🧑 Cooperative Learning

MEETING the NCTM STANDARDS

Problem Solving

Strategies and Skills	• using data from a picture pp. 131–132 • guess and test pp. 139–140
Applications	• **Decision Making** lesson p. 141 • **Problem of the Day** TE pp. 126, 128B, 130B, 132B, 136B, 138B, 140B
Mathematical Investigations	• **Thinking Mathematically** lesson p. 133

Communication

Language	• using the language of mathematics TE pp. 127–128, 129–130, 135–136
Oral/Written	• using cooperative learning activities pp. 126, 127, 128, 133, 141; TE pp. 124I–124L • **Journal Writing** opportunities TE pp. 128, 130, 132, 136

Reasoning

Critical Thinking	• answering questions that analyze and extend concepts pp. 125, 128, 129, 132, 136, 141, 142, 148

Connections

To other subject areas	• Literature p. 125; Literature TE pp. 125–126, 137, 141

Concept Development

Number Sense and Numeration	• using models to explore the concept of money p. 126 • giving the value of a group of coins pp. 127–128, 129–130; TE pp. 124I–124J • giving the value of a group of bills and coins pp. 135–136, 137–138; TE pp. 124K–124L

ASSESSMENT OPTIONS

PERFORMANCE ASSESSMENT

Preassessment Activity

Before beginning Chapter 4, have children imagine that they receive an allowance of $1.00 per week. Ask them to draw pictures (circles) of and use models to show any combinations of quarters, dimes, nickels, and pennies that total $1.00.

Ongoing Assessment

The Ongoing Assessment cards under MEETING INDI-VIDUAL NEEDS on TE pp. 130 and 136 provide criteria and questions for assessing children's understanding of the key mathematical concepts developed in the chapter.

Journal Writing opportunities encourage children to write about mathematics. Their responses can be recorded either pictorially or in words. The journal writing opportunities on the Ongoing Assessment cards also allow you to assess children's understanding of the lessons.

In addition to the Ongoing Assessment cards, other assessment and journal writing opportunities in this chapter include:

• **CLOSE** TE pp. 128, 132, 136

Performance Assessment Activity

The Performance Assessment activity on p. 147 provides an alternative to formal assessment. This activity assesses children's understanding of the key concepts of the chapter.

For performance assessment activities that are keyed to individual chapter objectives, see the *Performance Assessment* booklet.

BUILDING A PORTFOLIO

Children should be encouraged to keep a selection of their best work in portfolios. The portfolios provide a way of documenting children's growth in understanding mathematical concepts. Portfolio opportunities in this chapter include:

• **Performance Assessment** p. 147
• **Class Project** TE p. 141A

If you wish to provide additional opportunities for portfolio work, you may choose to use:

• **MAC Activities** 83, 86, 88

You may also wish to have children include their journal writing from the Ongoing Assessment on TE pp. 130 and 136 in their portfolio.

Formal Assessment

The **Chapter Review/Test** assesses children's understanding of the concepts and skills developed in the chapter. The **Cumulative Review** assesses children's understanding of the concepts and skills developed from the beginning of the year.

You can use **Form A** or **Form B** of the **Chapter Test** found in the *Testing Program Blackline Masters and Teacher's Manual* if you wish to use a multiple-choice

format to assess children's understanding of the chapter concepts and skills. You can use **Form C** if you wish to use a free-response format. Any of the forms may be used as a pretest, posttest, or for retesting.

The **COMPUTER MANAGEMENT SYSTEM**, or **CMS**, enables you to score **Forms A** and **B** of the **Chapter Test** quickly and automatically. It also prescribes learning activities based on children's test results.

For more information about Assessment, see the *Professional Handbook*.

MEETING INDIVIDUAL NEEDS

Common Error and Remediation

The Teacher's Edition notes for each Develop/Understand (Transitional/Abstract) lesson provide a common error analysis and a remediation activity. Some errors defy quick analysis and can only be identified by interviewing the child.

ALTERNATIVE TEACHING STRATEGY

Alternative Teaching Strategies appear frequently in the chapter. These strategies provide other presentations of the lessons for children who might benefit from instruction in different learning modalities: kinesthetic, visual, and/or auditory.

For Students Acquiring English (SAE)

Before beginning this chapter, introduce the coin names and values to SAE children. Have children explore real coins with a magnifying glass. Guide the exploration with questions that will develop familiarity and vocabulary. For example, ask: *Can you find any letters on the penny that are in your name?* Have children practice saying the names of the coins and the value of each using poems and chants. For example, say: *Penny, nickel, quarter, dime—don't be late, but be on time!*

SAE notes appear periodically in the chapter. These notes provide suggestions for how to work with children to improve comprehension and build vocabulary.

MANIPULATIVES WORKSHOP

Coins and dollar bills are used in this chapter to demonstrate money concepts. They provide a concrete model of the different denominations of coins and their relationships to one another and to the dollar.

USING MANIPULATIVES

Here a child begins sorting the bills and coins to find the total amount of money.

The child counts on, beginning with the bills.

Then the child continues counting on, beginning with the coins of greatest value. The total is $2.89.

MAKING MANIPULATIVES See the Manipulatives section of the *Professional Handbook* for materials that can be used as a substitute for coins and dollar bills.

COOPERATIVE LEARNING WORKSHOP

GETTING STARTED

Class Community and Pairs: A sequence of individual work, then partner comparison, and finally consultation/comparison with another pair are helpful at this point. This can be done within the family group; however, pairs can also reemphasize community when you use **pair concentric circles** for practice or review. Make two circles, with Partner Ones on the inside circle, Partner Twos on the outside circle, facing one another. Ask a question or give a problem, and the pair either takes turns answering or works it out jointly. After one question or problem, the outside circle turns left and moves forward two children. The new partners answer the next question or problem. Next time the children on the inside circle can turn right, and move forward three persons, and so on. In this way children learn they can work with everyone.

IDEAS TO TRY

Using Money: When working in pairs with money, children need to learn ways to **help one another learn** the value of the coins.

Model for them how to give clues or hints rather than simply telling one another the answer. This not only makes it more fun, but gives each a chance to learn better. Write both verbal and nonverbal responses on the chalkboard for pairs to refer to as they work together.

You can apply the above cooperative skills in these lessons:
4-1 *Money* p. 126
4-2 *Pennies, Nickels, and Dimes* pp. 127–128
4-3 *Quarters* pp. 129–130

What's It Worth? After working the problems together, have each pair review with another pair. Have the first partner in the "presenting pair" ask the other pair what they think each item is worth. The second partner handles the play money and is the "banker." When the second pair suggests an amount, the banker asks how many and which coins and bills, and the "buying pair" must say what coins and bills they need to buy the item. When the play money is counted out, the first pair checks whether it

is the correct amount. If so, the money goes to the buying pair. If not, it goes back in the bank. Then the pairs switch roles. Both pairs add up their play money at the end of the game, total the two amounts together, and combine it in a class total aimed at reaching a certain figure, after which there is a celebration.

You can apply the above rotating-pairs strategy in these lessons:
4-6 *Dollars and Cents* pp. 135–136
4-7 *More Dollars and Cents* pp. 137–138

SEE ALSO

Cooperative Learning Tip for lessons 4-4 Problem Solving p. 132; 4-8 Problem Solving p. 140

The Cooperative Learning section of the *Professional Handbook* for additional information

---

INTERACTIVE BULLETIN BOARD

SETUP Cover a bulletin board with black background paper. Distribute grocery circulars, newspapers, and scissors to the children.

PROCEDURE Have each child cut out two advertisements of products. Remind children to include each product's price. Then have each child tack his or her ads to the bulletin board to create a collage. Draw rings around the prices of the pictured items. Discuss the items and their prices with the children. Have them tell whether they would buy that item, if they think the price is high or low, and so on. Accept all responses.

19
TRADING MONEY

OBJECTIVE
Explore regrouping by trading coins.

MATERIALS
Classroom Materials
game markers
Manipulatives 1 number cube*, 150 P, 30 N, and 15 D coins (or punchouts) per group of four
Teacher Resources
*Teacher Aids 1, 17

SMALL GROUP ACTIVITY

Prepare a game board on a copy of Teacher Aid 1 (filling in each box) and duplicate it.

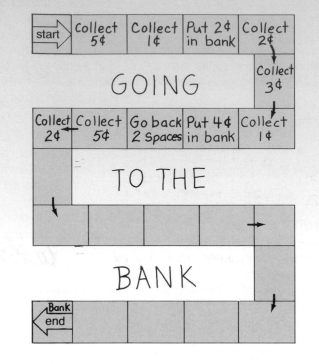

Have children play in small groups of four. Distribute 1 game board, 1 number cube, 3 game markers, 150 pennies, 30 nickels, and 15 dimes to each small group. Assign one child to be the BANKER.

Have the other three children take turns rolling the number cube and moving that number of spaces on the game board. Players should follow the directions written in the boxes. If the player is supposed to receive an amount of money, the BANKER gives the player the appropriate coins. When possible, players are to trade pennies for nickels and nickels for dimes, but only when it is their turn. The child with the most dimes at the end of the game wins.

EXTENDING THE ACTIVITY

Distribute 1 blank game board to each group. Have groups decide what to write in the boxes of the game board. Have them play the game using their own game boards.

ONGOING ASSESSMENT

✓ Are children able to appropriately trade pennies, nickels, and dimes and recognize their values?

For use before LESSON 4.3, pp. 129-130

20

GOING SHOPPING

OBJECTIVE
Count sets of coins for a given amount.

MATERIALS
Classroom Materials classroom objects, such as a ruler, pencils, crayons, notepads
Manipulatives 50¢ in assorted play coins (or punchouts) per child

WHOLE GROUP ACTIVITY ⏱

Assemble classroom objects and make up a price tag for each as indicated.

Set up a classroom store using the priced objects. Distribute 50¢ in assorted coins to each child. Assign a child to be the storekeeper. Allow each child an opportunity to purchase an item and pay the storekeeper. Children should pay using the exact amount, if possible. The storekeeper can write a receipt and make change. Allow children to switch roles.

Have children help in keeping the store stocked by finding classroom objects and making price tags for them.

EXTENDING THE ACTIVITY

Use lower prices on the objects and have children purchase one or more items with their 50¢. Encourage them to use whatever strategy works for finding the total cost of the items purchased.

ONGOING ASSESSMENT
✓ Are children able to appropriately model money amounts using coins?

MANIPULATIVES plus ACTIVITY

For use before LESSON 4.6, pp. 135-136

21
ONE DOLLAR

OBJECTIVE
Show one dollar as a set of coins.

MATERIALS
Classroom Materials small boxes (EXTENDING THE ACTIVITY only)
Manipulatives 7 D, 6 N coins; 150¢ in assorted play coins (or punchouts) per pair

WHOLE GROUP ACTIVITY 🕐

Display 7 dimes and 5 nickels. Review the value of each coin and then count with children to establish the amount of money shown. [95¢] Write the amount on the chalkboard and have the children read it aloud. Place another nickel with the coins and ask children to tell how many cents there are in all. [100¢] Have children count the coins with you. Explain that 100 cents equal 1 dollar.

PAIRS ACTIVITY 🔄 👫

Assign children to work in pairs. Give each pair 150¢ in assorted coins. Have one child show a group of coins with a value less than 75¢. Have the other child add coins to the group to make 100¢. Then have children reverse roles.

EXTENDING THE ACTIVITY

Give each pair a small box. Tell children to place their coins in the box. Have one child reach in and take out three coins without looking. Tell the child to place the coins on the desk and count the value. The other child adds coins to make 100¢. Then have children reverse roles.

ONGOING ASSESSMENT

✔ Are children able to appropriately model money amounts and find the total for coin combinations shown?

For use before LESSON 4.7, pp. 137-138

22

COMPARING MONEY

OBJECTIVE
Compare money amounts.

MATERIALS
Classroom Materials
money amount cards for 1¢–99¢; paper bag (EXTENDING THE ACTIVITY only)
Manipulatives 200¢ in assorted play coins (or punchouts) per pair

PAIRS ACTIVITY 🕐 👥

Prepare money amount cards for various amounts from 1¢ to 99¢.

| 6¢ | 84¢ | 73¢ | 24¢ | 52¢ | 47¢ |

Have children work in pairs. Give each pair of children a set of cards and a set of coins. Tell children to mix the cards and place them facedown in a stack. Have each child choose a card and show the amount using coins.

Children should then compare their sets of coins to see who has the greater amount of money. That child scores one point.

Then children should play for a bonus point. Using the lesser amount, challenge each child to show the amount using the least number of coins. Children should share coins, if needed. They may record by drawing pictures of the coins. Have them compare their guesses. The child who shows the amount using the least number of coins scores one point. If both children use the same number of coins, both children score one point.

EXTENDING THE ACTIVITY

Place the coins in a paper bag. Have each child in a pair reach in the bag and grab a set of coins. Have children count and compare their sets of coins. The child who has the most amount of money scores one point.

ONGOING ASSESSMENT

✔ Are children able to compare money amounts to find the amounts that are greater and lesser?

Mathematics and Literature

Listening and Speaking

The Read-Aloud selection can be used with the Chapter 4 Opener and Lesson 4-1 on pages 125-126.

Tape 1, Side 2
Selection 1

Penelope Gets Wheels

By Esther Allen Peterson

It was Penelope's birthday, and she got 10 one dollar bills, 4 quarters, and 5 dimes.

She counted the money many times, and it always came out the same: $11.50.

"I am rich and I am older now," she said to her mom. "I don't need to walk anymore. I will go on wheels."

"Wheels?" asked her mom.

"Yes," said Penelope. "I would like a car, but I know I am not rich enough or old enough. I think I will buy a bicycle."

"A bicycle costs a lot of money," said her mom.

"I have lots of money," Penelope said. And before her mother could say another word, she ran outside and went to the nearest department store.

"Today is my birthday," she said to the saleslady. "I would like to buy that silver racing bike."

"That bicycle costs one hundred and nineteen dollars," the saleslady said.

Penelope pointed to a smaller bike. "How much is that one?"

"Seventy-nine dollars and ninety-five cents," said the saleslady.

"I'm not that rich," Penelope said, and she put the money back in her pocket.

Penelope looked at badminton sets, paint-by-number kits, and baseball bats and gloves. But she didn't want to buy anything she saw.

Then she saw some roller skates. They were $9.95 a pair.

124M

She picked up a skate and spun its wheels. "I guess these are all I can afford."

"That will be ten dollars and forty-five cents with tax," the saleslady said.

Penelope paid for the skates.

She went outside, put them on, and started skating home. She still wished she was old enough to drive a car or rich enough to own a bicycle.

When she got home her mom and dad were in the kitchen. "I didn't have enough money for a bicycle," she said. "All I could afford were roller skates."

"But roller skates are the best wheels a kid can have," said her dad.

Penelope shoved one of the skates across the floor. "Skating is better than walking, but I'd still rather have a bike."

The next day everyone was going to the ball park to see Slugger Jones hit his five-hundredth home run. Slugger Jones was Penelope's favorite ballplayer, and she was going, too.

As she sat on the steps putting on her roller skates, Mr. Smith came out of his house and got into his car.

"Are you going to the game?" Penelope asked.

"Sure am," answered Mr. Smith.

"I'm skating to the game," said Penelope.

"Be sure you don't get any speeding tickets," he said, and he drove off.

Penelope skated toward the ball park. Her friend Jim rode by on his bicycle.

"Going to the game?" she asked.

"Yep," he said.

"I am too," said Penelope.

"Let's race," said Jim.

Penelope skated as fast as she could, but Jim got ahead of her. Soon she couldn't see him at all.

Penelope skated fast for six blocks and then stopped. Cars were lined up waiting to get into the parking lot.

Penelope skated past Mr. Smith. "I didn't get any speeding tickets," she said.

"Really!" said Mr. Smith.

Near the entrance to the ball park Penelope saw Jim looking for a place to lock his bike. She skated past him. "Does the winner get a prize?"

Penelope took off her skates, strapped them together, and waited in line to buy her ticket.

Then she went straight to her favorite seat in the grandstand.

Soon everyone stood up and sang the national anthem. The umpire yelled, "PLAY BALL!"

Jim walked by looking for a seat.

During the second inning Mr. Smith came in.

Penelope giggled and said, "Roller skates are the best wheels a kid can have."

124N

AT·A·GLANCE pp. 125-126

LESSON OBJECTIVES
Explore mathematical concepts through literature.
Explore the relative value of coins.

ASSIGNMENT GUIDE

COURSE	EXERCISES
Basic	p. 125: All; p. 126: All
Average	p. 125: All; p. 126: All
Challenge	p. 125: All; p. 126: All

MATERIALS
Manipulatives 60 P, 12 N, 4 D coins (or punchouts), spinner for 1–5 per group of 4

Teacher Resources
Math Anthology, pp. 149–150
Read-Aloud Cassette 1, Side 2, Selection 1

SKILLS TRACE
MONEY

Explore (Concrete) 126	Develop/Understand (Transitional/Abstract) 127–128, 129–130, 135–136, 137–138
Practice 134, 143, 144, 145–146, 149, 156, 183	Apply 131–132, 133, 139–140, 141, 148

Money

CHAPTER 4

Listen to the story Penelope Gets Wheels.

Tell why Penelope could not get the kind of wheels she wanted. Children should note that Penelope did not have enough money for a bicycle.

125

PREPARE **WARM-UP** To review the value of coins, display pennies, nickels, and dimes and have children identify the name of each coin. Display the following sets of coins and have children count by ones, by fives, or by tens to find the total amount of money in each set.

6 pennies [6¢]	5 nickels [25¢]
11 pennies [11¢]	3 dimes [30¢]
3 nickels [15¢]	7 dimes [70¢]

TEACH **DISCUSSING** Before reading the story *Penelope Gets Wheels,* read the title aloud and ask children to predict what kind of wheels Penelope might get. Explain they will check their predictions after reading the story.

Mathematics and Literature

PUPIL'S EDITION pp. 125-126

Page 125 Read *Penelope Gets Wheels* found on pages 124M–124N or in *Math Anthology* to children, or play Read-Aloud Cassette 1, Side 2, Selection 1 for them.

■ **Why was Penelope feeling so rich?** [She had gotten $11.50 for her birthday.]

■ **How did Penelope plan to spend her money?** [She planned to buy a new bicycle.]

■ **What kind of wheels did Penelope end up buying?** [a pair of roller skates]

Discuss the question on the page.

Page 126 ■ **Working Together** Assign children to work in groups of four or five. Give each group 60 pennies, 12 nickels, 4 dimes, and a

ACTiViTY

Money

Working Together

1–5 spinner

Use 60 , 12 🏛, 4 🪙, and a 🎡.

Trade pennies for nickels or dimes if you can.

Spin to find how many pennies to take.

Trade nickels for dimes if you can.

Take turns spinning for pennies.
Play until everyone
has pennies, nickels, and dimes.

Trade this way:
5 pennies = 1 nickel
10 pennies = 1 dime
2 nickels = 1 dime

MEETING INDIVIDUAL NEEDS

For Students Acquiring English (SAE)

Model **spinning** and **trading pennies** for other coins before the groups begin to play the game. Be sure to group children heterogeneously.

ALTERNATIVE TEACHING STRATEGY

ACTIVITY

MATERIALS 60 P, 12 N, 4 D coins (or punchouts) per pair; spinner for 1–5

VISUAL/AUDITORY Assign each child a partner and give the pair 60 pennies, 12 nickels, and 4 dimes. Have them place the coins in the middle of the desk. Explain that you will spin to determine how many pennies each pair will take. When each pair has 5 or more pennies, discuss how 5 pennies can be traded for 1 nickel. Have children make the trade. Continue spinning until children have traded pennies and nickels for the four dimes. Have children explain each trade.

spinner for 1–5. Discuss the picture with the children. Review the trading information on the piggy bank.

Check for Understanding

■ **How many nickels do you need to trade for 1 dime?** [2 nickels]

GUIDED PRACTICE   Have children take one turn each. Remind them to take pennies and then trade the pennies for nickels. Explain that the coins from previous turns should be combined with the pennies they get after each new spin.

For reteaching, use Alternative Strategy.

3 PRACTICE•APPLY

PRACTICE   Have children complete the activity. Remind them to use the trading information on the piggy bank.

CLOSE   Guide children to summarize the lesson:
■ **What coins could you get if you had 19 pennies?** [Possible response: 1 dime, 1 nickel, 4 pennies]

Problem of the Day

Betsy had 3 nickels and 7 pennies. What is the fewest number of coins she could trade for ? [2 dimes, 2 pennies]

CHAPTER 4 • Lesson 2

LESSON OBJECTIVES
Recognize the value of a penny, nickel, dime.
Find the value of a set of coins.

ASSIGNMENT GUIDE

COURSE	EXERCISES
Basic	p. 127: 1–4; p. 128: 1–4
Average	p. 127: 1–4; p. 128: 1–4
Challenge	p. 127: 1–4; p. 128: 1–4

MATERIALS
Classroom Materials large hundred chart*, small paper bags
Manipulatives 30 P, 20 N, and 11 D coins (or punchouts) per child

Teacher Resources
Reteaching 42   Practice 42   Enrichment 42
MAC Act. 83, 84   *Teacher Aid 2

SKILLS TRACE
MONEY

Explore (Concrete)	Develop/Understand (Transitional/Abstract)
126	127–128, 129–130, 135–136, 137–138
Practice 134, 143, 144, 145–146, 149, 156, 183	**Apply** 131–132, 133, 139–140, 141, 148

See **MANIPULATIVES PLUS 19**, p. 124I.

Name _____

Pennies, Nickels, and Dimes

I **penny** I cent I ¢	I **nickel** 5 cents 5¢	Talk about different ways to show 5¢.

Troy has these coins. Count to find how much.

5¢   10¢   15¢   16¢   17¢   18¢

First count by fives.   Then count by ones.

How much money? 18¢

Working Together
Use 8 🪙 and 10 🪙.

You choose some of the nickels and pennies.
Your partner counts to find how much.
Take turns.

Write how many of each coin. Write how much.

1.	3	3	18¢
	Answers will vary.		
2.			
3.			
4.			

ZOO 5¢

Chapter 4   Money

---

1 PREPARE

WARM-UP To review counting on and skip counting, display a large hundred chart. Point to the number 7. Have children count on the next five numbers by ones. Continue the activity by starting with other numbers, such as 16, 33, and 62.

Next point to the number 5. Have children skip count the next five numbers by fives. Continue the activity by pointing to other numbers, such as 35, 40, and 55.

2 TEACH

DISCUSSING Give each child a set of punchout pennies, nickels, and dimes. Help children name the coins as **penny, nickel,** and **dime,** and identify both sides of the coins by introducing the terms **heads** and **tails.** Write a ¢ on the chalkboard and review its meaning.

Next have children show 5 pennies on their desk tops. Explain that 5 pennies equal 1 nickel. Have children sort all their pennies into stacks of five and tell how many nickels their stacks equal. Have children replace their stacks with the appropriate number of nickels. Then call on volunteers to count on by fives as they count their nickels.

Then have children show 5 dimes and count them by tens. Repeat this procedure, using combinations of dimes, nickels, and pennies, having children count on to find each total amount.

PUPIL'S EDITION pp. 127-128

Page 127 Read the example at the top of the page with the children. Discuss the different ways to show 5¢.

WORKING TOGETHER Have children work in pairs. Distribute play coins to each pair.

1 dime
10 cents
10¢

Talk about different ways to show 10¢.
Answers will vary.

Bev has 3 dimes, 2 nickels, and 3 pennies.
Count to find how much.

10¢ 20¢ 30¢ 35¢ 40¢ 41¢ 42¢ 43¢

(First count by tens.) (Then count by fives.) (Then count by ones.)

How much money? 43¢

Working Together

Use a paper bag,
5 🪙 , 4 🪙 ,
and 5 🪙 .

Place all the
coins in a bag.
Take out some
coins.
Count to find
how much.
Take turns.

	How many of each?			How much?
1.	3 🪙	2 🪙	3 🪙	43¢
2.	Answers will vary. 🪙	🪙	🪙	
3.	🪙	🪙	🪙	
4.	🪙	🪙	🪙	

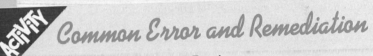

ALTERNATIVE TEACHING STRATEGY

MATERIALS 5 P, 5 N, and 5 D coins (or punchouts)

KINESTHETIC Give each child punchout coins, 5 pennies, nickels, dimes. Have children display the following coins, one at a time, and tell the value of each group. Have children start the counting with the coin(s) of greatest value.

1. 1 nickel, 2 pennies [7¢]   **2.** 1 dime, 1 nickel, 5 pennies [20¢]
3. 2 dimes, 2 nickels [30¢]   **4.** 3 dimes, 3 nickels, 4 pennies [49¢]

For Students Acquiring English (SAE)

Make and display posters of counting sequences for each coin. For example: Nickel = 5, 10, 15, 20, 25. Use the posters to practice counting with the class. Model the difference between **how many** and **how much.**

Common Error and Remediation

MATERIALS 5 P, 5 N, and 5 D coins

Some children may confuse coins and their values. Work individually with each child. Ask the child to tell you which is smaller in size, a nickel or a dime. [a dime] Ask how a penny is different from both a nickel and a dime. [color, value] Then have the child show a specified number of nickels and move each coin while counting by fives. Repeat the activity with dimes. Finally have the child count combinations of coins.

Check for Understanding

■ If I had 1 nickel and 3 pennies, how much money would I have? [8¢]

GUIDED PRACTICE   ex. 1–4: For reteaching, use Common Error and Remediation or Alternative Strategy.

Page 128   Read the example at the top of the page with the children. Discuss the different ways to show 10¢. Guide children to complete the exercise in the middle of the page.

PRACTICE•APPLY   **PRACTICE** ■ Working Together   ex. 1–4: Have children continue to work together to complete these exercises.

CLOSE   Guide children to summarize the lesson:

■ **How would you count to find the value of this set of coins: 3 dimes, 1 nickel, 3 pennies?** [10, 20, 30, 35, 36, 37, 38; 38¢]

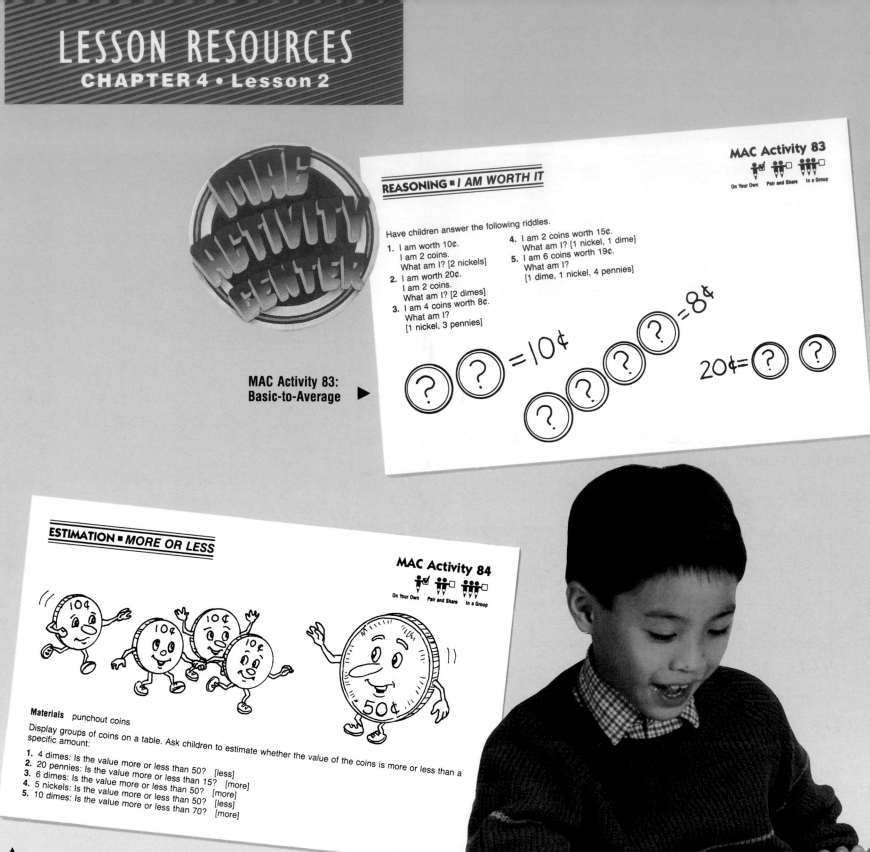

MAC ACTIVITY CENTER

MAC Activity 83

On Your Own Pair and Share In a Group

REASONING ▪ I AM WORTH IT

Have children answer the following riddles.

1. I am worth 10¢.
   I am 2 coins.
   What am I? [2 nickels]
2. I am worth 20¢.
   I am 2 coins.
   What am I? [2 dimes]
3. I am 4 coins worth 8¢.
   What am I?
   [1 nickel, 3 pennies]
4. I am 2 coins worth 15¢.
   What am I? [1 nickel, 1 dime]
5. I am 6 coins worth 19¢.
   What am I?
   [1 dime, 1 nickel, 4 pennies]

$(?)(?) = 10¢$

$(?)(?)(?)(?) = 8¢$

$20¢ = (?)(?)$

MAC Activity 83:
Basic-to-Average ▶

ESTIMATION ▪ MORE OR LESS

MAC Activity 84

On Your Own Pair and Share In a Group

Materials punchout coins

Display groups of coins on a table. Ask children to estimate whether the value of the coins is more or less than a specific amount:

1. 4 dimes: Is the value more or less than 50? [less]
2. 20 pennies: Is the value more or less than 15? [more]
3. 6 dimes: Is the value more or less than 50? [more]
4. 5 nickels: Is the value more or less than 50? [less]
5. 10 dimes: Is the value more or less than 70? [more]

▲
MAC Activity 84:
Average-to-Challenge

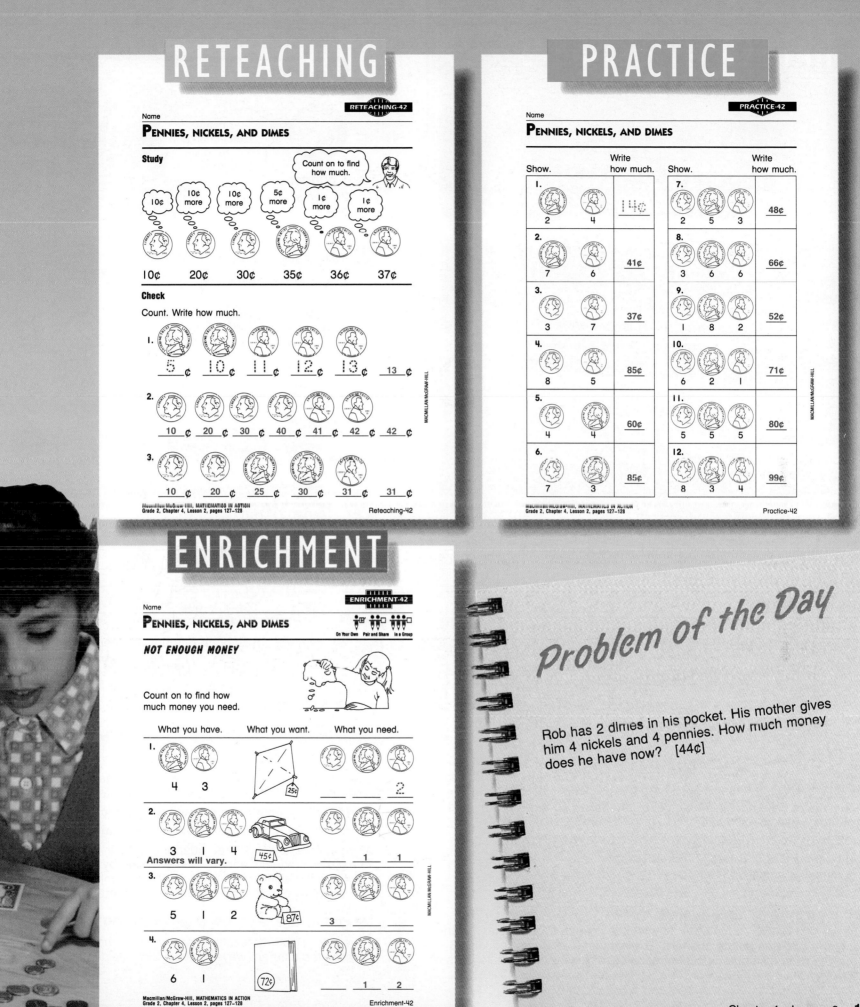

RETEACHING

RETEACHING-42

Name

PENNIES, NICKELS, AND DIMES

Study

Count on to find how much.

10¢   10¢ more   10¢ more   5¢ more   1¢ more   1¢ more

10¢   20¢   30¢   35¢   36¢   37¢

Check

Count. Write how much.

1. 5 ¢   10 ¢   11 ¢   12 ¢   13 ¢   13 ¢

2. 10 ¢   20 ¢   30 ¢   40 ¢   41 ¢   42 ¢   42 ¢

3. 10 ¢   20 ¢   25 ¢   30 ¢   31 ¢   31 ¢

Macmillan/McGraw-Hill, MATHEMATICS IN ACTION
Grade 2, Chapter 4, Lesson 2, pages 127–128

Reteaching-42

PRACTICE

PRACTICE-42

Name

PENNIES, NICKELS, AND DIMES

Show.		Write how much.	Show.		Write how much.
1.	2 4	14¢	7.	2 5 3	48¢
2.	7 6	41¢	8.	3 6 6	66¢
3.	3 7	37¢	9.	1 8 2	52¢
4.	8 5	85¢	10.	6 2 1	71¢
5.	4 4	60¢	11.	5 5 5	80¢
6.	7 3	85¢	12.	8 3 4	99¢

Macmillan/McGraw-Hill, MATHEMATICS IN ACTION
Grade 2, Chapter 4, Lesson 2, pages 127–128

Practice-42

ENRICHMENT

ENRICHMENT-42

Name

PENNIES, NICKELS, AND DIMES

On Your Own   Pair and Share   In a Group

NOT ENOUGH MONEY

Count on to find how
much money you need.

What you have.	What you want.	What you need.
1. 4 3	25¢	2
2. 3 4	45¢	1 1
Answers will vary.		
3. 5 1 2	87¢	3
4. 6 1	72¢	1 2

Macmillan/McGraw-Hill, MATHEMATICS IN ACTION
Grade 2, Chapter 4, Lesson 2, pages 127–128

Enrichment-42

Problem of the Day

Rob has 2 dimes in his pocket. His mother gives
him 4 nickels and 4 pennies. How much money
does he have now?   [44¢]

AT·A·GLANCE pp. 129-130

LESSON OBJECTIVES

Recognize the value of a quarter.
Find the value of a set of coins.

ASSIGNMENT GUIDE

COURSE	EXERCISES
Basic	p. 129: 2–4; p. 130: 1–3, Challenge
Average	p. 129: 2–4; p. 130: 1–3, Challenge
Challenge	p. 129: 2–4; p. 130: 1–3, Challenge
Extra Practice, p. 134	Practice Plus, p. 144

MATERIALS

Manipulatives 30 P, 20 N, 11 D, 3 Q coins (or punchouts)
per child

Teacher Resources
Reteaching 43   Practice 43   Enrichment 43
MAC Act. 85, 86

SKILLS TRACE	
MONEY	
Explore (Concrete) 126	**Develop/Understand (Transitional/Abstract)** 127–128, 129–130, 135–136, 137–138
Practice 134, 143, 144, 145–146, 149, 156, 183	**Apply** 131–132, 133, 139–140, 141, 148

See **MANIPULATIVES PLUS 20**, p. 124J.

PREPARE **WARM-UP** To review counting sets of coins, begin by distributing punchout pennies, nickels, and dimes to pairs of children. Have them show the following sets of coins and tell the value of each set.

5 nickels [25¢]; 4 dimes [40¢];
8 pennies [8¢]; 2 dimes, 2 nickels [30¢];
8 dimes, 4 pennies [84¢]

TEACH **DISCUSSING** Distribute punchout quarters to each child. Identify the coin as a **quarter** and identify the sides as heads and tails. Explain that one quarter equals 25 cents. Then distribute punchout pennies, nickels, and dimes to pairs of children.

Quarters

I **quarter**
25 cents
25¢

I need exact change for a quarter.

Talk about different ways to show 25¢.
Answers will vary.
Count to find how much.   How much?

1.   91¢

25¢ 50¢ 75¢ 85¢ 90¢ 91¢

2.   86¢

25¢   50¢   75¢   80¢   85¢   86¢

3.   72¢

25¢   50¢   60¢   70¢   71¢   72¢

4. Can you show each amount another way?

Work with a partner. Use some 🪙 , 🪙 , 🪙 , and 🪙 .

Chapter 4   Money   one hundred twenty-nine   129

Have them work together to show 25 pennies next to one quarter. Then have children arrange their pennies into groups of five.

■ **How many pennies are equal to one nickel?** [5]
■ **How many nickels are equal to one quarter?** [5]

Have children display three quarters on their desks. Have them point to each coin as you lead them in counting by twenty-fives: 25, 50, 75. Continue the activity by having children count combinations of quarters and pennies, quarters and nickels, and quarters and dimes.

PUPIL'S EDITION pp. 129-130

Page 129 Read the example at the top of the page with the children. Discuss the different ways to show 25¢. Guide children through ex. 1.

Ring the set of coins that buys each thing.

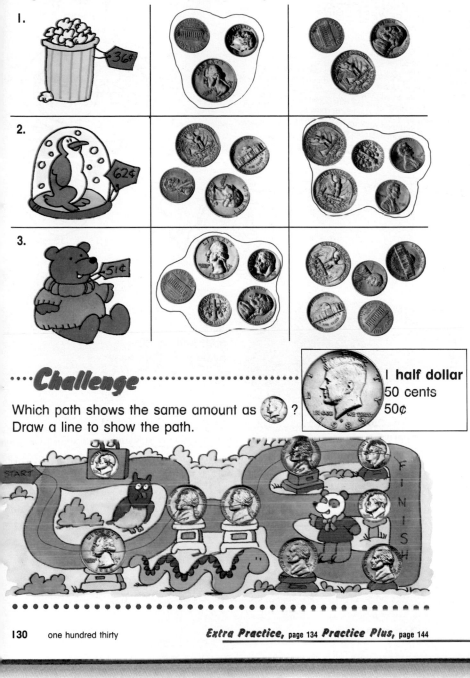

Extra Practice, page 134 **Practice Plus,** page 144

····**Challenge**··

Which path shows the same amount as ?
Draw a line to show the path.

	I **half dollar**
---	50 cents
	50¢

ACTIVITY ALTERNATIVE TEACHING STRATEGY

MATERIALS 2 Q, 3 D, 3 N, 7 P coins (or punchouts)

KINESTHETIC Name the coins in each set below. Have children place them on their desks in order from greatest to least value, count, and write the amount.

1. 2 pennies, 2 dimes, 1 nickel [d, d, n, p, p = 27¢]
2. 1 penny, 1 quarter, 2 nickels [q, n, n, p = 36¢]
3. 1 dime, 1 quarter, 4 pennies [q, d, p, p, p, p = 39¢]

ONGOING ASSESSMENT

INTERVIEW Provide a set of coins. **(1) Show me 2 quarters and 2 dimes. How much is that? (2) Show me 1 quarter, 1 dime, and 2 nickels. How much is that?**

JOURNAL WRITING You may wish to have children record their responses in their math journals.

ACTIVITY Common Error and Remediation

MATERIALS real coins for 20 N, 10 D, 1 Q

Some children may not be able to count coins of different values when the coins are combined. Begin by giving the child a set of nickels. Have the child skip count by fives as he or she touches each nickel in the row. Repeat the activity, using only dimes, and have the child skip count by tens. Repeat using quarters, and have the child skip count by twenty-fives. Next display 1 quarter and 1 nickel. Have the child count on from 25. Continue with other combinations of quarters, dimes, and nickels.

Check for Understanding
■ **How many pennies are equal to one quarter?** [25]

GUIDED PRACTICE ex. 2–4: For reteaching, use Common Error and Remediation or Alternative Strategy.

Page 130 Identify the pictures and have the price tags read aloud.

PRACTICE·APPLY **PRACTICE** ex. 1–3

CHALLENGE Introduce a **half dollar** and explain that this coin equals 50 cents. Ask children to name other coin combinations that are equal to a half dollar. [Possible responses: 5 dimes, 2 quarters, 50 pennies, 10 nickels]

CLOSE Guide children to summarize the lesson:
■ **What is the value of this set of coins: 1 quarter, 1 dime, and 2 nickels?** [45¢]

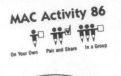

REASONING ■ FEWEST COINS

MAC Activity 86

On Your Own   Pair and Share   In a Group

Materials punchout coins

Assign each child a partner. Give each pair of children punchout quarters, dimes, nickels, and pennies. Have one child choose an amount between 11 cents and 99 cents and say it aloud. Tell the other child to show that amount using the fewest number of coins possible. Then have them record their work on a chart similar to the one below. Have children alternate roles.

Amount	Quarters	Dimes	Nickels	Pennies

**MAC Activity 86:
Average-to-Challenge**

CAREERS—CASHIER ■ PAY AT THE REGISTER

MAC Activity 85

On Your Own   Pair and Share   In a Group

Materials punchout coins, restaurant bills

Discuss the job of a cashier, and have children list different places in the community where cashiers work. Discuss why it is important that a cashier know about the value of different coins. Encourage children to talk about other skills that a cashier needs, such as knowing how to operate a cash register and being polite to customers.

Assign children to work in small groups. Have children take turns playing the role of cashier. Have other group members pretend to be customers at a restaurant. Give each customer a bill for less than 99¢. Tell them to present their bills to the cashier as they pay with punchout coins. The cashier should count the coins to make sure the amounts are correct.

**MAC Activity 85:
Basic-to-Average**

RETEACHING-43

Name _____

QUARTERS

Study

25¢ | 25¢ more | 25¢ more | 1¢ more | 1¢ more | Remember 25, 50, 75.

25¢   50¢   75¢   76¢   77¢

Check

Count. Write how much.

1. 25 ¢   35 ¢   45 ¢   55 ¢   55 ¢

2. 25 ¢   50 ¢   55 ¢   60 ¢   60 ¢

3. 25 ¢   50 ¢   75 ¢   85 ¢   86 ¢   86 ¢

MACMILLAN McGRAW-HILL

Reteaching-43

Macmillan/McGraw-Hill MATHEMATICS IN ACTION
Grade 2, Chapter 4, Lesson 3, pages 129–130

PRACTICE-43

Name _____

QUARTERS

Ring the set of coins that buys each thing.

1. 32¢

2. 56¢

3. 47¢

4. 61¢

5. 71¢

MACMILLAN McGRAW-HILL

Practice-43

Macmillan/McGraw-Hill MATHEMATICS IN ACTION
Grade 2, Chapter 4, Lesson 3, pages 129–130

ENRICHMENT-43

Name _____

QUARTERS

On Your Own   Pair and Share   In a Group

IN THE BANK

Write how many of each coin are in the bank.

1. 10
    5 coins in all.   ___ 1 1 3

2. 27
    3 coins in all.   1 ___ ___ 2

3. 65
    4 coins in all.   2 1 1 ___

4. 58
    6 coins in all.   2 ___ 1 3

5. 40
    4 coins in all.   1 1 1 1

MACMILLAN McGRAW-HILL

Enrichment-43

Macmillan/McGraw-Hill MATHEMATICS IN ACTION
Grade 2, Chapter 4, Lesson 3, pages 129–130

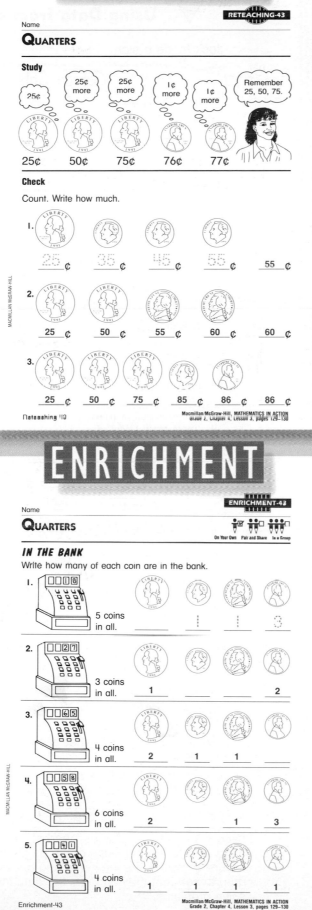

Problem of the Day

Jonathan receives an allowance of 35¢ a week. Usually his father gives him 1 quarter and 1 dime. What other coins could his father use to pay Jonathan's allowance? [Possible responses: 35 pennies; 1 nickel and 30 pennies; 1 dime and 25 pennies]

AT·A·GLANCE pp. 131-132

LESSON OBJECTIVE
Use data from a picture to solve problems.

ASSIGNMENT GUIDE

COURSE	EXERCISES
Basic	p. 131: 1–5; p. 132: 1–5
Average	p. 131: 1–5; p. 132: 1–5
Challenge	p. 131: 1–5; p. 132: 1–5
Extra Practice, p. 134	

MATERIALS
Classroom Materials index cards, book, box of crayons
Manipulatives 20 P coins (or punchouts) per pair

Teacher Resources
Reteaching 44   Practice 44   Enrichment 44
Prob. Solv. 16   MAC Act. 87, 88

Macmillan/McGraw-Hill

Name _____

Problem Solving

UNDERSTAND
PLAN
TRY
CHECK
EXTEND

Using Data from a Picture

Jack made a sign.

> The picture has information.
> Information is called **data**.

Garage Sale

Find the data.

1. How much does a shell cost? __6__ ¢

2. How much is a car? __7__ ¢

Solve. Use coins, mental math, or paper and pencil.

3. A ball costs __9__ ¢.

   A bear costs __5__ ¢.

   How much do a ball and a bear cost? __14__ ¢

---

4. Jack had 14¢.

   He bought a car for __7__ ¢.

   How much money does Jack have left? __7__ ¢

---

5. Mary bought a book.
   She bought a car.

   What was the total cost? __15__ ¢

Chapter 4   Money   one hundred thirty-one   131

---

1 PREPARE
WARM-UP To prepare children for using data from a picture to solve a problem, have them give the following sums and differences.

8¢ + 8¢ [16¢]   7¢ + 9¢ [16¢]
15¢ − 6¢ [9¢]   12¢ − 7¢ [5¢]
6¢ + 7¢ [13¢]   9¢ − 3¢ [6¢]

2 TEACH
MODELING Display a book and a box of crayons. Write 6¢ on one index card and place it next to the book. Write 7¢ on another index card and place it next to the box of crayons.

Assign children to work in pairs. Give each pair of children 20 punchout pennies. Explain that you will read a problem aloud and they should use their pennies to help them solve the problem.

Bill bought a book and a box of crayons. How much did he spend?
■ **What do you need to do?** [Find the price of each item and then add the numbers.]
■ **How do you find out what each item costs?** [Look at the prices on the items.]
■ **How will you find how much Bill spent?** [Use pennies to model each price, and then add: 6¢ + 7¢ = 13¢.]

PUPIL'S EDITION pp. 131-132

Page 131 Have a volunteer read aloud the information at the top left-hand and right-hand sides of the page. Have a volunteer tell what the picture shows. Have the items and prices identified. Then guide children to see that they can use the data in the picture to help them solve problems.

The shopkeeper put this picture in the paper.

Toy Sale

Find the data. Solve.

1. A baseball costs __9__ ¢.

   A basketball costs __8__ ¢.

   How much do a baseball and a basketball cost? __17__ ¢

2. Juan had 11¢.

   He bought a bus for __8__ ¢.

   Does Juan have enough money left to buy a car? __No.__

3. Ruth bought a baseball.
   Duve bought a football.

   How much did the two of them spend? __16__ ¢

4. Write a problem about the things that you would buy. **Answers will vary.**

   Use your own paper.

5. Talk about places where data can be found. **Answers will vary.**

Extra Practice, page 134

TEACHER to TEACHER

COOPERATIVE LEARNING TIP  My children use what they learned from this lesson to list the items sold in the weekly auction. They also list the prices of the items in terms of the play money we use in our class to reward good cooperative work. In pairs, students make lists of the white elephant items donated and decide what they should cost. In **concentric circles,** pairs compare prices they have estimated for the items. On Friday we hold the auction. We then compare what the item actually sold for with our earlier estimates.

For Students Acquiring English (SAE)

Scan the pages for vocabulary that may be new to SAE children. Introduce new words by using visuals, gestures, and body movements to convey meaning. Ask questions frequently to check comprehension. Attach a price tag to the picture card or real item and have SAE children follow oral directions similar to the word problems in the lesson. More verbal SAE children could give directions for others to follow.

■ **What do you need to do to find out how much a book and a ball cost?** [Find the prices in the picture.]

■ **How much does each item cost?** [book—8¢; ball—9¢]

■ **Suppose you had 15¢ and you wanted to find out how much money you would have left after buying the ball. What do you need to do?** [Find the price of the ball. Subtract it from 15¢.]

■ **How much money would you have left?** [6¢]

■ **What did you learn?** [Possible response: You can use data from a picture to solve problems.]

Encourage children to suggest other ways to solve these problems.

Check for Understanding

■ **How much money would Mary spend if she bought 2 puzzles?** [16¢]

GUIDED PRACTICE   ex. 1–5: Work through problem 1 with the children. Make sure they understand how to solve the problem using data from a picture.

Page 132   Have a volunteer read the sentence at the top of the page. Discuss the picture and help children identify the objects.

3 PRACTICE·APPLY   PRACTICE   ex. 1–5

CLOSE   Guide children to summarize the lesson:

■ **How do you use data from a picture to solve problems?** [Possible response: You find the information needed to answer the questions and solve the problem.]

MAC ACTIVITY CENTER

MAC Activity 87:
Basic-to-Average ▼

MATH AND CONSUMERS ▪ GOING SHOPPING

MAC Activity 87

On Your Own   Pair and Share   In a Group

Materials classroom objects, punchout pennies, index cards

Setup Set up a store display in one corner of the classroom, using classroom objects, such as books, crayons, plants, pencils, and rulers. Gather enough objects for all children to have a selection from which to buy. Use index cards as price tags. Price each item under 10¢.

Procedure Provide each child with 15 punchout pennies. Have children in turn, purchase two or three items from the display. Have the buyers tell how much they are spending as they count out the pennies. If a buyer chooses two objects that together cost more than 15¢, the buyer must choose again. Then have children report on what they bought, how much they spent, and how much money they have left, if any.

MAC Activity 88:
Average-to-Challenge ▼

SPEAKING MATHEMATICALLY ▪ NOW FOR SALE!

MAC Activity 88

On Your Own   Pair and Share   In a Group

Materials magazines, scissors, paste, index cards

Procedure Separate children into two teams. Give each team magazines, scissors, paste, and index cards (one for each child). Tell children that each team is going to create its own store by selecting objects from the magazines, pricing them, and making up problems for the opposing team.

Have each child cut out and paste one item on the index card, and write a price between 3¢ and 9¢ on the back of the card. When the cards are ready, have the teams make up money problems, based on the prices of items in their stores. Allow time for the teams to display their cards and present their problems.

RETEACHING-44

Name

PROBLEM SOLVING:
USING DATA FROM A PICTURE

Study

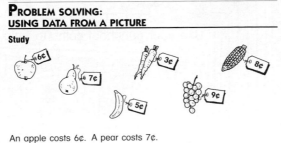

An apple costs 6¢. A pear costs 7¢.
Add to find how much they cost.

$$6¢ + 7¢ = 13¢$$

Check

Find the data. Solve.

1. How much do carrots and a banana cost?

   $$\underline{3¢} + \underline{5¢} = \underline{8¢}$$

2. Carl had 12¢.
   He bought grapes.
   How much money does he have left?

   $$\underline{12¢} - \underline{9¢} = \underline{3¢}$$

3. Ellen bought corn for __8¢__.

   She bought a pear for __7¢__.

   How much money did she spend? __15¢__

Macmillan/McGraw-Hill, MATHEMATICS IN ACTION
Grade 2, Chapter 4, Lesson 4, pages 131–132   Reteaching-44

PRACTICE-44

Name

PROBLEM SOLVING:
USING DATA FROM A PICTURE

School Fair

Find the data. Solve.

1. A toy horse costs __3__ ¢.

   A clown costs __7__ ¢.

   How much do a horse and a clown cost? __10__ ¢

2. Lee had 17¢.

   She bought a dog for __9__ ¢.

   How much money did she have left? __8__ ¢

3. Mack had 12¢.

   He bought a whistle for __7__ ¢.

   Does he have enough money for a top? __yes__

4. Dan bought a cat and a clown.

   How much money did he spend? __11¢__

Macmillan/McGraw-Hill, MATHEMATICS IN ACTION
Grade 2, Chapter 4, Lesson 4, pages 131–132   Practice-44

ENRICHMENT

ENRICHMENT-44

Name

PROBLEM SOLVING

On Your Own   Pair and Share   In a Group

THE PRICE IS RIGHT

Katie bought things for art class.
Some of the prices fell off.
Help her find the missing prices.

PAINTS — 8¢

12¢

9¢

11¢   CRAYONS

16¢   PASTE

Write the price on each tag.

1. Katie gave the clerk 15¢ for the paints.
   She got 6¢ back.

2. The scissors were 3¢ more than the paints.

3. Katie gave the clerk 10¢ for the paintbrush.
   She got 2¢ back.

4. The price of the paste is the same as 2 brushes.

5. The box of crayons was 5¢ less than the paste.

Katie went back to the store and spent 17¢.
What 2 things did she buy?

paints, paintbrush

Macmillan/McGraw-Hill, MATHEMATICS IN ACTION
Grade 2, Chapter 4, Lesson 4, pages 131–132   Enrichment-44

Problem of the Day

Maria had 16¢. She bought two pencils for 8¢.
She wanted to buy a pen for 9¢. How much more
money does she need? [1¢; 16¢ − 8¢ = 8¢;
9¢ − 8¢ = 1¢]

AT·A·GLANCE p. 133

LESSON OBJECTIVE
Solve problems involving money.

ASSIGNMENT GUIDE

COURSE	EXERCISES
Basic	p. 133: All
Average	p. 133: All
Challenge	p. 133: All

MATERIALS
Manipulatives 2 Q, 3 D, 7 N, and 10 P coins (or punchouts) per child

Teacher Resources
Crit. Think. 7

PROBLEM

THINKING MATHEMATICS

Name _____

PIGGY BANK

Use your punchout coins to help.

I have 56¢.
I have 5 coins.
I don't have any nickels.
I have 3 of 1 kind of coin.

Answer: __1__ __3__ __0__ __1__

I have 13¢.
I have 9 coins.

Answer: __0__ __0__ __1__ __8__

I have 56¢.
I don't have any dimes.
I have no more than 2 of any kind of coin.

Answer: __2__ __0__ __1__ __1__

133

1 PLAN

AIMS AND ATTITUDES This lesson develops number sense through the skill of counting money. It also develops logical reasoning by having children identify "mystery" coins from given clues.

Emphasize the gamelike nature of the lesson by encouraging children to pretend that they are piggy-bank detectives using clues to solve problems.

Encourage children to verbalize their strategies for finding the correct coins. Accept all strategies as valid, as long as it is used consistently by the child. A class discussion will reveal to children alternate ways to solve problems.

MANAGEMENT The activity is intended for all children and has been designed for independent work. It is also appropriate for pairs of children.

2 GUIDE

Before beginning the activity on page 133, have children model the following. Distribute a set of play quarters, dimes, nickels, and pennies to the children. Write 35¢ on the chalkboard.

■ **What coins can you use to show this amount?** [Possible responses: 7 nickels; 3 dimes and 1 nickel; 1 quarter and 1 dime]

Repeat the activity using other money amounts.

Read the directions at the top of page 133 with the children.

■ **How can you figure out which coins each customer has in a piggy bank?** [by using the clues next to each animal]

Have children use their coins to figure out which coins each bank customer has. Then have them write the answers.

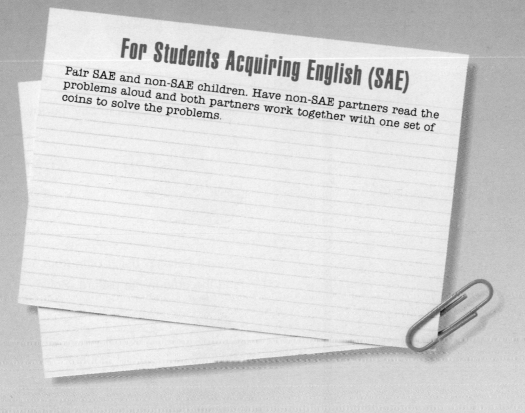

For Students Acquiring English (SAE)

Pair SAE and non-SAE children. Have non-SAE partners read the problems aloud and both partners work together with one set of coins to solve the problems.

After completing the page, ask volunteers to explain their strategy for finding the right coins. Accept all strategies as reasonable.

3 EXTEND

Allow children to repeat the activity, but change the amounts in the clues to 38¢, 18¢, and 37¢, respectively. All other clues remain the same. [Answers: 1 quarter, 1 dime, 0 nickels, 3 pennies; 0 quarters, 1 dime, 0 nickels, 8 pennies; 1 quarter, 0 dimes, 2 nickels, 2 pennies]

Once again, encourage volunteers to explain their strategies for solving the problems.

CHAPTER 4

Extra Practice items are provided so that children may have an opportunity for further practice.

The *Additional Practice* section also provides practice you may wish to assign.

Extra Practice

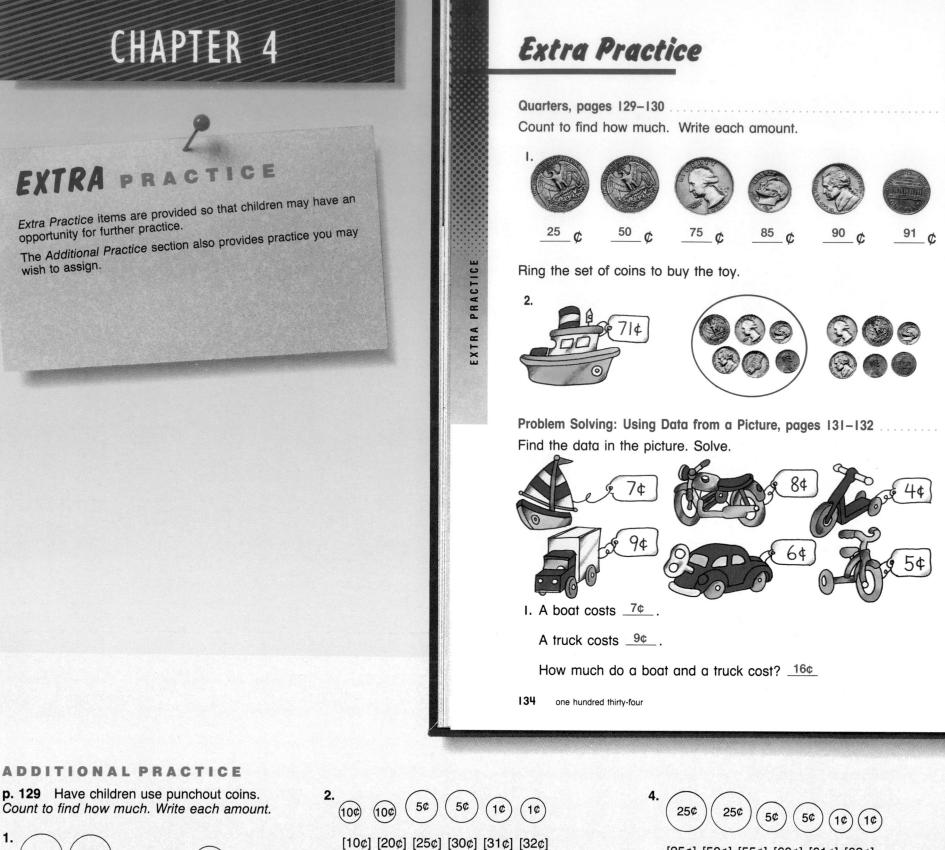

Quarters, pages 129–130 . . . .

Count to find how much. Write each amount.

1.

__25__ ¢   __50__ ¢   __75__ ¢   __85__ ¢   __90__ ¢   __91__ ¢

Ring the set of coins to buy the toy.

2.

71¢

Problem Solving: Using Data from a Picture, pages 131–132 . . . .

Find the data in the picture. Solve.

7¢   8¢   4¢

9¢   6¢   5¢

1. A boat costs __7¢__ .

   A truck costs __9¢__ .

   How much do a boat and a truck cost? __16¢__

ADDITIONAL PRACTICE

p. 129 Have children use punchout coins.
Count to find how much. Write each amount.

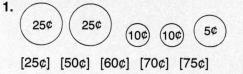

1.

(25¢) (25¢) (10¢) (10¢) (5¢)

[25¢] [50¢] [60¢] [70¢] [75¢]

2.

(10¢) (10¢) (5¢) (5¢) (1¢) (1¢)

[10¢] [20¢] [25¢] [30¢] [31¢] [32¢]

3.

(25¢) (10¢) (5¢) (5¢) (1¢) (1¢) (1¢)

[25¢] [35¢] [40¢] [45¢] [46¢] [47¢] [48¢]

4.

(25¢) (25¢) (5¢) (5¢) (1¢) (1¢)

[25¢] [50¢] [55¢] [60¢] [61¢] [62¢]

p. 129 *Use your punchout coins to show each amount. Have your partner count your coins.*

1. 86¢   2. 75¢
3. 48¢   4. 99¢

p. 131 *Find the data in the picture. Solve.*

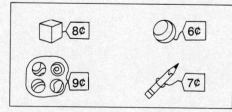

1. A box costs _____. [8¢]
2. A ball costs _____. [6¢]
3. How much do a box and a ball cost?
   _____ [14¢]

AT·A·GLANCE pp. 135-136

LESSON OBJECTIVES
Recognize the value of a dollar.
Find the value of a set of bills and coins.

ASSIGNMENT GUIDE

COURSE	EXERCISES
Basic	p. 135: 1–4; p. 136: 1–6
Average	p. 135: 1–4; p. 136: 1–6
Challenge	p. 135: 1–4; p. 136: 1–6
Extra Practice, p. 143	

MATERIALS
Manipulatives 100 P, 20 N, 10 D, 4 Q coins, 3 $1 bills (or punchouts) per pair

Teacher Resources
Reteaching 45   Practice 45   Enrichment 45
Prob. Solv. 17   MAC Act. 89, 90

SKILLS TRACE		
MONEY		
Explore (Concrete) 126	**Develop/Understand (Transitional/Abstract)** 127–128, 129–130, 135–136, 137–138	
Practice 134, 143, 144, 145–146, 149, 156, 183	**Apply** 131–132, 133, 139–140, 141, 148	

See *MANIPULATIVES PLUS 21*, p. 124K.

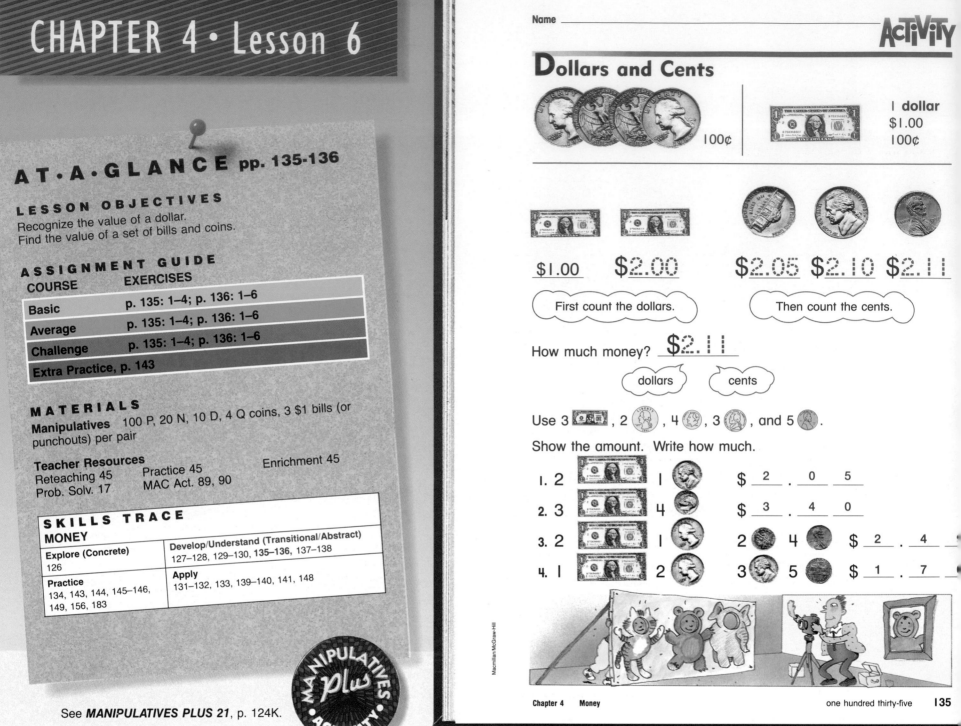

ACTIVITY

Dollars and Cents

I dollar
$1.00
100¢

100¢

$1.00 $2.00 $2.05 $2.10 $2.11

First count the dollars.   Then count the cents.

How much money? $2.11

dollars   cents

Use 3 🏦, 2 🪙, 4 🪙, 3 🪙, and 5 🪙.

Show the amount. Write how much.

I. 2 I $ __2__ . __0__ __5__

2. 3 4 $ __3__ . __4__ __0__

3. 2 I 2 4 $ __2__ . __4__

4. I 2 3 5 $ __1__ . __7__

Macmillan/McGraw-Hill

PREPARE   **WARM-UP**   To prepare children to discuss dollars and cents, distribute punchout coins to pairs of children. Have them count out a set of coins for each of the following amounts: 90¢, 74¢, 81¢, 79¢, 99¢.

TEACH   **DISCUSSING**   Distribute punchout coins and bills. Identify the bill as a **1 dollar bill.** Point out that the punchout dollar bill is smaller than a real dollar bill. Have children show 99¢ with their coins. Then have them add one penny.

■ **How many cents do you have?** [100 cents]

Note that a dollar is worth 100 cents. Have children work with a partner to show the following equivalents of 1 dollar: 100 pennies, 20 nickels, 10 dimes, 4 quarters.

Then write the following on the chalkboard:
   1 dollar equals 100¢
   100¢ equals $1.00

Identify the **dollar sign** and the **decimal point.** Explain that amounts equal to or greater than 1 dollar are written with a dollar sign and a decimal point.

Have children show 1 dollar, 1 quarter, and 2 dimes. Write $1.45 on the chalkboard. Read it aloud as 1 dollar *and* 45 cents. Repeat with other combinations of bills and coins.

PUPIL'S EDITION pp. 135-136

Page 135   Work through the example at the top of the page with the children. Identify all the coins and bills pictured. Make sure children read the decimal point as *and.*

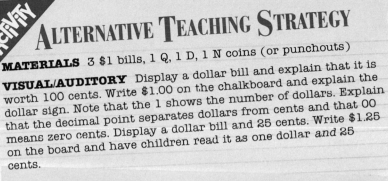

Ring the exact amount you need. **Answers will vary.**

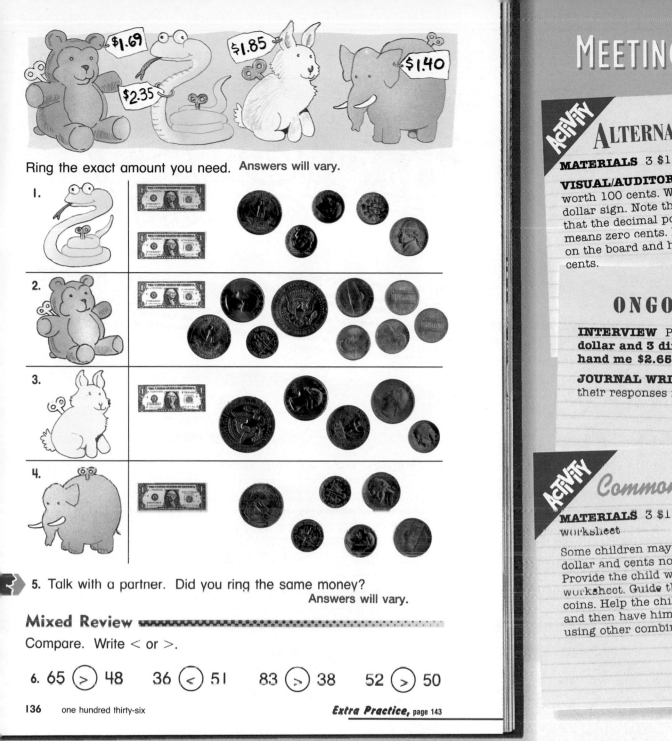

1.

2.

3.

4.

5. Talk with a partner. Did you ring the same money?

Answers will vary.

Mixed Review

Compare. Write < or >.

6. 65 ⧀>⧀ 48   36 ⧀<⧀ 51   83 ⧀>⧀ 38   52 ⧀>⧀ 50

Extra Practice, page 143

ACTIVITY ALTERNATIVE TEACHING STRATEGY

MATERIALS 3 $1 bills, 1 Q, 1 D, 1 N coins (or punchouts)

VISUAL/AUDITORY Display a dollar bill and explain that it is worth 100 cents. Write $1.00 on the chalkboard and explain the dollar sign. Note that the 1 shows the number of dollars. Explain that the decimal point separates dollars from cents and that 00 means zero cents. Display a dollar bill and 25 cents. Write $1.25 on the board and have children read it as one dollar and 25 cents.

ONGOING ASSESSMENT

INTERVIEW Provide a set of coins and bills. **(1) Show me 1 dollar and 3 dimes. How much is that? (2) If you were to hand me $2.65, what bills and coins would you give me?**

JOURNAL WRITING You may wish to have children record their responses in their math journals.

ACTIVITY Common Error and Remediation

MATERIALS 3 $1 bills, 2 Q, 4 D, 5 N, 6 P coins (or punchouts), worksheet

Some children may have difficulty writing money amounts in dollar and cents notation. Work individually with each child. Provide the child with punchout dollar bills, assorted coins, and a worksheet. Guide the child to show a combination of bills and coins. Help the child write the amount beginning with the bills, and then have him or her read it aloud. Continue the activity, using other combinations of bills and coins.

Check for Understanding

■ If I had 2 quarters and 5 dimes, would I have a dollar? [Yes.]

GUIDED PRACTICE ex. 1–4: For reteaching, use Common Error and Remediation or Alternative Strategy.

Page 136 Have children identify the toys at the top of the page and read the amount shown on each price tag.

3 PRACTICE•APPLY

PRACTICE ex. 1–6: Have children compare their answers.

CLOSE Guide children to summarize the lesson:

■ **Which coins are equal to one dollar?** [Possible responses: 4 quarters; 10 dimes; 2 quarters and 1 half dollar]

Chapter 4 • Lesson 6   **136**

CALCULATOR ■ CALCULATING DOLLARS AND CENTS

MAC Activity 90

On Your Own   Pair and Share   In a Group

Materials   calculator, punchout coins and dollar bills

Begin by showing children how to enter a dollar and cents amount into the calculator. After they enter the dollar amount, have them punch the decimal key and enter the cents amount.

Assign each child a partner. Give each pair punchout bills, coins, and a calculator. Have one child use the bills and coins to show an amount. Have the other child say the amount and enter it into the calculator. The first child then checks that the amount displayed is correct. After each entry the calculator should be cleared. Have children take turns using the punchouts and the calculator.

▲
MAC Activity 90:
Average-to-Challenge

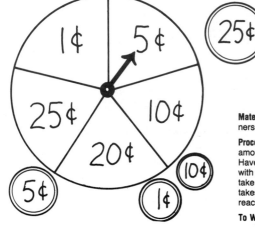

MANIPULATIVES ■ SPIN FOR DOLLARS

MAC Activity 89

On Your Own   Pair and Share   In a Group

Materials   punchout coins and dollar bills, punchout spinners

Procedure   Make five-part spinners with the money amounts 1¢, 5¢, 10¢, 20¢, and 25¢ written in the parts. Have children play in groups and provide each group with a pile of punchout coins and bills. Tell children to take turns spinning the spinner. For each spin, the child takes the indicated coins from the pile. The goal is to reach 100 and trade the coins for a dollar bill.

To Win   The first child to reach $1.00 wins the round.

▲
MAC Activity 89:
Basic-to-Average

RETEACHING-45

Name

DOLLARS AND CENTS

Study

I dollar *41 cents*

dollars	cents
1	41

$1.41

Check

Write how much.

1.

dollars	cents
2	15

$ 2 . 1 5

2.

dollars	cents
1	57

$ 1 . 5 7

3.

dollars	cents
3	50

$ 3 . 5 0

Reteaching-45

Macmillan/McGraw-Hill, MATHEMATICS IN ACTION
Grade 2, Chapter 4, Lesson 6, pages 135–136

PRACTICE-45

Name

DOLLARS AND CENTS

Color the exact amount you need.　　　**Answers may vary.**

1. $1.62

2. $2.17

3. $1.70

4. $2.31

5. $1.85

Practice-45

Macmillan/McGraw-Hill, MATHEMATICS IN ACTION
Grade 2, Chapter 4, Lesson 6, pages 135–136

ENRICHMENT

ENRICHMENT-45

Name

DOLLARS AND CENTS

On Your Own　Pair and Share　In a Group

AT THE COSTUME SHOP

Show how each child paid for a mask.
Write how many of each coin.

$1.50

	ONE				
1. Jim: 1 bill 1 coin	⋮	⋮			
2. Carol: 6 coins			6		
3. Bob: 1 bill 4 coins	1		1	2	1
4. Lou: 1 bill 6 coins	1		1		5
5. Jill: 16 coins				14	2

Enrichment-45

Macmillan/McGraw-Hill, MATHEMATICS IN ACTION
Grade 2, Chapter 4, Lesson 6, pages 135–136

Problem of the Day

A hamster costs $4.79 Mark has 4 one-dollar
bills, 1 quarter, 3 dimes, and 5 nickels. Does Mark
have enough to buy a hamster?   [Yes. Children
may work it out this way: $4.79 < $4.80.]

AT·A·GLANCE pp. 137-138

LESSON OBJECTIVE
Compare money amounts.

ASSIGNMENT GUIDE

COURSE	EXERCISES
Basic	p. 137: 1–3; p. 138: 1–6
Average	p. 137: 1–3; p. 138: 1–6
Challenge	p. 137: 1–3; p. 138: 1–6
Extra Practice, p. 143	Practice Plus, p. 144

MATERIALS
Manipulatives 10 P, 10 N, 10 D, 4 Q coins, 3 $1 bills (or punchouts) per pair

Teacher Resources
Reteaching 46   Practice 46   Enrichment 46
Prob. Solv. 18   MAC Act. 91, 92   Calculator 4
Math Anthology, pp. 200–201

SKILLS TRACE

MONEY	
Explore (Concrete) 126	Develop/Understand (Transitional/Abstract) 127–128, 129–130, 135–136, 137–138
Practice 134, 143, 144, 145–146, 149, 156, 183	Apply 131–132, 133, 139–140, 141, 148

See **MANIPULATIVES PLUS 22**, p. 124L.

MANIPULATIVES *plus* ACTIVITY

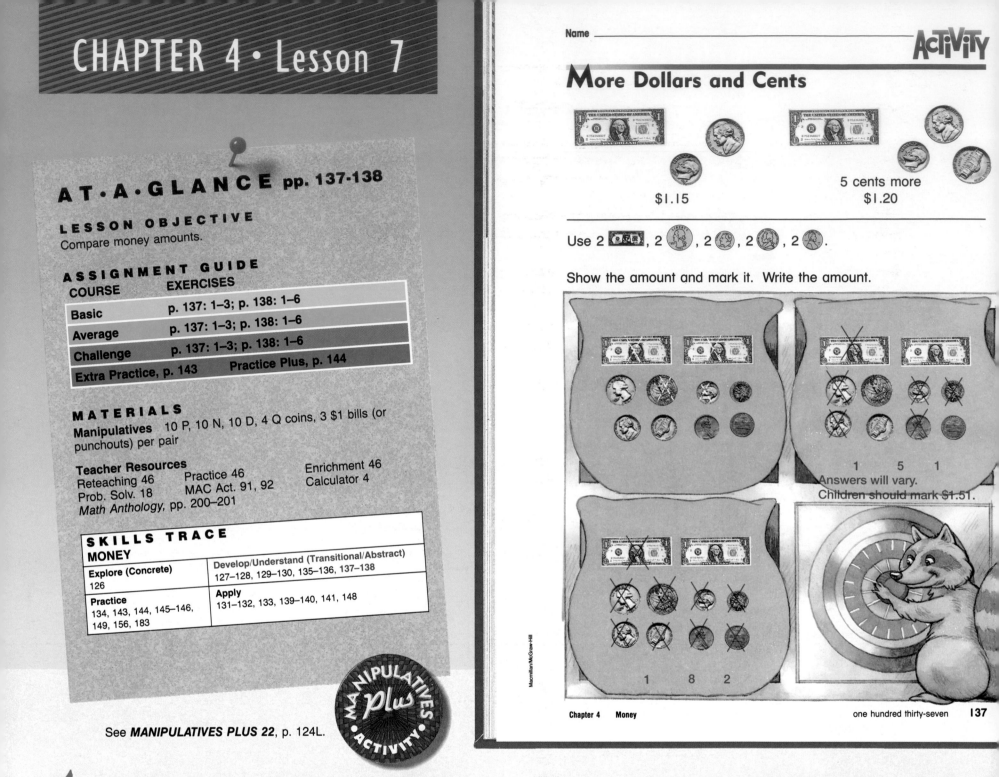

ACTIVITY

More Dollars and Cents

$1.15   5 cents more $1.20

Use 2 [bill], 2 [quarter], 2 [dime], 2 [nickel], 2 [penny].

Show the amount and mark it. Write the amount.

1   5   1
Answers will vary.
Children should mark $1.51.

1   8   2

Macmillan/McGraw-Hill

Chapter 4   Money   one hundred thirty-seven   **137**

PREPARE
WARM-UP To review dollar and cents notation, have children rewrite the following amounts using a dollar sign and a decimal point.

352 cents [$3.52]   412 cents [$4.12]
899 cents [$8.99]   107 cents [$1.07]
278 cents [$2.78]   543 cents [$5.43]

TEACH
DISCUSSING Assign each child a partner. Distribute play bills and coins to each pair of children. Have them work together to show the following sets of coins and determine their values.

2 quarters, 3 dimes, 1 nickel   [85¢]
1 quarter, 1 dime, 7 nickels   [70¢]

Discuss how to compare numbers to determine which set of coins has the greater value. Help children conclude that since 85 is greater than 70, 85¢ has a greater value than 70¢.

Next have children show the following sets of bills and coins and determine their values.

3 dollar bills, 3 quarters, 3 pennies   [$3.78]
3 dollar bills, 7 dimes, 4 nickels   [$3.90]
■ **Compare the dollar amounts.** [They are the same.]
■ **Compare the cents. Which amount is more?** [$3.90]

PUPIL'S EDITION pp. 137-138

Page 137 Discuss the picture at the top of the page. Have children use their play money to check the answer.

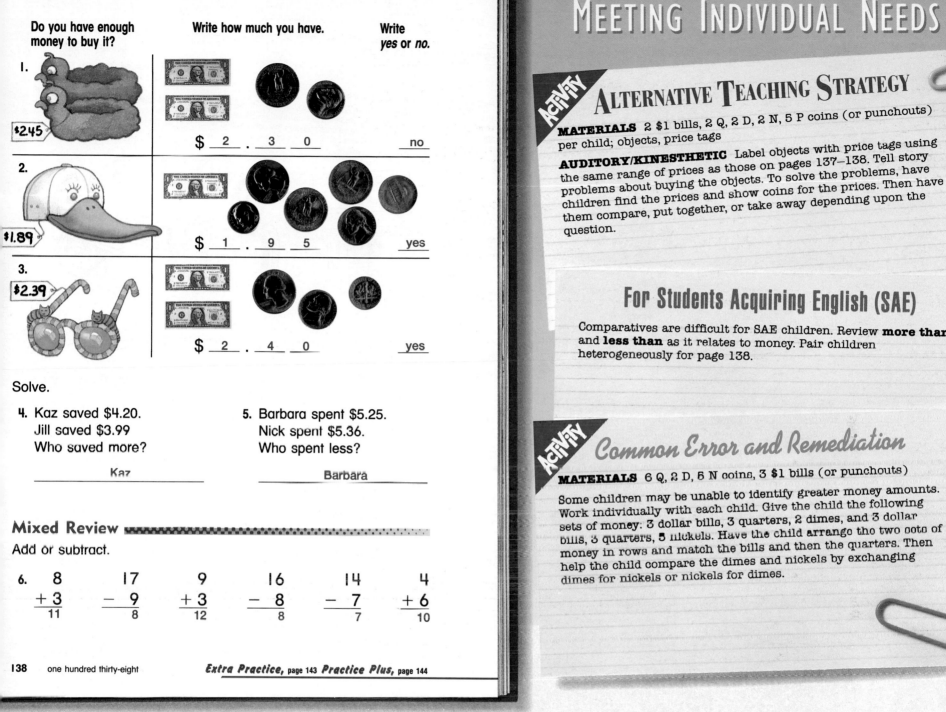

Do you have enough money to buy it?   **Write how much you have.**   **Write yes or no.**

1.

$2.45

$ 2 . 3 0   no

2.

$1.89

$ 1 . 9 5   yes

3.

$2.39

$ 2 . 4 0   yes

Solve.

4. Kaz saved $4.20.
   Jill saved $3.99
   Who saved more?

   _____Kaz_____

5. Barbara spent $5.25.
   Nick spent $5.36.
   Who spent less?

   _____Barbara_____

Mixed Review

Add or subtract.

6.
$$\begin{array}{r} 8 \\ +3 \\ \hline 11 \end{array}$$
$$\begin{array}{r} 17 \\ -9 \\ \hline 8 \end{array}$$
$$\begin{array}{r} 9 \\ +3 \\ \hline 12 \end{array}$$
$$\begin{array}{r} 16 \\ -8 \\ \hline 8 \end{array}$$
$$\begin{array}{r} 14 \\ -7 \\ \hline 7 \end{array}$$
$$\begin{array}{r} 4 \\ +6 \\ \hline 10 \end{array}$$

138 one hundred thirty-eight   *Extra Practice*, page 143 *Practice Plus*, page 144

ACTIVITY ALTERNATIVE TEACHING STRATEGY

MATERIALS 2 $1 bills, 2 Q, 2 D, 2 N, 5 P coins (or punchouts) per child; objects, price tags

AUDITORY/KINESTHETIC Label objects with price tags using the same range of prices as those on pages 137–138. Tell story problems about buying the objects. To solve the problems, have children find the prices and show coins for the prices. Then have them compare, put together, or take away depending upon the question.

For Students Acquiring English (SAE)

Comparatives are difficult for SAE children. Review **more than** and **less than** as it relates to money. Pair children heterogeneously for page 138.

ACTIVITY *Common Error and Remediation*

MATERIALS 6 Q, 2 D, 5 N coins, 3 $1 bills (or punchouts)

Some children may be unable to identify greater money amounts. Work individually with each child. Give the child the following sets of money: 3 dollar bills, 3 quarters, 2 dimes, and 3 dollar bills, 3 quarters, 5 nickels. Have the child arrange the two sets of money in rows and match the bills and then the quarters. Then help the child compare the dimes and nickels by exchanging dimes for nickels or nickels for dimes.

Check for Understanding

■ If I have 5¢ less than $1.50, how much money do I have? [$1.45]

GUIDED PRACTICE ex. 1–3: For reteaching, use Common Error and Remediation or Alternative Strategy.

Page 138 Read the column heads at the top of the page with the children. Have them identify the items and read the price tags.

Mathematics and Literature

PRACTICE•APPLY   PRACTICE ex. 1–6

CLOSE Guide children to summarize the lesson:

■ Which amount is more than $1.75: $1.87 or $1.65? [$1.87]

To extend the lesson, read *Bit by Bit* from *Math Anthology* to the class. Invite children to respond to the story by sharing experiences they may have had saving to buy a desired item, using a bank account, or earning money of their own. Then reread the parts of the story that mention coins or money amounts. Have children show them with coins and/or bills as volunteers write the amounts on the chalkboard with proper money notation. Pose questions based on the listed money amounts, such as **Which amounts are less than a dollar? Which amount has no cents? Which amount can be made with one coin?**

LESSON RESOURCES
CHAPTER 4 • Lesson 7

MAC ACTIVITY CENTER

MAC Activity 91

ESTIMATION ■ LESS MONEY

On Your Own   Pair and Share   In a Group

Materials punchout coins and dollar bills, tray

Place two separate sets of punchout coins and bills on a tray. Make sure the coins and bills are clearly visible. Display the money for a short time, and then ask children to estimate which set is worth less. After the estimates have been made and recorded, have volunteers count the coins to find which set has the lesser value. Repeat the activity, using different sets of bills and coins.

▲ MAC Activity 91:
Basic-to-Average

MAC Activity 92:
Average-to-Challenge ▼

MATH AND CONSUMERS ■ AUCTION

MAC Activity 92

On Your Own   Pair and Share   In a Group

Materials pictures of toys or sports equipment, punchout coins and dollar bills

Have children pretend that they are at an auction. Display pictures of toys or sports equipment. Distribute varying amounts of punchout coins and bills to the children. Briefly explain bidding rules. Remind children that they may not bid more money than they have. After each pictured item has been "sold," the child with the highest bid must count out his or her punchout money to pay for the item. If a buyer does not have enough money to pay for an item, it may be reauctioned. Continue until everyone has bought at least one item.

RETEACHING-46

Name

MORE DOLLARS AND CENTS

Study

> Yes, I have enough money to buy the hat.

$1.00 $1.25 $1.30

Check

Count the money.
Is there enough? Ring *yes* or *no*.

1. $\underline{\$1.00}$ $\underline{\$1.25}$ $\underline{\$1.50}$ (yes)   no

2. $\underline{\$1.00}$ $\underline{\$1.50}$ $\underline{\$1.75}$ $\underline{\$2.00}$ yes   no

3. $\underline{\$1.00}$ $\underline{\$1.25}$ $\underline{\$1.50}$ $\underline{\$1.55}$ yes   (no)

Macmillan/McGraw-Hill, MATHEMATICS IN ACTION
Grade 2, Chapter 4, Lesson 7, pages 137–138
Reteaching-46

PRACTICE-46

Name

MORE DOLLARS AND CENTS

Do you have enough money to buy it?
Write how much you have.
Write *yes* or *no*.

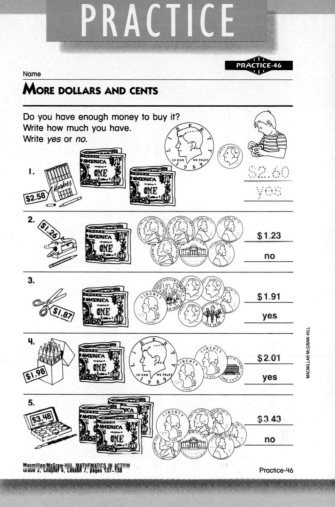

1. $2.58   — $2.60   yes

2. $1.26   — $1.23   no

3. $1.87   — $1.91   yes

4. $1.98   — $2.01   yes

5. $3.48   — $3.43   no

Grade 2, Chapter 4, Lesson 7, pages 137–138
Practice-46

ENRICHMENT-46

Name

MORE DOLLARS AND CENTS

On Your Own   Pair and Share   In a Group

HOW MUCH?

Work with a friend.
Use punchout money to help.

1. Jan saved $3.20.
   Mark saved 2 dollars more.
   How much did Mark save?   **$5.20**

2. Tom spent $1.15.
   Jody spent 4 nickels more.
   How much did Jody spend?   **$1.35**

3. Ms. Hill spent $8.30.
   Ms. Shore spent 3 quarters more.
   How much did Ms. Shore spend?   **$9.05**

4. Mr. Neel saved $1.30.
   Mr. Frank saved 4 dimes less.
   How much did Mr. Frank save?   **90¢ or $.90**

5. Mary saved $5.25.
   Larry saved 6 quarters more.
   How much did Larry save?   **$6.75**

6. Ann spent $3.45.
   Noel spent 3 dimes and 1 nickel less.
   How much did Noel spend?   **$3.10**

7. Ted spent $2.10.
   Bobby spent 2 half dollars and
   1 quarter more.
   How much did Bobby spend?   **$3.35**

Macmillan/McGraw-Hill, MATHEMATICS IN ACTION
Grade 2, Chapter 4, Lesson 7, pages 137–138
Enrichment-46

Problem of the Day

Kate wants to buy a new baseball mitt that costs $9.67. She has 8 dollar bills, 2 quarters, 7 dimes, and 5 nickels. Does she have enough money for the mitt?   [No. Children may work it out this way: $9.45 < $9.67.]

AT·A·GLANCE pp. 139–140

LESSON OBJECTIVE
Use a guess and test strategy to solve problems.

ASSIGNMENT GUIDE

COURSE	EXERCISES
Basic	p. 139: 1–2; p. 140: 1–6
Average	p. 139: 1–2; p. 140: 1–6
Challenge	p. 139: 1–2; p. 140: 1–6

MATERIALS
Manipulatives   10 P, 10 D coins (or punchouts) per child

Teacher Resources
Reteaching 47   Practice 47   Enrichment 47
Prob. Solv. 19   MAC Act. 93, 94

Name _____

Problem Solving

Strategy: Guess and Test

There were drinks and snacks
at the stand.
Tara has 13¢.
She wants 1 drink and 1 snack.
Which two can she buy?

First make a guess.
Then test it.

Drinks	Snacks
Lemonade 8¢	Popcorn 6¢
Orangeade 9¢	Raisins 5¢

Yard Sale Refreshments

Guess 9¢ and 6¢.
15¢ is too large.

Guess 8¢ and 6¢.
14¢ is too large.

Guess 8¢ and 5¢.
13¢ is correct.

Suppose your first guess was too large.
How should you choose your next guess?
Possible answer: choose smaller numbers to add.

Toys   7¢   6¢   9¢

Books   7¢   8¢

Solve.   Use coins, mental math, or paper and pencil.

1. Greg spent 15¢.
He bought two toys.
How much did each cost?

 __9__ ¢ and __6__ ¢

2. Sally has 12¢.
Does she have enough
money to buy a toy and

a book? **No.**

Chapter 4   Money   one hundred thirty-nine   **139**

Macmillan/McGraw-Hill

---

1 PREPARE   **WARM-UP**   To prepare children for using a guess
and test strategy to solve problems, have them give
the following sums:

7¢ + 6¢ [13¢]   5¢ + 8¢ [13¢]
4¢ + 7¢ [11¢]   8¢ + 2¢ + 2¢ [12¢]

2 TEACH   **QUESTIONING**   Write the following list on the
chalkboard:

Banana 6¢   Orange 4¢   Apple 5¢   Peach 7¢

Tell children to listen to the problem you will read about these items.
 Franklin had 10¢. He wants to buy two pieces of fruit. Which two
pieces can he buy?

Have children look at the prices. Ask volunteers to make a guess
about which two pieces of fruit Franklin can buy.

■ **What is the total cost of the two fruits you chose?** [Answers will
vary.]

■ **Was the cost more than 10¢ or less?** [Answers will vary.]

■ **If the cost was more than 10¢, what should you do?** [Possible
response: Choose a price combination with smaller numbers.]

Have children try until they find the fruits. [apple and orange—9¢; banana and orange—10¢]

PUPIL'S EDITION pp. 139–140

Page 139   Have a volunteer read the problem at the top of the page.
Have the drinks, snacks, and their prices read aloud.

Solve. Use coins, mental math, or paper and pencil.

1. Ron spent 13¢.
   Which two items did he buy?

   __bear__ and __boat__

2. Maya had 11¢.
   She bought a stuffed bear.
   Did she have enough money
   for another stuffed bear?

   __No.__

3. Wes bought two toys.
   He spent 11¢.
   How much did each toy cost?

   __5__ ¢ and __6__ ¢

TOYS

MORE TOYS

4. Andy spent 12¢.
   Which two items did he buy?

   __kite__ and __puppet__

5. Dawn bought 3 toys.
   She spent 14¢.
   How much did each toy cost?

   __3__ ¢, __3__ ¢, and __8__ ¢

6. Stu had 15¢.
   He bought a ball and a kite.
   Did he have enough money
   left to buy a puppet?

   Yes.

TEACHER to TEACHER

COOPERATIVE LEARNING TIP 👫 Guess and test activities can often be more fun in a small group than in an entire class. My students form pairs and take turns being Guesser and Tester. Then they compare answers with the other pair in their group of four. At this point, one child is the Checker and checks the answers with a calculator. This enables him or her to concentrate on the strategy rather than the computation.

■ **What do you need to do?** [Find the drink and snack that together cost 13¢ or less.]

■ **What do you know?** [Tara has 13¢ to buy 1 drink and 1 snack.]

Read aloud the sentences that tell what to do and the text in the speech bubbles. Have the text under the children's pictures read aloud and the question answered. [Choose smaller numbers.]

■ **What did you learn?** [Possible response: You may need to guess and test more than one set of numbers to solve a problem.]

Check for Understanding

■ **Could Tara buy 2 snacks and no drinks with 13¢?** [Yes; 6¢ + 5¢ = 11¢; and 11¢ < 13¢.]

GUIDED PRACTICE   ex. 1–2: Work through problem 1 with the children. Make sure they understand how to solve the problem using the guess and test strategy. They may also use coins.

Page 140   Have a volunteer read the directions at the top of the page. Discuss the pictures and help children identify the objects. Children may use coins as needed.

3 PRACTICE•APPLY   **PRACTICE**   ex. 1–6

C L O S E   Guide children to summarize the lesson:

■ **How do you use a guess and test strategy to solve a problem?** [Possible response: You choose two numbers to try and then compare the answer to see if it is correct. If it is not correct, you try again.]

LESSON RESOURCES
CHAPTER 4 • Lesson 8

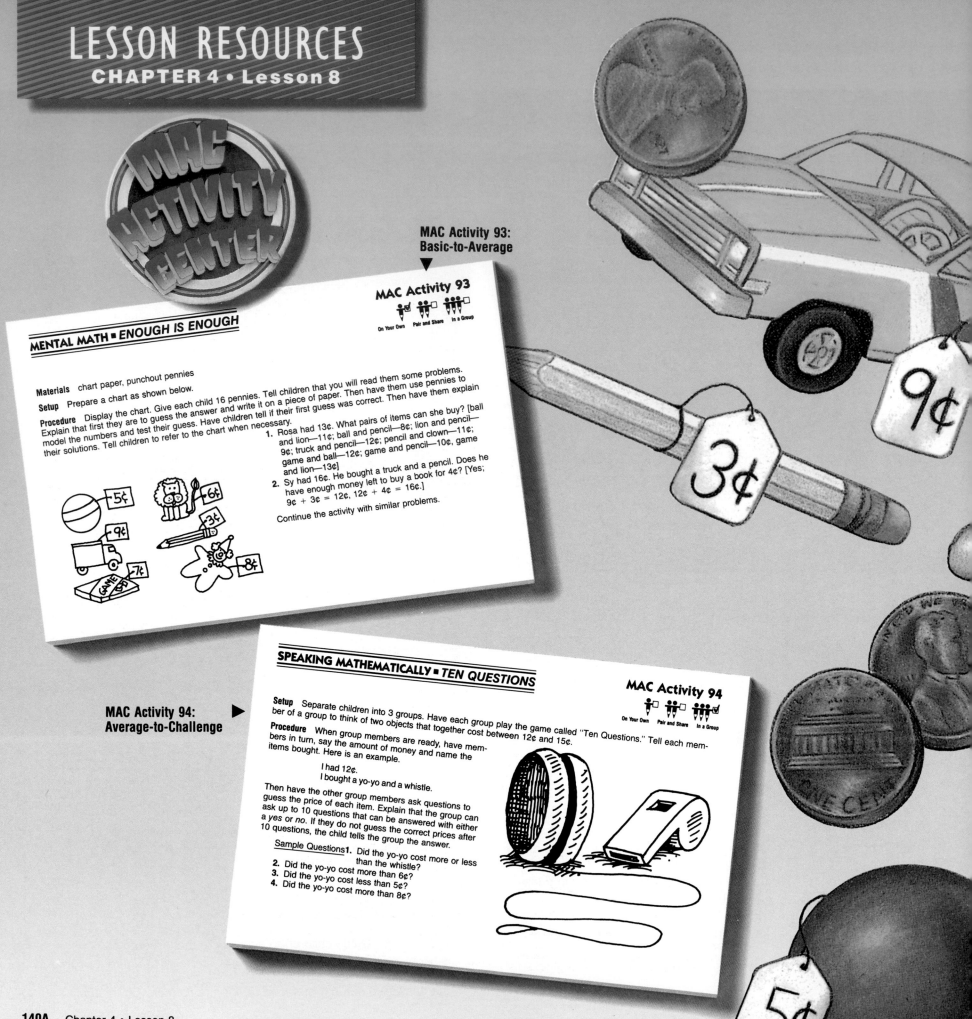

MAC Activity 93:
Basic-to-Average

MAC Activity 93

On Your Own   Pair and Share   In a Group

MENTAL MATH ■ ENOUGH IS ENOUGH

Materials   chart paper, punchout pennies

Setup   Prepare a chart as shown below.

Procedure   Display the chart. Give each child 16 pennies. Tell children that you will read them some problems. Explain that first they are to guess the answer and write it on a piece of paper. Then have them use pennies to model the numbers and test their guess. Have children tell if their first guess was correct. Then have them explain their solutions. Tell children to refer to the chart when necessary.

1. Rosa had 13¢. What pairs of items can she buy? [ball and lion—11¢; ball and pencil—8¢; lion and pencil— 9¢; truck and pencil—12¢; pencil and clown—11¢; game and ball—12¢; game and pencil—10¢, game and lion—13¢]
2. Sy had 16¢. He bought a truck and a pencil. Does he have enough money left to buy a book for 4¢? [Yes; 9¢ + 3¢ = 12¢, 12¢ + 4¢ = 16¢.]

Continue the activity with similar problems.

MAC Activity 94:
Average-to-Challenge

SPEAKING MATHEMATICALLY ■ TEN QUESTIONS

MAC Activity 94

On Your Own   Pair and Share   In a Group

Setup   Separate children into 3 groups. Have each group play the game called "Ten Questions." Tell each member of a group to think of two objects that together cost between 12¢ and 15¢.

Procedure   When group members are ready, have members in turn, say the amount of money and name the items bought. Here is an example.

> I had 12¢.
> I bought a yo-yo and a whistle.

Then have the other group members ask questions to guess the price of each item. Explain that the group can ask up to 10 questions that can be answered with either a *yes* or *no*. If they do not guess the correct prices after 10 questions, the child tells the group the answer.

<u>Sample Questions</u>
1. Did the yo-yo cost more or less than the whistle?
2. Did the yo-yo cost more than 6¢?
3. Did the yo-yo cost less than 5¢?
4. Did the yo-yo cost more than 8¢?

RETEACHING

RETEACHING-47

Name

PROBLEM SOLVING STRATEGY: GUESS AND TEST

Study

Fran bought a toy for her dog
and a toy for her cat.
She spent 11¢.
Which two toys did she buy?

Cat Toys	Dog Toys
yarn 6¢	bone 7¢
mouse 8¢	ball 5¢

Pick two toys.
Test the prices to see
if they add to 11¢.

I guess 6¢ + 7¢.
13¢ is too large.
I guess 5¢ + 6¢.
That makes 11¢.
She got yarn and a ball.

Check

Solve. First make a guess.
Then test it.

1. Judy spent 14¢.
She bought two toys.
One toy was a train.
What was the other toy?

   <u>doll</u>

2. Mike had 11¢.
He bought a horse.
Does he have enough
money left for a boat?

   <u>no</u>

3. Dina spent 10¢.
She bought two toys.
How much did each
toy cost?

   <u>4</u> ¢ and <u>6</u> ¢

Reteaching-47

Macmillan/McGraw-Hill, MATHEMATICS IN ACTION
Grade 2, Chapter 4, Lesson 8, pages 139–140

PRACTICE

PRACTICE-47

Name

PROBLEM SOLVING STRATEGY: GUESS AND TEST

Solve. First make a guess. Then test it.

1. Ben went to the gift shop.
He spent 10¢.
Which two items did
he buy?

   <u>star</u> and <u>rock</u>

2. Lisa had 14¢.
She bought a plant.
Did she have enough
money left for a book?

   <u>no</u>

3. Jesse bought two items.
He spent 9¢.
How much did each
item cost?

   <u>5</u> ¢ and <u>4</u> ¢

4. Tanya had 16¢.
Did she have enough
money for a plant
and a plane?

   <u>yes</u>

5. Abe bought three items.
He spent 15¢. How
much did each item cost?

   <u>5</u> ¢, <u>4</u> ¢, and <u>6</u> ¢

6. Dave got two items for 13¢.
One item was a rocket.
What was the second item?

   <u>star</u>

Practice-47

Macmillan/McGraw-Hill, MATHEMATICS IN ACTION
Grade 2, Chapter 4, Lesson 8, pages 139–140

ENRICHMENT

ENRICHMENT-47

Name

PROBLEM SOLVING

On Your Own   Pair and Share   In a Group

ON THE ROAD

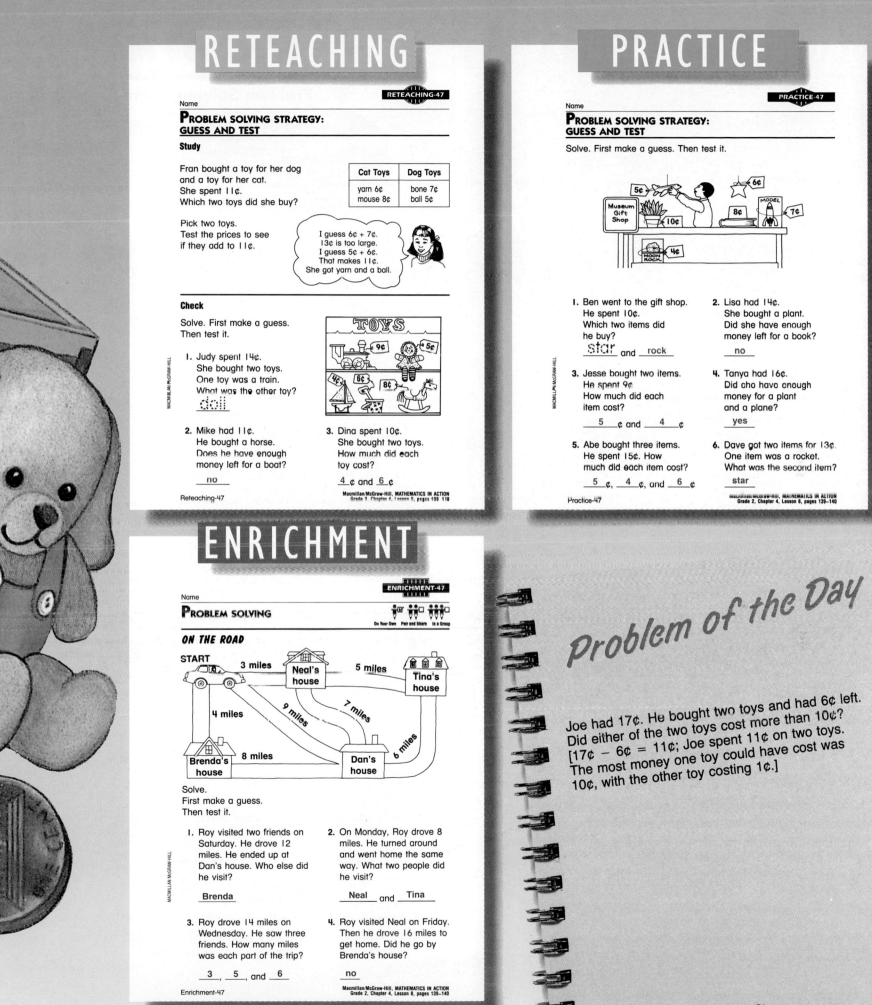

Solve.
First make a guess.
Then test it.

1. Roy visited two friends on
Saturday. He drove 12
miles. He ended up at
Dan's house. Who else did
he visit?

   <u>Brenda</u>

2. On Monday, Roy drove 8
miles. He turned around
and went home the same
way. What two people did
he visit?

   <u>Neal</u> and <u>Tina</u>

3. Roy drove 14 miles on
Wednesday. He saw three
friends. How many miles
was each part of the trip?

   <u>3</u>, <u>5</u>, and <u>6</u>

4. Roy visited Neal on Friday.
Then he drove 16 miles to
get home. Did he go by
Brenda's house?

   <u>no</u>

Enrichment-47

Macmillan/McGraw-Hill, MATHEMATICS IN ACTION
Grade 2, Chapter 4, Lesson 8, pages 139–140

Problem of the Day

Joe had 17¢. He bought two toys and had 6¢ left.
Did either of the two toys cost more than 10¢?
[17¢ − 6¢ = 11¢; Joe spent 11¢ on two toys.
The most money one toy could have cost was
10¢, with the other toy costing 1¢.]

CHAPTER 4 • Lesson 9

AT·A·GLANCE p. 141

LESSON OBJECTIVE
Make decisions using information.

ASSIGNMENT GUIDE

COURSE	EXERCISES
Basic	p. 141: 1–3
Average	p. 141: 1–3
Challenge	p. 141: 1–3

Teacher Resources
Crit. Think. 8   Prob. Solv. 20
Math Anthology p. 151
Math Songs Cassette, Side 2, Selection 9

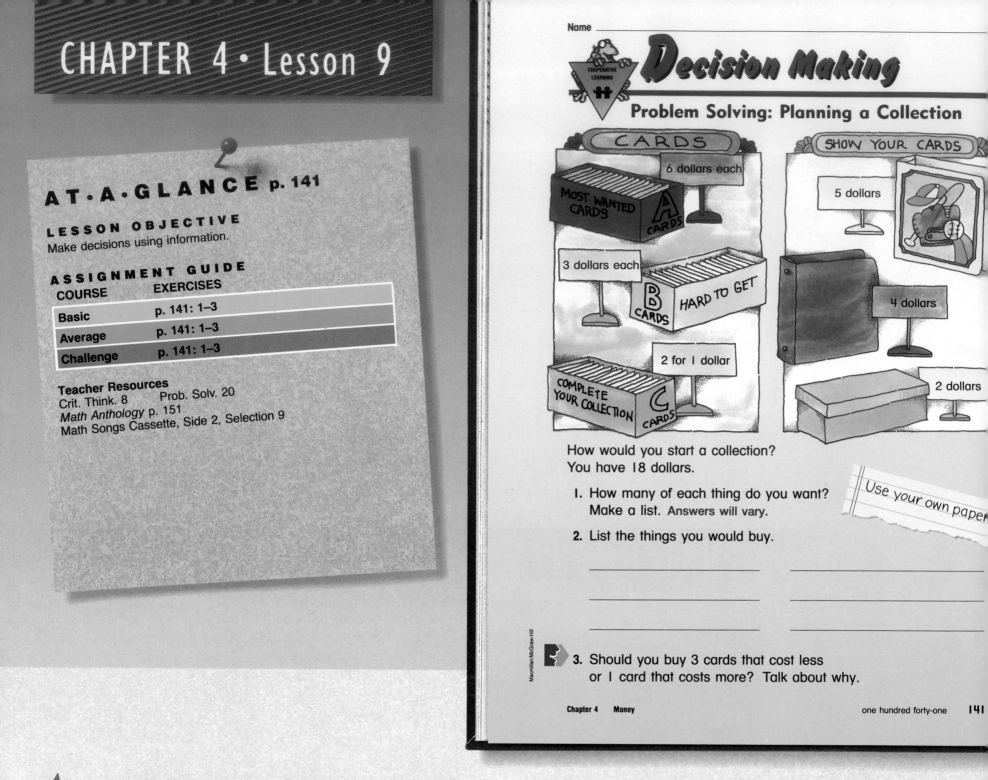

Name _____

COOPERATIVE LEARNING

Decision Making

Problem Solving: Planning a Collection

CARDS

6 dollars each

MOST WANTED CARDS   A CARDS

3 dollars each

B CARDS   HARD TO GET

2 for I dollar

COMPLETE YOUR COLLECTION   C CARDS

SHOW YOUR CARDS

5 dollars

4 dollars

2 dollars

How would you start a collection?
You have 18 dollars.

Use your own paper

1. How many of each thing do you want?
   Make a list. Answers will vary.

2. List the things you would buy.

   _____   _____

   _____   _____

   _____   _____

3. Should you buy 3 cards that cost less
   or I card that costs more? Talk about why.

Macmillan/McGraw-Hill

Chapter 4   Money   one hundred forty-one   **141**

PREPARE

WARM-UP To review money concepts, ask children the following questions.

■ **How many one-dollar bills are equal to a five-dollar bill?** [5]

■ **How many dollars will you get for a ten-dollar bill?** [10]

■ **How much change would you receive if you spent $8.00 and gave the clerk a ten-dollar bill?** [$2.00]

■ **How many five-dollar bills would you get for a ten-dollar bill?** [2]

TEACH

Mathematics and Literature

DISCUSSING Sing the song "Hot Cross Buns" found in *Math Anthology* with the class, or play the tape. Explain that the buns are sweet rolls with an icing *X* on top.

Discuss the money amounts in the song. Help children understand how there might be two prices for hot cross buns. [Possible answer: They come in two sizes.]

■ **If you had a nickel, how many hot cross buns could you buy?** [5 one-a-penny or 10 two-a-penny buns]

PUPIL'S EDITION p. 141

Identify the pictures and prices at the top of the page with the children.

Check for Understanding

■ **How many C cards could you buy with $1.00?** [2]

■ **What could you buy with $3.00?** [Possible responses: 1 B card; a $2.00 display box and 1C card; 6 C cards]

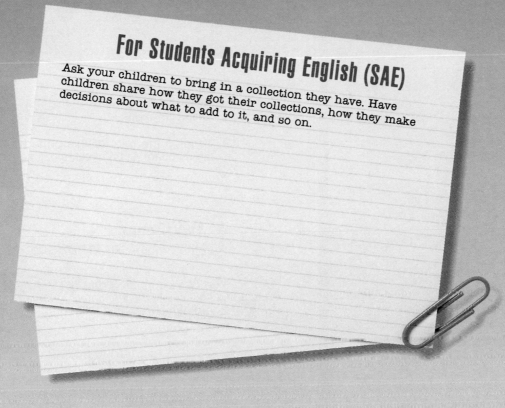

For Students Acquiring English (SAE)

Ask your children to bring in a collection they have. Have children share how they got their collections, how they make decisions about what to add to it, and so on.

PRACTICE·APPLY Have children complete ex. 1–3. Call on volunteers to tell about the card collections they will start, how they decided which items to buy, and how many of each item they will buy.

CLOSE Guide children to summarize the lesson:

■ **What should you do before you start a baseball card collection?** [Decide which things are needed, how much money you have to spend, and which things to buy.]

CLASS PROJECT

Materials magazines, drawing paper, scissors, paste

Provide children with magazines, drawing paper, scissors, and paste. Tell them to think of objects to collect such as cars, glasses, hats. Then have children cut out pictures from magazines of the things they want to "collect." Remind children to collect only one kind of thing.

Tell children to paste their pictures on drawing paper and label their collection.

When children have completed the project, call on volunteers to display and discuss their pictures.

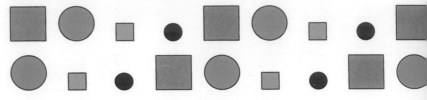

AT·A·GLANCE p. 142

OBJECTIVE
Use a computer to generate patterns.

MATERIALS
Computer

Teacher Resources
Computer Software   *Computer Workshop:*   PATTERNS 2

Computer: Patterns

You know how to make patterns using shapes.

The part of the pattern that repeats
is called the **rule.**

1. What is the rule for this pattern?
   large square, large circle, small square, small circle

You can also make patterns on a computer.

At the Computer

Run the program PATTERNS 2.

You can complete patterns.

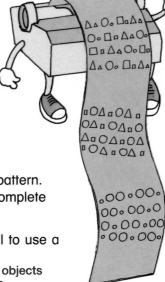

2. Tell which shapes will complete
   the pattern.

3. Tell the rule for the pattern.

You can make your own patterns.

4. You pick the shapes and show the pattern.
   Your partner shows which shapes complete
   the pattern. Take turns.

5. Talk about why you think it is helpful to use a
   computer to make patterns.
   Possible answer: A computer can draw objects
   accurately and repeat a rule many times.

142   one hundred forty-two

 **PREPARE**   **WARM-UP**   To prepare children to complete patterns of shapes on a computer, draw the following
on the chalkboard.
1. ☐ ○ ☆ ☐ ○ ☆ ☐ ○ ☆ ☐ __ [○]
2. X ○ X X ○ X X ○ X __ [X]
3. ☐ ○ ☐ ○ ☐ ○ __ ○ ☐ ○ [☐]
4. ☆ ☆ ☐ ☆ ☆ __ ☐ ☆ ☆ ☐ [☆]
Have volunteers tell the next or missing object in the patterns.

TEACH   **PATTERNING**   Draw the following pattern on the
chalkboard.

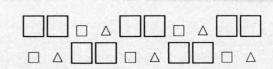

■ **What kinds of shapes make up the pattern?** [large square, small
square, triangle]

■ **What is the order of the shapes in the pattern?** [large square,
large square, small square, triangle]

Explain that *large square, large square, small square, triangle* is the
rule for this pattern. Discuss that the rule for other patterns may be
different and the rule is the part of the pattern that repeats.

■ **What happens to the pattern at the end of the first line?** [It
continues on the next line.]

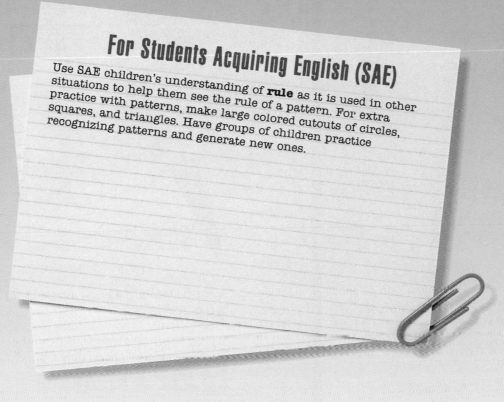

For Students Acquiring English (SAE)

Use SAE children's understanding of **rule** as it is used in other situations to help them see the rule of a pattern. For extra practice with patterns, make large colored cutouts of circles, squares, and triangles. Have groups of children practice recognizing patterns and generate new ones.

Have a volunteer identify the next four shapes in the pattern. Draw the shapes as they are identified. Then erase one of the shapes anywhere in the pattern and have a volunteer identify the missing shape. Have children cover their eyes while you erase another shape. Then allow them to identify the missing shape.

PRACTICE•APPLY   Discuss the pattern pictured at the top of the page. Guide children to see that the pattern continues on the second line.

AT THE COMPUTER   Have children work in pairs using the computer program PATTERNS 2. To begin, tell children to look for the rule in the pattern on the screen. Discuss that some shapes in the pattern are missing. Have children complete the patterns shown and then type in the rule for the pattern using the number for each shape.

When children are comfortable completing patterns, have them make their own patterns on the computer and challenge each other to complete them.

CLOSE   Guide children to summarize the lesson:

■ **How does a computer help you make different patterns?** [Possible response: A computer can draw shapes in a pattern for you, while you make up the rule.]

EXTRA PRACTICE

Extra Practice items are provided so that children may have an opportunity for further practice.

The Additional Practice section also provides practice you may wish to assign.

Name _____

Dollars and Cents, pages 135–136

Ring the exact amount you need.

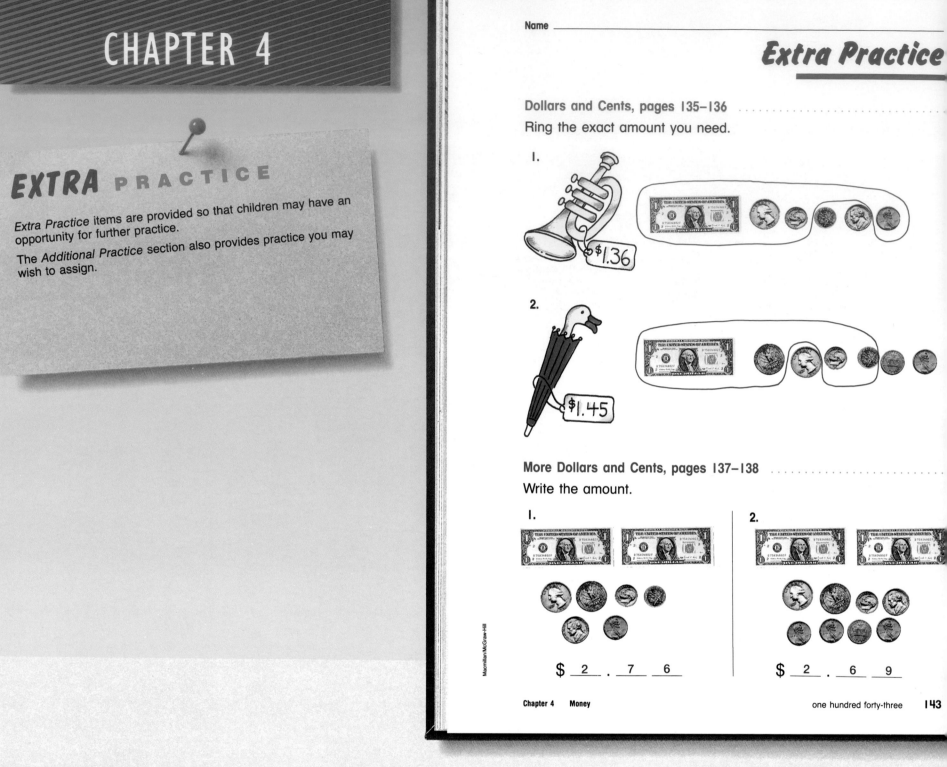

1. $1.36

2. $1.45

More Dollars and Cents, pages 137–138

Write the amount.

1. $ _2_ . _7_ _6_

2. $ _2_ . _6_ _9_

Macmillan/McGraw-Hill

Chapter 4   Money   one hundred forty-three   **143**

ADDITIONAL PRACTICE

p. 135 Have children use punchout dollars and coins.
Show these amounts with your money. Make sure you use your dollar bills.

1. $2.25	**2.** $4.35
3. $1.68	**4.** $1.97
5. $3.12	**6.** $2.59

p. 137 *Show these amounts with punchout dollars and coins. Write the amount.*

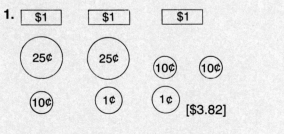

1. [$1] [$1] [$1]
(25¢) (25¢) (10¢) (10¢)
(10¢) (1¢) (1¢)   [$3.82]

2. [$1] [$1] [$1] [$1]
(25¢) (10¢)   [$4.35]

Practice Plus

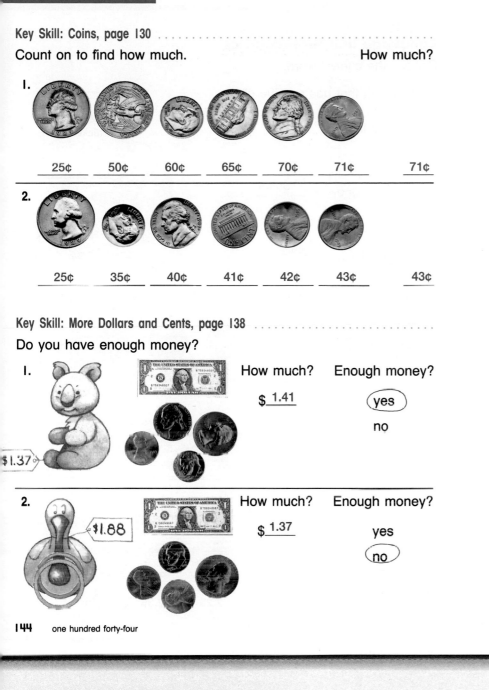

Key Skill: Coins, page 130 . . . .

Count on to find how much.   How much?

1.

25¢   50¢   60¢   65¢   70¢   71¢   71¢

2.

25¢   35¢   40¢   41¢   42¢   43¢   43¢

Key Skill: More Dollars and Cents, page 138 . . . .

Do you have enough money?

1.   How much?   Enough money?

$ 1.41   (yes)

no

$1.37

2.   How much?   Enough money?

$ 1.37   yes

$1.88   (no)

144   one hundred forty-four

PRACTICE **PLUS**

Practice Plus is provided to supply additional practice for the two key skills in this chapter.

Key Skills
    Page 130: Quarters
    Page 138: More Dollars and Cents

The *Additional Practice* also provides practice you may wish to assign for key skills in this chapter.

ADDITIONAL PRACTICE

p. 130 *Use your coins. Count on to find how much. Write how much.*

1.
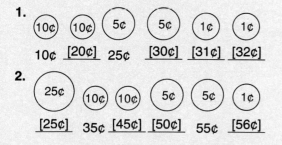
(10¢) (10¢) (5¢) (5¢) (1¢) (1¢)
10¢ [20¢] 25¢ [30¢] [31¢] [32¢]

2.
(25¢) (10¢) (10¢) (5¢) (5¢) (1¢)
[25¢] 35¢ [45¢] [50¢] 55¢ [56¢]

3.
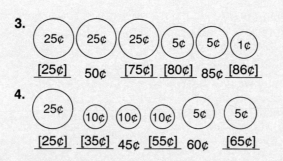
(25¢) (25¢) (25¢) (5¢) (5¢) (1¢)
[25¢] 50¢ [75¢] [80¢] 85¢ [86¢]

4.
(25¢) (10¢) (10¢) (10¢) (5¢) (5¢)
[25¢] [35¢] 45¢ [55¢] 60¢ [65¢]

p. 138 *Show these amounts. Use your punchout dollars and coins.*

1. $2.56   **2.** $3.41

3. $1.79   **4.** $2.87

5. $1.06   **6.** $3.15

AT·A·GLANCE 145-146

OBJECTIVE
Review/test the concepts and skills presented in Chapter 4.

4A. Give the value of a group of coins.
4B. Give the value of a group of bills and coins.
4C. Solve problems including those that involve using data from a picture.

Teacher Resources
Testing Program, pp. 37–48

Name _____

Chapter Review/Test

Language and Mathematics

Choose the correct word.

1. The coin that has a value of

   5 cents is a _____nickel_____ .

2. The coin that has a value of

   25 cents is a _____quarter_____ .

3. $1.00 is another way

   to write I _____dollar_____ .

> quarter
> nickel
> dollar

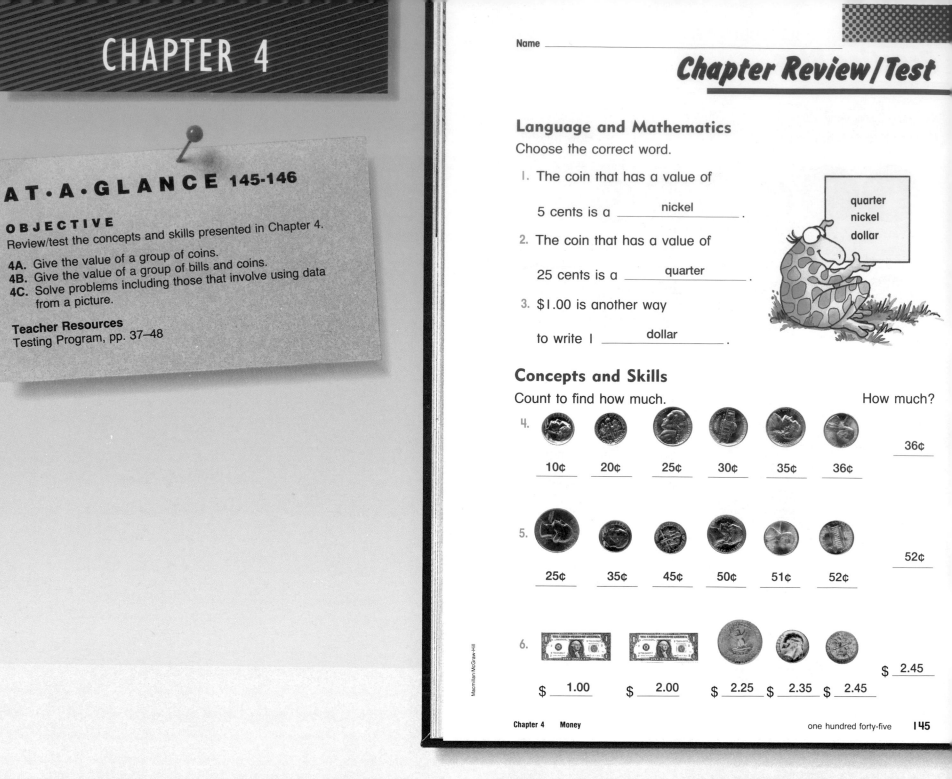

Concepts and Skills

Count to find how much.   How much?

4.

| 10¢ | 20¢ | 25¢ | 30¢ | 35¢ | 36¢ |

_____36¢_____

5.

| 25¢ | 35¢ | 45¢ | 50¢ | 51¢ | 52¢ |

_____52¢_____

6.

| $ 1.00 | $ 2.00 | $ 2.25 | $ 2.35 | $ 2.45 |

$ _____2.45_____

Macmillan/McGraw-Hill

USING THE CHAPTER REVIEW/TEST

The Chapter Review/Test may be used as a review to survey children's knowledge and understanding of the chapter material. Or it may be used as a test to formally assess children's understanding of the concepts and skills taught in the chapter. If used as a test, you may wish to assign one or more of the resources listed in *Reinforcement and Remediation* on p. 146 after reviewing children's test results.

If the Chapter Review/Test is used as a review, you may wish to have children work in pairs to complete it. Have them talk about different ways to make 25¢. Then, you can use the Chapter Tests—Forms A, B, and C—provided in the *Testing Program Blackline Master and Teacher's Manual* for testing purposes. Any of these forms may be used for pretesting, posttesting, or retesting.

A performance assessment activity for the key concept in this chapter is provided on page 147.

Ring the set of coins needed to buy the item.

7.

Ring the exact amount you need to buy the item.

8.

Problem Solving

Solve.

9. How much does the

 pitcher cost? ___18¢___

10. Al bought the pail.
 Lea bought the shovel.
 How much did they spend

 in all? ___16¢___

11. Who spent more money,

 Al or Lea? ___Al___

12. How much more does
 the pitcher cost than the pail? ___9¢___

146   one hundred forty-six

Reinforcement and Remediation

CHAP. OBJ.	TEST ITEMS	PUPIL'S EDITION pp.			TEACHER'S EDITION pp.	TEACHER RESOURCES	
		Lesson	Extra Practice	Practice Plus	Alt. Teaching Strategy	Reteaching	Practice
4A	1–2, 4–5, 7	127–130	134	144	128, 130	42, 43	42, 43
4B	3, 6, 8	135–138	143				
4C	9–12	131–132, 134		144	136, 138	45, 46	45, 46
		139–140				44, 47	44, 47

For Students Acquiring English (SAE)

Before beginning the Chapter Review/Test with SAE children, scan the pages for any unfamiliar vocabulary that should be pretaught. You may wish to pair or group SAE children with non-SAE children. You may also wish to repeat some of the activities and techniques for SAE children that were suggested earlier in this chapter.

CHAPTER 4

AT·A·GLANCE p. 147

OBJECTIVE
Assess whether children can solve problems involving the value of money.

MATERIALS
Manipulatives 2 $1 bills, 2 Q, 2 D, 1 N, 5 P coins (or punchouts) per pair

Teacher Resources
Performance Assessment booklet, pp. 20–22

For Students Acquiring English (SAE)

Before beginning the performance assessment with SAE children, scan the page for any unfamiliar vocabulary that should be pretaught. You may wish to pair or group SAE children with non-SAE children. You may also wish to repeat some of the activities and techniques for SAE children that were suggested earlier in this chapter.

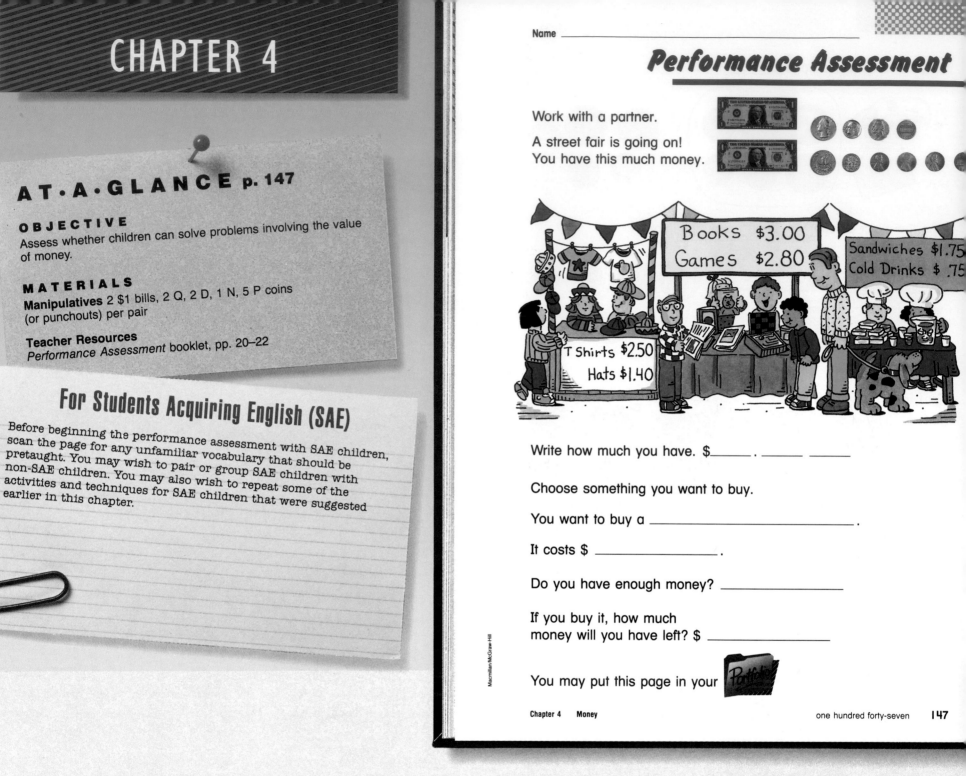

Name _____

Performance Assessment

Work with a partner.

A street fair is going on!
You have this much money.

Books $3.00
Games $2.80
Sandwiches $1.75
Cold Drinks $ .75
T Shirts $2.50
Hats $1.40

Write how much you have. $_____ . _____ _____

Choose something you want to buy.

You want to buy a _____ .

It costs $ _____ .

Do you have enough money? _____

If you buy it, how much
money will you have left? $ _____

You may put this page in your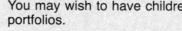

Chapter 4   Money

one hundred forty-seven **147**

USING PERFORMANCE ASSESSMENT
The Performance Assessment activity may be used to informally assess children's understanding of the key concept(s) of the chapter. Additional assessment activities and Math Journal Options are provided in the *Performance Assessment* booklet.

Performing the Activity
Assign children to work in pairs. Distribute play money. You may want to act as a banker for any coin exchanges. Have them work together to complete the problem. Children should record their results individually.

Evaluation Guidelines
Use these criteria to help determine the holistic score for each child. The holistic scoring scale can be found in the Teacher's Reference Section.

- Can children find the number facts they need from the picture?
- Can children compute the money amount they have?
- Can children choose the correct operation to solve their problems?

[Example Response: A problem might be: Nancy wants to buy a T-shirt for $2.50. If she buys it, she will have $.30 left. $2.80 − $2.50 = $.30]

If children do not have a full understanding of the key concept(s), you may wish to use the Alternative Teaching Strategies or the MAC Activities within the chapter.

You may wish to have children put their final revised work in their portfolios.

A formal assessment of the concepts and skills taught in this chapter is provided on pages 145–146.

147   Chapter 4 • Performance Assessment

Enrichment For All

Making Change

Stan bought a pencil that cost 28¢. He paid the clerk 50¢. What was his change?

Start with the **cost** and count up to the amount **paid**.

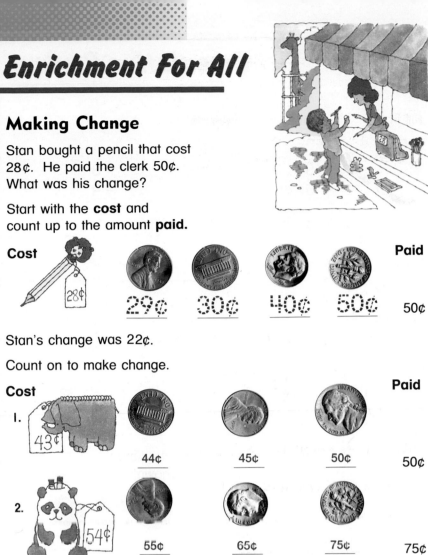

Cost					Paid
28¢	29¢	30¢	40¢	50¢	50¢

Stan's change was 22¢.

Count on to make change.

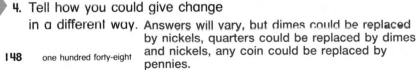

Cost				Paid
1. 43¢	44¢	45¢	50¢	50¢
2. 54¢	55¢	65¢	75¢	75¢
3. 69¢	70¢	75¢	$1.00	$1.00

4. Tell how you could give change in a different way. Answers will vary, but dimes could be replaced by nickels, quarters could be replaced by dimes and nickels, any coin could be replaced by pennies.

AT·A·GLANCE p. 148

OBJECTIVE
Count money.

ASSIGNMENT GUIDE

COURSE	EXERCISES
Basic	p. 148: 1–4
Average	p. 148: 1–4
Challenge	p. 148: 1–4

MATERIALS
Manipulatives   10 P, 10 N, 5 D, 1 Q coin models (or punch-outs) per child

For Students Acquiring English (SAE)

Read the page aloud to SAE children, explaining and demonstrating key vocabulary. Make sure SAE children understand the word **change** as used on the page. Use visuals, gestures, and body movements to convey meaning. To check comprehension of the directions, ask SAE children to restate them. It will be especially helpful to SAE children to use coins or punchouts as they complete ex. 1–4.

 **PREPARE**   **WARM-UP**   To prepare children to make change, display play coins on a table, such as 1 nickel, 1 quarter, 1 dime, and 1 penny. Hold up each coin and have it identified. Ask children to tell the value of each coin.

TEACH   **DISCUSSING**   Read the word problem at the top of the page with the children.

■ **Why should Stan get change?** [He paid the clerk 50¢ for a 27¢ item. He gave the clerk more money than the price of the item.]

Work through the example at the top of the page with the children.

PRACTICE·APPLY   Have children complete ex. 1–4. For ex. 4, call on volunteers to tell how they would give change in a different way. You may wish to have children show their answers with play coins.

CLOSE   Guide children to summarize the lesson:

■ **If you gave a store owner 75¢ to buy a quart of milk that cost 68¢, how much change would you get?** [7¢]

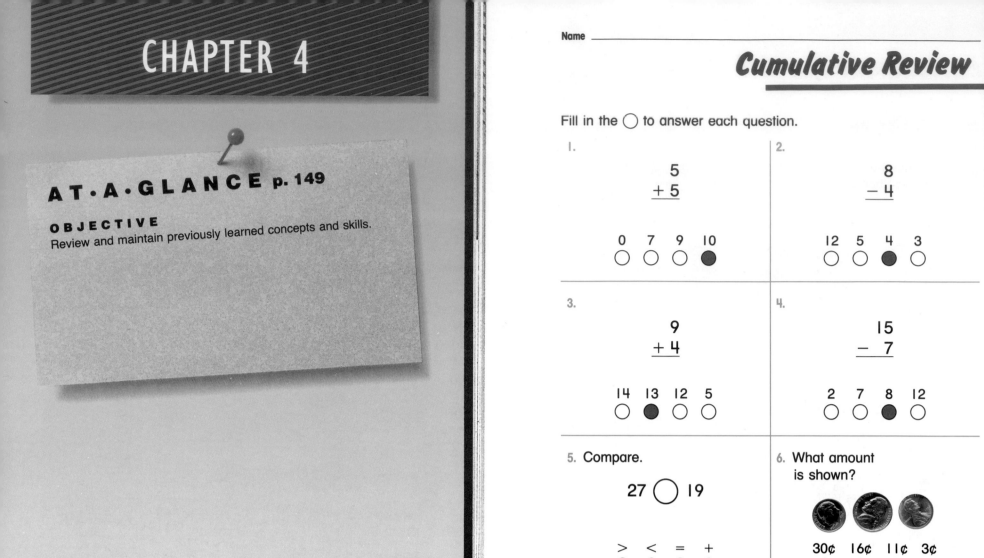

Name _____

Cumulative Review

Fill in the ○ to answer each question.

1.
$$5 + 5$$

| 0 | 7 | 9 | 10 |
| ○ | ○ | ○ | ● |

2.
$$8 - 4$$

| 12 | 5 | 4 | 3 |
| ○ | ○ | ● | ○ |

3.
$$9 + 4$$

| 14 | 13 | 12 | 5 |
| ○ | ● | ○ | ○ |

4.
$$15 - 7$$

| 2 | 7 | 8 | 12 |
| ○ | ○ | ● | ○ |

5. Compare.

$$27 \bigcirc 19$$

| > | < | = | + |
| ● | ○ | ○ | ○ |

6. What amount is shown?

| 30¢ | 16¢ | 11¢ | 3¢ |
| ○ | ● | ○ | ○ |

7. Which number sentence solves the problem?
Alison bought 4 red party hats.
She bought 6 blue hats.
How many party hats did she buy?

● $4 + 6 = 10$
○ $6 - 4 = 2$

Macmillan/McGraw-Hill

USING THE CUMULATIVE REVIEW
The Cumulative Review is presented in a multiple-choice format to provide practice in taking a standardized test. It gives children an opportunity to review previously learned skills. An answer sheet, similar to those used when taking standardized tests, can be found in the *Testing Program Blackline Masters and Teacher's Manual.*

The table that follows correlates the review items to the lesson pages on which the skills are taught.

Review Items	Text Pages	Review Items	Text Pages
1	35–36	5	75–76
2	29–30	6	127–128
3	100	7	39–40
4	108		

Testing Program Blackline Masters
In addition to the Cumulative Review in the Pupil's Edition, there are quarterly Cumulative Tests and an End-Year Test. These tests are multiple choice and provide additional opportunities for children to practice taking standardized tests.

Cumulative Tests measure children's performance on major skills and concepts taught during the previous quarters. The **End-Year Test** measures children's performance on major skills and concepts taught throughout the year.

Home Activity

Your child has been learning how to count money. Here is an activity that you can do with your child to help him or her practice this skill.

Materials:
coins
dollar bills
slips of paper

Directions:

1. Use slips of paper to make "price tags" for several items in the house. Prices should be under $10.00.

2. Give your child an assortment of coins and bills. Let your child "buy" the items by showing you the exact amount of money that is written on each price tag.

Variations:

1. Ask your child to show more than one way to make the same amount.

2. Let your child make up some price tags for items that you can "buy." Your child should be able to tell you if you have shown the correct amount.

150   one hundred fifty

A·T·A·GLANCE p. 150

OBJECTIVE

Give family members an opportunity to share in their child's mathematics learning.

For Students Acquiring English (SAE)

Before assigning this Home Activity to SAE children, find out if someone at home will be able to work with them in English. If not, prepare them to complete the activity independently at home. Explain the directions of the activity and ask SAE children to restate them so you can check comprehension. Scan the page and preteach any difficult vocabulary or phrases that they may not know. If you feel that an SAE child will need extra help with the activity, you might assign that student a non-SAE partner and arrange a time for them to work on the activity in or out of school.

USING THE ACTIVITY

Have children look at the page. Explain that the page has an activity that an adult in the family can help them complete. Read the page with the children, making sure that they understand what needs to be done. Tell children that they will do this page at home.

MEASUREMENT

> **"IN CHAPTER 5, you will introduce your children to measurement. You will also have the opportunity to explore the concept of attributes, units of measure, and using standard units."**

Notes
FROM THE AUTHOR

Here are some notes on the concepts presented in this chapter and how your children can apply them to solve problems.

ATTRIBUTES

Encourage your children to recognize their own familiarity with measurement concepts and choosing an attribute—length, weight, temperature, or capacity. When children compare heights, talk about how cold it is, or discuss which glass holds the most milk, they are choosing an attribute. Children should use their measurement experiences to help them make accurate comparisons and measurements.

To compare the lengths of two objects children learn to align the objects at one end. They should understand that in Example **A**, for example, it is obvious that the top pencil is longer because the pencils are aligned.

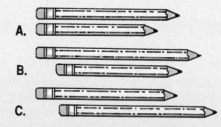

Children should recognize that in **B** they can tell that the top pencil is longer but cannot tell how much longer, and that in **C** there is no good point of reference for comparison.

Audrey Jackson

DEVELOPING MEASURING SKILLS

Your children learn to select the correct unit of measure for a given attribute and to compare it with the item to be measured to determine how many units are needed to match.

Children discover the need for standard units by first using arbitrary units, such as their own feet, to measure length.

To compare the capacity of containers, children take part in activities in which they explore how many small containers it would take to fill a larger container.

In the same way, by comparing objects to determine which is heavier (or lighter), children gain a foundation for measuring in standard units.

USING STANDARD UNITS

Introduce children to the following standard units.

Metric Units Length: centimeter, decimeter, meter. Capacity: liter. Mass: kilogram. Temperature: °Celsius.

Customary Units Length: inch, foot, yard. Capacity: cup, pint, quart. Weight: pound. Temperature: °Fahrenheit.

Participating in many measuring and comparing activities enables children to develop an intuitive feel and mental image of standard units and other benchmark measures. Children have many hands-on experiences using rulers, scales, thermometers and measuring devices for measuring capacity.

PROBLEM SOLVING

In **Problem Solving** your children (1) use number sense to solve problems and (2) solve problems by choosing the operation.

In **Thinking Mathematically** children use logical reasoning to compare capacity and mass. Children place the cutout fish in their correct containers and order the dogs by mass in the pet store.

In **Decision Making** children use information to plan a garden. Children decide where on a 30 x 30 inch grid they will plant flowers that must be placed certain numbers of inches apart.

Mathematics and Literature

■ To use literature in the application of mathematics. ■ To promote appreciation of the contributions of all cultures to mathematics. ■ Children are introduced to a Chinese folk song in the K–2 *Math Anthology* on page 157. By reading and singing "Spring in China," children explore measurement and time.

CULTURAL DIVERSITY

CHAPTER 5 · ORGANIZER

CHAPTER PLANNING GUIDE

CHAPTER OBJECTIVES
WITH STANDARDIZED TEST CORRELATIONS

A. Estimate and measure length in metric and customary units	SAT, ITBS, CTBS
B. Estimate and measure capacity using metric and customary units	SAT, ITBS
C. Estimate and measure mass using metric units and weight using customary units	SAT, ITBS
D. Read temperature in °C and °F	ITBS
E. Solve problems including those that involve choosing the correct operation	MAT, CAT, SAT, ITBS, CTBS

SUGGESTED PACING-15 DAYS

LESSONS	NCTM STANDARDS	ASSIGNMENTS Basic/Average/Challenge	STUDENT EDITION Extra Practice/ Practice Plus	Manip. Plus	Reteach	Practice	Enrich	MAC Activities
Chapter Opener: *How Big Is a Foot?* page 151	1, 2, 3, 4, 10	p. 151: All						
✔ 1 Measurement 👥 page 152	1, 2, 3, 10	p. 152: All						
✔ 2 Using Centimeters 👥 pages 153–154	1, 2, 3, 10	p. 153: 1–4; p. 154: 1–5	pp. 164, 178	23	48	48	48	95, 96
✔ 3 Using Centimeters, Decimeters, and Meters 👥 pages 155–156	1, 2, 3, 10	p. 155: 1–4; p. 156: 1–8		24	49	49	49	97, 98
✔ 4 Measuring Capacity 👥 pages 157–158	1, 2, 3, 10	p. 157: 1–4; p. 158: 1–8	p. 164	25	50	50	50	99, 100
✔ 5 Measuring Mass page 159	1, 2, 3, 10	p. 159: 1–6	p. 164	26, 27	51	51	51	101, 102
6 Measuring Temperature page 160	1, 2, 3, 10	p. 160: 1–4	p. 164		52	52	52	103, 104
7 PS: Using Number Sense pages 161–162	1, 2, 3, 6	p. 161: 1–2; p. 162: 1–5			53	53	53	105, 106
✔ 8 PS: Thinking Mathematically 👥 page 163	1, 2, 3, 10	p. 163: All						
✔ 9 Using Inches 👥 pages 165–166	1, 2, 3, 10	p. 165: 1–4; p. 166: 1–6	pp. 177, 178		54	54	54	107, 108
✔ 10 Inch, Foot, and Yard 👥 pages 167–168	1, 2, 3, 10	p. 167: 1–2; p. 168: 1–8		28	55	55	55	109, 110
✔ 11 Measuring Capacity 👥 pages 169–170	1, 2, 3, 10	p. 169: 1–4; p. 170: 1–4, Challenge	p. 177	29	56	56	56	111, 112
✔ 12 Measuring Weight 👥 page 171	1, 2, 3, 10	p. 171: 1–6	p. 177	30	57	57	57	113, 114
13 Measuring Temperature page 172	1, 2, 3, 10	p. 172: 1–4	p. 177		58	58	58	115, 116
14 PS: Choosing the Operation pages 173–174	1, 2, 3, 7, 8	p. 173: 1; p. 174: 1–4	p. 177		59	59	59	117, 118
15 PS: Decision Making 👥 page 175	1, 2, 3, 10	p. 175: 1–2						

Technology: Computer page 176

Chapter Review/Test pages 179–180

Performance Assessment page 181

Cumulative Review page 183

Enrichment for All/Home Activity pages 182, 184

NATIONAL COUNCIL OF TEACHERS OF MATHEMATICS Grades K–4

1. Problem Solving
2. Communication
3. Reasoning
4. Connections
5. Estimation
6. Number Sense and Numeration
7. Concepts of Whole Number Operations
8. Whole Number Computation
9. Geometry and Spatial Sense
10. Measurement
11. Statistics and Probability
12. Fractions and Decimals
13. Patterns and Relationships

✔ Activity   👥 Cooperative Learning

MEETING the NCTM STANDARDS

Problem Solving

Strategies and Skills	• using number sense pp. 161–162 • choosing the operation pp. 173–174
Applications	• **Decision Making** lesson p. 175 • **Problem of the Day** TE pp. 152, 154B, 156B, 158B, 159C, 160C, 162B, 166B, 168B, 170B, 171C, 172C, 174B
Mathematical Investigations	• **Thinking Mathematically** lesson p. 163

Communication

Language	• using the language of mathematics TE pp. 153–154, 155–156, 157–158, 159, 160, 165–166, 167–168, 169–170, 171, 172
Oral/Written	• using cooperative learning activities pp. 152, 154, 156, 157, 163, 166, 168, 169, 171, 175; TE pp. 150I–150P • **Journal Writing** opportunities TE pp. 152, 154, 159A, 160A, 170, 172A

Reasoning

Critical Thinking	• answering questions that analyze and extend concepts pp. 151, 152, 153, 155, 157, 166, 176

Connections

To other subject areas	• Literature p. 151; Literature TE pp. 151–152, 167, 172
To all cultures	• Chinese folk song, "Spring in China," *Math Anthology* p. 157

Concept Development

Measurement	• using models to explore the concept of measurement p. 152 • estimating and measuring length using metric and customary units pp. 153–154, 155–156, 165–166, 167–168; TE pp. 150I–150J, 150N • estimating and measuring capacity, mass, and weight using metric and customary units pp. 157–158, 159, 169–170, 171; TE pp. 150L–150M, 150O–150P • reading a thermometer to find temperature in °C and °F pp. 160, 172

ASSESSMENT OPTIONS

PERFORMANCE ASSESSMENT

Preassessment Activity

Before beginning Chapter 5, display a pencil. Have children discuss and write about ways to measure the length of the pencil. Display a jug or bottle of juice. Have children discuss and write about how they would guess and measure the amount of juice the container holds.

Ongoing Assessment

The Ongoing Assessment cards under MEETING INDIVIDUAL NEEDS on TE pp. 159A and 170 provide criteria and questions for assessing children's understanding of the key mathematical concepts developed in the chapter.

Journal Writing opportunities encourage children to write about mathematics. Their responses can be recorded either pictorially or in words. The journal writing opportunities on the Ongoing Assessment cards also allow you to assess children's understanding of the lessons.

In addition to the Ongoing Assessment cards, other assessment and journal writing opportunities in this chapter include:

• **CLOSE** TE pp. 152, 154, 160A, 172A

Performance Assessment Activity

The Performance Assessment activity on p. 181 provides an alternative to formal assessment. This activity assesses children's understanding of the key concepts of the chapter.

For performance assessment activities that are keyed to individual chapter objectives, see the *Performance Assessment* booklet.

BUILDING A PORTFOLIO

Children should be encouraged to keep a selection of their best work in portfolios. The portfolios provide a way of documenting children's growth in understanding mathematical concepts. Portfolio opportunities in this chapter include:

• **Performance Assessment** p. 181
• **Class Project** TE p. 175A

If you wish to provide additional opportunities for portfolio work, you may choose to use:

• **MAC Activities** 96, 99, 100, 103, 104, 109, 110, 111, 115, 117, 118

You may also wish to have children include their journal writing from the Ongoing Assessment on TE pp. 159A and 170 in their portfolio.

Formal Assessment

The **Chapter Review/Test** assesses children's understanding of the concepts and skills developed in the chapter. The **Cumulative Review** assesses children's understanding of the concepts and skills developed from the beginning of the year.

You can use **Form A** or **Form B** of the **Chapter Test** found in the *Testing Program Blackline Masters and Teacher's Manual* if you wish to use a multiple-choice

format to assess children's understanding of the chapter concepts and skills. You can use **Form C** if you wish to use a free-response format. Any of the forms may be used as a pretest, posttest, or for retesting.

The **COMPUTER MANAGEMENT SYSTEM**, or **CMS**, enables you to score **Forms A** and **B** of the **Chapter Test** quickly and automatically. It also prescribes learning activities based on children's test results.

For more information about Assessment, see the *Professional Handbook*.

Common Error and Remediation

The Teacher's Edition notes for each Develop/Understand (Transitional/Abstract) lesson provide a common error analysis and a remediation activity. Some errors defy quick analysis and can only be identified by interviewing the child.

ALTERNATIVE TEACHING STRATEGY

Alternative Teaching Strategies appear frequently in the chapter. These strategies provide other presentations of the lessons for children who might benefit from instruction in different learning modalities: kinesthetic, visual, and/or auditory.

For Students Acquiring English (SAE)

Measurement activities in this chapter will require that SAE children understand comparative terms such as **more, less, same, most, least, big, bigger, biggest, long, longer,** and **longest.** Use picture cards or real objects to demonstrate these concepts. Preteach the vocabulary. For example, say: *The orange ribbon is longer than the purple ribbon, but the green ribbon is the longest.*

SAE notes appear periodically in the chapter. These notes provide suggestions for how to work with children to improve comprehension and build vocabulary.

MANIPULATIVES WORKSHOP

Metric and customary measurement tools are used in this chapter to explore length. They provide children with opportunities to read and compare units of measure and to develop their measurement sense.

USING MANIPULATIVES

Here a child finds the length of a pencil in centimeters.

The child aligns the end of the pencil with the 0 end of the ruler.

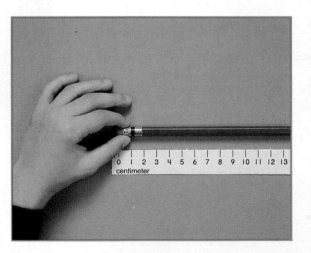

The child finds the length of the pencil by noting the number on the ruler where the pencil ends.

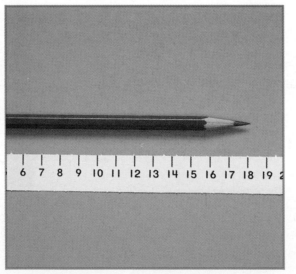

Here the child measures the same pencil with an inch ruler, again aligning the end of the pencil with the 0 end of the ruler.

The pencil is about 7 inches long.

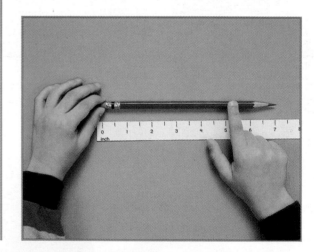

MAKING MANIPULATIVES   See the Manipulatives section of the *Professional Handbook* for materials that can be used as a substitute for the various measurement tools.

COOPERATIVE LEARNING WORKSHOP

GETTING STARTED

Individuals and the Group: Consider using team-building structures with groups of two pairs which emphasize the benefits of individual diversity (alternative methods, viewpoints, resources) while building group unity.

The **one-and-all** structure helps four children talk about similarities and differences within their group. Each group folds one large square sheet of paper into quarters, and then draws a large circle in the middle. Each member puts his or her name on one quarter of the paper, and the word *All* in the center of the circle. They first try to think of things to go in the center circle that they all have in common and draw a symbol for each. Then they think of things that are true only for each child and each child draws these in his or her outside area. Remind the children that they must check with all the other members to be sure someone does not have the same characteristic or preference before they draw its symbol in their area.

IDEAS TO TRY

How Long? The human body was the first source of units of measurement. Have groups investigate such things as "how long a line do all of us make, stretched out head to toes?" (outside activity), "how many spread hands does it take to measure from one end of the chalkboard to the other?" Partners help each other make measurements to answer questions such as "what differences do we have in arm span, leg lengths, or space between little finger and elbow?"

You can apply the above partner-building ideas in these lessons:
5-1 *Measurement* p. 152
5-2 *Using Centimeters* pp. 153–154
5-3 *Using Centimeters, Decimeters, and Meters* pp. 155–156
5-9 *Using Inches* pp. 165–166

Cooperative Skills: When starting to work together to apply measurement principles to everyday tasks, children need the skills of **asking for help, giving help, valuing differences,** and **restating** other people's strategies and solutions. Assign only one of these skills per lesson and find many ways for children to practice it in pairs and then in groups of four. The group then celebrates successes and sets goals for improving the skill next time.

You can apply the above cooperative skills in these lessons:
5-4 *Measuring Capacity* pp. 157–158
5-5 *Measuring Mass* p. 159
5-11 *Measuring Capacity* pp. 169–170
5-12 *Measuring Weight* p. 171

SEE ALSO

Cooperative Learning Tip for lessons 5-7 Problem Solving p. 162; 5-8 Thinking Mathematically p. 163A; 5-15 Decision Making p. 175A

The Cooperative Learning section of the *Professional Handbook* for additional information

---

INTERACTIVE BULLETIN BOARD

SETUP Collect small objects, and place each group of objects in a container. Label each container. Give each child a sheet of paper. Have each child trace his or her hand on the paper and then carefully cut it out.

PROCEDURE Have children, in turn, reach into one of the containers and pick up as many of the objects as they can with one hand. Then have each child count the handful and, on the paper hand, record the number and the name of the object. Display children's paper hands on the bulletin board.

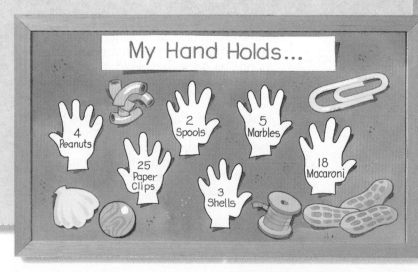

For use before LESSON 5.2, pp. 153-154

23

MEASURING LENGTH WITH ARBITRARY UNITS

OBJECTIVE
Measure length in arbitrary units.

MATERIALS
Classroom Materials
1 yard of string per child, markers, labels

PAIRS ACTIVITY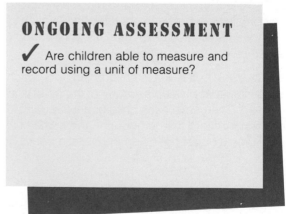

Assign children to work in pairs. Give each child a length of string about 1 yard long. Tell children that they are going to measure themselves using a unit of measurement called "wrists."

Demonstrate how children should use the string to measure each other's wrists. Wrap a length of string once around your wrist and mark the string to show the unit. Then fold the string on the mark and make another mark. Continue until the string is about ten "wrists" long.

Have children work together to find their wrist measurements. Help children make their measuring strings as necessary. Fold a small self-sticking label over the end of each child's measuring string and write the child's name on it.

Discuss that children should have partners help them to use their measuring strings to measure their own necks, arms, and finger lengths. Demonstrate with a volunteer how to measure each and record the measures on the chalkboard. Use your own measuring string for your own measures.

Neck	2 wrists
Arm	5 wrists
Finger	$\frac{1}{2}$ wrist

Then have partners work together to measure and record. Remind them that each child's measurements should be taken with that child's measuring string.

EXTENDING THE ACTIVITY

Have children write a story about how they might use the wrist measurements they recorded. Have children share their stories.

ONGOING ASSESSMENT

✔ Are children able to measure and record using a unit of measure?

For use before LESSON 5.3, pp. 155-156

24
DECIMETER AND METER

OBJECTIVE
Explore measuring length in decimeters and meters.

MATERIALS
Classroom Materials
tape; measuring string (EXTENDING THE ACTIVITY only)
Manipulatives metric measuring tape* per child
Teacher Resources
*Teacher Aid 7

WHOLE GROUP ACTIVITY ⬍

Give each child a metric measuring tape. Teacher Aid 7 may be used to make a metric measuring tape by overlapping the pieces of the ruler and taping them.

Demonstrate how to use the ruler to measure in centimeters. Have children measure their desks in centimeters.

Explain that another way to use the ruler is to read the darker numbers below the centimeter marks.

■ **How many centimeters are there in 1 decimeter?** [10]

Have children measure their desks in decimeters. Compare the centimeter and decimeter measurements.

■ **Did the length of your desk change?** [No, only the unit changed.]

Have children measure other objects in centimeters and decimeters. Then discuss whether both units are always appropriate.

■ **Should you use decimeters to measure a paper clip? Why or why not?** [No. The unit is too large.]

Introduce **meter** to children using the length of the entire tape. Discuss the relationships between a meter, a decimeter, and a centimeter. Have children measure the length and width of the room in meters.

EXTENDING THE ACTIVITY

Have children use their metric measuring tapes to measure one of their wrists on their own measuring strings from Manipulatives Plus 23.

■ **How many centimeters is your wrist?**

■ **How many decimeters is your wrist?** [Answers will vary.]

ONGOING ASSESSMENT

✔ Are children able to measure length using metric units of measure?

For use before LESSON 5.4, pp. 157-158

25

EXPLORING CAPACITY

OBJECTIVE
Explore the concept of capacity.

MATERIALS
Classroom Materials
various-sized unbreakable containers, plastic buckets of water, plastic buckets of sand; eyedroppers and nickels (EXTENDING THE ACTIVITY only)

SMALL GROUP ACTIVITY

Assign children to work in small groups of three. Provide each group with containers of several sizes labeled A, B, C . . ., a bucket of water, and a bucket of sand.

Have each group find the smallest container in their group of containers. Discuss that the group should decide on one of the other containers to measure. Then each child in the group should estimate how many smaller containers of sand will fill the chosen container.

Children should work together to pour and measure the sand from the small containers to the chosen containers. Then have them compare their estimates to the actual measure. Have children repeat the activity using water.

■ **Do the containers hold more water or sand?**
[They hold the same amount of each.]

Have children repeat the activity using the other containers. Then pose the following question:

■ **Does the amount of water in the small container change each time we pour it into a different container?** [Answers may vary.]

Pour the same amount of water into several variously sized and shaped containers. Then pour the water from each into a measuring device to show that the measures are the same.

EXTENDING THE ACTIVITY

Display an eyedropper and describe that a drop can be a small unit of measure. Distribute a nickel and an eyedropper to each small group of three. Have groups make predictions on how many drops of water will fit on a nickel, then conduct the experiment and describe the results.

ONGOING ASSESSMENT

✔ Are children able to measure capacity using a unit of measure?

MANIPULATIVES plus ACTIVITY

For use before LESSON 5.5, p. 159

26

EXPLORING MASS

OBJECTIVE
Explore the concept of mass.

MATERIALS
Classroom Materials
small classroom objects to measure, paper clips and beans to use as units of measure
Manipulatives 📦 to use as units of measure, balance

WHOLE GROUP ACTIVITY 🔃

Display a balance and tell children that it is used to measure how heavy things are.

Display various small classroom objects. Have a volunteer choose one of the objects to measure and place it on one of the pans of the balance.

Have another volunteer place paper clips on the other pan until the pans are balanced, or even.

■ **How many paper clips does the object measure?**

Then have other volunteers measure the same object using beans, and then cubes. Guide children to see that the measures are different because the units are different, but the object does not change.

EXTENDING THE ACTIVITY

Place the balance in an activity center and allow all children the opportunity to measure objects using the balance, paper clips, beans, and cubes, throughout the year.

ONGOING ASSESSMENT

✔ Are children able to measure mass using a unit of measure?

27

GRAMS AND KILOGRAMS

OBJECTIVE
Explore mass in grams and kilograms.

MATERIALS
Classroom Materials
objects to measure, paper clips and beans to use as units of measure
Manipulatives to use as units of measure, balance, gram and kilogram measures or objects that measure 1 gram and 1 kilogram

WHOLE GROUP ACTIVITY

Display a balance and review how it is used. Also display sets of paper clips, beans, and cubes, and review how these objects could be used as units of measure.

Then show children a gram measure and explain that it is a standard unit of measure. Demonstrate on the balance that a gram measure is about the same as a paper clip.

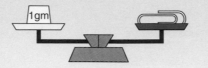

Discuss that grams are often used to measure very light objects.

Then show children a kilogram measure and explain that it is also a standard unit of measure. Discuss that a kilogram measure is about the same as 1,000 paper clips.

Discuss that kilograms are often used to measure heavy objects.

Have children measure various objects using the kilogram and gram measures. Tell them to first estimate if the object is more or less than the unit and then measure it on the balance.

EXTENDING THE ACTIVITY

Place the balance in an activity center and allow all children the opportunity to measure objects using grams and kilograms throughout the year.

ONGOING ASSESSMENT

✓ Are children able to measure mass using grams and kilograms?

For use before LESSON 5.10, pp. 167-168

28
INCH, FOOT, AND YARD

OBJECTIVE
Measure in inches, feet, and yards.

MATERIALS
Classroom Materials
yardstick,* string, objects to measure
Manipulatives 1 inch-ruler punchout per child (may be taped together to make yardsticks)

WHOLE GROUP ACTIVITY

Distribute 1-inch ruler to each child. Have children examine the ruler. Review the inch as a unit and how to use the ruler to measure. Introduce the term *foot*.

■ **Look at your ruler. How many inches in a foot?** [12]

Assign children to work in pairs. Have them measure the lengths of their feet and tell if their feet are longer or shorter than a foot.

Then have them measure the width of the hallway, first with rulers and then with their feet by using heel-to-toe steps. Have them compare both measures.

Have children cut two pieces of string to show the width of the hallway. Then lay one out to show a straight road and the other to show a winding road. Have children discuss whether the lengths of the roads are the same or different. To check, have them measure both pieces of string in feet.

Ask children to estimate how many feet equal the length of a yardstick. Then place three punchout rulers along the yardstick to show that 3 feet equal 1 yard.

Have children measure the length and width of the school yard in yards.

EXTENDING THE ACTIVITY

After introducing the units, have children measure and record their heights in feet and inches. Repeat at two-month intervals and have children graph their growth rates.

ONGOING ASSESSMENT

✓ Are children able to measure length using inches, feet, and yards?

**For use before
LESSON 5.11,
pp. 169-170**

29
EXPLORING
CAPACITY

OBJECTIVE
Explore measuring
capacity.

MATERIALS
Classroom Materials
1 cup measure, 1 pint
measure, 1 quart measure,
about 3 quarts of beans or
sand in a pail, unbreakable
various-sized containers to
be measured (such as a
small mixing bowl, a
pitcher, a large drink cup);
masking tape

PAIRS ACTIVITY

Use tape to label the cup, pint, and quart measures
"small," "medium," and "large." Assign children to
work in pairs. Provide each pair with 1 cup measure, 1 pint measure, 1 quart measure, 3 quarts of
beans or sand in a pail, 1 small mixing bowl, 1
pitcher, and 1 large drink cup.

Identify each object. Then discuss the activity:

■ **Choose one of the 3 containers to measure.**

■ **Estimate whether the container holds less
than, more than, or the same as the small measure.**

■ **Measure the container by pouring beans from
the small measure into the container.**

■ **Next try estimating and measuring the same
container using the medium measure, and then
the large measure.**

Then have children use pouring to find the following
quantities:

   [2] small measures = 1 medium measure
   [2] medium measures = 1 large measure
   [4] small measures = 1 large measure

■ **Now try estimating and measuring the last
two containers using the small, medium, and
large measures.**

EXTENDING THE ACTIVITY

After exploring "small," "medium," and "large" measures, introduce the terms *cup, pint,* and *quart.*
Have small groups exchange containers and use
the new terms as they measure the new containers.

ONGOING ASSESSMENT

✓ Are children able to measure capacity using units of measure?

**For use before
LESSON 5.12,
p. 171**

30

OUNCES AND POUNDS

OBJECTIVE
Explore measuring weight
in ounces and pounds.

MATERIALS
Classroom Materials
objects to be measured,
including paper clips and
beans
Manipulatives 1 balance,
a set of 1-ounce weights
and 1-pound weights, a set
of 🔲

WHOLE GROUP ACTIVITY ↕

Display a balance and review that it is used to measure how heavy things are. Show children an ounce
weight and let them feel it. Place the weight on one
pan of the balance.

■ **About how many paper clips will it take to
balance the ounce weight?** [Estimates will vary.]

Have a volunteer place paper clips on the other pan
until both pans are balanced, or even.

Repeat the activity with beans and then cubes.

Show children a pound weight and let them feel it
along with the ounce weight. Place the weight on
the balance.

■ **About how many ounces will it take to balance the pound weight?** [Estimates will vary.]

Tell children that 16 ounces equal 1 pound.

Have children measure various objects using the
ounce and pound weights. Tell them to first estimate if the object is more or less than the unit and
then measure it on the balance.

EXTENDING THE ACTIVITY

Place the balance in an activity center and allow all
children the opportunity to measure objects using
the balance, ounces, and pounds throughout the
year.

ONGOING ASSESSMENT

✔ Are children able to measure weight
using units of measure?

Mathematics and Literature

Listening and Speaking

The Read-Aloud selection can be used
with the Chapter 5 Opener and Lesson 5-1
on pages 151-152.

Tape 1, Side 2
Selection 2

How Big Is A FOOT?

BY ROLF MYLLER

Once upon a time there lived a King and his wife, the Queen. They were a happy couple for they had everything in the World.

However . . . when the Queen's birthday came near the King had a problem: What could he give to Someone who had Everything?

The King thought and he thought and he thought. Until suddenly, he had an idea! HE WOULD GIVE THE QUEEN A BED. The Queen did not have a bed because at the time beds had not been invented. So even Someone who had Everything—did not have a bed.

The King called his Prime Minister and asked him to please have a bed made.

The Prime Minister called the Chief Carpenter and asked him to please have a bed made.

The Chief Carpenter called the apprentice and told him to make a bed.

"How big is a bed?" asked the apprentice, who didn't know because at the time nobody had ever seen a bed.

"How big is a bed?" the Carpenter asked the Prime Minister.

"A good question," said the Prime Minister. And he asked the King, "HOW BIG *IS* A BED?

The King thought and he thought and he thought. Until suddenly he had an idea! THE BED MUST BE BIG ENOUGH TO FIT THE QUEEN.

The King called the Queen. He told her to put on her new pajamas and told her to lie on the floor.

The King took off his shoes and with his big feet walked carefully around the Queen. He counted that the bed must be THREE FEET WIDE AND SIX FEET LONG to be big enough to fit the Queen. (Including the crown which the Queen sometimes liked to wear to sleep.)

The King said "Thank you," to the Queen, and told the Prime Minister, who told the Chief Carpenter, who told the apprentice: "The bed must be three feet wide and six feet long to be big enough to fit the Queen." (Including the crown which she sometimes liked to wear to sleep.)

The apprentice said "Thank you," and took off his shoes, and with his little feet he measured three feet wide and six feet long and made a bed to fit the Queen.

When the King saw the bed, he thought it was beautiful. He could not wait for the Queen's Birthday. Instead, he called the Queen at once and told her to put on her new pajamas.

Then he brought out the bed and told the Queen to try it. BUT the bed was much too small for the Queen.

The King was so angry that he immediately called the Prime Minister who called the Chief Carpenter who called the jailer who threw the apprentice into jail.

The apprentice was unhappy. WHY WAS THE BED TOO SMALL FOR THE QUEEN?

He thought and he thought and he thought. Until suddenly he had an idea! A bed that was three King's feet wide and six King's feet long was naturally bigger than a bed that was three apprentice feet wide and six apprentice feet long.

"I CAN MAKE A BED TO FIT THE QUEEN IF I KNOW THE SIZE OF THE KING'S FOOT," he cried.

He explained this to the jailer, who explained it to the Chief Carpenter, who explained it to the Prime Minister, who explained it to the King, who was much too busy to go to the jail.

Instead, the King took off one shoe and called a famous sculptor. The sculptor made an exact marble copy of the King's foot. This was sent to the jail.

The apprentice took the marble copy of the King's foot, and with it he measured three feet wide and six feet long and built a bed to fit the Queen!

The Bed was ready just in time for the Queen's Birthday. The King called the Queen and told her to put on her new pajamas. Then he brought out the New Bed and told the Queen to try it. The Queen got into bed and . . . THE BED FIT THE QUEEN PERFECTLY. (Including the crown which she sometimes liked to wear to sleep.)

It was, without a doubt, the nicest gift that the Queen had ever received.

The King was very happy. He immediately called the apprentice from jail and made him a royal prince.

He ordered a big parade, and all the people came out to cheer the little apprentice prince.

And forever after, anyone who wanted to measure anything used a copy of the King's foot. And when someone said, "My bed is six feet long and three feet wide," everyone knew exactly how big it was.

Measurement

CHAPTER **5**

AT·A·GLANCE pp. 151-152

LESSON OBJECTIVES
Explore mathematical concepts through literature.
Explore the concept of measurement.

ASSIGNMENT GUIDE

COURSE	EXERCISES
Basic	p. 151: All; p. 152: All
Average	p. 151: All; p. 152: All
Challenge	p. 151: All; p. 152: All

MATERIALS
Classroom Materials drinking straws, drawing paper, markers, scissors

Teacher Resources
Math Anthology, pp. 152–153
Read-Aloud Cassette 1, Side 2, Selection 2

SKILLS TRACE
MEASUREMENT

Explore (Concrete) 152	Develop/Understand (Transitional/Abstract) 153–154, 155–156, 157–158, 159, 160, 165–166, 167–168, 169–170, 171, 172
Practice 164, 177, 178, 179–180, 213, 245, 301	**Apply** 161–162, 163, 173–174, 175, 176, 182

READ ALOUD

HOW BIG IS A FOOT?

HOW BIG IS A FOOT?
By Rolf Myller

Listen to the story *How Big Is a Foot?*
2 different units were used to measure the first bed.
Tell why the first bed was too small for the queen.

Tell why the second bed was just right.
The same unit was used to measure the second bed.

 **PREPARE** **WARM-UP** To introduce the concept of a unit of measure, have children use drinking straws to measure their desktops. Then have children measure again with straws cut to various lengths. Discuss why their measurements differ.

TEACH **DISCUSSING** Before reading the story *How Big Is a Foot?*, remind children that the word *foot* names a body part and also refers to a unit of measure.

PUPIL'S EDITION pp. 151-152

Page 151 Read *How Big Is a Foot?* found on pages 150Q–150R or in *Math Anthology* or play Read-Aloud Cassette 1, Side 2, Selection 2.

■ **What happened when the Queen tried out her new bed?** [It was too small.]

■ **What did the apprentice need to know to make a bed that would fit the Queen?** [the size of the King's foot]

■ **What did the apprentice use to make the second bed?** [a marble copy of the King's foot]

■ **In what way is the marble copy of the King's foot like a measuring stick we use today?** [It is a standard measure that does not change.]

Discuss the directives on the page. Remind children to think about the measuring units used in making each bed.

Page 152 ■ Working Together Discuss the pictures and read the directions aloud.

Measurement

Find out how your foot can be
a unit of measure.

Working Together

Use sheets of paper.
Trace around your foot.
Cut out 6 copies.

Measure your desk.

My desk is ____  long.
Answers will vary.

Compare your measurements.
Did you each get the same number? Answers will vary.
Tell why or why not. In their own words, children may note that feet of
similar lengths gave the same measurement; feet
of different lengths gave different measurements.

Check for Understanding
■ **What unit of measure will you use to measure your desk?** [a
cutout of the outline of my own foot]

GUIDED PRACTICE Have children trace around their shoe, keeping
the pencil upright. Then have them use this as a pattern to cut out 5
more copies. Have them use these units to measure their desks. For
reteaching, use Alternative Strategy.

3 PRACTICE•APPLY   **PRACTICE** Have children complete
the page and compare their
measurements.

MEETING INDIVIDUAL NEEDS

ALTERNATIVE TEACHING STRATEGY

MATERIALS construction paper, scissors

VISUAL Select one child with large feet and another child with
small feet. Using two different colors of construction paper, make
a pattern for each child's foot. Distribute these patterns and have
children make copies of their own. Then have children place the
units side-by-side and compare how many are needed to measure
the length of a desk.

CLOSE Guide children to summarize the lesson:
■ **What happens when different units of measure are used to
measure the same thing?** [The measurements will differ.]

Problem of the Day

Jeff's foot is twice as big as Chris's foot. When
Jeff measures his desk, he finds it is 4 of his feet
long. How long would the desk be if Chris used
his foot as a unit? [8 "feet" long]

AT·A·GLANCE pp. 153-154

LESSON OBJECTIVE
Estimate and measure length in centimeters.

ASSIGNMENT GUIDE

COURSE	EXERCISES
Basic	p. 153: 1–4; p. 154: 1–5
Average	p. 153: 1–4; p. 154: 1–5
Challenge	p. 153: 1–4; p. 154: 1–5
Extra Practice, p. 164	Practice Plus, p. 178

MATERIALS
Classroom Materials crayons, pencils, chalk, erasers
Manipulatives centimeter ruler punchouts per child

Teacher Resources
Reteaching 48   Practice 48   Enrichment 48
MAC Act. 95, 96

SKILLS TRACE
MEASURING LENGTH

Explore (Concrete)	Develop/Understand (Transitional/Abstract)
152	153–154, 155–156, 165–166, 167–168
Practice	Apply
164, 177, 178, 179–180, 213	161–162, 173–174, 175, 176

See **MANIPULATIVES PLUS 23**, p. 150l.

Name _____

ACTiViTY

Using Centimeters

It measures between 1 and 2. It is closer to 2.

1 centimeter
1 cm

0 1 2 3 4 5 6 7 8 9 10
centimeter

The pin is about 2 centimeters long.

How long?
Use a ⬚⬚⬚⬚⬚⬚⬚. cm ruler
Look at the picture.
Estimate. Then measure.

1. For exercises 1–3 answers will vary.

Estimate: about _____ cm   **Measure:** about __4__ cm

2.

Estimate: about _____ cm   **Measure:** about __12__ cm

3.

Estimate: about _____ cm   **Measure:** about __10__ cm

4. Talk about how to solve the problem.

My ruler is much shorter than the ribbon. How do I measure the ribbon?

Answers will vary. Possible answer: Use the ruler to measure parts of the ribbon, one part at a time.

Chapter 5   Measurement   one hundred fifty-three   **153**

Macmillan/McGraw-Hill

PREPARE **WARM-UP** To prepare children for measuring length, demonstrate how they can use their handspans to measure the length or width of their desks. Record each child's measurement on the chalkboard. Point out that the measurements of the same-size desks are different and explain why. [Each child has a different-sized hand.]

TEACH **DISCUSSING** Remind children of the different results that were obtained when they used their handspans to measure their desks. Tell children that this problem can be avoided when everyone uses the same **unit** of measurement.

Write the term **centimeter** on the chalkboard and read it aloud. Explain that it is a unit of measurement. Then write **cm** next to the word and tell children that it is the symbol for, or a short way to write, centi-

meter. Distribute punchout centimeter rulers to the children. Have them place one pointer finger on the 0 mark and one pointer finger on the 1 mark. Identify the distance between as 1 centimeter.

Hold up a pencil.

■ **How long do you think this pencil is? Write down your estimates.** [Answers will vary.]

Demonstrate how to use the centimeter ruler to measure the pencil. Discuss the importance of lining up the 0 mark with the end of the object. Explain to children how they can find measures to the nearest centimeter. Tell children the measure of the pencil and have them compare it to their estimates.

Point out that when you measure to the nearest centimeter the object may be shorter or longer than the measurement recorded. This is why

Working Together

Find the real object.
You estimate how long.
Your partner measures.
Take turns.

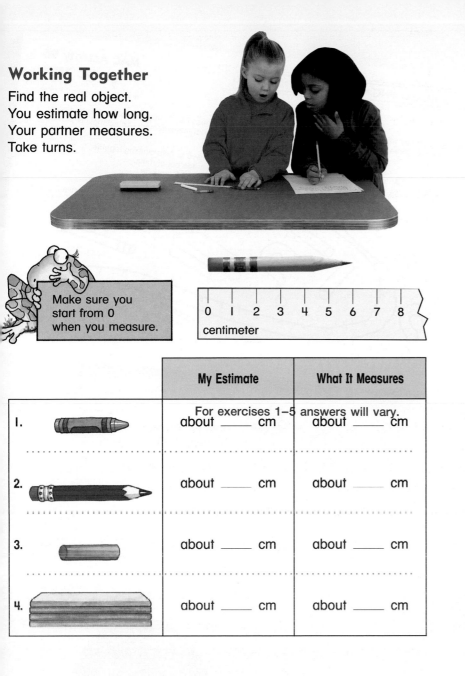

Make sure you start from 0 when you measure.

		My Estimate	What It Measures
		For exercises 1–5 answers will vary.	
1.		about _____ cm	about _____ cm
2.		about _____ cm	about _____ cm
3.		about _____ cm	about _____ cm
4.		about _____ cm	about _____ cm

5. Find four more objects. Estimate and measure.

Extra Practice, page 164 *Practice Plus,* page 178

---

we say it is "about" that measurement. As children become more familiar with this concept, the "about" can be dropped.

PUPIL'S EDITION pp. 153-154

Page 153 Discuss the example at the top of the page with the children.

Check for Understanding

■ **What if the end of the safety pin was closer to the 4 on the ruler? How long would the safety pin be?** [about 4 cm]

GUIDED PRACTICE ex. 1–4: For reteaching, use Common Error and Remediation or Alternative Strategy.

Page 154 WORKING TOGETHER Be sure to have an adequate supply of crayons, pencils, chalk, and erasers for children to measure.

MEETING INDIVIDUAL NEEDS

ACTIVITY *Common Error and Remediation*

MATERIALS punchout centimeter ruler, classroom objects, marker

Some children may not position the ruler correctly. Work individually with each child. Use a bright color to mark the end of the centimeter ruler, directly under the 0. This mark should remind the child to align the ruler with the end of the object to be measured. Provide classroom objects to be measured, such as an eraser, a paper clip, or a piece of chalk. Observe the child to make sure he or she is aligning the ruler correctly.

TEACHER to TEACHER

MANAGEMENT TIP My children resisted estimating until I assured them that their estimates would be *close* or *not close,* but never wrong.

ACTIVITY ALTERNATIVE TEACHING STRATEGY

MATERIALS centimeter ruler; small objects

VISUAL Hold up a centimeter ruler and have it identified. Demonstrate measuring different objects with the ruler. Emphasize the correct placement of the ruler. Call on volunteers, in turn, to read the number aligned with the right end of the object and give the measurement in centimeters. Write each measurement on the chalkboard.

 PRACTICE·APPLY **PRACTICE** ex. 1–5

CLOSE Guide children to summarize the lesson:

■ **What is the most important thing to remember when measuring with a centimeter ruler?** [Always start from 0 when you measure.]

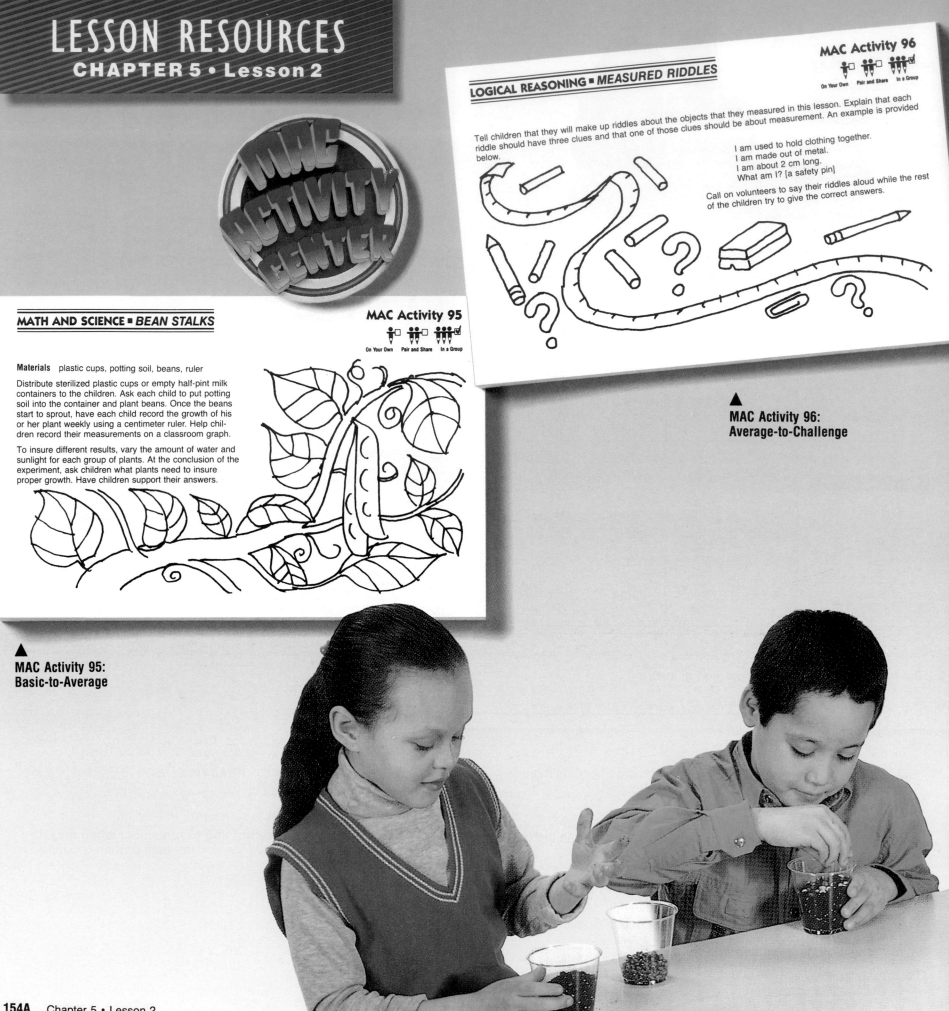

MATH AND SCIENCE ▪ BEAN STALKS

MAC Activity 95

On Your Own   Pair and Share   In a Group

Materials   plastic cups, potting soil, beans, ruler

Distribute sterilized plastic cups or empty half-pint milk containers to the children. Ask each child to put potting soil into the container and plant beans. Once the beans start to sprout, have each child record the growth of his or her plant weekly using a centimeter ruler. Help children record their measurements on a classroom graph.

To insure different results, vary the amount of water and sunlight for each group of plants. At the conclusion of the experiment, ask children what plants need to insure proper growth. Have children support their answers.

▲
MAC Activity 95:
Basic-to-Average

LOGICAL REASONING ▪ MEASURED RIDDLES

MAC Activity 96

On Your Own   Pair and Share   In a Group

Tell children that they will make up riddles about the objects that they measured in this lesson. Explain that each riddle should have three clues and that one of those clues should be about measurement. An example is provided below.

I am used to hold clothing together.
I am made out of metal.
I am about 2 cm long.
What am I? [a safety pin]

Call on volunteers to say their riddles aloud while the rest of the children try to give the correct answers.

▲
MAC Activity 96:
Average-to-Challenge

Name

USING CENTIMETERS

Study

About 10 cm long.

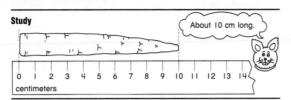

0 1 2 3 4 5 6 7 8 9 10 11 12 13 14
centimeters

Check

Measure the length of each object.

1.

0 1 2 3 4 5 6 7 8 9 10 11 12 13 14
centimeters

about ___ cm

2.

0 1 2 3 4 5 6 7 8 9 10 11 12 13 14
centimeters

about __7__ cm

3.

about __10__ cm

4.

about __6__ cm

5.

about __8__ cm

Macmillan/McGraw-Hill, MATHEMATICS IN ACTION
Grade 2, Chapter 5, Lesson 2, pages 153–154

Reteaching-48

Name

USING CENTIMETERS

Estimate how long.
Then use a centimeter ruler to measure.

	Estimate. Answers will vary.	Measure.
1.	about ___ cm	about __2__ cm
2.	about ___ cm	about __3__ cm
3.	about ___ cm	about __6__ cm
4.	about ___ cm	about __4__ cm

Measure each jump.

5. about __9__ cm

6. about __5__ cm

7. about __11__ cm

8. about __7__ cm

Macmillan/McGraw-Hill, MATHEMATICS IN ACTION
Grade 2, Chapter 5, Lesson 2, pages 153–154

Practice-48

Name

USING CENTIMETERS

On Your Own   Pair and Share   In a Group

ANT TOWN ZOO

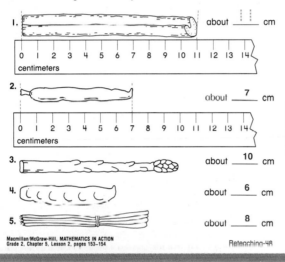

Complete.
Use a centimeter ruler to measure.

Path	About How Long
1. Parking Lot to Lions	9 cm
2. Monkeys to Elephants	2 cm
3. Parking Lot to Seals to Snack Bar	7 cm
4. Monkeys to Snack Bar to Elephants	9 cm
5. Parking Lot to Seals to Tigers to Elephants	23 cm

Macmillan/McGraw-Hill, MATHEMATICS IN ACTION
Grade 2, Chapter 5, Lesson 2, pages 153–154

Enrichment-48

Problem of the Day

Adam estimated that the chalkboard eraser was 5 centimeters long. Toby estimated that the eraser was 15 centimeters long. Whose estimate is probably closer?   [Toby's]

AT·A·GLANCE pp. 155-156

LESSON OBJECTIVE
Estimate and measure in centimeters, decimeters, and meters.

ASSIGNMENT GUIDE

COURSE	EXERCISES
Basic	p. 155: 1–4; p. 156: 1–8
Average	p. 155: 1–4; p. 156: 1–8
Challenge	p. 155: 1–4; p. 156: 1–8

MATERIALS
Manipulatives metric measuring tape*; centimeter/decimeter ruler (or punchout) per pair

Teacher Resources
Reteaching 49
MAC Act. 97, 98
Practice 49
*Teacher Aid 7
Enrichment 49

SKILLS TRACE
MEASURING LENGTH

Explore (Concrete)	Develop/Understand (Transitional/Abstract)
152	153–154, 155–156, 165–166, 167–168
Practice 164, 177, 178, 179–180, 213	**Apply** 161–162, 173–174, 175, 176

See **MANIPULATIVES PLUS 24**, p. 150J.

Using Centimeters, Decimeters, and Meters

10 centimeters equal 1 decimeter.
100 centimeters equal 1 meter.

|–––| 1 centimeter

|– – – – – – – – – – – –| 1 **decimeter**

A baseball bat is about 1 **meter** long.

Which animal is about 1 cm long? Possible answers: ant, lady bug;
Which animal is about 1 decimeter long? worm, grasshopper;
Which animal is about 1 meter long? snake, dog.

How long?
Think of the real object.
Ring the better estimate.

1.
about 1 meter
(about 1 decimeter)

2.
(about 2 meters)
about 2 centimeters

3.
(about 8 centimeters)
about 8 decimeters

4.
about 1 decimeter
(about 1 meter)

Macmillan/McGraw-Hill

PREPARE

WARM-UP To review measuring in centimeters, write the following on the chalkboard: 3 cm, 8 cm, 1 cm, 6 cm, 10 cm. Have the measurements read aloud. Call on volunteers to tell which measure is longest and which is shortest. [10 cm, 1 cm]

TEACH

DISCUSSING Draw a 10-cm line on the chalkboard. Explain that 10 centimeters equals 1 decimeter. Write the word **decimeter** on the chalkboard and pronounce it. Write **dm** and tell children that this is the symbol for decimeter. Ask children to look at their punchout rulers and identify the number of decimeters on it. [3 dm]

Display a metric measuring tape and explain that it is another tool that is used to measure length. Write **meter** and its symbol **m** on the chalkboard. Read and explain the term to the children. Tell them that 10 decimeters equal 1 meter. Compare relative sizes by naming two measures, such as 2 cm and 2 m, asking children to identify which is longer or shorter.

PUPIL'S EDITION pp. 155-156

Page 155 Work through the example at the top of the page. Display a metric measuring tape and then discuss children's answers to the questions.

Check for Understanding

■ **Are your scissors about 12 cm or 12 dm long?** [12 cm]

GUIDED PRACTICE ex. 1–4: Remind children to think of the real object, not the picture in the book.

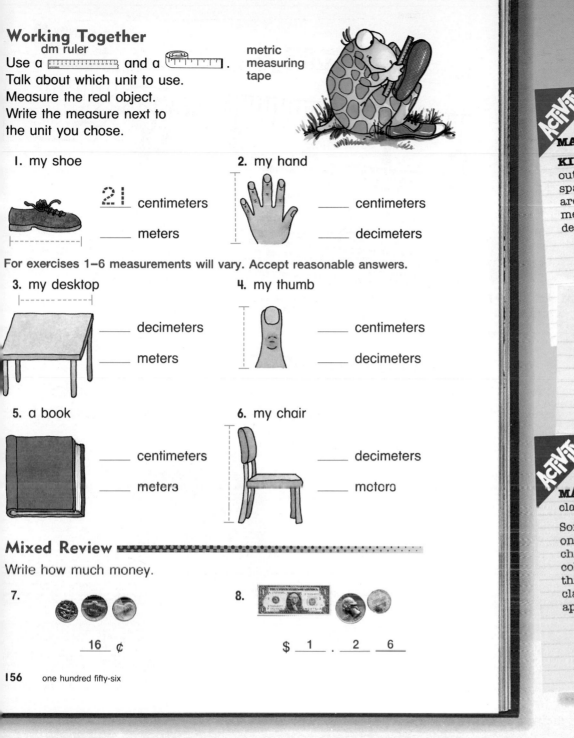

Working Together

Use a [dm ruler] and a [metric measuring tape].
Talk about which unit to use.
Measure the real object.
Write the measure next to
the unit you chose.

1. my shoe

___21___ centimeters

_____ meters

2. my hand

_____ centimeters

_____ decimeters

For exercises 1–6 measurements will vary. Accept reasonable answers.

3. my desktop

_____ decimeters

_____ meters

4. my thumb

_____ centimeters

_____ decimeters

5. a book

_____ centimeters

_____ meters

6. my chair

_____ decimeters

_____ meters

Mixed Review

Write how much money.

7.

___16___ ¢

8.

$ __1__ . __2__ __6__

MEETING INDIVIDUAL NEEDS

ACTIVITY ALTERNATIVE TEACHING STRATEGY

MATERIALS metric measuring tape (Teacher Aid 7)

KINESTHETIC/VISUAL Display a metric measuring tape. Point out that there are 10 centimeters in a decimeter. Identify the space between 0 and 10 as 1 decimeter. Then tell children there are 100 centimeters in a meter. Use the measuring tape to measure each child's height to the nearest centimeter and decimeter. Discuss children's heights relative to 1 meter.

For Students Acquiring English (SAE)

Explain the difference between a **measuring tape** and a **ruler**. Do page 155 orally, having SAE volunteers restate/paraphrase. Pair or group children heterogeneously for page 156.

ACTIVITY Common Error and Remediation

MATERIALS ribbon or hem binding, colored markers, classroom objects

Some children may not be able to read centimeters or decimeters on a meter measure. Work individually with each child. Help the child make a meter tape from a piece of ribbon. Use different-colored markers to mark centimeters and decimeters. Then have the child write the numbers in the same colors. Give the child classroom objects to measure. Have him or her identify the appropriate measuring unit and then measure the object.

For reteaching, use Common Error and Remediation or Alternative Strategy.

Page 156 ■ WORKING TOGETHER Discuss the display at the top of the page with the children. Assign partners. Before measuring, children should discuss which unit to use.

3 PRACTICE•APPLY   PRACTICE   ex. 1–8

CLOSE Guide children to summarize the lesson:
■ **Which unit of measure would you use to measure a stapler?** [centimeter] **the length of a book?** [decimeter or centimeter] **the length of the room?** [meter]

SPEAKING MATHEMATICALLY ▪ I SPY

On Your Own   Pair and Share   In a Group

Materials   classroom objects, punchout cm ruler, metric measuring tape (Teacher Aid 7)

Have children work in pairs. Each child should collect several classroom objects of different lengths and bring them to the work area. Then the first child says, "I spy something about..." and supplies the estimated length in centimeters, decimeters, or meters. The second child looks at the collection of objects and guesses which object is being described. The pair should then measure the item to confirm the estimate. Have children alternate roles until all of the objects have been described and identified.

To make the activity even more challenging, let the children describe the length of any visible object in the classroom.

MATH AND ART ▪ WE'RE THIS BIG

MAC Activity 97

On Your Own   Pair and Share   In a Group

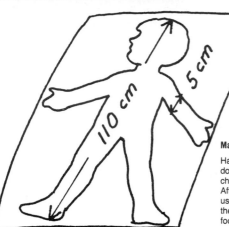

Materials   mural paper, crayons

Have children work in pairs. Tell each child, in turn, to lie down on a large sheet of mural paper while the other child traces the outline of that child's body with crayons. After children's outlines have been traced, have them use centimeter, decimeter, and meter units to measure the following: body height; length of an arm, leg, head, foot, and hand. Have these measurements recorded directly on the body outlines. You may wish to display these life-sized silhouettes on a bulletin board or on a wall.

▲ **MAC Activity 97:**
Basic-to-Average

▲ **MAC Activity 98:**
Average-to-Challenge

Name _____

RETEACHING-49

USING CENTIMETERS, DECIMETERS, AND METERS

Study

10 centimeters equal 1 decimeter

Check

Use your centimeter ruler to measure. Color the ribbons that are longer than 1 decimeter.

1. 12 cm
2. 9 cm
3. 11 cm
4. 8 cm
5. 6 cm
6. 13 cm
7. 7 cm

Reteaching-49

Macmillan/McGraw-Hill, MATHEMATICS IN ACTION
Grade 2, Chapter 5, Lesson 3, pages 155–156

Name _____

PRACTICE-49

USING CENTIMETERS, DECIMETERS, AND METERS

Find these objects.
Ring which unit to use.
Estimate. Then measure.

	Estimate.	Measure.
	Answers will vary.	
	Accept reasonable answers.	

1. a paper clip

   (centimeter)   meter   about _____   about _____

2. an eraser

   meter   (decimeter)   about _____   about _____

3. a sheet of paper

   (decimeter)   meter   about _____   about _____

4. the door

   (meter)   decimeter   about _____   about _____

Practice-49

Macmillan/McGraw-Hill, MATHEMATICS IN ACTION
Grade 2, Chapter 5, Lesson 3, pages 155–156

Name _____

ENRICHMENT-49

On Your Own   Pair and Share   In a Group

USING CENTIMETERS, DECIMETERS, AND METERS

ME AND MY SHADOW

Does your shadow change during the day?
Try this to find out.

Stand with the
Sun behind you.

Your partner draws a
line near your feet.

Your partner draws
another line at the
end of your shadow.

Measure between the
lines. Write the
length. Write the time.

Do this every 2 hours.
Stand on the same line each time.

Length of Shadow	Time
about _____	____ : ____
about _____	____ : ____
about _____	____ : ____

Use another sheet of paper. Write about what happened.

Enrichment-49

Macmillan/McGraw-Hill, MATHEMATICS IN ACTION
Grade 2, Chapter 5, Lesson 3, pages 155–156

Problem of the Day

It takes the road crew 1 minute to paint a section of a center line that is 5 meters long. Could they paint a center line 100 meters long in 15 minutes? [No. Possible solution: skip count by fives 15 times; 75 < 100.]

AT·A·GLANCE pp. 157–158

LESSON OBJECTIVE
Estimate and measure capacity in liters.

ASSIGNMENT GUIDE

COURSE	EXERCISES
Basic	p. 157: 1–4; p. 158: 1–8
Average	p. 157: 1–4; p. 158: 1–8
Challenge	p. 157: 1–4; p. 158: 1–8
Extra Practice, p. 164	

MATERIALS
Classroom Materials liter measure, unbreakable containers that are smaller and larger than a liter, plastic glasses, water

Teacher Resources
Reteaching 50   Practice 50   Enrichment 50
Prob. Solv. 21   MAC Act. 99, 100

SKILLS TRACE
MEASURING CAPACITY

Explore (Concrete) 152	Develop/Understand (Transitional/Abstract) 157–158, 169–170
Practice 164, 177, 179–180	Apply 161–162, 163, 173–174

See **MANIPULATIVES PLUS 25**, p. 150K.

Measuring Capacity

> 4 glasses hold about 1 liter.

1 liter

Working Together

Possible answers:
Name a container that holds about 1 liter. pitcher, watering can;
Name a container that holds more than 1 liter. sink, washtub;
Name a container that holds less than 1 liter. drinking glass, juice box.

Talk about a plan to find out if
your estimates are close.

Ring the container that holds about 1 liter.

1. 1 liter

2. 1 liter

3. 1 liter

4. 1 liter

PREPARE   **WARM-UP** To prepare children to measure in liters, display various measuring containers in pairs. Ask volunteers to compare each pair and tell which of the two containers is larger or smaller, shorter or taller, and so on. Then ask children to estimate which container could hold more water.

TEACH   **DISCUSSING** Display a 1-liter container and identify it. Explain that a **liter** is a unit used to measure capacity, or how much something holds. Write **L** on the chalkboard and explain that this is the symbol for liter. Fill the 1-liter container with water and display it next to six large plastic glasses. Have children estimate how many of the glasses the liter of water can fill. Then pour the water. Have children compare their estimates with the actual measurement, which should be close to four large glasses.

Show containers of different sizes and have children identify a container that they estimate holds less than 1 liter. Have a child pour water from the 1-liter container to check this estimate. Repeat this procedure, having children identify which containers hold about 1 liter, more than 1 liter, and less than 1 liter. In each case have children confirm their estimates by measuring.

PUPIL'S EDITION pp. 157-158

Page 157 Guide children through the example at the top of the page.

WORKING TOGETHER Discuss the kinds of containers that can be found in the classroom before children make their estimates.

Check for Understanding
■ **Which objects can hold about 1 liter?** [Possible responses: pitcher, watering can]

Ring the better estimate.

1.
   less than 1 liter (ringed)
   about 1 liter
   more than 1 liter

2.
   less than 1 liter
   about 1 liter
   more than 1 liter (ringed)

3.
   less than 1 liter
   about 1 liter (ringed)
   more than 1 liter

4.
   less than 1 liter
   about 1 liter
   more than 1 liter (ringed)

5.
   less than 1 liter (ringed)
   about 1 liter
   more than 1 liter

6.
   less than 1 liter
   about 1 liter (ringed)
   more than 1 liter

Read the recipe. Solve the problem.

FRUIT PUNCH

Mix

4 liters
   orange juice

2 liters
   pineapple juice

1 liter
   lemonade

7. How many liters of fruit punch will the recipe make?

   __7__ liters

8. Write another problem about the recipe. _Answers will vary._

   Possible problem: How much more

   orange juice is used than lemonade?

Extra Practice, page 164

ACTIVITY ALTERNATIVE TEACHING STRATEGY

MATERIALS various-shaped 1-liter unbreakable containers, dried beans

VISUAL   Display a tall, narrow 1-liter container and a short, wide 1-liter container next to a standard 1-liter measure. Ask children to estimate which container holds more than, less than, or about 1 liter. Check their estimates by pouring 1 liter of beans into each container. Guide children to understand that 1-liter containers can come in different sizes and shapes.

For Students Acquiring English (SAE)

Teach the names of the containers in the lesson: **pitcher, watering can, sink,** and so on, showing the real items. Have SAE children practice saying the names. Pair children for the recipe exercise.

ACTIVITY Common Error and Remediation

MATERIALS half-gallon milk carton, liter container, scissors, various-sized containers, sand

Some children may not be able to estimate whether a container holds more or less than 1 liter. Work with each child. Help the child make a liter measure from a milk carton. Pour a liter of sand into the carton. Mark the level, empty the carton, and cut along the line. Have the child estimate whether various containers hold more or less than 1 liter, then pour sand from the liter measure into each to check.

GUIDED PRACTICE   ex. 1–4: For reteaching, use Common Error and Remediation or Alternative Strategy.

Page 158   Have the pictures identified. Read the recipe with the children before assigning ex. 7–8.

3 PRACTICE·APPLY

PRACTICE   ex. 1–8: Call on volunteers to share their problems with the rest of the class.

C L O S E   Guide children to summarize the lesson:
■ **Which unit could you use to measure the amount of water in a bathtub, a liter or a meter?** [a liter]

MAC ACTIVITY CENTER

MAC Activity 99

On Your Own   Pair and Share   In a Group

MATH AND CONSUMER ▪ LITERS AROUND US

Materials   construction paper, magazines, scissors, glue

Tell children to make a list of things they see at home or in stores that are sold by the liter. Have them complete this activity over a specific time period.

In class, combine children's lists to make a class list of "Liters Around Us." Have children choose things from the list to illustrate. Set up a display with the children's pictures and list.

▲
MAC Activity 99:
Basic-to-Average

MAC Activity 100:
Average-to-Challenge
▼

NUMBER SENSE ▪ MEASUREMENT TRUE OR FALSE

MAC Activity 100

On Your Own   Pair and Share   In a Group

Read statements, such as the following, to the children. After each sentence is read, ask volunteers to tell if the statement is true or false. If the statement is false, have another volunteer provide a replacement measure to make the statement true.

I drink about 100 liters of milk a day.
[False; about 1 liter or less than a liter.]
A milk container could hold about 1 liter. [True.]
A large pot could hold up to 10 liters of water. [True.]

To continue the activity, have children make up their own statements to present to their classmates.

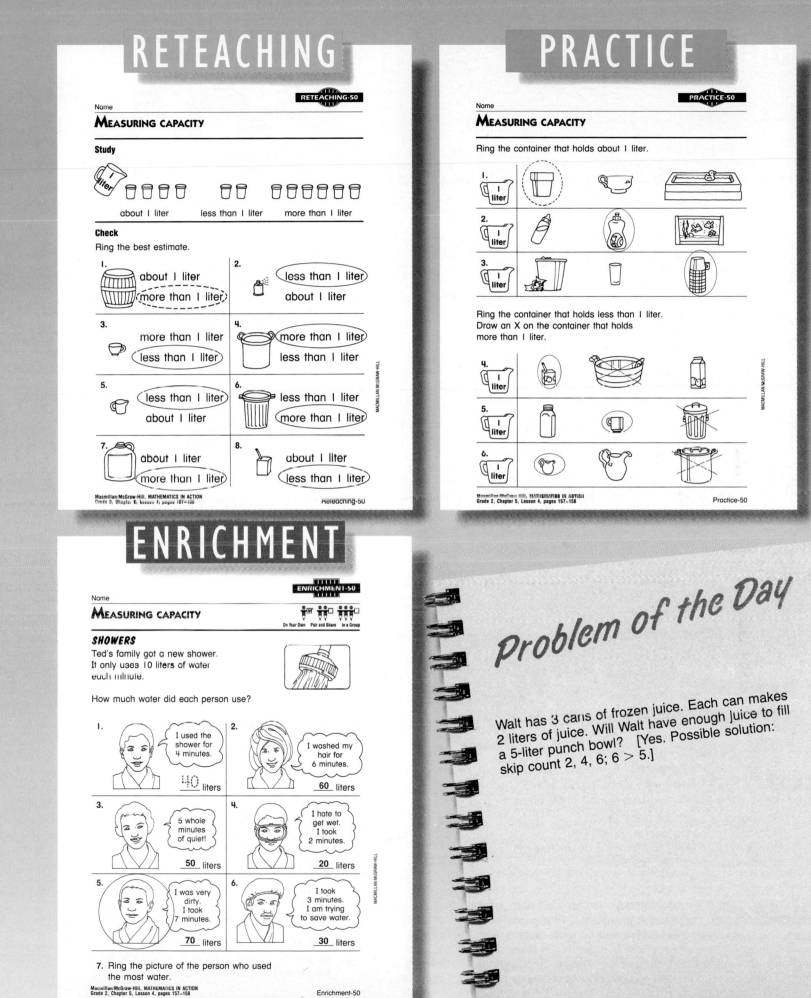

RETEACHING

Name

RETEACHING-50

MEASURING CAPACITY

Study

about 1 liter   less than 1 liter   more than 1 liter

Check

Ring the best estimate.

1. about 1 liter
   (more than 1 liter)

2. (less than 1 liter)
   about 1 liter

3. more than 1 liter
   (less than 1 liter)

4. (more than 1 liter)
   less than 1 liter

5. (less than 1 liter)
   about 1 liter

6. less than 1 liter
   (more than 1 liter)

7. about 1 liter
   (more than 1 liter)

8. about 1 liter
   (less than 1 liter)

Macmillan/McGraw-Hill, MATHEMATICS IN ACTION
Grade 2, Chapter 5, Lesson 4, pages 157–158

Reteaching-50

PRACTICE

Name

PRACTICE-50

MEASURING CAPACITY

Ring the container that holds about 1 liter.

1.
2.
3.

Ring the container that holds less than 1 liter.
Draw an X on the container that holds
more than 1 liter.

4.
5.
6.

Macmillan/McGraw-Hill, MATHEMATICS IN ACTION
Grade 2, Chapter 5, Lesson 4, pages 157–158

Practice-50

ENRICHMENT

Name

ENRICHMENT-50

On Your Own   Pair and Share   In a Group

MEASURING CAPACITY

SHOWERS

Ted's family got a new shower.
It only uses 10 liters of water
each minute.

How much water did each person use?

1. I used the shower for 4 minutes.
   40 liters

2. I washed my hair for 6 minutes.
   60 liters

3. 5 whole minutes of quiet!
   50 liters

4. I hate to get wet. I took 2 minutes.
   20 liters

5. I was very dirty. I took 7 minutes.
   70 liters

6. I took 3 minutes. I am trying to save water.
   30 liters

7. Ring the picture of the person who used
   the most water.

Macmillan/McGraw-Hill, MATHEMATICS IN ACTION
Grade 2, Chapter 5, Lesson 4, pages 157–158

Enrichment-50

Problem of the Day

Walt has 3 cans of frozen juice. Each can makes
2 liters of juice. Will Walt have enough juice to fill
a 5-liter punch bowl?   [Yes. Possible solution:
skip count 2, 4, 6; 6 > 5.]

AT·A·GLANCE p. 159

LESSON OBJECTIVE
Estimate and measure mass in kilograms.

ASSIGNMENT GUIDE

COURSE	EXERCISES
Basic	p. 159: 1–6
Average	p. 159: 1–6
Challenge	p. 159: 1–6

MATERIALS
Classroom Materials classroom objects that are more and less than 1 kilogram
Manipulatives pan balance, spring scale, 1-kilogram measures

Teacher Resources
Reteaching 51   Practice 51   Enrichment 51
MAC Act. 101, 102

SKILLS TRACE
MEASURING MASS AND WEIGHT

Explore (Concrete) 152	Develop/Understand (Transitional/Abstract) 159, 171
Practice 164, 177, 179–180	Apply 161–162, 163, 173–174

See **MANIPULATIVES PLUS 26–27**, pp. 150L–150M

ACTIVITY

Measuring Mass

| 1 **kilogram** 1 kg | less than 1 kilogram | more than 1 kilogram |

How do you know that 🍒 are less than | 1 kg | ?

Hold the real object.
Ring the better estimate.

In their own words, children should note that the tilted pan shows the 1 kg mass has more mass than the cherries.

1.
less than 1 kilogram
(more than 1 kilogram)

2.
(less than 1 kilogram)
more than 1 kilogram

3.
less than 1 kilogram
(more than 1 kilogram)

4.
(less than 1 kilogram)
more than 1 kilogram

How many kilograms?

5.   __2__ kilograms

6.   __7__ kilograms

Extra Practice, page 164   one hundred fifty-nine   **159**

PREPARE

WARM-UP To review measurement, read the following questions aloud. Have children identify the unit of measure they could use to find each answer.

How long is a school bus? [meter]
How much does a pitcher hold? [liter]
How long is a belt? [centimeter or decimeter]
How wide is a glove? [centimeter]

TEACH

DISCUSSING Display a balance scale and several 1-kilogram measures. Place one measure in each pan. Point out that when both pans contain objects with the same mass, the pans are level and the scale is "in balance." Allow all the children to handle the 1-kilogram measure. Explain that **kilogram** is a unit of measurement used to describe how heavy something is. Write

the term **kilogram** on the chalkboard and pronounce it. Write **kg** and explain that this is the symbol for kilogram.

Have children identify concrete unit models for a kilogram. Have them estimate which classroom objects measure about 1 kilogram. Then allow them to use the balance scale to compare the object(s) to a 1-kilogram measure.

Place an object greater than 1 kilogram in one of the pans.
■ **What happens?** [The pan sinks and the scale is no longer in balance.]

Help children conclude that the object is heavier than 1 kilogram.

Display a spring scale and have children use it to measure the mass of several classroom objects. Show them how to read the dial to determine mass to the nearest kilogram.

ACTIVITY Common Error and Remediation

MATERIALS 1-kilogram measure; classroom objects

Some children may not be able to estimate the relative mass of objects. Work individually with each child. Ask the child to pretend to be a balance scale. Have the child hold a light object and a heavy object and tilt his or her shoulders to show the difference in mass. Ask which object is heavier. Repeat several times with different objects. Then have the child hold a 1-kilogram measure and a light object and pretend to be a balance scale. Ask if the object is more or less than 1 kilogram. [less] Use other objects.

ACTIVITY ALTERNATIVE TEACHING STRATEGY

MATERIALS 1-kilogram measure, pan balance; classroom objects

VISUAL/KINESTHETIC Display a balance scale and demonstrate how it is used. Measure a classroom object, such as a book, to determine if it is more or less than 1 kilogram. Display a collection of classroom objects. Have children take turns holding a 1-kilogram measure. Tell each child to choose an object to measure and estimate if it is more or less than 1 kilogram. Then have the child compare the object and the 1-kilogram measure on the balance scale.

ONGOING ASSESSMENT

INTERVIEW (1) What weighs about 1 kilogram? Give me an example. (2) What weighs less than 1 kilogram? Give me an example.

JOURNAL WRITING You may wish to have children record their responses in their math journals.

PUPIL'S EDITION p. 159

Identify the objects on the pictured scales with the children. Discuss the examples shown at the top of the page.

Check for Understanding

■ **How do you know that the cherries are less than 1 kilogram by looking at the picture?** [Possible response: The pan with 1 kilogram sinks, showing that the cherries are less than 1 kilogram.]

GUIDED PRACTICE ex. 1–4: For reteaching, use Common Error and Remediation or Alternative Strategy.

CLOSE Guide children to summarize the lesson:

■ **What things are heavier than 1 kilogram?** [Possible responses: book, bag of potatoes]

3 PRACTICE·APPLY **PRACTICE** ex. 5–6

MAC ACTIVITY CENTER

MAC Activity 101:
Basic-to-Average
▼

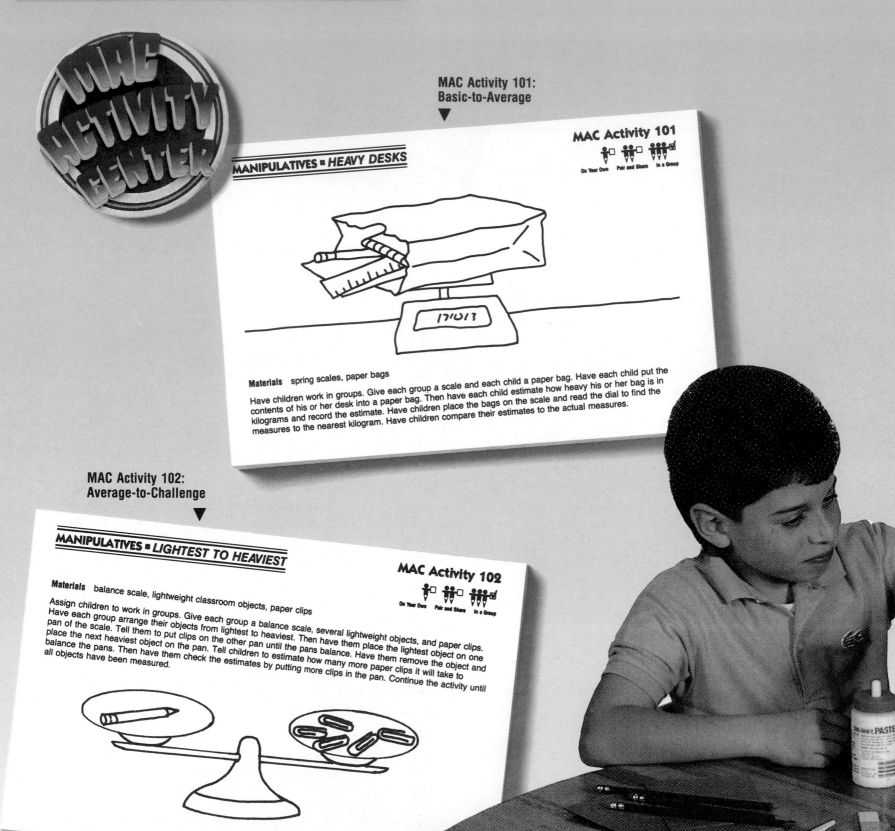

MANIPULATIVES • HEAVY DESKS

MAC Activity 101

On Your Own   Pair and Share   In a Group

Materials   spring scales, paper bags

Have children work in groups. Give each group a scale and each child a paper bag. Have each child put the contents of his or her desk into a paper bag. Then have each child estimate how heavy his or her bag is in kilograms and record the estimate. Have children place the bags on the scale and read the dial to find the measures to the nearest kilogram. Have children compare their estimates to the actual measures.

MAC Activity 102:
Average-to-Challenge
▼

MANIPULATIVES • LIGHTEST TO HEAVIEST

MAC Activity 102

On Your Own   Pair and Share   In a Group

Materials   balance scale, lightweight classroom objects, paper clips

Assign children to work in groups. Give each group a balance scale, several lightweight objects, and paper clips. Have each group arrange their objects from lightest to heaviest. Then have them place the lightest object on one pan of the scale. Tell them to put clips on the other pan until the pans balance. Have them remove the object and place the next heaviest object on the pan. Tell children to estimate how many more paper clips it will take to balance the pans. Then have them check the estimates by putting more clips in the pan. Continue the activity until all objects have been measured.

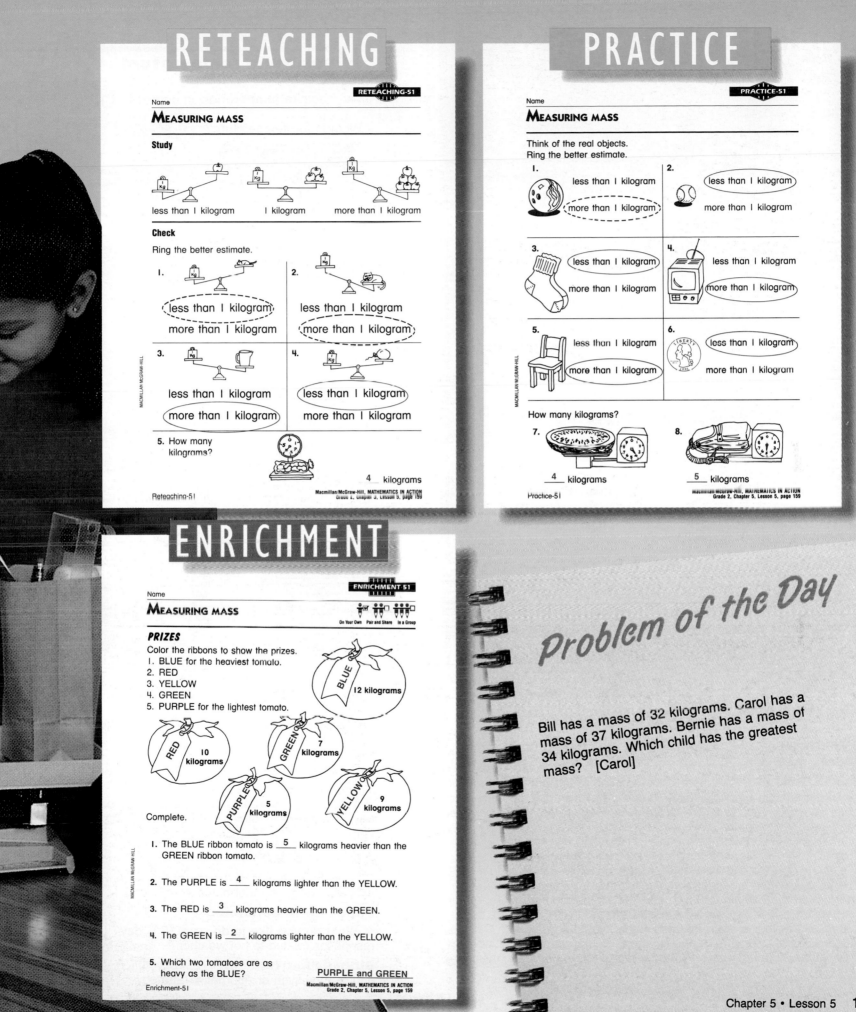

RETEACHING

Name

MEASURING MASS

Study

less than 1 kilogram   1 kilogram   more than 1 kilogram

Check

Ring the better estimate.

1. (less than 1 kilogram)
   more than 1 kilogram

2. less than 1 kilogram
   (more than 1 kilogram)

3. less than 1 kilogram
   (more than 1 kilogram)

4. (less than 1 kilogram)
   more than 1 kilogram

5. How many kilograms?

   _4_ kilograms

Reteaching-51

Macmillan/McGraw-Hill, MATHEMATICS IN ACTION
Grade 2, Chapter 5, Lesson 5, page 159

PRACTICE

Name

MEASURING MASS

Think of the real objects.
Ring the better estimate.

1. less than 1 kilogram
   (more than 1 kilogram)

2. (less than 1 kilogram)
   more than 1 kilogram

3. (less than 1 kilogram)
   more than 1 kilogram

4. less than 1 kilogram
   (more than 1 kilogram)

5. less than 1 kilogram
   (more than 1 kilogram)

6. (less than 1 kilogram)
   more than 1 kilogram

How many kilograms?

7. _4_ kilograms

8. _5_ kilograms

Practice-51

Macmillan/McGraw-Hill, MATHEMATICS IN ACTION
Grade 2, Chapter 5, Lesson 5, page 159

ENRICHMENT

On Your Own   Pair and Share   In a Group

Name

MEASURING MASS

PRIZES

Color the ribbons to show the prizes.
1. BLUE for the heaviest tomato.
2. RED
3. YELLOW
4. GREEN
5. PURPLE for the lightest tomato.

BLUE — 12 kilograms

RED — 10 kilograms

GREEN — 7 kilograms

PURPLE — 5 kilograms

YELLOW — 9 kilograms

Complete.

1. The BLUE ribbon tomato is _5_ kilograms heavier than the GREEN ribbon tomato.

2. The PURPLE is _4_ kilograms lighter than the YELLOW.

3. The RED is _3_ kilograms heavier than the GREEN.

4. The GREEN is _2_ kilograms lighter than the YELLOW.

5. Which two tomatoes are as heavy as the BLUE? **PURPLE and GREEN**

Enrichment-51

Macmillan/McGraw-Hill, MATHEMATICS IN ACTION
Grade 2, Chapter 5, Lesson 5, page 159

Problem of the Day

Bill has a mass of 32 kilograms. Carol has a mass of 37 kilograms. Bernie has a mass of 34 kilograms. Which child has the greatest mass? [Carol]

AT·A·GLANCE p. 160

LESSON OBJECTIVE
Read temperature in °C.

ASSIGNMENT GUIDE

COURSE	EXERCISES
Basic	p. 160: 1–4
Average	p. 160: 1–4
Challenge	p. 160: 1–4

MATERIALS
Classroom Materials Celsius thermometer

Teacher Resources
Reteaching 52   Practice 52   Enrichment 52
MAC Act. 103, 104

SKILLS TRACE	
MEASURING TEMPERATURE	
Explore (Concrete) 152	**Develop/Understand (Transitional/Abstract)** 160, 172
Practice 164, 177, 179–180, 245, 301	**Apply** 161–162, 182

Measuring Temperature

We measure **temperature** in degrees (°C).

What is the temperature? ___26___ °C

Write the temperature.

1. ___28___ °C

2. ___10___ °C

3. ___0___ °C

4. ___22___ °C

1 PREPARE

WARM-UP To prepare children to read a thermometer, discuss the meaning of **temperature** (how hot or cold something is). Display a **Celsius thermometer** and give each child an opportunity to look at it carefully. Explain that a thermometer measures temperature.

2 TEACH

DISCUSSING Show children how to read a Celsius thermometer by showing the point where the mercury ends. Explain that with this kind of thermometer, temperature is measured in units called **degrees Celsius**. Write °C on the chalkboard and further explain that this is the symbol for degrees Celsius. Then demonstrate what happens when the thermometer is placed in ice water and in hot water. Write the temperatures on the chalkboard.

Tell children that room temperature is around 20°C, water boils at 100°C, and water freezes at 0°C.

■ **What would you wear on a 30°C day? on a 5°C day? on a 18°C day?** [lightweight clothing, very warm clothing, medium-weight clothing]

PUPIL'S EDITION p. 160

Discuss the example at the top of the page. Have a volunteer read the temperature on the thermometer.

Check for Understanding

■ **What do you like to do on a 32°C day?** [Accept all reasonable responses related to hot weather.]

GUIDED PRACTICE ex. 1–2: For reteaching, use Common Error and Remediation or Alternative Strategy.

Activity
Common Error and Remediation

MATERIALS thermometer

Some children may not be able to relate the degrees on a thermometer to the temperature. Work individually with each child. Help the child read the thermometer to find the room's temperature. Then have the child hold the thermometer in the sun and tell what is happening. [The mercury goes up.] Ask the child to describe how the sun feels. [warm or hot] Read the temperature with the child and establish that it is hotter than room temperature.

For Students Acquiring English (SAE)

For oral language development, discuss how different temperatures relate to various seasonal pictures/settings.

ALTERNATIVE TEACHING STRATEGY

VISUAL Draw a large thermometer on the chalkboard. Explain how the instrument is read and how it is used. Shade in the "mercury" to 0° and tell children that water freezes at 0°C. Have a volunteer describe frozen water. [It is ice.] Then extend the "mercury" to 20° and tell children that the temperature in the room is about 20°C. Extend the "mercury" to 100° and tell children that water boils at 100°C. Call on a volunteer to tell the uses of boiling water. [Possible responses: cook food, make beverages]

3 PRACTICE•APPLY PRACTICE ex. 3–4

CLOSE Guide children to summarize the lesson:

■ **Why is it important to learn to read a thermometer?** [Possible response: It tells you the temperature, which can help you in deciding which kinds of clothing to wear on given days.]

MAC ACTIVITY CENTER

MATH AND SCIENCE ■ TEMPERATURE RANGE

MAC Activity 104

On Your Own   Pair and Share   In a Group

Materials   outdoor Celsius thermometer

Place an outdoor thermometer outside the classroom window. Tell children that the temperature outdoors changes during the day. Explain that they will work together to find how much it changes. Write the following chart on the chalkboard. Use times to fit your schoolday schedule.

Time	Temperature
9:00	_____
10:00	_____
11:00	_____
12:00	_____
1:00	_____
2:00	_____

Assign two or three children to read the thermometer at their appointed time and write the temperature on the chart. When the chart is complete, discuss the range of temperatures. You may want to repeat the activity on a day when the weather is different (cloudy versus sunny).

▲
MAC Activity 104:
Average-to-Challenge

MATH AND ART ■ THE FOUR SEASONS

MAC Activity 103

On Your Own   Pair and Share   In a Group

SUMMER   FALL   WINTER   SPRING

Materials   magazines, scissors, paste, large sheets of construction paper

Assign children to work in groups of four. Give each group several old magazines, four sheets of large construction paper, scissors, and paste. Explain to children that they will make a collage of pictures to show the four seasons of the year. Remind them that the seasons are summer, fall, winter, and spring.

Tell children to decide among themselves which season each member of the group will be responsible for. Have each child label a sheet of paper with the name of his or her season. Then have children look through magazines for pictures that show the seasons or events that occur in the seasons. Have them paste their pictures on their construction paper.

Display each group's complete collages and have a volunteer from each group tell about the pictures.

▲
MAC Activity 103:
Basic-to-Average

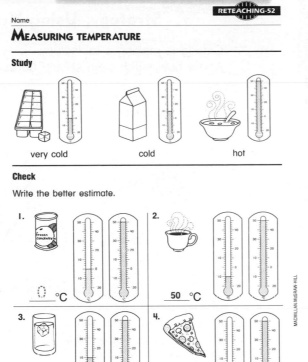

RETEACHING-52

Name

MEASURING TEMPERATURE

Study

very cold   cold   hot

Check

Write the better estimate.

1. 0 °C
2. 50 °C
3. 10 °C
4. 50 °C

Macmillan/McGraw-Hill, MATHEMATICS IN ACTION
Grade 2, Chapter 5, Lesson 6, page 160

Reteaching-52

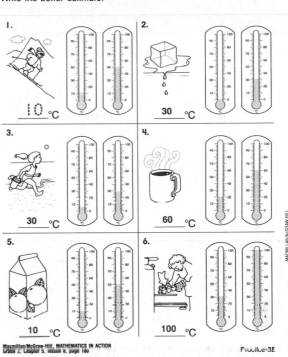

PRACTICE-52

Name

MEASURING TEMPERATURE

Write the better estimate.

1. 10 °C
2. 30 °C
3. 30 °C
4. 60 °C
5. 10 °C
6. 100 °C

Macmillan/McGraw-Hill, MATHEMATICS IN ACTION
Grade 2, Chapter 5, Lesson 6, page 160

Practice-52

ENRICHMENT-52

On Your Own   Pair and Share   In a Group

Name

MEASURING TEMPERATURE

WEATHER REPORT

You can write a weather report.
Find the weather map in a newspaper.
Choose 4 cities.
Color to show the high temperature.
Write a weather report.
Tell if it is hot or cold or warm or cool.
Tell what people should wear.
  Answers will vary.

1. City: _____
2. City: _____
3. City: _____
4. City: _____

Macmillan/McGraw-Hill, MATHEMATICS IN ACTION
Grade 2, Chapter 5, Lesson 6, page 160

Enrichment-52

Problem of the Day

Jack wears a heavy coat if the temperature falls below 10°C. Monday's temperature was 14°C. Tuesday's temperature was 8°C lower than Monday's. Wednesday's temperature was 5°C higher than Tuesday's. On which day did Jack wear a heavy coat?   [Tuesday]

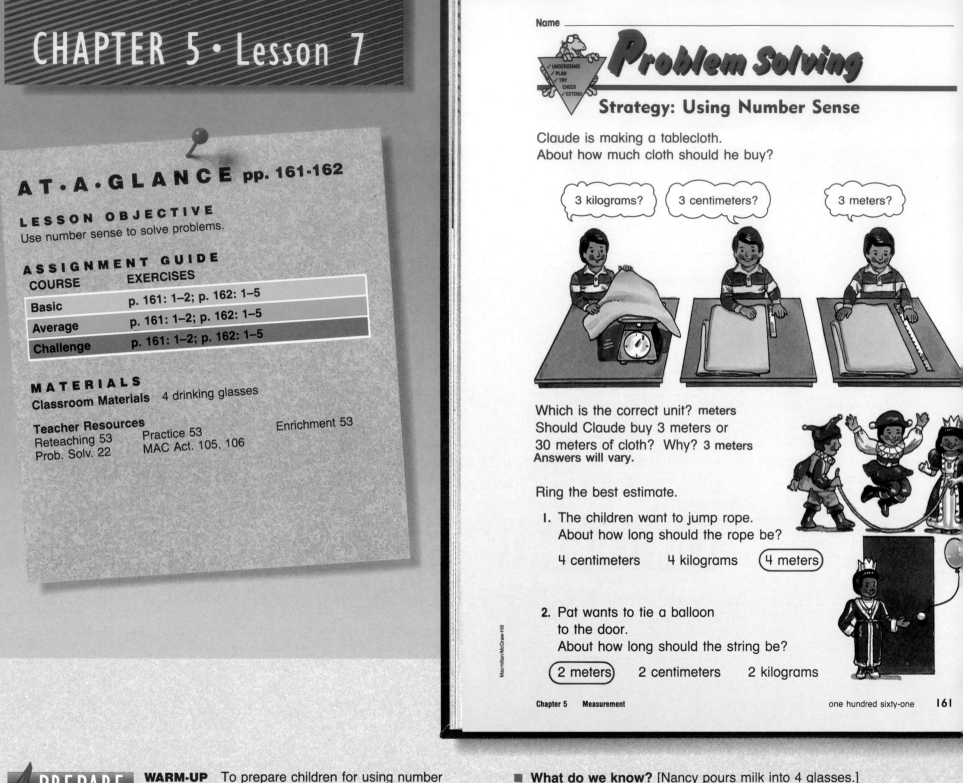

Problem Solving

UNDERSTAND
PLAN
TRY
CHECK
EXTEND

Strategy: Using Number Sense

Claude is making a tablecloth.
About how much cloth should he buy?

3 kilograms?   3 centimeters?   3 meters?

Which is the correct unit? **meters**
Should Claude buy 3 meters or
30 meters of cloth? Why? **3 meters**
Answers will vary.

Ring the best estimate.

1. The children want to jump rope.
   About how long should the rope be?

   4 centimeters   4 kilograms   (4 meters)

2. Pat wants to tie a balloon
   to the door.
   About how long should the string be?

   (2 meters)   2 centimeters   2 kilograms

Macmillan/McGraw-Hill

Chapter 5   Measurement   one hundred sixty-one   161

AT·A·GLANCE pp. 161-162

LESSON OBJECTIVE
Use number sense to solve problems.

ASSIGNMENT GUIDE

COURSE	EXERCISES
Basic	p. 161: 1–2; p. 162: 1–5
Average	p. 161: 1–2; p. 162: 1–5
Challenge	p. 161: 1–2; p. 162: 1–5

MATERIALS
Classroom Materials 4 drinking glasses

Teacher Resources
Reteaching 53   Practice 53   Enrichment 53
Prob. Solv. 22   MAC Act. 105, 106

---

1 PREPARE

WARM-UP To prepare children for using number sense to solve a problem, ask them whether they would measure the following in centimeters, meters, liters, or kilograms:

■ **how heavy a bag of oranges is** [kilograms]
■ **the distance from their desk to the door** [meters]
■ **the length of a pencil** [centimeters]
■ **the amount of water in a pail** [liters]

2 TEACH

DISCUSSING Display 4 drinking glasses. Read the following problem aloud.

Nancy pours milk for herself and 3 friends. Does she use about 1 kilogram, 1 liter, or 1 meter of milk?

■ **What do we know?** [Nancy pours milk into 4 glasses.]
■ **How can we find out which amount makes the most sense?** [We need to think about how each unit of measure is used.]
■ **Which measure makes the most sense?** [One liter; Liters are used to measure liquid, and milk is a liquid.]

PUPIL'S EDITION pp. 161-162

Page 161 Have a volunteer read the problem at the top of the page.
■ **What do you know?** [Claude is buying cloth to make a tablecloth.]
■ **What do you need to find out?** [which unit measures cloth]
Have children look at the pictures and read the text around them.

■ **What do you need to do?** [You need to think about what each measure is used for and which measure makes the most sense.]

Ring the best estimate.

1. Pat wants to make a banner for the party.
   About how long should the cloth be?

   1 centimeter   (1 meter)   1 liter

2. George wants to serve some apples and oranges as a snack.
   About how much fruit does he need?

   (3 kilograms)   3 meters   30 kilograms

3. Jim and Lara made a dragon costume.
   About how much cloth did they use?

   (5 meters)   5 kilograms   50 meters

4. Toni's mother brought a bowl of punch.
   About how much punch was in the bowl?

   6 meters   6 kilograms   (6 liters)

5. There were 4 children.
   Each child drank 1 glass of juice.
   About how much juice did they drink?

   40 liters   (1 liter)   4 liters

For Students Acquiring English (SAE)

Review the units of measure and the measuring device with SAE children, as well as the vocabulary for approximating length, weight, and volume.

TEACHER to TEACHER

COOPERATIVE LEARNING TIP I find children work well on this lesson in pairs and small groups. The day before the lesson, I ask family groups to bring in various household objects for everyone to measure. Together the pairs decide the appropriate measurement for each object and alternate measuring with recording the measurement. Then they compare results with the other pair(s) in their family group. Finally, I call on family representatives to present their findings to the **class community** with a **stand and share,** where each group presents new information.

Have children ring the best estimate. [3 meters] Then ask children to explain why 3 meters is the most sensible answer. [Cloth can be measured in meters; 3 meters is about enough for a tablecloth.] Discuss why 30 meters of cloth would not be a sensible answer. [Answers will vary but children should realize that 30 meters is too large an amount of cloth.]

■ **What did you learn?** [You can use number sense or what you know about amounts and measures to solve problems.]

Check for Understanding

■ **What if Claude wanted to make a tablecloth for a little doll table? Would he need about 3 meters or 3 centimeters of cloth? Why?** [He would need 3 centimeters. A doll's table is very small, and centimeters are used to measure small amounts.]

GUIDED PRACTICE   ex. 1–2: Work through problem 1 with the children. Make sure they understand how to solve the problem using number sense.

Page 162   Have a volunteer read the directions at the top of the page.

 **PRACTICE•APPLY**   **PRACTICE**   ex. 1–5

C L O S E   Guide children to summarize the lesson:

■ **How do you use number sense to solve problems?** [Possible response: You think about amounts and units of measure and what makes the most sense, according to what you already know.]

MATH AND CONSUMERS ■ STORE SMARTS

MAC Activity 105

On Your Own   Pair and Share   In a Group

Materials   grocery store circulars

Procedure   Assign children to work in groups of three or four. Give each group a grocery circular from a local store. Tell children that you will name a unit of measure. Explain that they are to look through their circular and find a picture of something that could be bought in that unit of measure. Demonstrate for the children what to do before they begin; for example, tell children that you are looking for something in kilograms. Volunteers may suggest fruits or meats. If there is a picture, ask children to guess the mass of the fruit in kilograms. Discuss whether the answer is sensible. Then continue the activity with meters, centimeters, and liters.

▲
MAC Activity 105:
Basic-to-Average

MAC Activity 106:
Average-to-Challenge
▼

SPEAKING MATHEMATICALLY ■ IS IT?

MAC Activity 106

On Your Own   Pair and Share   In a Group

Materials   classroom objects such as books, a crayon, a sheet of paper, scissors, a water pitcher, a plastic gallon-sized jug

Setup   Display a book, crayon, sheet of paper, scissors, and other materials. Make sure these objects can be measured in varying amounts of centimeters, meters, and kilograms. Also display containers of various sizes, such as a water pitcher and a plastic gallon-sized jug.

Procedure   Assign children to play in pairs. Have one child sit with closed eyes, while the other chooses one of the objects and says, "I see an object that is about 2 kilograms." The partner gives one clue about the object, such as "You can use it to learn the meanings of words." The other child then opens his or her eyes and tries to find the object by asking, "Is it (a dictionary)?" Tell children that they can make three guesses. If the child has not guessed the answer, he or she should be told. Have children take turns so that they have played at least three rounds.

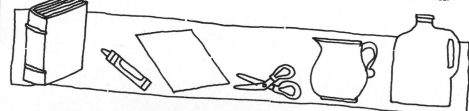

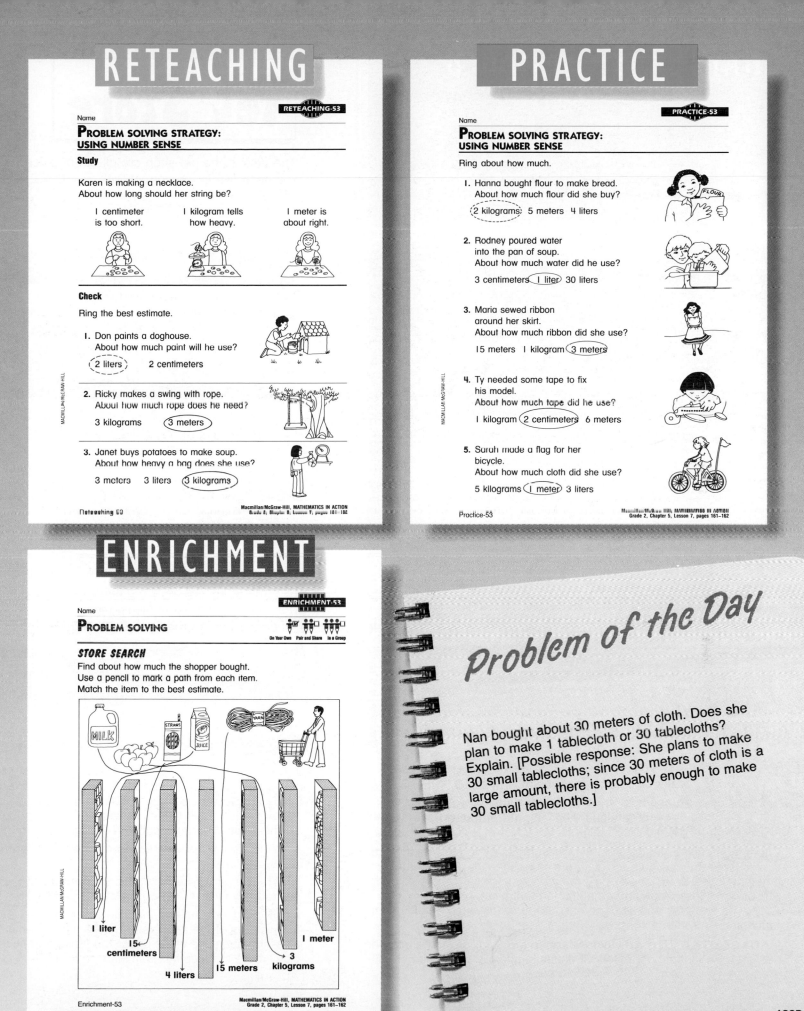

RETEACHING

Name _____

PROBLEM SOLVING STRATEGY: USING NUMBER SENSE

Study

Karen is making a necklace.
About how long should her string be?

I centimeter is too short.	I kilogram tells how heavy.	I meter is about right.

Check

Ring the best estimate.

1. Don paints a doghouse.
   About how much paint will he use?

   (2 liters)   2 centimeters

2. Ricky makes a swing with rope.
   About how much rope does he need?

   3 kilograms   (3 meters)

3. Janet buys potatoes to make soup.
   About how heavy a bag does she use?

   3 meters   3 liters   (3 kilograms)

Reteaching-53

Macmillan/McGraw-Hill, MATHEMATICS IN ACTION
Grade 2, Chapter 5, Lesson 7, pages 161-162

PRACTICE

Name _____

PROBLEM SOLVING STRATEGY: USING NUMBER SENSE

Ring about how much.

1. Hanna bought flour to make bread.
   About how much flour did she buy?

   (2 kilograms)   5 meters   4 liters

2. Rodney poured water into the pan of soup.
   About how much water did he use?

   3 centimeters   (I liter)   30 liters

3. Maria sewed ribbon around her skirt.
   About how much ribbon did she use?

   15 meters   I kilogram   (3 meters)

4. Ty needed some tape to fix his model.
   About how much tape did he use?

   I kilogram   (2 centimeters)   6 meters

5. Sarah made a flag for her bicycle.
   About how much cloth did she use?

   5 kilograms   (I meter)   3 liters

Practice-53

Macmillan/McGraw-Hill, MATHEMATICS IN ACTION
Grade 2, Chapter 5, Lesson 7, pages 161-162

ENRICHMENT

On Your Own   Pair and Share   In a Group

Name _____

PROBLEM SOLVING

STORE SEARCH

Find about how much the shopper bought.
Use a pencil to mark a path from each item.
Match the item to the best estimate.

I liter

15 centimeters

4 liters

15 meters

3 kilograms

I meter

Enrichment-53

Macmillan/McGraw-Hill, MATHEMATICS IN ACTION
Grade 2, Chapter 5, Lesson 7, pages 161-162

Problem of the Day

Nan bought about 30 meters of cloth. Does she plan to make 1 tablecloth or 30 tablecloths? Explain. [Possible response: She plans to make 30 small tablecloths; since 30 meters of cloth is a large amount, there is probably enough to make 30 small tablecloths.]

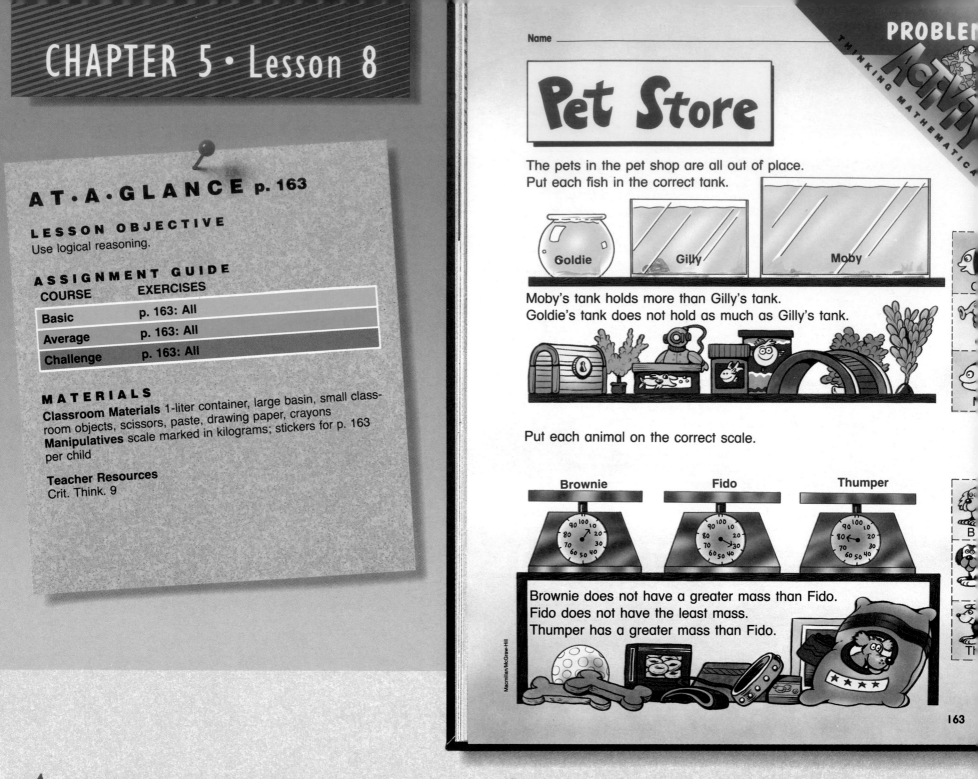

Name _____

PROBLEM

THINKING MATHEMATICS

Pet Store

The pets in the pet shop are all out of place.
Put each fish in the correct tank.

Goldie   Gilly   Moby

Moby's tank holds more than Gilly's tank.
Goldie's tank does not hold as much as Gilly's tank.

Put each animal on the correct scale.

Brownie   Fido   Thumper

Brownie does not have a greater mass than Fido.
Fido does not have the least mass.
Thumper has a greater mass than Fido.

163

PLAN   **AIMS AND ATTITUDES** This lesson develops logical reasoning involving clues about capacity and mass. Children must eliminate choices for answers only after considering all clues presented.

Encourage children to develop their own methods for solving the problems. Some may be able to retain the clues mentally. Others may find it helpful to draw and revise pictures as new information is obtained. Still other children may find it helpful to manipulate physical models. Accept all methods as valid and encourage children to verbalize their reasoning.

MANAGEMENT The activity is intended for all children and has been designed for independent work. It is also appropriate for pairs of children.

GUIDE   Assemble a 1-liter container, large basin, small objects, and a scale marked in kilograms. Measure 3 liters of water, then 6 liters of water. Place various classroom objects on the scale. Then ask children the following questions.

■ **Which tank would hold more, a 10-liter tank or a 15-liter tank?** [a 15-liter tank]

■ **Which has a greater mass, something that is 10 kilograms or something that is 3 kilograms?** [something that is 10 kilograms]

Read the directions and the clues on page 163. Have children cut out the pictures of the animals or use stickers. Remind them to consider all of the sentence clues under the tanks and scales before they decide where to place the animals.

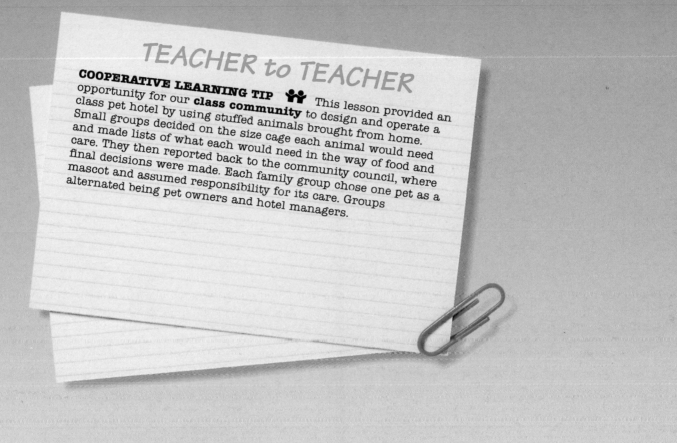

TEACHER to TEACHER

COOPERATIVE LEARNING TIP This lesson provided an opportunity for our **class community** to design and operate a class pet hotel by using stuffed animals brought from home. Small groups decided on the size cage each animal would need and made lists of what each would need in the way of food and care. They then reported back to the community council, where final decisions were made. Each family group chose one pet as a mascot and assumed responsibility for its care. Groups alternated being pet owners and hotel managers.

After children have decided where to place the stickers, discuss the clues and the placement. Then have children paste the animals in place on the page.

3 EXTEND Distribute drawing paper and crayons to each child. Write the following clues on the chalkboard. Ask children to repeat the activity they just did using these new clues and placing the stickers or cutouts (whichever were not used for page 163) in the correct order on the drawing paper. Children may wish to draw the tanks and scales on the drawing paper.

Gilly's tank holds more than Goldie's tank.
Goldie's tank holds less than Moby's tank.
[Answer: Goldie, Moby, Gilly]

Thumper does not have a greater mass than Brownie.
Brownie does not have the greatest mass.
[Answer: Thumper, Brownie, Fido]

Encourage volunteers to discuss the method they used to solve the problem.

EXTRA PRACTICE

Extra Practice

Using Centimeters, pages 153–154
Estimate. Then measure. Use ▭.

		Estimate	Measure
1.	_____	about ___ cm	about _5_ cm
2.	_____	about ___ cm	about _3_ cm
3.	_____	about ___ cm	about _2_ cm

Measuring Capacity, pages 157–158
Ring the better estimate.

1. less than 1 liter
about 1 liter
(more than 1 liter)

2. (less than 1 liter)
about 1 liter
more than 1 liter

Measuring Mass and Temperature, pages 159–160
Ring the better estimate.   Write the temperature.

1. (more than 1 kg)
less than 1 kg

2. 24 °C

ADDITIONAL PRACTICE

p. 153 Draw the length of line of the number indicated at the left.

Estimate. Then measure with ruler.

		Estimate [Answers will vary.]	**Measure**
1.	3.8 cm	about ___ cm	about [4] cm
2.	1.7 cm	about ___ cm	about [2] cm
3.	4.1 cm	about ___ cm	about [4] cm
4.	2.6 cm	about ___ cm	about [3] cm

Draw these lines. Use your ruler.
[Check students' drawings.]

5. 6 cm
6. 3 cm
7. 2 cm
8. 5 cm

p. 157 Show children the container illustrated below.

Tell the better estimate.

1.

[less than 1 liter]
about 1 liter
more than 1 liter

p. 159 *Tell the better estimate.*

1.

more than 1 kg
[less than 1 kg]

2. *Write the temperature.*

[94°C]

AT·A·GLANCE pp. 165-166

LESSON OBJECTIVE
Estimate and measure length in inches.

ASSIGNMENT GUIDE

COURSE	EXERCISES
Basic	p. 165: 1–4; p. 166: 1–6
Average	p. 165: 1–4; p. 166: 1–6
Challenge	p. 165: 1–4; p. 166: 1–6
Extra Practice, p. 177	Practice Plus, p. 178

MATERIALS
Classroom Materials book, small classroom objects suitable for measuring length
Manipulatives 1 inch ruler punchout per child

Teacher Resources
Reteaching 54   Practice 54   Enrichment 54
MAC Act. 107, 108

SKILLS TRACE MEASURING LENGTH	
Explore (Concrete) 152	**Develop/Understand (Transitional/Abstract)** 153–154, 155–156, 165–166, 167–168
Practice 164, 177, 178, 179–180, 213	**Apply** 161–162, 173–174, 175, 176

ACTIVITY

Using Inches

It measures between 1 and 2. It is closer to 2.

I **inch**

0   I   2   3   4
inch

The eraser is about 2 inches long.

How long?
Use an ▭ . inch ruler
Look at the picture.
Estimate. Then measure.

1. For exercises 1–4 answers will vary.

   Estimate: about ____ inches   **Measure:** about __4__ inches

2. ◁━━

   Estimate: about ____ inches   **Measure:** about __2__ inches

3. ━━━━━━

   Estimate: about ____ inches   **Measure:** about __5__ inches

4. How many inches long are the red part and blue part together?

   Estimate: about ____ inches   **Measure:** about __2__ inches

Macmillan/McGraw-Hill

Chapter 5   Measurement   one hundred sixty-five   **165**

PREPARE **WARM-UP** To prepare children to measure length in inches, demonstrate heel-to-toe steps. Then call on volunteers to measure the length of the room using heel-to-toe steps. Record these nonstandard measurements on the chalkboard and explain why some of the measurements are different. [Each child's foot is a different size.]

TEACH **DISCUSSING** Display an inch ruler and tell children that **inch** is another unit used to measure length. Write the word **inch** on the chalkboard and have children read it. Distribute punchout inch rulers to the children and have them locate the 0 mark and the 1 mark. Explain that the distance between these two marks equals 1 inch.

Hold up a classroom book. Ask children to estimate the length of the book. Next demonstrate how to measure the length of the book using the ruler.

■ **Where do you put the 0 mark on the ruler when you measure?** [at the end of the object being measured]

Have children measure other small classroom objects. Show children how to measure to the nearest inch.

Remind children that when you measure to the nearest inch the object may be shorter or longer than the measurement recorded. This is why we say it is "about" that measurement. As children become more familiar with this concept the "about" can be dropped.

PUPIL'S EDITION pp. 165-166

Page 165 Guide children through the example at the top of the page.

Working Together

Use an ▭▭▭▭ .
Find the object.
You estimate how long.
Your partner measures.
Take turns.

> Remember to start from zero when you measure.

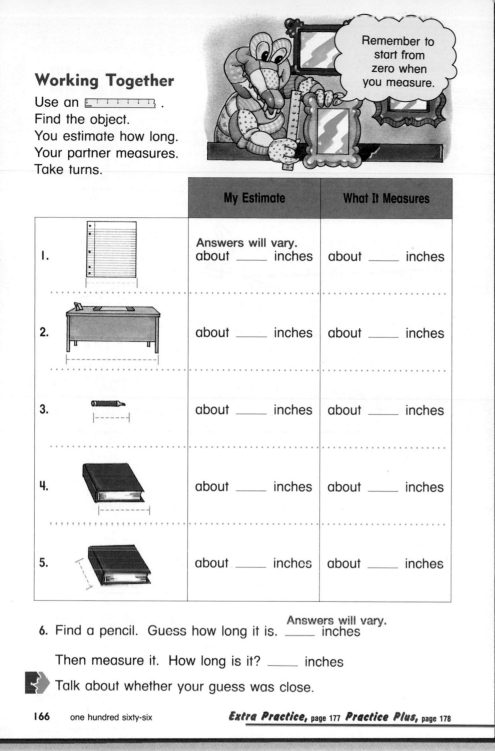

		My Estimate	What It Measures
		Answers will vary.	
1.		about ___ inches	about ___ inches
2.		about ___ inches	about ___ inches
3.		about ___ inches	about ___ inches
4.		about ___ inches	about ___ inches
5.		about ___ inches	about ___ inches

6. Find a pencil. Guess how long it is. **Answers will vary.** ___ inches

Then measure it. How long is it? ___ inches

▶ Talk about whether your guess was close.

Extra Practice, page 177 *Practice Plus,* page 178

ACTIVITY *Common Error and Remediation*

MATERIALS punchout inch ruler; chalk; classroom objects

Some children may not be able to measure to the nearest inch. Work individually with each child. Give the child a piece of chalk that measures between 2 and 3 inches. Line up one end of the chalk with the inch ruler. Explain that the other end of the chalk does not fall exactly on an inch mark, but rather between two marks. Have the child identify the two inch marks. [2 and 3] Guide children to see to which mark the end of the chalk is closer. Have the child repeat with other small classroom objects.

ACTIVITY **ALTERNATIVE TEACHING STRATEGY**

MATERIALS 1 punchout inch ruler per child; classroom objects

KINESTHETIC Distribute punchout inch rulers to each child. As children examine the ruler, draw a number line for 0 to 12 on the chalkboard. Call on volunteers to tell how the number line and the ruler are the same. [They each have units marked off with lines; they each have the same numbers.] Tell children they are different because the space on a number line can be any length, but 1 inch is always 1 inch long. Review counting on the number line and have children do the same on their rulers. Then have children measure classroom objects by counting on the ruler from 0 to the end of the object.

Check for Understanding

■ **What could you measure with an inch ruler?** [Possible responses: eraser, book]

GUIDED PRACTICE ex. 1–4: For reteaching, use Common Error and Remediation or Alternative Strategy.

Page 166 WORKING TOGETHER Identify the pictured objects. Assign partners and have children find each pictured object, write an estimate of its length, and then measure it.

PRACTICE•APPLY **PRACTICE** ex. 1–6

C L O S E Guide children to summarize the lesson:

■ **How many inches long is your pointer finger?** [Answers will vary but should be given in inches.]

MAC Activity 107

On Your Own Pair and Share In a Group

CAREER—CARPENTER ■ BUILDING PROBLEMS

Discuss the work of a carpenter with the children. As part of the discussion, encourage children to describe briefly any personal or family woodworking projects they have participated in or observed. Discuss why it is important that carpenters measure accurately. Ask what might happen if a carpenter read a measurement incorrectly.

Then have children solve the following measurement problems related to woodworking and building.

Tom had a 17-inch board.
He cut off a piece 9 inches long.
How many inches were left?
[8 inches]

Lila plans to make 3 shelves for her doll house. One will be 6 inches long, one will be 4 inches long, and one will be 3 inches long. How many inches of wood does she need? [13 inches]

▲
MAC Activity 107:
Basic-to-Average

MAC Activity 108:
Average-to-Challenge
▼

MAC Activity 108

On Your Own Pair and Share In a Group

MANIPULATIVES ■ SUBTRACTING INCHES

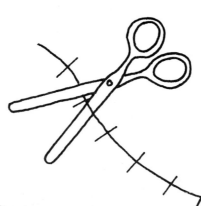

6 INCHES–2 INCHES =_____

Materials punchout inch rulers, scissors, string, drawing paper, paste

Assign children to work in pairs. Give each pair a punchout inch ruler, a pair of scissors, and some string. Have one child write a simple addition or subtraction sentence at the top of a sheet of drawing paper, such as 6 in. − 2 in. = ____. The other child illustrates the sentence by measuring and cutting a piece of string 6 inches long and then cutting off 2 inches. The child then measures the length of string that is left, pastes that piece of string on the paper below the corresponding number sentence, and writes the answer. Then have children exchange roles.

RETEACHING-54

Name

USING INCHES

Study

about
5 inches
long

| 0 | 1 | 2 | 3 | 4 | 5 | 6 |

Check

Measure the length of each object.

1. about __3__ inches

| 0 | 1 | 2 | 3 | 4 | 5 | 6 |

2. about __1__ inch

| 0 | 1 | 2 | 3 | 4 | 5 | 6 |

3. about __4__ inches

4. about __6__ inches

5. about __2__ inches

Macmillan/McGraw-Hill, MATHEMATICS IN ACTION
Grade 2, Chapter 5, Lesson 9, pages 165–166

Reteaching-54

PRACTICE-54

Name

USING INCHES

Estimate how long. Then measure.

1. Estimate: about ____ inches   Measure: about __3__ inches
Answers will vary.

2. Estimate: about ____ inch   Measure: about __1__ inch

3. Estimate: about ____ inches   Measure: about __4__ inches

4. Estimate: about ____ inches   Measure: about __5__ inches

How many inches long?

5. about __4__ inches

6. about __5__ inches

Macmillan/McGraw-Hill, MATHEMATICS IN ACTION
Grade 2, Chapter 5, Lesson 9, pages 165–166

Practice-54

ENRICHMENT-54

Name

USING INCHES

On Your Own   Pair and Share   In a Group

INCHING ALONG

Use your inch ruler.
How many inches did each worm travel?

1. about __7__ inches

2. about __12__ inches

3. about __11__ inches

I wonder if string could help me measure?

4. about __10__ inches

5. about __11__ inches

Macmillan/McGraw-Hill, MATHEMATICS IN ACTION
Grade 2, Chapter 5, Lesson 9, pages 165–166

Enrichment-54

Problem of the Day

Kim needs 10 inches of ribbon to make a bookmark. A spool has 87 inches of ribbon. Can Kim make bookmarks for 9 friends? [No; possible solution: 10, 20, 30, . . . , 90; 90 inches needed.]

AT·A·GLANCE pp. 167-168

LESSON OBJECTIVE
Estimate and measure in inches, feet, and yards.

ASSIGNMENT GUIDE

COURSE	EXERCISES
Basic	p. 167: 1–2; p. 168: 1–8
Average	p. 167: 1–2; p. 168: 1–8
Challenge	p. 167: 1–2; p. 168: 1–8

MATERIALS

Classroom Materials yardstick
Manipulatives 1 12-inch ruler, 1 measuring tape, 1 punchout inch ruler per pair

Teacher Resources
Reteaching 55   Practice 55   Enrichment 55
Prob. Solv. 23   MAC Act. 109, 110
Math Anthology, pp. 154–156

SKILLS TRACE
MEASURING LENGTH

Explore (Concrete) 152	Develop/Understand (Transitional/Abstract) 153–154, 155–156, 165–166, 167–168
Practice 164, 177, 178, 179–180, 213	Apply 161–162, 173–174, 175, 176

See *MANIPULATIVES PLUS 28*, p. 150N.

ACTiViTy

Inch, Foot, and Yard

A nail is about 1 inch long.
A hammer is about 1 **foot** long.
An umbrella is about 1 **yard** long.

> 12 inches equal 1 foot.
> 3 feet equal 1 yard.

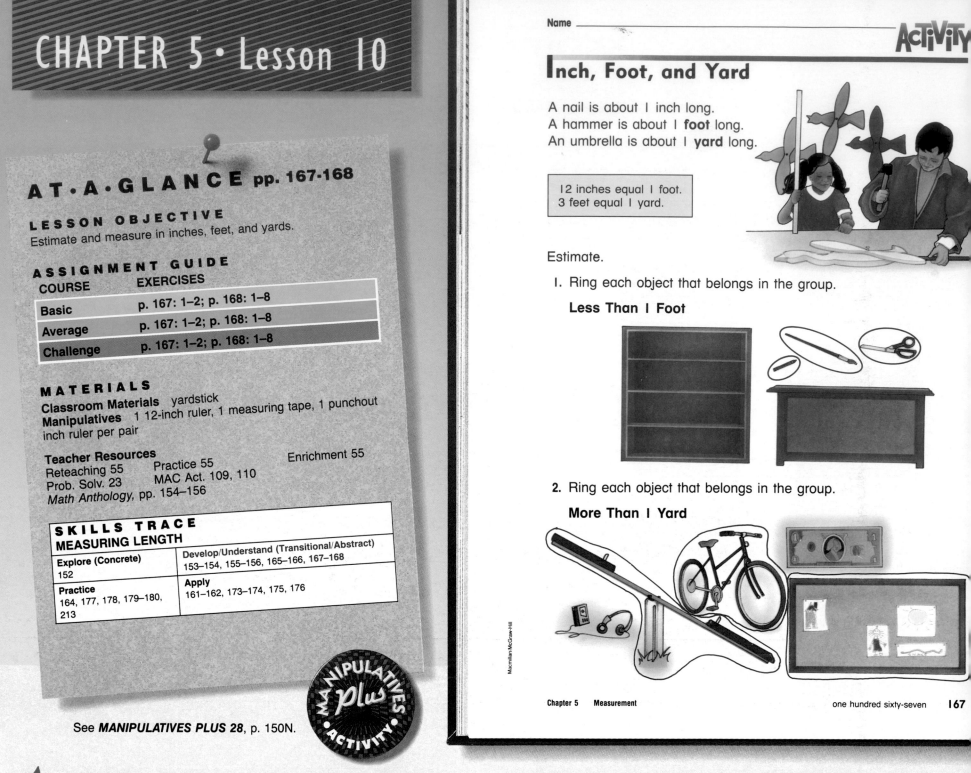

Estimate.

1. Ring each object that belongs in the group.

   Less Than 1 Foot

2. Ring each object that belongs in the group.

   More Than 1 Yard

---

1 PREPARE

WARM-UP To review measuring in inches, write the following on the chalkboard.

3 inches	9 inches	5 inches
7 inches	1 inch	12 inches

Have children use inch rulers to draw and label lines for each length.

2 TEACH

DISCUSSING Point to a 12-inch line drawn for the Warm-Up. Explain that 12 inches equal 1 **foot.**

Display a yardstick and identify it. Explain that a **yard** is another unit of measure for length. Have three volunteers hold 1-foot rulers directly under the yardstick.

■ **How many feet are there in 1 yard?** [3 feet]

Compare relative sizes by naming two units and asking children to identify which is longer or shorter.

PUPIL'S EDITION pp. 167-168

Page 167 Work through the example at the top of the page with the children. Display 12-inch rulers and yardsticks for children who need help in visualizing these lengths.

Check for Understanding

■ **Can you name three things that are less than 1 foot long?**
[Possible responses: pencil, crayon, piece of chalk, eraser]

GUIDED PRACTICE ex. 1–2: For reteaching, use Common Error and Remediation or Alternative Strategy.

Working Together

Use an ▭▭▭▭ and a ⬭▭ .
Measure the real object. customary measure tape
Write the measure next to the unit you used.

> Talk about which unit to use.

For exercises 1–6 measurements will vary. Accept reasonable answers.

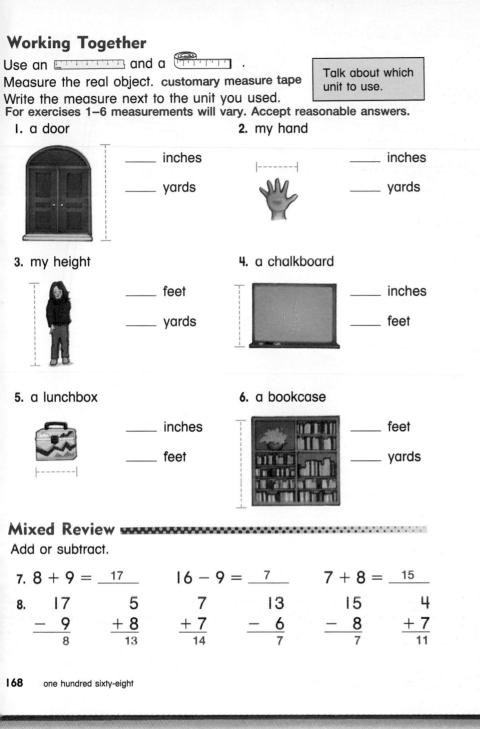

1. a door
_____ inches
_____ yards

2. my hand
_____ inches
_____ yards

3. my height
_____ feet
_____ yards

4. a chalkboard
_____ inches
_____ feet

5. a lunchbox
_____ inches
_____ feet

6. a bookcase
_____ feet
_____ yards

Mixed Review

Add or subtract.

7. $8 + 9 =$ __17__ $16 - 9 =$ __7__ $7 + 8 =$ __15__

8.
17 − 9 8	5 + 8 13	7 + 7 14	13 − 6 7	15 − 8 7	4 + 7 11

ACTIVITY ALTERNATIVE TEACHING STRATEGY

MATERIALS 12-inch ruler, yardstick

VISUAL Draw a 12-inch line on the chalkboard. Demonstrate how to measure the line with a ruler. Tell children that 12 inches equal 1 foot. Then draw three continuous 12-inch lines on the chalkboard.

■ **How many feet long is this line?** [3]

Measure with a yardstick. Tell children that 3 feet equal 1 yard.

For Students Acquiring English (SAE)

Preteach or review with SAE children the words for the items pictured on pages 167 and 168; use real items if possible. Have children predict which of the items measures more than a yard.

ACTIVITY Common Error and Remediation

MATERIALS 12-inch ruler; paper streamers

Some children may not be able to measure an object that is longer than their ruler. Work individually with each child. Using a foot ruler, have the child measure strips of paper streamers several feet in length. Show the child how to make a small tick mark on the paper at the 1-foot mark. Demonstrate how to position the ruler at this tick mark to measure the next foot. Explain that the tick marks can be erased after measuring.

Page 168 Working Together   Assign children to work in pairs. Have children discuss with their partners which unit to use for measuring each object.

Mathematics and Literature

PRACTICE·APPLY   **PRACTICE**   ex. 1–8

Read *A New Coat for Anna* found in *Math Anthology* to the class. Talk about the importance of measuring length in the story.

■ **Why did the tailor take Anna's measurements?** [so he would know what size to make the coat]

■ **What would have happened if he had not measured Anna, or if he had not measured her accurately?** [The coat might have come out too big or too small.]

Reread the paragraph on page 156 of the story that describes how the tailor measured Anna. Demonstrate on a child where those measurements would be, and discuss the importance of each one in making a coat. Then have pairs of children use measuring tapes to take the same measurements of each other. Talk about the problems that might occur in trying to take the measurements using a ruler or a yardstick. [Because rulers and yardsticks are not flexible, it would be hard to get exact measurements around the curves of the body.]

C L O S E   Guide children to summarize the lesson:

■ **Which units can be used to measure length?** [inches, feet, yards]

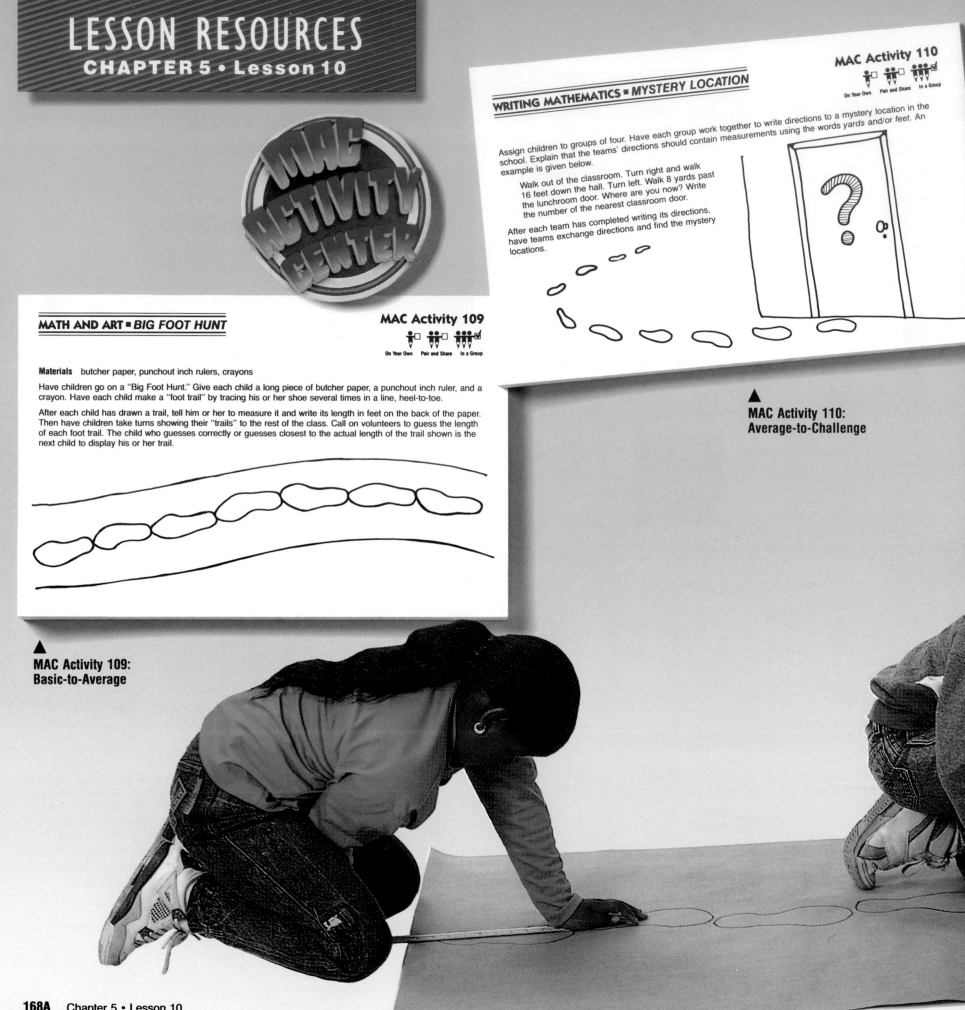

MAC Activity 110

WRITING MATHEMATICS ▪ MYSTERY LOCATION

On Your Own   Pair and Share   In a Group

Assign children to groups of four. Have each group work together to write directions to a mystery location in the school. Explain that the teams' directions should contain measurements using the words *yards* and/or *feet*. An example is given below.

Walk out of the classroom. Turn right and walk 16 feet down the hall. Turn left. Walk 8 yards past the lunchroom door. Where are you now? Write the number of the nearest classroom door.

After each team has completed writing its directions, have teams exchange directions and find the mystery locations.

▲
MAC Activity 110:
Average-to-Challenge

MATH AND ART ▪ *BIG FOOT HUNT*

MAC Activity 109

On Your Own   Pair and Share   In a Group

Materials   butcher paper, punchout inch rulers, crayons

Have children go on a "Big Foot Hunt." Give each child a long piece of butcher paper, a punchout inch ruler, and a crayon. Have each child make a "foot trail" by tracing his or her shoe several times in a line, heel-to-toe.

After each child has drawn a trail, tell him or her to measure it and write its length in feet on the back of the paper. Then have children take turns showing their "trails" to the rest of the class. Call on volunteers to guess the length of each foot trail. The child who guesses correctly or guesses closest to the actual length of the trail shown is the next child to display his or her trail.

▲
MAC Activity 109:
Basic-to-Average

Name

INCH, FOOT, AND YARD

Study

A small paper clip is about 1 inch long.

A football is about 1 foot long.

A baseball bat is about 1 yard long.

Check

Color the objects that belong in the group.

1. Less Than a Foot

2. More Than a Yard

Reteaching-55

Macmillan/McGraw-Hill, MATHEMATICS IN ACTION
Grade 2, Chapter 5, Lesson 10, pages 167–168

Name

INCH, FOOT, AND YARD

Measure the real object.
Write the measure next to
the unit you used.

Answers will vary.

1. your chair
—— inches
—— feet

2. your math book
—— inches
—— yards

3. your arm
—— feet
—— yards

4. your pencil
—— inches
—— feet

5. your shoe
—— inches
—— feet

6. your desktop
—— feet
—— yards

7. your notebook
—— inches
—— yards

8. your leg
—— feet
—— yards

Practice-55

Macmillan/McGraw-Hill, MATHEMATICS IN ACTION
Grade 2, Chapter 5, Lesson 10, pages 167–168

Name

INCH, FOOT, AND YARD

On Your Own   Pair and Share   In a Group

DIFFERENT UNITS

1 foot = 12 inches

1 yard = 3 feet
1 yard = 36 inches

Work with a partner.
Use different units to measure.

Answers will vary.

1. Your height.
—— inches
—— feet —— inches
—— yards —— inches

2. Your partner's height.
—— inches
—— feet —— inches
—— yards —— inches

3. The door.
—— inches
—— feet —— inches
—— yards —— inches

4. A window.
—— inches
—— feet —— inches
—— yards —— inches

5. The width of your
classroom.
—— feet —— inches
—— yards —— feet —— inches

6. The length of your
classroom.
—— feet —— inches
—— yards —— feet —— inches

Enrichment-55

Macmillan/McGraw-Hill, MATHEMATICS IN ACTION
Grade 2, Chapter 5, Lesson 10, pages 167–168

Problem of the Day

There are 15 yards of fabric. It takes 2 yards of fabric to make a bird costume and 3 yards to make a fox costume. How many yards will be left after costumes for 2 birds and 1 fox have been made?   [8 yards; possible solution: 2 + 2 = 4; 4 + 3 = 7; 15 − 7 = 8]

CHAPTER 5 • Lesson 11

AT·A·GLANCE pp. 169-170

LESSON OBJECTIVE
Estimate and measure capacity in cups, pints, and quarts.

ASSIGNMENT GUIDE

COURSE	EXERCISES
Basic	p. 169: 1–4; p. 170: 1–4, Challenge
Average	p. 169: 1–4; p. 170: 1–4, Challenge
Challenge	p. 169: 1–4; p. 170: 1–4, Challenge

MATERIALS
Classroom Materials unbreakable containers of various sizes, water or sand, sand or beans
Manipulatives 1 unbreakable cup, pint, and quart measures per group

Teacher Resources
Reteaching 56   Practice 56   Enrichment 56
MAC Act. 111, 112

SKILLS TRACE	
MEASURING CAPACITY	
Explore (Concrete) 152	**Develop/Understand (Transitional/Abstract)** 157–158, 169–170
Practice 164, 177, 179–180	**Apply** 161–162, 163, 173–174

See **MANIPULATIVES PLUS 29**, p. 150O.

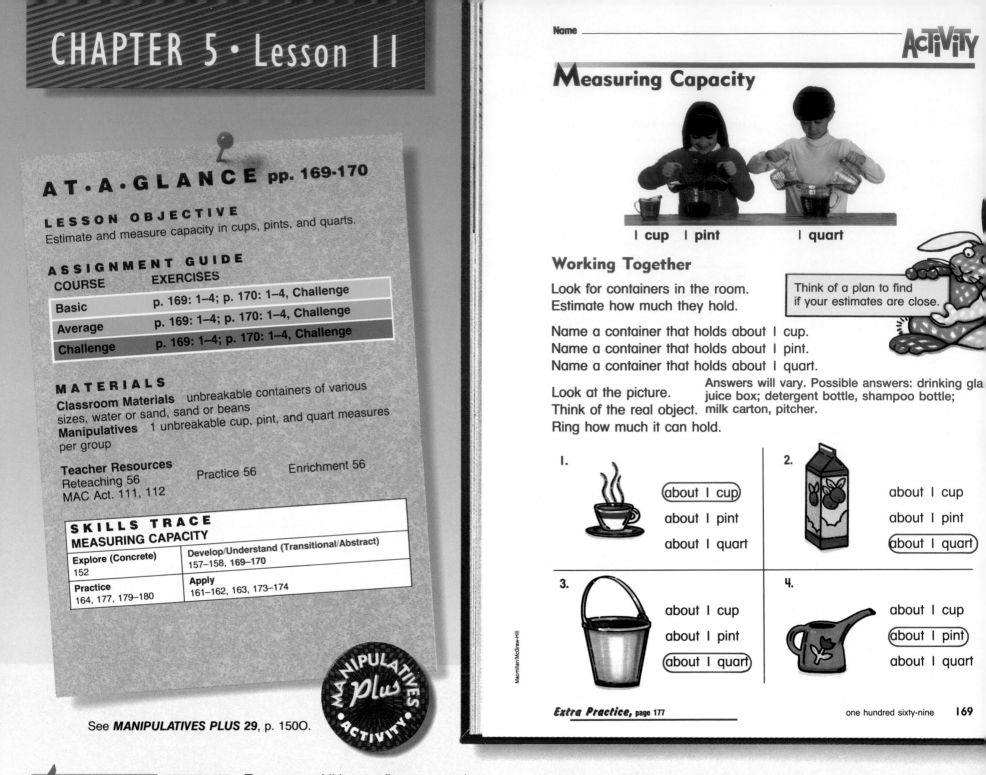

Measuring Capacity

I cup   I pint   I quart

Working Together

Look for containers in the room.
Estimate how much they hold.

Think of a plan to find if your estimates are close.

Name a container that holds about I cup.
Name a container that holds about I pint.
Name a container that holds about I quart.

Look at the picture.
Think of the real object.
Ring how much it can hold.

Answers will vary. Possible answers: drinking gla
juice box; detergent bottle, shampoo bottle;
milk carton, pitcher.

1. about I cup (ringed)
   about I pint
   about I quart

2. about I cup
   about I pint
   about I quart (ringed)

3. about I cup
   about I pint
   about I quart (ringed)

4. about I cup
   about I pint (ringed)
   about I quart

Macmillan/McGraw-Hill

Extra Practice, page 177   one hundred sixty-nine **169**

---

1 PREPARE
WARM-UP To prepare children to discuss capacity, display cup, pint, and quart measures. Without identifying the units, ask children to identify the containers that can hold the most and the least. Have them arrange the containers in order of size.

2 TEACH
DISCUSSING Display a **cup** measure and identify it as a unit for measuring how much a container can hold. Then display and identify a **pint** measure. Explain that 2 cups equal 1 pint. Demonstrate this fact by filling the pint measure with 2 cups of water or sand. Introduce a **quart** measure, using the same procedure.

PUPIL'S EDITION pp. 169-170

Page 169 Discuss the example at the top of the page with the children.

WORKING TOGETHER Have children work in groups to do the activity. Be sure there are several containers visible in the classroom. Have children estimate if a given container holds less than, more than, or the same as a cup. Then verify by pouring sand or beans from the cup measure to the container. Repeat for pint and quart.

Check for Understanding
■ **Which size container can hold more, a pint or a quart?** [a quart]

GUIDED PRACTICE ex. 1–4: Remind children to think of the real object, not the picture.

Ring the better estimate.

1.
about 10 cups
(about 2 cups)

2.
(about 2 pints)
about 7 pints

3.
about 1 quart
(about 6 quarts)

4.
(about 1 pint)
about 4 pints

····Challenge····

Make up a recipe for fruit punch to serve 8 people.

PARTY PUNCH

<u>2</u> cups 🍒 juice   <u>2</u> cups 🍎 juice

<u>2</u> cups 🍍 juice   <u>2</u> cups 🍇 juice

1. How much punch altogether? <u> 8 </u> cups punch

2. Talk about how to write the total measurement in pints and in quarts.
   Possible answer: 4 pints; 2 quarts

ACTIVITY *Common Error and Remediation*

MATERIALS beans or sand; unbreakable liquid measures

Some children may not see the relationship between units of capacity. Work with each child. Provide cup, pint, quart containers and beans. Have the child fill the pint container, then use the contents to fill 2 cups. Ask how much 1 pint equals. [2 cups] Have the child refill the pint container with the 2 cups. Ask how much 2 cups equal. [1 pint] Repeat with pints and quarts.

ONGOING ASSESSMENT MATH JOURNAL

OBSERVATION Determine whether children identify cup, pint, and quart containers correctly in the activity on p. 169.

INTERVIEW (1) About how much milk do you drink at a meal—1 cup, 1 pint, or 1 quart? Tell me how you know. (2) Show me a container that holds about 1 quart.

JOURNAL WRITING You may wish to have children record their responses in their math journals.

ACTIVITY **ALTERNATIVE TEACHING STRATEGY**

MATERIALS unbreakable containers of various sizes, water or sand

VISUAL Display containers of different sizes on the table. Give children an opportunity to study the containers.

■ **Which container do you think can hold about 1 cup of water?** [Use water or sand to compare children's estimates.]
■ **Which container can hold about 1 pint?**
■ **Which container can hold about 1 quart?**

Compare children's estimates.

For reteaching, use Common Error and Remediation or Alternative Strategy.

Page 170 Identify the pictures with the children. Remind children that their answers will be estimates.

3 PRACTICE•APPLY **PRACTICE** ex. 1–4

CHALLENGE Have the recipe read aloud. Remind children that the total amount of punch must equal at least 8 cups.

C L O S E Guide children to summarize the lesson:
■ **Which size container holds the most, a quart, cup, or pint?** [quart]

MAC Activity 111:
Basic-to-Average
▼

MAC Activity 111

On Your Own   Pair and Share   In a Group

MATH AND HEALTH ▪ HOW MUCH MILK?

MILK WE DRINK

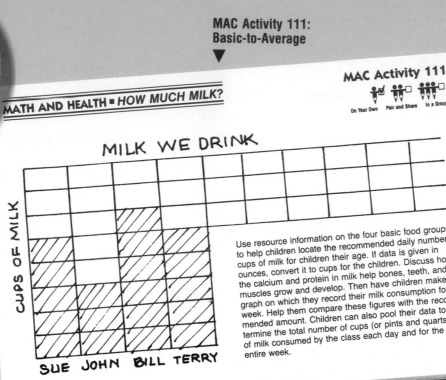

CUPS OF MILK

SUE   JOHN   BILL   TERRY

Use resource information on the four basic food groups to help children locate the recommended daily number of cups of milk for children their age. If data is given in ounces, convert it to cups for the children. Discuss how the calcium and protein in milk help bones, teeth, and muscles grow and develop. Then have children make a graph on which they record their milk consumption for a week. Help them compare these figures with the recommended amount. Children can also pool their data to determine the total number of cups (or pints and quarts) of milk consumed by the class each day and for the entire week.

MAC Activity 112:
Average-to-Challenge
▼

MATH AND CONSUMERS ▪ PRICES, PRICES

MAC Activity 112

On Your Own   Pair and Share   In a Group

Materials   unbreakable containers of various sizes, punchout coins

Tell children that fruit juices are sold in different-sized containers. Explain that the cost of juice per cup may vary, depending upon the size of the container bought. Point out that the lower the price is per cup, the better the buy.

Then have children work in pairs to draw and label three containers with the following prices: 1 cup at 30¢; 1 pint at 50¢; and 1 quart at 80¢. Tell children to use coins and what they know about measurement to find the price per cup for each size. [1 cup container is 30¢ per cup, 1 pint container is 25¢ per cup, and 1 quart container is 20¢ per cup.] Have children use this information to determine the best buy.   [1 quart]

½ PT.
1 CUP
30¢ EA.

1 PT.
2 CUPS.
25¢ EA.

1 QT.
4 CUPS.
20¢ EA.

BARGAIN BUY!

RETEACHING

Name

MEASURING CAPACITY

Study

I cup   I pint   I quart

Check

Color [yellow] if it holds about a cup.
Color [blue] if it holds about a pint.
Color [green] if it holds about a quart.

yellow   blue   green

green   yellow   blue

PRACTICE

Name

MEASURING CAPACITY

Ring the better estimate.

1.	I cup / I quart	2.	I pint / 2 quarts
3.	4 quarts / 8 quarts	4.	I cup / I quart

Match.

5.

ENRICHMENT

Name

MEASURING CAPACITY

On Your Own   Pair and Share   In a Group

MEASURE, STIR, AND SIP

Choose a drink. Make it together with your teacher.

Orange Milk Shake

2 cups orange juice	1. Put water in container.
3 cups lowfat powdered milk	2. Add powdered milk and mix well.
6 cups water	3. Add orange juice and stir.
4 ice cubes	4. Add ice cubes.
large container	

1. Ring how much orange juice to buy.

2. Ring how much water you need.

3. Estimate how many people can have a I cup drink.   1 to 2   8 to 10   20 to 22

Slumber Under

8 cups lowfat milk	1. Mix milk and cider and heat.
4 cups cider	2. Pour into mugs.
12 cinnamon sticks	3. Stir with a cinnamon stick.

4. Ring how much milk to buy.

5. Ring how much cider to buy.

6. Estimate how many people can have a I cup drink.   4 to 5   10 to 12   18 to 20

Problem of the Day

There will be 10 children at the cookout. If each child will drink 2 cups of juice, how many cups of juice will be needed?   [20 cups]

AT·A·GLANCE p. 171

LESSON OBJECTIVE
Estimate and measure weight in pounds.

ASSIGNMENT GUIDE

COURSE	EXERCISES
Basic	p. 171: 1–6
Average	p. 171: 1–6
Challenge	p. 171: 1–6
Extra Practice, p. 177	

MATERIALS
Classroom Materials balance scale, spring scale, 1-pound weights, clay

Teacher Resources
Reteaching 57   Practice 57   Enrichment 57
MAC Act. 113, 114

SKILLS TRACE
MEASURING MASS AND WEIGHT

Explore (Concrete) 152	Develop/Understand (Transitional/Abstract) 159, 171
Practice 164, 177, 179–180	Apply 161–162, 163, 173–174

See **MANIPULATIVES PLUS 30**, p. 150P.

Measuring Weight

I **pound**

How much does the flour weigh?
5 pounds

Working Together
Pick up the real object.
Estimate the weight.
Write *less than* or *more than*.

1.
less than _____ I pound

2.
more than _____ I pound

3.
less than _____ I pound

4.
more than _____ I pound

5.
How much does
the cat weigh?

  6 pounds

6.
How much more does the dog
weigh than the cat?

  6 pounds

Macmillan/McGraw-Hill

---

1 PREPARE   **WARM-UP** To review measurement, list these measurements on the chalkboard as you read them aloud: inch, foot, yard, cup, pint, quart. Ask children to name the unit of measure that answers each of these questions.

- **How much can a vase hold?** [pint or quart]
- **How wide is an auditorium stage?** [yard]
- **How tall is a plant?** [inch or foot]
- **How much can a bottle hold?** [cup, pint, or quart]

2 TEACH   **DISCUSSING** Distribute 1-pound weights and have children take turns holding them. Explain that **pound** is a unit used to measure weight. Then ask children to name objects in the classroom that they think weigh about 1 pound. Place each object on a balance scale. Have children determine if the object weighs about 1 pound, less than 1 pound, or more than 1 pound.

Display a spring scale and have children use it to measure the weight of other classroom objects. Demonstrate how to read the dial to determine weight to the nearest pound.

PUPIL'S EDITION p. 171

Page 171 Discuss the example at the top of the page with the children. Discuss whether the butter would weigh more, less, or the same if it were made into a different shape. Verify by taking one pound of clay and making it into a cube and weighing it. Then roll out the clay into a rope and weigh it. Discuss that the clay weighed the same each time.

ACTIVITY Common Error and Remediation

MATERIALS balance scale, empty crayon box, small eraser, classroom objects

Some children may think that the larger of two objects always weighs more. Work individually with each child. Have the child use a balance scale to compare the weight of an empty crayon box and a small eraser. Explain that it is not necessarily the size that determines if one object is heavier than the other. Repeat activity with other objects. Have the child estimate which is heavier and then compare on scale.

For Students Acquiring English (SAE)

Point out **flour** versus **flower**. Have children complete the page in heterogeneous pairs. Have the real objects available to pick up and hold for ex. 1–4.

ACTIVITY ALTERNATIVE TEACHING STRATEGY

MATERIALS 1-pound weight, balance scale, lightweight classroom objects, heavy classroom objects

VISUAL Hold up one object at a time and have it identified. Then call on volunteers to tell whether each object weighs more or less than 1 pound. Check children's estimates by placing each object on the balance scale to compare its weight with 1 pound.

Check for Understanding

■ When you weigh yourself on a scale, what label should you write after the number, pounds or inches? [pounds]

GUIDED PRACTICE ex. 1–2.

WORKING TOGETHER Have partners discuss their estimates. For reteaching, use Common Error and Remediation or Alternative Strategy.

3 PRACTICE•APPLY

PRACTICE ex. 3–6

CLOSE Guide children to summarize the lesson:

■ Do you weigh more or less than a cat? [more]

MAC ACTIVITY CENTER

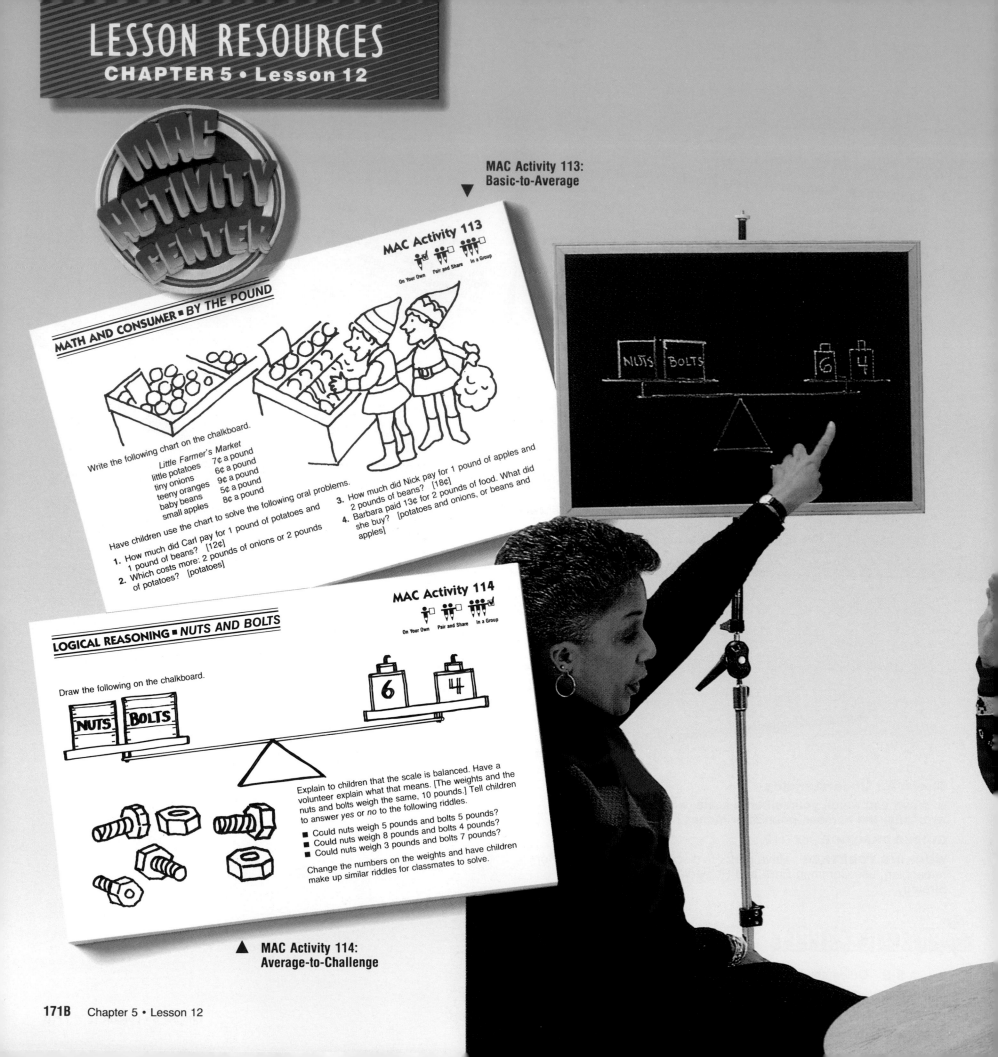

MAC Activity 113:
Basic-to-Average

MAC Activity 113

On Your Own   Pair and Share   In a Group

MATH AND CONSUMER ■ BY THE POUND

Write the following chart on the chalkboard.

Little Farmer's Market

little potatoes   7¢ a pound
tiny onions   6¢ a pound
teeny oranges   9¢ a pound
baby beans   5¢ a pound
small apples   8¢ a pound

Have children use the chart to solve the following oral problems.

1. How much did Carl pay for 1 pound of potatoes and 1 pound of beans?   [12¢]
2. Which costs more: 2 pounds of onions or 2 pounds of potatoes?   [potatoes]
3. How much did Nick pay for 1 pound of apples and 2 pounds of beans?   [18¢]
4. Barbara paid 13¢ for 2 pounds of food. What did she buy?   [potatoes and onions, or beans and apples]

MAC Activity 114

On Your Own   Pair and Share   In a Group

LOGICAL REASONING ■ NUTS AND BOLTS

Draw the following on the chalkboard.

Explain to children that the scale is balanced. Have a volunteer explain what that means. [The weights and the nuts and bolts weigh the same, 10 pounds.] Tell children to answer *yes* or *no* to the following riddles.

■ Could nuts weigh 5 pounds and bolts 5 pounds?
■ Could nuts weigh 8 pounds and bolts 4 pounds?
■ Could nuts weigh 3 pounds and bolts 7 pounds?

Change the numbers on the weights and have children make up similar riddles for classmates to solve.

▲ **MAC Activity 114:**
Average-to-Challenge

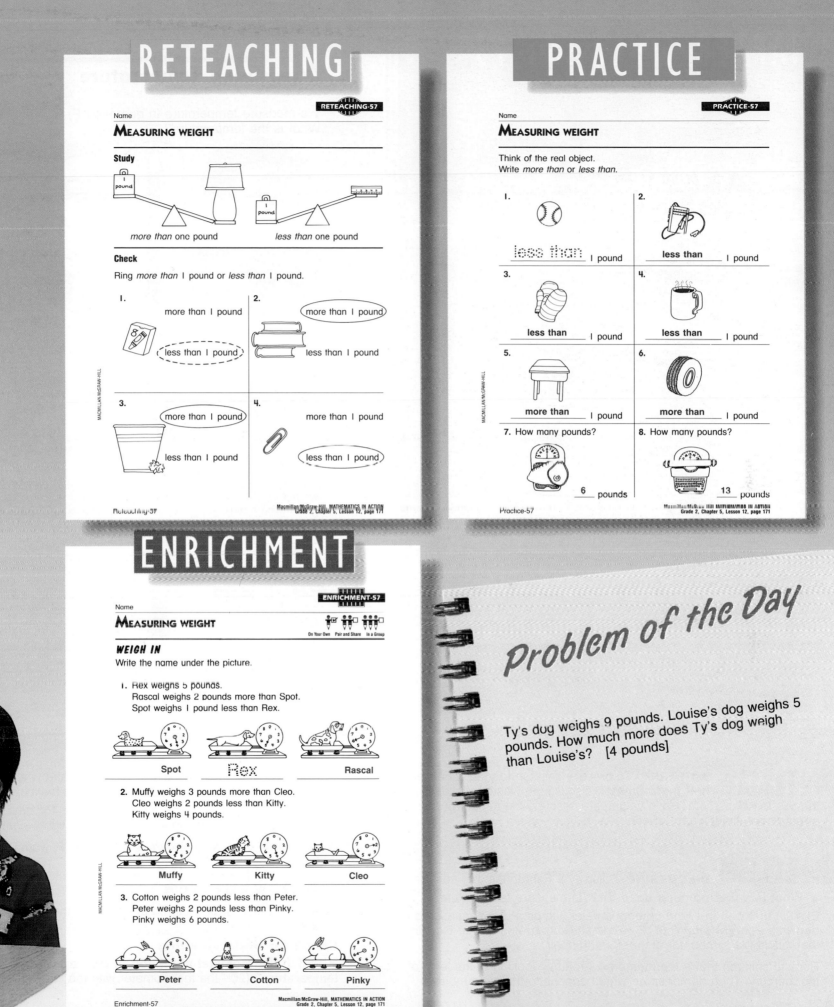

RETEACHING-57

Name _____

MEASURING WEIGHT

Study

more than one pound   *less than* one pound

Check

Ring *more than* 1 pound or *less than* 1 pound.

1.
   more than 1 pound

   (less than 1 pound)

2.
   (more than 1 pound)

   less than 1 pound

3.
   (more than 1 pound)

   less than 1 pound

4.
   more than 1 pound

   (less than 1 pound)

Reteaching-57

Macmillan/McGraw-Hill, MATHEMATICS IN ACTION
Grade 2, Chapter 5, Lesson 12, page 171

PRACTICE-57

Name _____

MEASURING WEIGHT

Think of the real object.
Write *more than* or *less than*.

1.
less than ___ 1 pound

2.
less than ___ 1 pound

3.
less than ___ 1 pound

4.
less than ___ 1 pound

5.
more than ___ 1 pound

6.
more than ___ 1 pound

7. How many pounds?

6 ___ pounds

8. How many pounds?

13 ___ pounds

Practice-57

Macmillan/McGraw-Hill MATHEMATICS IN ACTION
Grade 2, Chapter 5, Lesson 12, page 171

ENRICHMENT-57

On Your Own   Pair and Share   In a Group

Name _____

MEASURING WEIGHT

WEIGH IN

Write the name under the picture.

1. Rex weighs 5 pounds.
   Rascal weighs 2 pounds more than Spot.
   Spot weighs 1 pound less than Rex.

   Spot   Rex   Rascal

2. Muffy weighs 3 pounds more than Cleo.
   Cleo weighs 2 pounds less than Kitty.
   Kitty weighs 4 pounds.

   Muffy   Kitty   Cleo

3. Cotton weighs 2 pounds less than Peter.
   Peter weighs 2 pounds less than Pinky.
   Pinky weighs 6 pounds.

   Peter   Cotton   Pinky

Enrichment-57

Macmillan/McGraw-Hill, MATHEMATICS IN ACTION
Grade 2, Chapter 5, Lesson 12, page 171

Problem of the Day

Ty's dog weighs 9 pounds. Louise's dog weighs 5 pounds. How much more does Ty's dog weigh than Louise's?   [4 pounds]

AT·A·GLANCE p. 172

LESSON OBJECTIVE
Read temperature in °F.

ASSIGNMENT GUIDE

COURSE	EXERCISES
Basic	p. 172: 1–4
Average	p. 172: 1–4
Challenge	p. 172: 1–4
Extra Practice, p. 177	

MATERIALS
Classroom Materials Fahrenheit thermometer

Teacher Resources
Reteaching 58   Practice 58   Enrichment 58
MAC Act. 115, 116   Calculator 5   *Math Anthology*, p. 157
Math Songs Cassette, Side 2, Selection 10

SKILLS TRACE
MEASURING TEMPERATURE

Explore (Concrete) 152	Develop/Understand (Transitional/Abstract) 160, 172
Practice 164, 177, 179–180, 245, 301	Apply 161–162, 182

Measuring Temperature

We measure temperature in degrees (°F).
What is the temperature?

90 °F   20 °F

Write the temperature.

1. 80 °F

2. 50 °F

3. 10 °F

4. 70 °F

Extra Practice, page 177

PREPARE

WARM-UP To prepare children to read a **Fahrenheit thermometer,** discuss the weather inside and outside the classroom. Have volunteers describe the temperature in terms of hot, cold, warm, or cool.

TEACH

DISCUSSING Display a Fahrenheit thermometer.

■ **What is a thermometer used for?** [to measure temperature]

Explain that with this kind of thermometer, temperature is measured in **degrees Fahrenheit.** Write **°F** on the chalkboard and further explain that this is the symbol for degrees Fahrenheit.

Remind children that a thermometer is read by looking at the level of the mercury. Then demonstrate what happens to the mercury level when the thermometer is placed in ice water and when it is placed in hot water. Record these temperatures on the chalkboard.

■ **What would you wear on a 55° day; on a 15° day; on a 95° day?** [medium-weight clothing; very warm clothing; lightweight clothing]

Point out that room temperature is around 65°F, water boils at 212°F, and water freezes at 32°F.

PUPIL'S EDITION p. 172

Page 172 Discuss the pictures at the top of the page with the children.

Check for Understanding

■ **Which thermometer at the top of the page shows the colder temperature?** [20°; the thermometer with the snowy scene]

ACTIVITY

Common Error and Remediation

MATERIALS thermometer, 2 containers, ice water, warm water

Some children may not be able to relate the degrees on a thermometer to the temperature. Work individually with each child. Provide the child with a thermometer, a container filled with warm water, and a container filled with ice water. Have the child place his or her hand and the thermometer in the warm water and observe what happens to the mercury. [It rises.] Guide the child in reading the temperature and describing what the water feels like. Repeat the activity with the container of ice water.

ALTERNATIVE TEACHING STRATEGY

VISUAL Draw a large thermometer on the chalkboard. Explain how the instruction is read and how it is used. Shade in the "mercury" to 32° and tell children that water freezes at 32°F. Then extend the "mercury" to 65° and tell children that the temperature of the room is about 65°F. Extend the "mercury" to 212° and tell children that water boils at 212°F.

Using the thermometer as a reference, ask children if various temperatures are hot, warm, cool, or cold.

TEACHER to TEACHER

MANAGEMENT TIP I do not allow children to work with glass thermometers without supervision. I remind them often that glass is easily broken.

GUIDED PRACTICE ex. 1–2: For reteaching, use Common Error and Remediation or Alternative Strategy.

Mathematics and Literature **CULTURAL CONNECTION**

3 PRACTICE•APPLY **PRACTICE** ex. 3–4

Discuss typical characteristics of spring in your area in terms of temperature, changes among animals, features of the land, and weather conditions. Play the song "Spring in China" or read the lyrics found in *Math Anthology* for the class. Have children identify ideas in the song that relate to temperature [sunshine, melting snow, warm rains] as they compare spring in China with spring in your area. Have the children pick the thermometers on page 172 that might be springtime temperatures and which are typical of other seasons.

CLOSE Guide children to summarize the lesson:
■ **What does a thermometer measure?** [Possible response: It tells you the temperature, how hot or cold something is.]

MATH AND SCIENCE ■ *TEMPERATURE EXPERIMENT*

MAC Activity 116

On Your Own   Pair and Share   In a Group

— BODY
  TEMPERATURE
— ROOM
  TEMPERATURE

Materials 1 small bottle, a one-hole stopper to fit the bottle, 8 inches of glass tubing, colored water, grease pencil

Demonstrate the following for the children. Tell them this experiment will show that water expands when heated.

Fit the glass tubing into the stopper so that it is even with the small end of the stopper. About 7 inches of tubing should extend upward. Fill the bottle to 1/4 inch from the top with colored water (use food coloring). Push the stopper into the bottle so it fits firmly and so the water rises in the tube. Mark the water level of the tube with a grease pencil and explain that this is water at room temperature.

Heat the bottle with your hands. The water level will rise. Mark the point at which it stops rising and explain to children that this is body temperature.

You now have two temperatures marked on the tube—room temperature and body temperature. Have children predict what will happen as the water cools to room temperature.   [The water in the tube will fall to the first mark.] Have children suggest other ways to raise and lower the water level in the tube.

▲
MAC Activity 116:
Average-to-Challenge

MATH AND SOCIAL STUDIES ■ *TEMPERATURE USE*

MAC Activity 115

On Your Own   Pair and Share   In a Group

46° Seattle
Minneapolis 44°
52° Boston
55° New York
Denver 48°
54° Chicago
61° Washington D.C.
San Francisco 55°
63°
Los Angeles
70°
63° Dallas
64°
66° New Orleans
78° Miami
Phoenix
Houston

Materials maps of the United States, newspaper weather reports

Have children work in groups and provide each group with a newspaper report of temperatures in major U.S. cities. Give each child a map of the United States. Tell children to match the names of cities in the report to cities on the maps. Then have them write the temperatures for the cities. When the maps are completed, discuss which parts of the country are coldest and warmest.

▲
MAC Activity 115:
Basic-to-Average

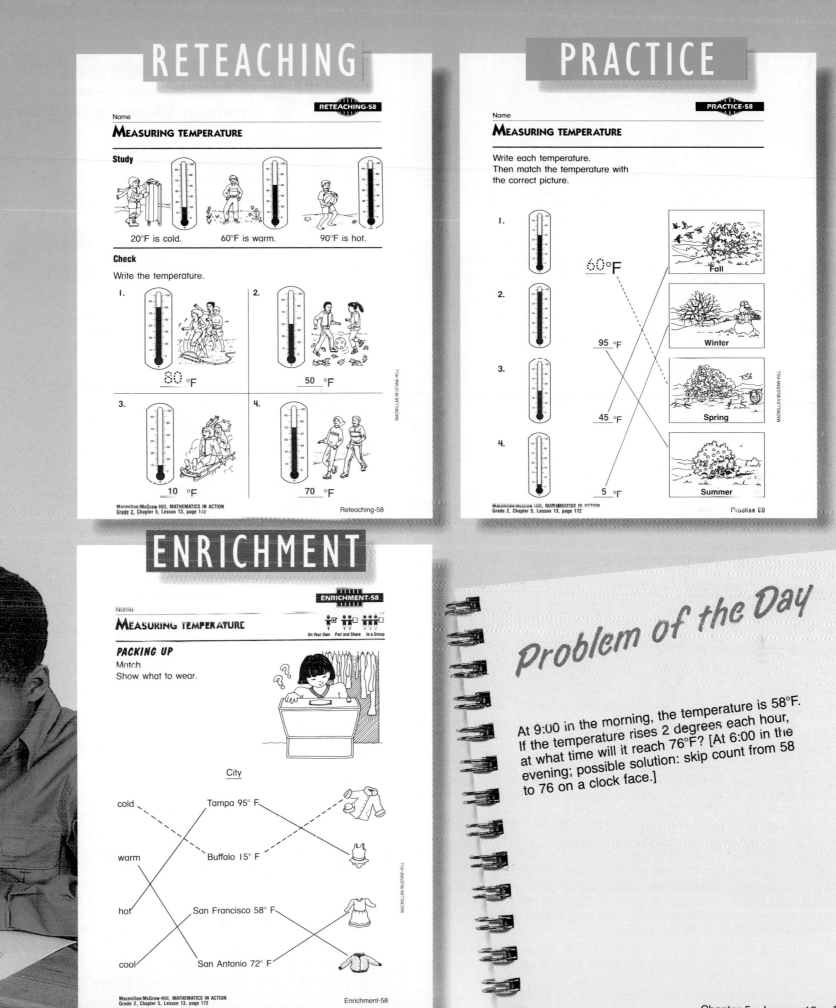

RETEACHING-58

Name

MEASURING TEMPERATURE

Study

20°F is cold.   60°F is warm.   90°F is hot.

Check

Write the temperature.

1. 80 °F

2. 50 °F

3. 10 °F

4. 70 °F

Macmillan/McGraw-Hill, MATHEMATICS IN ACTION
Grade 2, Chapter 5, Lesson 13, page 172   Reteaching-58

PRACTICE-58

Name

MEASURING TEMPERATURE

Write each temperature.
Then match the temperature with
the correct picture.

1. 60°F   Fall

2.   Winter

3. 95 °F   Spring

4. 45 °F   Summer

5 °F

Macmillan/McGraw-Hill, MATHEMATICS IN ACTION
Grade 2, Chapter 5, Lesson 13, page 172   Practice-58

ENRICHMENT-58

Name

MEASURING TEMPERATURE

On Your Own   Pair and Share   In a Group

PACKING UP
Match
Show what to wear.

City

cold ---- Tampa 95° F

warm   Buffalo 15° F

hot   San Francisco 58° F

cool   San Antonio 72° F

Macmillan/McGraw-Hill, MATHEMATICS IN ACTION
Grade 2, Chapter 5, Lesson 13, page 172   Enrichment-58

Problem of the Day

At 9:00 in the morning, the temperature is 58°F.
If the temperature rises 2 degrees each hour,
at what time will it reach 76°F? [At 6:00 in the
evening; possible solution: skip count from 58
to 76 on a clock face.]

AT·A·GLANCE pp. 173-174

LESSON OBJECTIVE
Choose the operation to solve problems.

ASSIGNMENT GUIDE

COURSE	EXERCISES
Basic	p. 173: 1; p. 174: 1–4
Average	p. 173: 1; p. 174: 1–4
Challenge	p. 173: 1; p. 174: 1–4
Extra Practice, p. 177	

MATERIALS
Classroom Materials small paper cups
Manipulatives 19 ◯ (or punchouts) per child

Teacher Resources
Reteaching 59   Practice 59   Enrichment 59
Prob. Solv. 24   MAC Act. 117, 118

Problem Solving

✓ UNDERSTAND
✓ PLAN
✓ TRY
✓ CHECK
✓ EXTEND

Strategy: Choosing the Operation

The children each made punch.
Dom used 8 cups orange juice.
Joyce used 5 cups orange juice.
How many more cups did Dom
use than Joyce?

You can draw a
picture to find
how many more.

You can use
subtraction to find
how many more.

$$\begin{array}{r} 8 \\ -5 \\ \hline 3 \end{array}$$

Dom used ___3___ more cups than Joyce.

Did Joyce use fewer cups than Dom?
How many fewer? Yes, 3 fewer.

Solve. Use addition or subtraction.
Use ◯, mental math, or paper and pencil.

1. Helen makes punch.
   She uses 7 cups of grapefruit juice.
   She uses 5 cups of pineapple juice.
   How many more cups of grapefruit juice
   than pineapple juice does she use?

   ___2___ more cups

Macmillan/McGraw-Hill

PREPARE   **WARM-UP** To prepare children for choosing the
operation to solve problems, have them give the following sums and differences.

8 − 6 [2]	12 − 5 [7]	9 + 7 [16]	13 − 8 [5]
9 − 4 [5]	11 − 7 [4]	6 + 5 [11]	4 + 4 [8]

TEACH   **MODELING** Assign children to work in pairs. Give
each pair of children 10 small paper cups. Explain
that you will read a problem aloud and they should use the cups to
model the numbers in the problem.

   Tracy and Dina are watering their plants. Tracy used 3 cups of
   water. Dina used 7 cups. How many more cups of water did Dina
   use than Tracy?

■ **What do we know?** [Tracy used 3 cups and Dina used 7 cups.]

■ **What do we need to find out?** [how many more cups Dina used]

■ **How can we use the cups to find out how many more cups
Dina used?** [Possible response: Have children line up the cups and
tell how many more cups; 4.]

■ **How else can we find out how many more cups of water Dina
used?** [Possible response: We can subtract 3 cups from 7 cups;
7 − 3 = 4. Dina used 4 more cups of water.]

Encourage children to explain other ways to solve the problem.

PUPIL'S EDITION pp. 173-174

Page 173 Distribute counters to children. Have a volunteer read the
problem at the top of the page.

■ **What do you know?** [Dom used 8 cups. Joyce used 5 cups.]

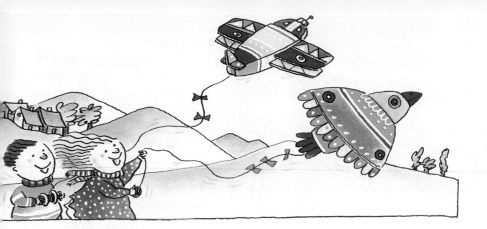

Solve. Use addition or subtraction.

1. Rod uses 3 yards of cloth to make a kite.
He uses 6 yards of cloth to make a blanket.
How many yards does he use in all?

____9____ yards

2. Nina uses 7 pounds of clay.
Betty uses 11 pounds of clay.
How many more pounds does Betty use
than Nina?

____4____ more pounds

3. Tia makes tablecloths.
She uses 6 feet of blue cloth.
She uses 9 feet of red cloth.
How many fewer feet of blue cloth than
red cloth does she use?

____3____ fewer feet

4. Kyle has 13 pounds of plant soil.
He uses 6 pounds of soil.
How many pounds are left?

____7____ pounds

Extra Practice, page 177

TEACHER to TEACHER

MANIPULATIVES TIP My children benefited from modeling the numbers in problems that called for finding the difference between two groups. They were better able to visualize how many more or how many fewer one group had than another by first using concrete objects to compare the groups.

For Students Acquiring English (SAE)

Preteach the vocabulary **fewer, more, in all,** and **are left** in context. Use real objects to act out word problems similar to the ones presented, having SAE children manipulate the objects and use the vocabulary orally.

■ **What do you need to find out?** [You need to find how many more cups Dom used than Joyce.]

■ **What do you need to do?** [Draw a picture or subtract.]

Have children count how many more and read aloud the subtraction sentence.

■ **What did you learn?** [Possible response: You can use subtraction to find how many more and how many fewer.]

Check for Understanding

■ **What if Dom used 9 cups of orange juice and Joyce used 4 cups of orange juice? How many fewer cups would Joyce have used than Dom? Explain.** [You can subtract to find out how many fewer; $9 - 4 = 5$, or 5 fewer cups.]

GUIDED PRACTICE ex. 1: Work through problem 1 with the children. Make sure they understand how to solve the problem by choosing the correct operation.

Page 174 Have a volunteer read the directions at the top of the page. Read the problems with the children as necessary.

PRACTICE•APPLY PRACTICE ex. 1–4

C L O S E Guide children to summarize the lesson:

■ **What can you do to solve a problem that asks how many more or how many fewer?** [Possible response: You can compare two groups or amounts and subtract to find the difference.]

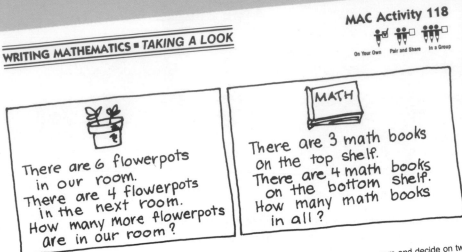

WRITING MATHEMATICS ▪ TAKING A LOOK

MAC Activity 118

On Your Own   Pair and Share   In a Group

There are 6 flowerpots in our room.
There are 4 flowerpots in the next room.
How many more flowerpots are in our room?

There are 3 math books on the top shelf.
There are 4 math books on the bottom shelf.
How many math books in all?

Materials drawing paper, crayons

Procedure Give each child writing paper and crayons. Have children look around the classroom and decide on two objects to use in two different problems. Tell children to draw a picture of one object on one side of the paper and the other object on the other side of the paper. Then ask children to write one addition problem and one subtraction problem involving the object they have just drawn. Have children exchange papers and solve the problems.

▲ **MAC Activity 118:**
Average-to-Challenge

LOGICAL REASONING ▪ TEAMWORK

MAC Activity 117

On Your Own   Pair and Share   In a Group

Materials sheet of writing paper, books, pencils, paper clips, scissors, crayons, jars.

Setup Display classroom objects by forming two groups of each object. Make 2 stacks of books, 2 groups of pencils, 2 groups of paper clips, 2 groups of crayons, and 2 groups of scissors. Each group should contain a different number of objects less than 10.

Procedure Assign the children to work in groups. Give each group a sheet of writing paper and a set of objects. Explain to children that you will ask them to find how many more objects are in one group than in the other, or how many objects there are in all. Go to each group and ask them "How many more?" or "How many in all?". Have most of the children in the group count the objects, and have one member write the numbers on the sheet of paper. The group should decide whether they need to add or subtract. Then the writer in the group should complete the problem on the paper and find the answer. Have groups report on their findings.

▲ **MAC Activity 117:**
Basic-to-Average

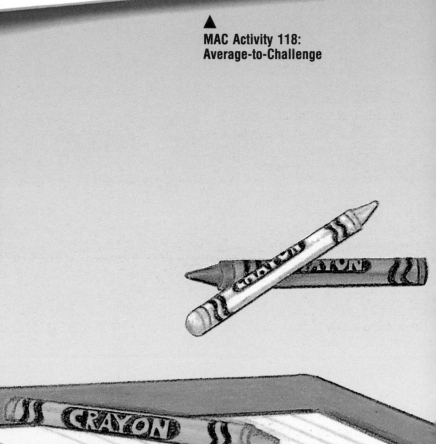

Name _____

PROBLEM SOLVING STRATEGY:
CHOOSING THE OPERATION

Study

Jim and Sandy are thirsty.
Jim drinks 4 cups of water.
Sandy drinks 2 cups of water.
How many more cups does
Jim drink than Sandy?
Subtract to find how many more.

Draw a picture. Subtract.

$$\begin{array}{r} 4 \\ -\ 2 \\ \hline ② \end{array}$$

Jim has 2 cups more.

Check

Write + or −.
Complete the exercise.

1. Luis has 3 pounds of apples.
   Helen has 4 pounds of apples.
   How many pounds do they
   have in all?

   __7__ pounds

   $$\begin{array}{r} 3 \\ +\ 4 \\ \hline 7 \end{array}$$

2. Rick uses 8 feet of ribbon.
   Pam uses 4 feet of ribbon.
   How many more feet of ribbon
   does Rick use than Pam?

   __4__ feet

   $$\begin{array}{r} 8 \\ -\ 4 \\ \hline 4 \end{array}$$

3. Bill buys 7 yards of cloth.
   He gives 2 yards to Lee.
   How many yards are left?

   __5__ yards

   $$\begin{array}{r} 7 \\ -\ 2 \\ \hline 5 \end{array}$$

Macmillan/McGraw-Hill, MATHEMATICS IN ACTION
Grade 2, Chapter 5, Lesson 14, pages 173–174

Name _____

PROBLEM SOLVING STRATEGY:
CHOOSING THE OPERATION

Solve. Use addition or subtraction.

1. Mandy has 9 cups of water.
   She uses 3 cups to mix poster paint.
   How many cups are left?

   __6__ cups

   $$\begin{array}{r} 9 \\ -\ 3 \\ \hline 6 \end{array}$$

2. Barry makes plates and bowls.
   He uses 5 pounds of brown clay.
   He uses 12 pounds of white clay.
   How many more pounds of white
   clay than brown clay does he use?

   __7__ more pounds

   $$\begin{array}{r} 12 \\ -\ 5 \\ \hline 7 \end{array}$$

3. Lynn draws on 6 feet of paper.
   Frank draws on 4 feet of paper.
   How many feet of paper do
   they use in all?

   __10__ feet

   $$\begin{array}{r} 6 \\ +\ 4 \\ \hline 10 \end{array}$$

4. Tom uses 11 yards of cloth for curtains.
   Kay uses 7 yards of cloth for drapes.
   How many fewer yards of cloth
   does Kay use than Tom?

   __4__ yards

   $$\begin{array}{r} 11 \\ -\ 7 \\ \hline 4 \end{array}$$

Macmillan/McGraw-Hill, MATHEMATICS IN ACTION
Grade 2, Chapter 5, Lesson 14, pages 173–174

Name _____

PROBLEM SOLVING

On Your Own   Pair and Share   In a Group

HIGH IN THE SKY
Solve.
Use addition or subtraction.

18 feet

14 feet

10 feet

6 feet

2 feet

1. How many feet higher is the bird than the balloon?

   __8__ feet

   $$\begin{array}{r} 14 \\ -\ 6 \\ \hline 8 \end{array}$$

2. How many feet is the balloon from the kite?

   __4__ feet

   $$\begin{array}{r} 10 \\ -\ 6 \\ \hline 4 \end{array}$$

3. If the balloon goes up 9 feet more, will it be
   as high as the plane?

   __no__

   $$\begin{array}{r} 6 \\ +\ 9 \\ \hline 15 \end{array}$$

Macmillan/McGraw-Hill, MATHEMATICS IN ACTION
Grade 2, Chapter 5, Lesson 14, pages 173–174

Problem of the Day

Pamela has 15 toy cars in all. Nine are green, the
rest are blue. How many toy cars are blue?
[15 − 9 = 6 blue cars]

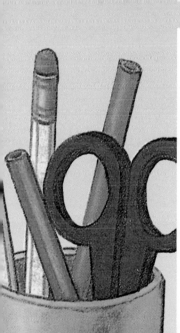

AT·A·GLANCE p. 175

LESSON OBJECTIVE
Make decisions using information.

ASSIGNMENT GUIDE

COURSE	EXERCISES
Basic	p. 175: 1–2
Average	p. 175: 1–2
Challenge	p. 175: 1–2

MATERIALS
Classroom Materials paper, crayons, pictures of flowers (optional)

Teacher Resources
Crit. Think. 10   Prob. Solv. 25

Name _____

Decision Making

Problem Solving: Planning a Garden

Plant	How Far Apart to Plant Each
Daffodil	6 inches
Bluebell	6 inches
Tulip	6 inches
Iris	4 inches
Snowdrop	3 inches

30 inches

30 inches

Plants You Have

5 Daffodil ○
5 Bluebell ●
5 Tulip ●
8 Iris ●
10 Snowdrop ○

How Tall Plants Will Grow

Daffodil	Bluebell	Tulip	Iris	Snowdrop
20 inches	10 inches	28 inches	24 inches	6 inches

How would you plan a garden?

1. Decide where each plant should be placed. Color to show where you would place each plant. Answers will vary.

Use your own paper.

2. Write about how you decided.

Chapter 5   Measurement   one hundred seventy-five   **175**

Macmillan/McGraw-Hill

PREPARE

WARM-UP To review measurement concepts, ask children the following questions.

■ **How many inches are in one foot?** [12]

■ **How many inches are in two feet?** [24]

■ **If a red toy truck is 6 inches long and a green toy truck is 1 foot long, which truck is longer? Why?** [the green truck, because it is 12 inches long]

TEACH

DISCUSSING Have children describe any gardens that they have seen. Explain that some people plant flower gardens, while others plant vegetable gardens. Tell children that gardens are usually planned and designed first and then planted.

If possible, provide pictures of flowers for children to study before they begin the page.

PUPIL'S EDITION p. 175
Read the tables at the top of the page with the children. Discuss the grid and the information provided about the heights of the plants.

Check for Understanding
■ **How many inches apart must the irises be planted?** [4 inches]

■ **Which plant grows to be 6 inches?** [snowdrop]

TEACHER to TEACHER

COOPERATIVE LEARNING TIP  Our class community decided to develop a cooperative garden. Each member of the class wrote a list of what to plant. Next, each student combined his or her list first with that of a partner, then with the lists of another pair. Each group of four plotted out one section of the garden for their crop and reported results to the community council. In deciding how much of their crop each small group could plant, the class had to consider the fact that some crops need more space in which to grow than do others.

For Students Acquiring English (SAE)

Enlarge the grid for planting using an overhead projector. Set up heterogeneous teams of four. Read aloud the information from the chart and have team members discuss where they would put the plants. Using the transparency, record each group's garden.

3 PRACTICE·APPLY

Have children complete ex. 1–2. Call on volunteers to tell how they would arrange the flowers in their gardens. Have them tell how they decided on which flowers to plant and where.

CLOSE Guide children to summarize the lesson:

■ **What should you do before you plant a flower garden?** [Decide on which flowers to plant, learn how tall each will grow and the color of each flower, and where each flower will go.]

CLASS PROJECT

Materials drawing paper, crayons, paste, scissors, tongue depressors or craft sticks, clay, large sheets of green construction paper

Provide children with drawing paper, scissors, crayons, paste, and tongue depressors. Have each child choose one kind of flower pictured on page 175 and then draw and cut out two of those flowers with stems. Reinforce the stems by pasting tongue depressors to the back of the stems.

Have groups of four children "plant" their gardens by placing the stems into small balls of clay and then pressing the clay to green construction paper.

AT·A·GLANCE p. 176

OBJECTIVE
Use a computer to make bar graphs.

MATERIALS
Computer

Teacher Resources
Computer Software *Computer Workshop:* BAR GRAPH 2

Computer Graphing: Bar Graphs

Lengths of Animals	
Animal	**Length in Feet**
Boa	14
Giant Salamander	4
Lion	10

You can use a computer to make
a bar graph with this data.

At the Computer
Run the program BAR GRAPH 2.

Complete the chart on the screen.
Make a bar graph.

1. Which animal is longest? _____boa_____

2. How long is it? _____14 feet_____

Go back to the chart.
Add another animal: Crocodile 16 feet
Make another bar graph.

3. Now how long is the longest animal? _____16 feet_____

4. What if the lion was 12 feet long?
   Change the chart. Make a new graph.
   How are the graphs different?

   Possible answer:
   The bar showing
   the length of the
   lion is longer for 12
   feet than for 10
   feet.

5. Talk about why it is useful to draw
   graphs on a computer. Possible answer: A computer can draw lines
   and bars accurately and use my data to show a picture.

PREPARE   **WARM-UP**   To review comparing measures, have
children identify the longer measure in each pair.

1. 15 feet   9 feet [15 feet]
2.   7 feet   4 feet [7 feet]
3.   8 feet   9 feet [9 feet]

TEACH   **DISCUSSING**   Draw the following chart on the
chalkboard:

Lengths of Some Ribbons			
red	blue	green	yellow
4 ft	2 ft	5 ft	3 ft

Discuss the data in the chart with the children. Then call on volunteers
to tell you how you could make a bar graph with the data in the chart.
Have other volunteers demonstrate each step in making the bar
graph.

PRACTICE·APPLY   Discuss the chart at the top of the
page.

■ **What would a bar graph of this data look like?** [Answers will
vary.]

AT THE COMPUTER   Have children work in pairs using the computer program BAR GRAPH 2. To begin, have children complete the
chart on the screen using the data from their page. Then have them

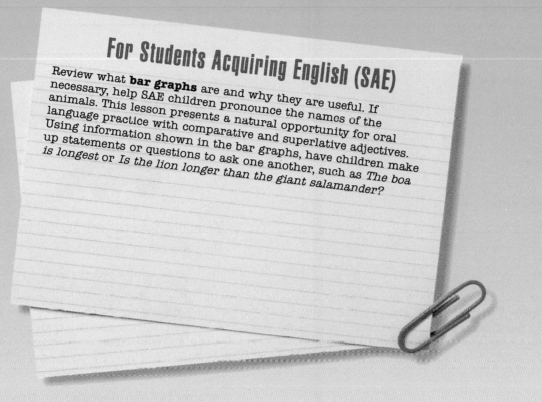

For Students Acquiring English (SAE)

Review what **bar graphs** are and why they are useful. If necessary, help SAE children pronounce the names of the animals. This lesson presents a natural opportunity for oral language practice with comparative and superlative adjectives. Using information shown in the bar graphs, have children make up statements or questions to ask one another, such as *The boa is longest* or *Is the lion longer than the giant salamander?*

follow the directions to make a bar graph. Tell them to use the graph to answer ex. 1 and 2.

Next have children revise the chart and make a new graph to answer ex. 3. Continue in the same manner for ex. 4.

Encourage children to discuss the benefits of using a computer to draw bar graphs.

CLOSE Guide children to summarize the lesson:

■ **How does a computer help when you have to change the data in a graph?** [Possible response: You just have to type in the new data, press the correct keys, and the new graph appears.]

CHAPTER 5

EXTRA PRACTICE

Extra Practice items are provided so that children may have an opportunity for further practice.

The Additional Practice section also provides practice you may wish to assign.

Using Inches, pages 165–166 . . . .

Estimate. Then measure. Use  .

	Estimate Answers will vary.	Measure
1. _____	____ inches	<u>2</u> inches
2. _____	____ inches	<u>3</u> inches

Measuring Weight, page 171 . . . .

Ring the better estimate.

1. 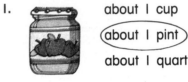 (more than 1 pound)
   less than 1 pound

Measuring Capacity and Temperature, pages 169, 172 . . . .

Ring the better estimate.

1. about 1 cup
   (about 1 pint)
   about 1 quart

2. 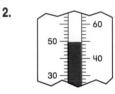   <u>50</u> °F

Problem Solving: Choosing the Operation, pages 173–174 . . . .

Solve.

1. Jody bought 5 pounds of tomatoes.
   He bought 12 pounds of potatoes.
   How many more pounds of potatoes

   than tomatoes did he buy? __7__ pounds

ADDITIONAL PRACTICE

p. 165 Draw the length of line indicated at the left.

Estimate. Then measure. Use your ruler.

	Estimate	Measure
	[Answers will vary.]	
1. 3 in.	____ in.	[3] in.
2. 6 in.	____ in.	[6] in.
3. 4 in.	____ in.	[4] in.

p. 169 *Tell the better estimate.*

1 cup
1 pint
[1 quart]

p. 171 Point to a pencil, a desk, a piece of paper.

Tell the better estimate: more than a pound, or less than a pound. [pencil, less; desk, more; piece of paper, less.]

p. 172 Display a large Fahrenheit thermometer. Have children read these temperatures.

1. 80°	**2.** 71°	**3.** 25°
4. 36°	**5.** 48°	**6.** 85°

p. 173 *Solve.*

1. Mary made 8 pounds of cookies. Then she made 9 pounds more. How many pounds of cookies did Mary make in all?
   [17] pounds

Practice Plus

Key Skill: Using Centimeters, page 154 . . . .

Look at the picture.
Estimate how long. Then measure.

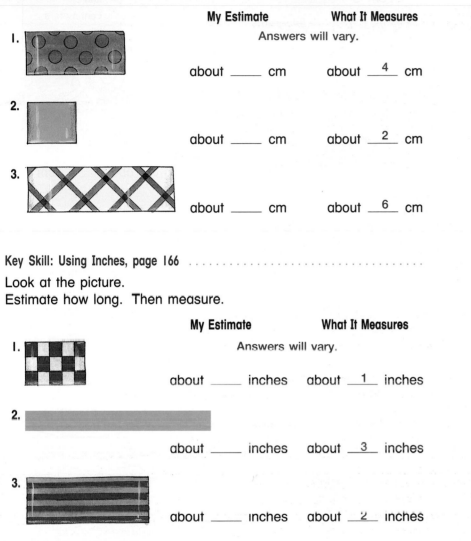

	My Estimate	What It Measures
	Answers will vary.	
1.	about _____ cm	about __4__ cm
2.	about _____ cm	about __2__ cm
3.	about _____ cm	about __6__ cm

Key Skill: Using Inches, page 166 . . . .

Look at the picture.
Estimate how long. Then measure.

	My Estimate	What It Measures
	Answers will vary.	
1.	about _____ inches	about __1__ inches
2.	about _____ inches	about __3__ inches
3.	about _____ inches	about __2__ inches

PRACTICE **PLUS**

Practice Plus is provided to supply additional practice for the two key skills in this chapter.

Key Skills
   Page 154: Using Centimeters
   Page 166: Using Inches

The *Additional Practice* also provides practice you may wish to assign for key skills in this chapter.

ADDITIONAL PRACTICE

p. 154 Draw the length of the line indicated at the left.

Estimate. Then measure. Use your ruler.

	Estimate		Measure
	[Answers will vary.]		
1.	1.8 cm	_____ cm	about [2] cm
2.	3.2 cm	_____ cm	about [3] cm
3.	4.6 cm	_____ cm	about [5] cm
4.	2.1 cm	_____ cm	about [2] cm

p. 166 *Draw these lines. Use your ruler.*

1. 2 inches

2. 4 inches

3. 1 inch

4. 5 inches

CHAPTER 5

AT·A·GLANCE pp. 179-180

OBJECTIVE
Review/test the concepts and skills presented in Chapter 5.

5A. Estimate and measure length in metric and customary units.

5B. Estimate and measure capacity using metric and customary units.

5C. Estimate and measure mass using metric units and weights using customary units.

5D. Read temperature in °C and °F.

5E. Solve problems including those that involve choosing the correct operation.

Teacher Resources
Testing Program, pp. 49–60

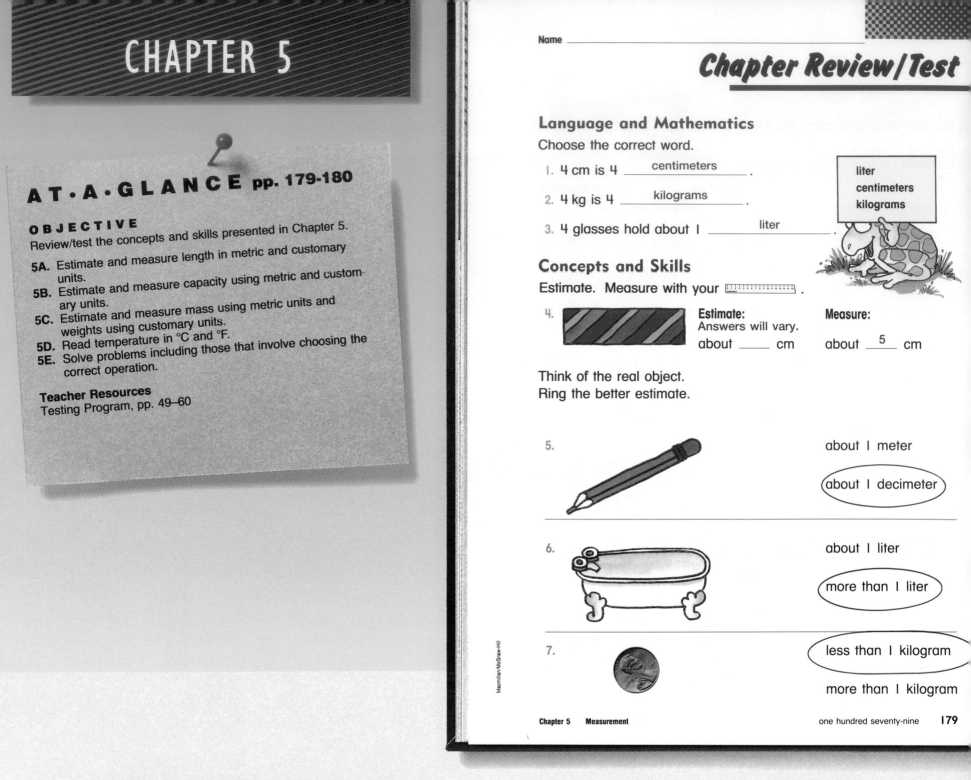

Language and Mathematics
Choose the correct word.

1. 4 cm is 4 ____centimeters____ .

2. 4 kg is 4 ____kilograms____ .

3. 4 glasses hold about 1 ____liter____ .

> liter
> centimeters
> kilograms

Concepts and Skills
Estimate. Measure with your ⬚⬚⬚⬚⬚ .

4. **Estimate:** Answers will vary.
    about ____ cm

    Measure: about __5__ cm

Think of the real object.
Ring the better estimate.

5. about 1 meter
   (about 1 decimeter)

6. about 1 liter
   (more than 1 liter)

7. (less than 1 kilogram)
   more than 1 kilogram

Macmillan/McGraw-Hill

USING THE CHAPTER REVIEW/TEST

The Chapter Review/Test may be used as a review to survey children's knowledge and understanding of the chapter material. Or it may be used as a test to formally assess children's understanding of the concepts and skills taught in the chapter. If used as a test, you may wish to assign one or more of the resources listed in *Reinforcement and Remediation* on p. 180 after reviewing children's test results.

If the Chapter Review/Test is used as a review, you may wish to have children work in pairs to complete it. Then, you can use the Chapter Tests—Forms A, B, and C—provided in the *Testing Program Blackline Master and Teacher's Manual* for testing purposes. Any of these forms may be used for pretesting, posttesting, or retesting.

A performance assessment activity for the key concept in this chapter is provided on page 181.

Estimate. Measure with your  .

8.

Estimate:
Answers will vary.

about _____ inches

Measure:

about __2__ inches

Think of the real object. Ring the better estimate.

9.

about 10 quarts

(about I quart)

10.

(less than I pound)

more than I pound

Write the temperature.

11.

__2__ °C

12.

__80__ °F

Problem Solving

Solve.

13. Irene's puppy weighs 9 kilograms.
Doug's kitten weighs 5 kilograms.
How many more kilograms does
the puppy weigh than the kitten?

__4__ more kilograms

14. How long is the path?

__8__ centimeters long

Reinforcement and Remediation

CHAP. OBJ.	TEST ITEMS	PUPIL'S EDITION pp.			TEACHER'S EDITION pp.	TEACHER RESOURCES	
		Lesson	Extra Practice	Practice Plus	Alt. Teaching Strategy	Reteaching	Practice
5A	1, 4–5, 8	153–156, 165–168	164– 177	178	154, 156, 166, 168 158, 170	48, 49, 54, 55 50, 56	48, 49, 54, 55 50, 56
5B	3, 6, 9	157–158, 169–170	164				
5C	2, 7, 10	159, 171	177				
5D	11–12	160, 172	177		159A, 171A 160A, 172A	51, 57 52, 58 53, 59	51, 57 52, 58 53, 59
5E	13–14	161–162, 173–174	177				

For Students Acquiring English (SAE)

Before beginning the Chapter Review/Test with SAE children,
scan the pages for any unfamiliar vocabulary that should be
pretaught. You may wish to pair or group SAE children with
non-SAE children. You may also wish to repeat some of the
activities and techniques for SAE children that were suggested
earlier in this chapter.

CHAPTER 5

AT·A·GLANCE p. 181

OBJECTIVE
Assess whether children can estimate and measure length in metric or customary units.

MATERIALS
Classroom Materials tape
Manipulatives metric or inch ruler (or punchouts) per group

Teacher Resources
Performance Assessment booklet, pp. 23–26

For Students Acquiring English (SAE)

Before beginning the performance assessment with SAE children, scan the page for any unfamiliar vocabulary that should be pretaught. You may wish to pair or group SAE children with non-SAE children. You may also wish to repeat some of the activities and techniques for SAE children that were suggested earlier in this chapter.

Performance Assessment

Work with your group to solve this problem.

How far can you and the other children in your group jump? Find out.

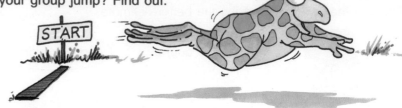

One at a time, stand on the starting line and jump!

Mark where each child lands.
Estimate how far each child jumps.
Measure the length of the jump with a ruler.

Ring the ruler used to measure.

Fill in the table.

Remember to include the unit!

Name	Estimate	Measure
	about	about
	about	about
	about	about
	about	about

You may put this page in your Portfolio

USING PERFORMANCE ASSESSMENT
The Performance Assessment activity may be used to informally assess children's understanding of the key concept(s) of the chapter. Additional assessment activities and Math Journal Options are provided in the *Performance Assessment* booklet.

Performing the Activity
Assign children to work in small groups of 4 or 5. Distribute materials. Have them do the "standing broad jump" activity as a group. Children should mark each jump with a piece of tape or a chalk line. Have them estimate the length of each jump and record the estimate first, then measure each jump afterward. Let them choose a metric or customary ruler for making measurements.

Evaluation Guidelines
Use these criteria to help determine the holistic score for each child.

The holistic scoring scale can be found in the Teacher's Reference Section.

● Can children estimate length in metric or customary units?
● Do children understand how to measure length?
● Can children write estimated and actual lengths on the table?

[Example Response: James, about 2 feet, 2 ft, 2 in.]

If children do not have a full understanding of the key concept(s), you may wish to use the Alternative Teaching Strategies or the MAC Activities within the chapter.

You may wish to have children put their final revised work in their portfolios.

A formal assessment of the concepts and skills taught in this chapter is provided on pages 179–180.

Enrichment For All

Collecting and Organizing Data

Which season do your friends like best?
Ask 10 friends.
Use the chart to collect your data.

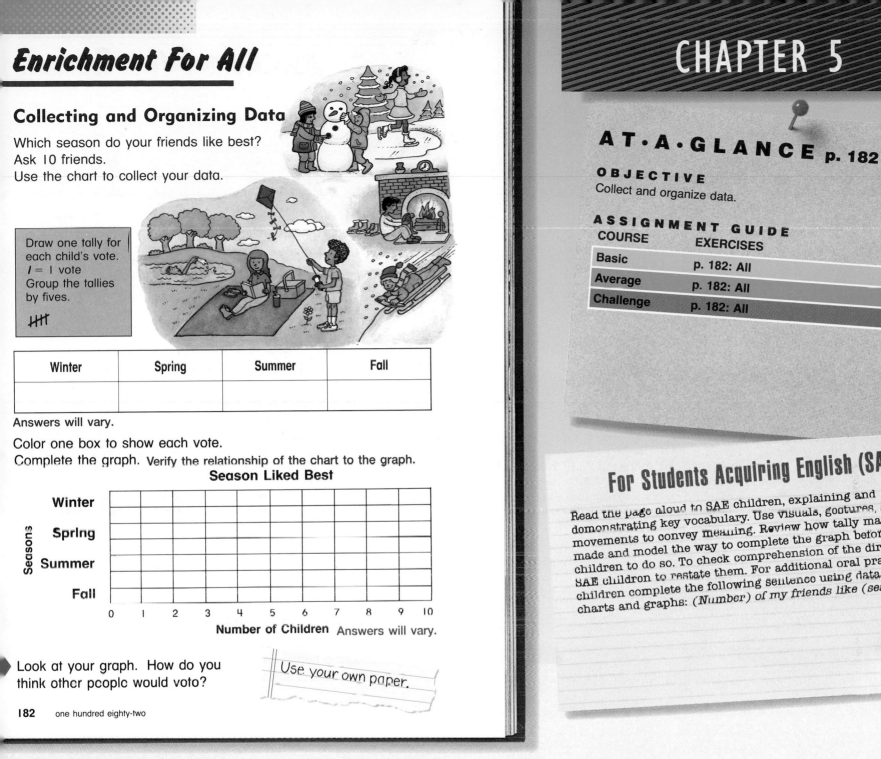

Draw one tally for
each child's vote.
/ = 1 vote
Group the tallies
by fives.

卌

Winter	Spring	Summer	Fall

Answers will vary.

Color one box to show each vote.
Complete the graph. Verify the relationship of the chart to the graph.

Season Liked Best

Seasons: Winter, Spring, Summer, Fall
Number of Children: 0 1 2 3 4 5 6 7 8 9 10

Answers will vary.

Look at your graph. How do you
think other people would vote?

Use your own paper.

AT·A·GLANCE p. 182

OBJECTIVE
Collect and organize data.

ASSIGNMENT GUIDE

COURSE	EXERCISES
Basic	p. 182: All
Average	p. 182: All
Challenge	p. 182: All

For Students Acquiring English (SAE)

Read the page aloud to SAE children, explaining and
demonstrating key vocabulary. Use visuals, gestures, and body
movements to convey meaning. Review how tally marks are
made and model the way to complete the graph before asking
children to do so. To check comprehension of the directions, ask
SAE children to restate them. For additional oral practice, have
children complete the following sentence using data from their
charts and graphs: *(Number) of my friends like (season) best.*

---

1 PREPARE **WARM-UP** To prepare children for collecting and
organizing data, review *data* as information that can
be shown in a picture or on a bar graph. Discuss the different kinds of
data that might be shown on a bar graph, such as number of votes for
a class president. Have children tell how they would know which item
on a bar graph showed the most or the least number. [the height of
the bars]

2 TEACH **ORGANIZING** Have children read the question at
the top of the page. Discuss what the children like
best about each season. List their ideas on the board. Then have
them look at the picture and read the text.

■ **What is a tally?** [a mark to show one vote]

■ **Why are tallies shown in groups of five?** [easier and faster to
count]

3 PRACTICE·APPLY Have each child ask 10 classmates to
name the season they each like best.
Have children tally the votes and then color the boxes on their bar
graphs to show the total number of votes.

CLOSE Guide children to summarize the lesson:

■ **Which season got the greatest number of votes? The least?**
[Answers will vary, depending on completed graphs.]

CHAPTER 5

OBJECTIVE
Review and maintain previously learned concepts and skills.

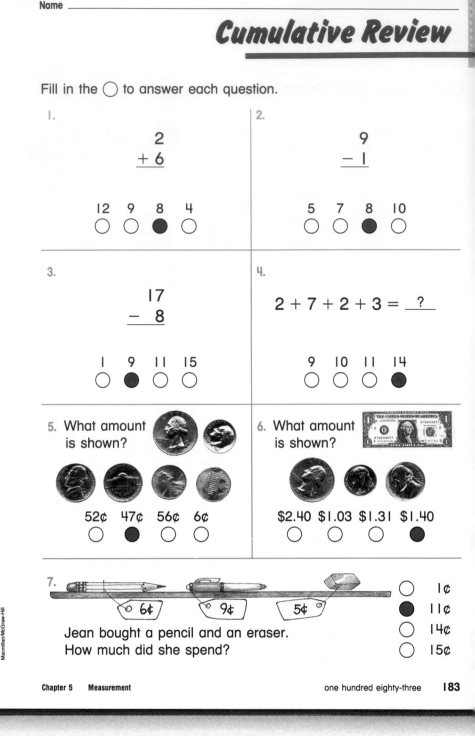

Fill in the ○ to answer each question.

1.
$$2 + 6$$

| 12 | 9 | 8 | 4 |
| ○ | ○ | ● | ○ |

2.
$$9 - 1$$

| 5 | 7 | 8 | 10 |
| ○ | ○ | ● | ○ |

3.
$$17 - 8$$

| 1 | 9 | 11 | 15 |
| ○ | ● | ○ | ○ |

4.
$$2 + 7 + 2 + 3 = \underline{?}$$

| 9 | 10 | 11 | 14 |
| ○ | ○ | ○ | ● |

5. What amount is shown?

| 52¢ | 47¢ | 56¢ | 6¢ |
| ○ | ● | ○ | ○ |

6. What amount is shown?

| $2.40 | $1.03 | $1.31 | $1.40 |
| ○ | ○ | ○ | ● |

7.

6¢   9¢   5¢

○ 1¢
● 11¢
○ 14¢
○ 15¢

Jean bought a pencil and an eraser. How much did she spend?

Macmillan/McGraw-Hill

Chapter 5   Measurement   one hundred eighty-three   **183**

USING THE CUMULATIVE REVIEW

The Cumulative Review is presented in a multiple-choice format to provide practice in taking a standardized test. It gives children an opportunity to review previously learned skills. An answer sheet, similar to those used when taking standardized tests, can be found in the *Testing Program Blackline Masters and Teacher's Manual.*

The table that follows correlates the review items to the lesson pages on which the skills are taught.

Review Items	Text Pages	Review Items	Text Pages
1	34	5	129–130
2	34	6	135–136
3	107–108	7	131–132
4	111		

Testing Program Blackline Masters

In addition to the Cumulative Review in the Pupil's Edition, there are quarterly Cumulative Tests and an End-Year Test. These tests are multiple choice and provide additional opportunities for children to practice taking standardized tests.

Cumulative Tests measure children's performance on major skills and concepts taught during the previous quarters. The **End-Year Test** measures children's performance on major skills and concepts taught throughout the year.

Home Activity

Your child has been learning how to measure, using metric and customary units. Here is an activity that will help your child practice this skill.

Players:
2 or more

Materials:
heavy string, yarn, or lightweight rope

Directions:

1. Help one another cut a string exactly as tall as each player is. Give each player that string to use in the next step.

2. Now have one player at a time stretch his or her arms out sideways. A helper measures that player's string along his or her outstretched arms.

   - If the player's string and reach are the same, the player is in Category A.
   - If the string is longer than the player's reach, the player is in Category B.
   - If the string is shorter than the player's reach, the player is in Category C.

3. Record the results for each person measured in the table below.

4. Later you may want to repeat the activity using a tape measure to get numerical measurements.

▨ Category A	▨ Category B	▬ Category C

AT·A·GLANCE p. 184

OBJECTIVE
Give family members an opportunity to share in their child's mathematics learning.

For Students Acquiring English (SAE)

Before assigning this Home Activity to SAE children, find out if someone at home will be able to work with them in English. If not, prepare them to complete the activity independently at home. Explain the directions of the activity and ask SAE children to restate them so you can check comprehension. Scan the page and preteach any difficult vocabulary or phrases that they may not know. If you feel that an SAE child will need extra help with the activity, you might assign that student a non-SAE partner and arrange a time for them to work on the activity in or out of school.

USING THE ACTIVITY

Have children look at the page. Explain that the page has an activity that an adult in the family can help them complete. Read the page with the children, making sure that they understand what needs to be done. Tell children that they will do this page at home.

Previewing
CHAPTER 6

ADDING 2-DIGIT NUMBERS

Richard Lodholz

> **"IN CHAPTER 6, you will introduce your children to adding 2-digit numbers. You will also have the opportunity to explore place value, regrouping, and the algorithm for adding 2-digit numbers."**

Notes
FROM THE AUTHOR

Here are some notes on the concepts presented in this chapter and how your children can apply them to solve problems.

PREREQUISITES

Your children must first understand place value, know the basic addition facts, and be able to follow steps in order to add 2-digit numbers with regrouping. Some children may need remediation in these areas to achieve success in adding 2-digit numbers.

REGROUPING

Using ones and tens models enables children to understand the concept of regrouping. Encourage children to use models to work through exercises and to discuss each step. For example:

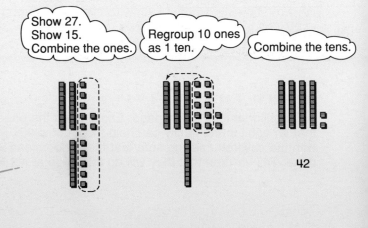

ADDING 2-DIGIT NUMBERS

After children demonstrate their understanding of regrouping, introduce them to the algorithm for adding 2-digit numbers. Children learn that an algorithm is a process or series of steps for solving a mathematics problem, and that the algorithm for adding 2-digit numbers helps them remember what to do. Children should understand that the algorithm is a multistep procedure and know how to do each step. Using ones and tens models allows them to discover why the algorithm works. Practicing adding 2-digit numbers with place-value models and without recording reinforces their understanding of the algorithm.

Children apply their understanding of the algorithm by working through carefully structured examples such as the following.

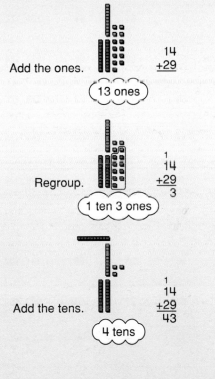

Add the ones.

$$\begin{array}{r} 14 \\ +29 \\ \hline \end{array}$$

(13 ones)

Regroup.

$$\begin{array}{r} 1 \\ 14 \\ +29 \\ \hline 3 \end{array}$$

(1 ten 3 ones)

Add the tens.

$$\begin{array}{r} 1 \\ 14 \\ +29 \\ \hline 43 \end{array}$$

(4 tens)

PROBLEM SOLVING

In **Problem Solving** your children (1) use data from a table to solve a problem and (2) solve a problem by using estimation.

In **Thinking Mathematically** children use logical reasoning to follow written clues about position. In Tree Trouble, children paste pictures of animals in their correct tree houses.

In **Decision Making** children read and use information to plan what rides they can take at a fair, given a number of tickets.

Mathematics and Literature

To use literature in the application of mathematics ■ To promote appreciation of the contributions of all cultures to mathematics. ■ Children are introduced to a story in the K–2 *Math Anthology* on page 158. By reading *Ninety-Nine Pockets*, children build addition and geometry skills, and develop number sense. ■ In the Curriculum Connection on page 206, children use Chinese counting rods, *chou*, and counting boards, and apply their knowledge of place value.

CULTURAL DIVERSITY

CHAPTER 6 • ORGANIZER

CHAPTER PLANNING GUIDE

CHAPTER OBJECTIVES
WITH STANDARDIZED TEST CORRELATIONS

A. Add 2-digit numbers with and without regrouping	MAT, CAT, SAT, ITBS, CTBS
B. Add three 2-digit numbers	MAT, CAT, SAT, ITBS, CTBS
C. Add money amounts to 99¢	MAT, CAT, SAT, ITBS, CTBS
D. Solve problems including those that involve using data from a table	CTBS

SUGGESTED PACING-13 DAYS

LESSONS	NCTM STANDARDS	ASSIGNMENTS Basic/Average/Challenge	STUDENT EDITION Extra Practice/ Practice Plus	Manip. Plus	Reteach	Practice	Enrich	MAC Activities
Chapter Opener: *Ninety-Nine Pockets* page 185	1, 2, 3, 4, 6, 7	p. 185: All						
✓ 1 Adding 2-Digit Numbers page 186	1, 2, 3, 7, 8	p. 186: All						
✓ 2 Regrouping Readiness pages 187–188	1, 2, 3, 7	p. 187: 1–4; p. 188: 1–7		31, 32, 33, 34				
✓ 3 More Regrouping Readiness pages 189–190	1, 2, 3, 7	p. 189: 1–2; p. 190: 1–2		35	60	60	60	119, 120
✓ 4 2-Digit Addition pages 191–192	1, 2, 3, 8	p. 191: 1–2; p. 192: 1–6, Mental Math			61	61	61	121, 122
5 More 2-Digit Addition pages 193–194	1, 2, 3, 8	p. 193: 1–4; p. 194: 1–11			62	62	62	123, 124
6 Addition Practice page 195	1, 2, 3, 8	p. 195: 1–4	pp. 200, 208	36	63	63	63	125, 126
7 Checking Addition page 196	1, 2, 3, 7, 8	p. 196: 1–5			64	64	64	127, 128
8 PS: Using Data from a Table pages 197–198	1, 2, 3, 11	p. 197: 1–4; p. 198: 1–5	p. 200		65	65	65	129, 130
✓ 9 PS: Thinking Mathematically page 199	1, 2, 3, 9	p. 199: All						
10 PS: Using Estimation pages 201–202	1, 2, 3, 5, 6	p. 201: 1; p. 202: 1–3			66	66	66	131, 132
11 Adding Money page 203	1, 2, 3, 8	p. 203: 1–5	p. 207	37	67	67	67	133, 134
12 Adding Three Numbers page 204	1, 2, 3, 8	p. 204: 1–2, Calculator	pp. 207, 208	38	68	68	68	135, 136
13 PS: Decision Making page 205	1, 2, 3, 6, 8	p. 205: 1–4						

Curriculum Connection: Social Studies page 206 **CC**

Chapter Review/Test pages 209–210

Performance Assessment page 211

Cumulative Review page 213

Enrichment for All/Home Activity pages 212, 214

NATIONAL COUNCIL OF TEACHERS OF MATHEMATICS Grades K–4

1. Problem Solving
2. Communication
3. Reasoning
4. Connections
5. Estimation
6. Number Sense and Numeration
7. Concepts of Whole Number Operations
8. Whole Number Computation
9. Geometry and Spatial Sense
10. Measurement
11. Statistics and Probability
12. Fractions and Decimals
13. Patterns and Relationships

✓ Activity   Cooperative Learning   **CC** Cultural Connection

MEETING the NCTM STANDARDS

Problem Solving

Strategies and Skills
- using data from a table pp. 197–198
- using estimation pp. 201–202

Applications
- **Decision Making** lesson p. 205
- **Problem of the Day** TE pp. 186, 188, 190B, 192B, 194B, 195C, 196C, 198B, 202B, 203C, 204C

Mathematical Investigations
- **Thinking Mathematically** lesson p. 199

Communication

Language
- using the language of mathematics TE pp. 187–188

Oral/Written
- using cooperative learning activities pp. 186, 187, 189, 199, 205, 206; TE pp. 184I–184P
- **Journal Writing** opportunities TE pp. 186, 190, 192, 194, 196A, 198, 202, 203A, 204A

Reasoning

Critical Thinking
- answering questions that analyze and extend concepts pp. 185, 191, 196, 205, 212

Connections

To other subject areas
- Literature p. 185, Social Studies p. 206; Literature TE pp. 185, 203

To all cultures
- Chinese counting rods, *chou* p. 206

Concept Development

Concepts of Whole Number Operations
- regrouping 10 ones for 1 ten pp. 186, 187–188, 189–190; TE pp. 184I–184M

Whole Number Computation
- adding 2-digit numbers with and without regrouping pp. 191–192, 193–194, 195, 196; TE p. 184N
- adding three 2-digit numbers p. 204; TE p. 184P
- adding money amounts to 99¢ p. 203; TE p. 184O

ASSESSMENT OPTIONS

PERFORMANCE ASSESSMENT

Preassessment Activity
Before beginning Chapter 6, display two sets of connecting cubes to represent the number of children in your class and another class. Have children discuss and write about as many ways as they can think of to find how many cubes there are in all. Assess children's knowledge and reasoning of grouping strategies.

Ongoing Assessment
The Ongoing Assessment cards under MEETING INDIVIDUAL NEEDS on TE pp. 190 and 194 provide criteria and questions for assessing children's understanding of the key mathematical concepts developed in the chapter.

MATH JOURNAL *Journal Writing* opportunities encourage children to write about mathematics. Their responses can be recorded either pictorially or in words. The journal writing opportunities on the Ongoing Assessment cards also allow you to assess children's understanding of the lessons.

In addition to the Ongoing Assessment cards, other assessment and journal writing opportunities in this chapter include:

• **CLOSE** TE pp. 186, 192, 194, 196A, 198, 202, 203A, 204A

Performance Assessment Activity
The Performance Assessment activity on p. 211 provides an alternative to formal assessment. This activity assesses children's understanding of the key concepts of the chapter.

For performance assessment activities that are keyed to individual chapter objectives, see the *Performance Assessment* booklet.

BUILDING A PORTFOLIO

Children should be encouraged to keep a selection of their best work in portfolios. The portfolios provide a way of documenting children's growth in understanding mathematical concepts. Portfolio opportunities in this chapter include:
• **Performance Assessment** p. 211
• **Class Project** TE p. 205A

If you wish to provide additional opportunities for portfolio work, you may choose to use:
• **MAC Activities** 120, 121, 122, 126, 128, 135

You may also wish to have children include their journal writing from the Ongoing Assessment on TE pp. 190 and 194 in their portfolio.

Formal Assessment

The **Chapter Review/Test** assesses children's understanding of the concepts and skills developed in the chapter. The **Cumulative Review** assesses children's understanding of the concepts and skills developed from the beginning of the year.

You can use **Form A** or **Form B** of the **Chapter Test** found in the *Testing Program Blackline Masters and Teacher's Manual* if you wish to use a multiple-choice format to assess children's understanding of the chapter concepts and skills. You can use **Form C** if you wish to use a free-response format. Any of the forms may be used as a pretest, posttest, or for retesting.

The **COMPUTER MANAGEMENT SYSTEM**, or **CMS**, enables you to score **Forms A** and **B** of the **Chapter Test** quickly and automatically. It also prescribes learning activities based on children's test results.

For more information about Assessment, see the *Professional Handbook*.

Common Error and Remediation

The Teacher's Edition notes for each Develop/Understand (Transitional/Abstract) lesson provide a common error analysis and a remediation activity. Some errors defy quick analysis and can only be identified by interviewing the child.

ALTERNATIVE TEACHING STRATEGY

Alternative Teaching Strategies appear frequently in the chapter. These strategies provide other presentations of the lessons for children who might benefit from instruction in different learning modalities: kinesthetic, visual, and/or auditory.

For Students Acquiring English (SAE)

Preteach the following vocabulary words: **regroup, trade, models, combine, tens,** and **ones.** Also preteach the vocabulary for any manipulatives you will be using. Use Workmat 2 and tens and ones models to illustrate the vocabulary. If possible, elicit from SAE children any known synonyms for the new words.

SAE notes appear periodically in the chapter. These notes provide suggestions for how to work with children to improve comprehension and build vocabulary.

MANIPULATIVES WORKSHOP

Tens and ones models are used in this chapter to demonstrate the addition of 2-digit numbers. They provide a concrete way to show the relationship between ones and tens and the equivalences used in regrouping.

USING MANIPULATIVES

Here a child models 34 + 28.

The child uses 3 tens 4 ones to model 34 and 2 tens 8 ones to model 28.

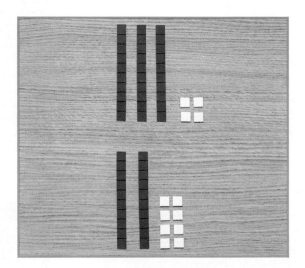

The child combines the ones, trading 10 ones for 1 ten.

The child then combines the tens. The model shows that 34 + 28 = 62.

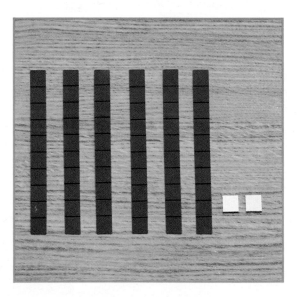

MAKING MANIPULATIVES See the Manipulatives section of the *Professional Handbook* for materials that can be used as a substitute for tens and ones models.

COOPERATIVE LEARNING WORKSHOP

GETTING STARTED

Pair Combinations: Three different pair groupings, A—B, C—D; A—C, B—D; and A—D, B—C, can work in turn in a group of four. Pairs interview each other before joining with another pair and then partners introduce one another to the other pair.

Partner text comprehension, in which each pair looks over a section of a lesson together and then reports their ideas to the other pair, creates interdependence. **Group graphic representations** (drawing, Venn diagrams, and so on) make recording the group's ideas easier for all to see. A **huddle** permits a quick consultation within the group before calling on one member to report the group's thinking.

IDEAS TO TRY

Coaching One Another: You can use a **partners-check** structure to model addition problems and regrouping situations. One partner models the initial number with manipulatives; the second partner checks the model and asks questions; the partners agree on the correct modeling; and the

second partner appreciates the first partner for good work. Then the partners trade roles. Repeat the process with each partner doing the modeling, writing the fact, and being coached before shifting roles. Monitor the pairs and celebrate when they have remembered to appreciate and cheer each other on. Pairs can then demonstrate some problems for another pair, or challenge the other pair with a problem they invent.

You may apply the above pair-coaching structures in these lessons:
6-1 *Adding 2-Digit Numbers* p. 186
6-2 *Regrouping Readiness* pp. 187–188
6-3 *More Regrouping Readiness* pp. 189–190

Pair Structures: Interview and introduction structures help pairs learn gradually how to work together as a group of four. In **six-step interview,** partners interview each other in turn (steps 1 and 2); then each faces another child in the group of four (2 pairs) and tells what they learned from their partner (steps 3 and 4). Finally, these new partners now interview each other (steps 5

and 6). Material for the interview can be discovering what each knows about the topic, considering an application of the knowledge, or comparing methods of arriving at an answer. To check for misinformation, the activity can end with a **think-write-pair-compare** structure: Each child thinks of one mathematical summary statement of what they heard, writes it, and then compares it with a partner's written statement.

You can apply the above pair structures in these lessons:
6-4 *2-Digit Addition* pp. 191–192
6-5 *More 2-Digit Addition* pp. 193–194
6-6 *Addition Practice* p. 195

SEE ALSO

Cooperative Learning Tip for lessons 6-1 p. 186; 6-8 Problem Solving p. 198; 6-10 Problem Solving p. 202

The Cooperative Learning section of the *Professional Handbook* for additional information

ACTIVITY
INTERACTIVE BULLETIN BOARD

SETUP Cover a bulletin board with white paper. Draw a fence on the paper, as shown in the illustration. Write a 2-digit addition fact on each picket. Use oaktag to make a cat pattern. Trace the pattern onto the construction paper, making enough cats to give one to each child.

PROCEDURE Have children cut out their cats. Then have them choose one of the facts on the pickets, and on their cat, write the sum for the addition fact. Then have children, in turn, place their cats on top of the appropriate pickets.

The Number Fence

| 60 | 35 | 77 | 58 | 66 | 99 | 76 | 81 | 62 | 93 |

| 24 +36 | 10 +25 | 41 +36 | 36 +22 | 55 +11 | 70 +29 | 47 +29 | 58 +23 | 23 +39 | 24 +69 |

MANIPULATIVES plus ACTIVITY

**For use before
LESSON 6.2,
pp. 187-188**

31

GROUPING BY FIVES

OBJECTIVE
Explore grouping by fives
and other numbers.

MATERIALS
Manipulatives 1 number
cube and 50 ☐ per pair

PAIRS ACTIVITY ⬆️ 🙌

Prepare number cubes by taping the numbers 0, 1,
2, 2, 3, and 4 on each cube.

Assign children to play in pairs. Give each pair of
children 1 number cube and at least 50 connecting
cubes or squares. Explain to children that they will
play a game called "Fives."

Call on a volunteer and demonstrate how the game
is played. Roll the number cube and show that
number of cubes or squares. Have the child do the
same. Continue rolling the number cube and showing cubes until one player has five cubes.

Explain that when a player has five cubes they
must be snapped together to make a *five*. (Have
squares stacked in a pile.) Show how this is done
and tell children that the player now has "1 five 2
ones."

Have children play the game together. The first
child in each pair to get 5 fives wins the round.

EXTENDING THE ACTIVITY

Present the following grouping to children "1 five 2
ones." Have pairs work together to find all the possible arrangements of the seven cubes. Discuss
that children may group the cubes in any way, not
only by fives, for example, 1 four 3 ones. Have
them record their findings and share them with the
class.

ONGOING ASSESSMENT

✓ Are children able to represent numbers by grouping by fives and other
numbers?

For use before LESSON 6.2, pp. 187-188

32

GROUPING BY TENS

OBJECTIVE
Explore grouping by tens.

MATERIALS
Classroom Materials
1 game board, game markers
Manipulatives
40 T and 40 O models, 1 spinner for 0–9 (or punchouts) per group; 200 ☐ per group (EXTENDING THE ACTIVITY only)

SMALL GROUP ACTIVITY 🔼 👫

Prepare a game board for each small group of three children as shown.

Assign children to play in groups of three. Distribute 1 game board, 1 spinner, and 40 tens and 40 ones models to each group. Give each child a game marker. Tell children that they will play the game "Around the World by Tens."

Discuss how to play the game.

■ **To begin, place your game marker on Start.**

■ **Take turns spinning the spinner and taking the same number of ones as shown on the spinner.**

■ **If you have 10 or more ones, trade the 10 ones for 1 ten, and then move forward one space.**

■ **The first player to go "around the world" wins.**

EXTENDING THE ACTIVITY

Have children play the game in the same way, but have them use connecting cubes and group by 5.

ONGOING ASSESSMENT

✓ Are children able to represent numbers by grouping by fives and other numbers?

MANIPULATIVES plus ACTIVITY

For use before LESSON 6.2, pp. 187-188

33

REGROUPING READINESS

OBJECTIVE
Explore regrouping ones as tens.

MATERIALS
Classroom Materials red and blue crayons
Manipulatives 3 🟥 and 20 🟦 (or square counter punchouts)
Teacher Resources Teacher Aid 8

WHOLE GROUP ACTIVITY ↕

Prepare a workmat as shown by drawing two squares on the top of a copy of Teacher Aid 8. Duplicate 1 copy for each child.

Give a workmat, 3 red cubes, and 20 blue cubes to each child. Tell children to color the square at the top of the right column blue and identify this column as the ones column. Then have children color the square at the top of the left column red and identify this column as the tens column. Discuss how to regroup.

■ **The ones column may hold only 9 or fewer blue cubes. If you have 10 blue cubes, trade them for 1 red cube. Place the red cube in the red column.**

Read the following story for children to model:

■ **Jan had 14 baseball cards of good players. She can trade 10 good-player baseball cards for 1 star-player baseball card. Show how the baseball cards should be placed. How many star-player baseball cards will the 14 good-player baseball cards get? How many good-player**

baseball cards will be left over? [Children should place 14 blue cubes in the ones column. They should then trade 10 of the 14 blue cubes for 1 red cube, placing the red cube in the tens column. The mat should show 1 red and 4 blue cubes.]

Repeat the activity using these numbers: 18 ones [1 ten 8 ones], 15 ones [1 ten 5 ones], 11 ones [1 ten 1 one].

EXTENDING THE ACTIVITY

Repeat the activity using numbers that begin with one ten, such as 1 ten 16 ones [2 tens 6 ones], 1 ten 19 ones [2 tens 9 ones], 1 ten 17 ones [2 tens 7 ones].

ONGOING ASSESSMENT

✔ Are children able to represent numbers by regrouping ones as tens?

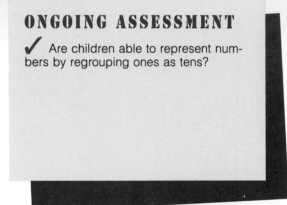

MANIPULATIVES plus ACTIVITY

**For use before
LESSON 6.2,
pp. 187-188**

34

MORE
REGROUPING
READINESS

OBJECTIVE
Explore regrouping ones
as tens.

MATERIALS
Classroom Materials
small plastic bowls, large
spoons, tape
Manipulatives 10 D and
40 P coins (or punchouts)
per pair
Teacher Resources
Teacher Aid 8

PAIRS ACTIVITY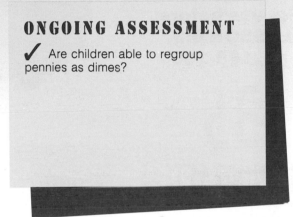

Prepare a workmat as shown by drawing two circles, (dime and penny), on the top of a copy of
Teacher Aid 8. Duplicate 1 copy for each child.

Assign children to play in pairs. Give each pair 10
dimes, 1 spoon, and 1 small bowl filled with at least
40 pennies. Give each child 1 workmat.

Tell children to tape a dime down at the top of the
left column of the workmat and a penny at the top
of the right column. Explain that dimes will be the
model for tens and pennies will be the model for
ones.

Have children take turns taking a spoonful of pennies out of the bowl and putting their pennies in the
ones column on their workmats. Have them trade
10 pennies for 1 dime whenever they can, and then
tell how many dimes and pennies they have. The

child in each pair with the most dimes scores one
point. The leftover pennies can serve as a tie
breaker. Repeat until one child scores 10 points.

EXTENDING THE ACTIVITY

Assign one child in each pair to play the role of a
bank teller. Have the other child be the customer.
The customer should choose a number of pennies
greater than 10 and ask the teller to trade the pennies for dimes. Have children switch roles.

ONGOING ASSESSMENT
✓ Are children able to regroup
pennies as dimes?

MA NIPULATIVES plus ACTIVITY

For use before LESSON 6.3, pp. 189-190

35
JOINING SETS

OBJECTIVE
Explore joining sets, with and without regrouping.

MATERIALS
Classroom Materials
number cards
Manipulatives 9 T and 20 O models (or punchouts), Workmat 2 per pair

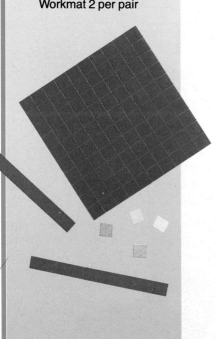

SMALL GROUP ACTIVITY
Prepare number cards for numbers between 8 and 49.

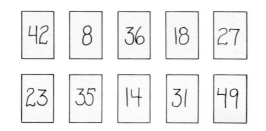

Assign children to teams of two and have two teams play the game together. Give each group of children a set of 10 number cards. Give each team 1 copy of Workmat 2 and 9 tens and 20 ones models. Work with one group of children to demonstrate the activity.

Mix the number cards and place them in a pile facedown between the two teams. Have each child from one team choose a number card. The first child should then model his or her number on the workmat; for example, 18. The other child then models his or her number below that number; for example, 49.

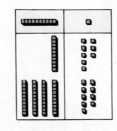

Tell children to work together to combine the models, regrouping as necessary. Repeat the sequence with the other team.

Next have a member of each team say the total for the two cards drawn, using the regrouped number, for example, 6 tens 7 ones. A correct total scores one point. Have children play the game for three rounds. Then rotate teams and number cards.

EXTENDING THE ACTIVITY
Have children work with mental math to join two numbers. Have groups turn over 2 number cards and each try to mentally solve the problem. Have individuals share and discuss their strategies and solutions.

ONGOING ASSESSMENT
✓ Are children able to represent numbers using ones and tens and regroup ones as tens?

**For use before
LESSON 6.6,
p. 195**

36

ADDING ON A
CALCULATOR

OBJECTIVE
Add on a calculator.

MATERIALS
Calculator

WHOLE GROUP ACTIVITY

Give each child a calculator. Review or demonstrate the process of adding 2-digit numbers.

Write 37 + 49 on the chalkboard. Have children enter 37 on the calculator. Then tell them to press the + key and enter 49. Next have them press the = key and read the sum. [86] Repeat with other exercises.

Write the following sets of numbers on the chalkboard. Challenge children to find the two numbers in each row whose sum equal the number in the box. Have children guess before testing.

46	37	50	49	95	[46 + 49]
15	23	34	36	49	[15 + 34]
51	27	45	31	72	[27 + 45]
47	27	11	53	64	[11 + 53]

EXTENDING THE ACTIVITY

Have children use calculators, if they wish, and work backward from the sum to find the two addends. First allow children the opportunity to find any two addends that can be added to make the target sum. Then provide them with clues to find the two addends you have in mind, as in the following:

■ I am thinking of two numbers that have a sum of 54. What two numbers could they be? [Answers may vary. Examples: 32 and 22, 25 and 29.]

■ Of the two numbers I am thinking of, the lesser number is less than 20. [Possible answers: 1–19]

■ The greater number has the same digit in both the tens place and the ones place. [44; 44 and 10]

ONGOING ASSESSMENT

✓ Are children able to use calculators to add two 2-digit numbers?

37

ADDING MONEY

OBJECTIVE
Add money amounts.

MATERIALS
Classroom Materials
index cards, game markers
Manipulatives 1 number
cube*, 10 D and 10 P coins
(or punchouts) per group
Teacher Resources
Teacher Aids 1, 17*

SMALL GROUP ACTIVITY

Prepare and duplicate 1 game board per small group of three on a copy of Teacher Aid 1 as shown. Write money amounts from 18¢ to 49¢ on index cards.

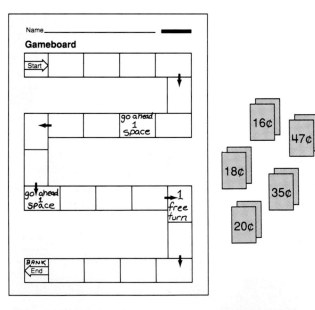

Have children play in small groups of three. Give each group 1 game board, 15 amount cards, 3 game markers, 1 number cube, 10 dimes, and 10 pennies.

Have groups play "Get to the Bank." Each player begins with a marker on *Start*. Players take turns rolling the number cube, moving that number of spaces on the game board, and taking an amount card.

Players should model the amount on the card using dimes and pennies, and then add 25¢ to the amount using 2 dimes 5 pennies. They should re-group when they can and say the total as dimes and pennies.

A player may move ahead one space with a correct response, and back one space with an incorrect response. The first player to reach the bank wins.

EXTENDING THE ACTIVITY

Write money amounts from 10¢ to 49¢ in the spaces on the game board. Have players take turns modeling the amount they land on and then draw-ing an amount card and modeling that amount. Players should add the two amounts, regrouping when they can.

ONGOING ASSESSMENT

✓ Are children able to model and add money amounts?

MANIPULATIVES plus ACTIVITY

For use before LESSON 6.12, p. 204

38

ADDING THREE NUMBERS

OBJECTIVE
Add three numbers.

MATERIALS
Classroom Materials red, yellow, blue, and white construction paper
Manipulatives 6 T and 19 O models (or punchouts) per group

SMALL GROUP ACTIVITY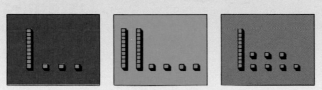

Assign children to work in small groups of three. Give each group 1 sheet of white construction paper and 6 tens and 19 ones models. Give each child in a group a different-colored sheet of paper: red, yellow, or blue.

Discuss that each child should model the number for her or his assigned color. Read the following:

Red: 13   Yellow: 24   Blue: 17

■ **Look at the ones. Do two of you have sets of ones that equal ten?** [Yes; 3 + 7 = 10.]

Have these children combine their ones models and trade them for 1 tens model. Tell them to put the ten on the white workmat.

■ **How many ones do you have now?** [4]
■ **How many tens do you have in all?** [5]
■ **What number is 5 tens 4 ones?** [54]

Repeat the activity with the following numbers.

Red: 25	Yellow: 15	Blue: 9	[49]
Red: 18	Yellow: 7	Blue: 23	[48]
Red: 36	Yellow: 19	Blue: 14	[69]
Red: 24	Yellow: 9	Blue: 31	[64]

EXTENDING THE ACTIVITY

Have children work with mental math to join three numbers. Read three numbers to children and write them on the chalkboard. Children should try to add the numbers mentally. Have individuals share and discuss their strategies and solutions.

ONGOING ASSESSMENT

✔ Are children able to regroup ones as tens given three sets of models for numbers?

Mathematics and Literature

Listening and Speaking

The Read-Aloud selection can be used with the Chapter 6 Opener and Lesson 6-1 on pages 185-186.

**Tape 1, Side 2
Selection 3**

NINETY-NINE POCKETS

BY JEAN MYRICK

"Jeremy, what would you like for your birthday?"

Jeremy jumped up from the floor where he was reading the funnies and ran over to his mother's chair. He had been waiting for that question for days and he had his answer all ready. "I would like to have you make me a pocket suit!"

"A suit? But you have your best Sunday suit, and you have corduroys for school and jeans for play. Why do you want another suit?"

"This would be a *pocket* suit. It would have pockets all over it—long skinny ones for pencils and rulers and my pocket knife, a round one for my compass, a big, squarish one for a book, a little one with a button for money, a bag-shaped one for an apple, one for nails, and one for my hammer—or maybe that could hang from a little loop like the one on Uncle Ted's white coveralls."

Jeremy stopped long enough to get his breath. Then he continued, "I'll need a pocket for my flashlight, and pockets for my collections of bottlecaps and rocks—I don't suppose I could carry all of them, just a few of the special ones—and some extra pockets for things I might find. Oh, and pockets for string and glue and marbles, and one for my rope and my magnifying glass, and—and—Boy, could I have a hundred pockets, Mom? Could I?"

"My goodness!" exclaimed Mother. "Where would I ever get a pattern for a suit like that? You had better draw a picture for me."

So Jeremy got a pencil and a big piece of paper and started making a picture of his pocket suit.

It was bedtime before he finished, so he put the paper under his pillow, in case he thought of anything in the middle of the night.

All the next day Jeremy worked on his suit pattern. He kept thinking of more and more things he would like to carry with him. His mother asked him to take a note to Aunt Beatrice, so he drew a note pocket on his collar. Then he decided to have one on each side, so he could carry notes coming and going and not get mixed up. Left going, right coming.

Hiram, his hamster, looked so lonesome when Jeremy put him back in his cage that Jeremy dashed up to his room and added a hamster pocket on the back of his right shoulder.

Jeremy's mother went downtown and bought seven yards of blue denim—three yards for the suit and four yards for all of the pockets.

Jeremy started carrying around a little notebook to write down more pockets as he thought of them. He decided to have a yardstick pocket on his left trouser leg and a saw pocket on his right leg. His telescope could go on his left sleeve, and the periscope he had made out of a wax paper tube could go on his right sleeve. No, it had better be the other way around, so the periscope wouldn't get smashed. His lunch pocket would be, naturally, right over his stomach.

The evening before Jeremy's birthday his mother straightened up from her sewing, bit off her thread, and said, "Jeremy, I think your suit is finished. Every last pocket is stitched in place."

"Does it really have a hundred pockets?"

"I'm sorry, Jeremy, but it has only ninety-nine."

"Couldn't we make just one more so it would have a hundred?"

"Jeremy Jason Jones!" said his mother. "This suit has round pockets, triangular pockets, square pockets, long, thin pockets, baggy pockets! It has pockets on pockets, pockets inside of pockets, and pockets inside of pockets on pockets! There is not room for one more pocket! Besides, I don't have any more denim."

"O.K. Thanks, Mom. Boy, I bet even the President doesn't have a suit with ninety-nine pockets! Wait till I show the kids tomorrow! Oh boy! Nine-nine pockets!"

Jeremy woke up early the next morning, he was so anxious to wear his new suit. It didn't take him long to get dressed *this* morning, but his mother called him to breakfast before he had more than eight pockets filled. He was just finishing his breakfast when Steve, Peter, and David stopped by for him. Jeremy ran upstairs while his mother went to the door.

"Ask them to wait a couple of minutes, and I'll show them something they've never seen before!" he called down the stairs. He hurried to put his police whistle, his squirt gun, his popsicle sticks, and his bubble gum funnies in the pockets designed for them.

"David says to hurry," Mother called up to him.

"Coming," Jeremy answered, and squeezed his bunch of keys, the chain from the bathtub plug, his oil can, his crayons, and his collapsible cup into their pockets.

"Hurry up, Jeremy," called Peter. "I have to be home by 11:30."

"I'm coming," yelled Jeremy, putting his notebook, his mouth organ, his magnet, and marbles in place.

"We're going on over to Mark's house. You come when you get ready," Steve called from the foot of the stairs.

"All right. I'll be there in a flash." Jeremy grabbed his little funnel, his camp shovel, his four big steel ball bearings, and the nutcracker and shoved them into their pockets. Now he just had to put in his rocks and spare batteries, and—OOOOPS! "Hey, Mom! Mother!"

His trousers had been sinking lower and lower on his hips. Now they dropped to the floor with a THUD! and a JANGLE! a CRASH! and a SMASH! and a SPLAT!

Mother and Father rushed upstairs in alarm. As they stood in the doorway staring at him, Jeremy felt that he had to say something. "I guess I need suspenders."

"Two pairs of suspenders—and a belt," Mother suggested.

"Or a portable derrick," added Father, smiling.

Jeremy could not move around very well with everything hanging around his ankles, so Mother found his old suspenders and then took the new ones from his Sunday suit. She finally added an old pair of Father's, which she shortened with safety pins. And then, somehow, she managed to buckle on two belts.

Jeremy found it a little difficult to bend down. "Would you mind handing me that file over there, please, Mother? And would you please slide that yardstick in this long pocket on my left leg, and the saw on the other side? Now my telescope goes on the right sleeve and the periscope on the left sleeve."

"Oh, oh!" said Father, laughing. "Do you think you can walk? Let's see you bend your arm."

Jeremy tried. He couldn't bend either his knees or his elbows!

"We forgot to put joints in this suit!" said Father. Jeremy finally agreed that he would have to get along with only his six-inch ruler for measuring and his pocket knife for cutting.

He was in a hurry to get over to Mark's house, so he decided to leave Hiram in his cage and not to take his shell collection along this time. Mother and Father insisted on helping him down the stairs, one on each side, holding an arm.

"Bye, Mom! Bye, Dad!" Jeremy shouted back as he started off for Mark's. "Thanks for helping me get ready. And thanks a million, Mother, for making my suit! I'll be ba—"

SPLASH! THUD! JANGLE! CRASH! SMASH! SPLAT! BOOM! and especially, OUCH! Jeremy's right side pockets with the rocks and ball bearings and the camp shovel and the nails had over-balanced the lighter left side and tumbled Jeremy into the big mud puddle he had made yesterday when he forgot to move the hose.

"Just look at that suit!" Mother cried, as soon as she was sure that Jeremy was not really hurt. "You take it off and put it in the wash this minute! And be sure you take every single thing out of the pockets!"

"But Mom, it will take me an hour to unload."

"I'll help you. Come up to your room, so we can put things away."

Mother and Father helped him up the stairs again, and Mother took out enough things so that Jeremy could move around to empty the rest.

"Mother," said Jeremy slowly, "I wouldn't want to hurt your feelings after you worked so hard, but do you think there could be such a thing as too many pockets?"

"It looks as though there might well be."

"How many pockets do you think a boy should have?"

"Well, I would say one on each side—"

"And maybe two in the back? Mom, do you know what? My jeans are just perfect. A pocket for each hand and two extra in the back. And I have two pockets in my shirt, besides. Six pockets ought to be enough for any boy, don't you think so, Mom?"

"But what shall we do with this suit? It took me so long to make it."

"I know!" said Jeremy, triumphantly. "I can hang it up on my coat-tree and store everything in its own pocket just as we planned. I guess I don't really need to carry everything around with me all the time. I bet I'll have the only hanging toy chest in the neighborhood!"

CHAPTER 6

Adding 2-Digit Numbers

LESSON OBJECTIVES
Explore mathematical concepts through literature.
Explore regrouping for addition.

ASSIGNMENT GUIDE

COURSE	EXERCISES
Basic	p. 185: All; p. 186: All
Average	p. 185: All; p. 186: All
Challenge	p. 185: All; p. 186: All

MATERIALS
Manipulatives 25 ☐ (or square counter punchouts) per pair

Teacher Resources
Math Anthology, pp. 158–161
Read-Aloud Cassette 1, Side 2, Selection 3

SKILLS TRACE
2-DIGIT ADDITION

Explore (Concrete) 186, 187–188	Develop/Understand (Transitional/Abstract) 189–190, 191–192, 193–194, 195, 196, 203, 204
Practice 200, 207, 208, 209–210, 213, 224, 245	Apply 197–198, 201–202, 205, 206, 212, 244, 291–292

🦻 Listen to the story *Ninety-Nine Pockets.*

🗣 Suppose one pocket suit had 10 pockets. Tell how many pockets 10 pocket suits would have. 100

READ ALOUD

NINETY-NINE POCKETS By Jean Myrick

185

Mathematics and Literature

Page 185 Read *Ninety-Nine Pockets* found on pages 184Q–184R or in *Math Anthology* to children, or play Read-Aloud Cassette 1, Side 2, Selection 3 for them.

■ **What did Jeremy want for his birthday?** [a pocket suit]

■ **How many pockets did he want on the suit?** [100]

■ **What are some things Jeremy wanted to carry in his pockets?** [Responses include: pencils, ruler, compass, money, books, and so on.]

Discuss the problem on the page. Guide children to find the answer by skip counting by tens.

Page 186 Discuss the picture with the children. Read the problem aloud.

WARM-UP To review tens and ones, give pairs of children 25 connecting cubes. Have them show the following numbers with the cubes.

14 [1 ten 4 ones]   23 [2 tens 3 ones]
17 [1 ten 7 ones]   25 [2 tens 5 ones]

Ask them to snap together the cubes for each number to make tens trains. Then have them tell how many tens and ones they have.

DISCUSSING Before reading the story *Ninety-Nine Pockets,* discuss with the children what they carry in their pockets. Have volunteers tell what they like to take with them when they go out.

ActiVity

Adding 2-Digit Numbers

Guess how many pockets you and your

classmates have altogether. _____
Answers will vary.

Working Together

Use .

Find how many pockets are
in your group.
Show 1 cube for each pocket.
Write how many pockets
each child has.

Put together all the cubes.
Make as many tens
as you can.
Write how many pockets are
in your group.

How many pockets are
in your class?
Think of a plan. Try it.

My Group

Name	Pockets
Pockets in My Group	

Meeting Individual Needs

For Students Acquiring English (SAE)

Begin Lesson 6–1 by sorting a group of children according to the kinds of pockets they have. Construct a real Venn diagram by taping large circles of masking tape to the floor as the set delineator. Have children stand inside the circles according to their pocket type; circles can overlap if a student has more than one type of pocket.

TEACHER to TEACHER

COOPERATIVE LEARNING TIP  My children love to line up according to how many pockets each has that day. First each students puts one connecting cube in each pocket, and then the small groups estimate how many pockets we have. When everyone is lined up according to the estimate, we check it out by connecting all the cubes in one long train. Finally each person counts aloud the cubes they contributed, and we compare the result to our estimate.

ActiVity ALTERNATIVE TEACHING STRATEGY

MATERIALS 4 T, 10 O models (or punchouts)

KINESTHETIC/VISUAL Gather children around a table and ask each child, in turn, to come forward. Help the child count the number of pockets on his or her clothing. Tell the child to count out ones models for the number of pockets. Have the next child come forward and do the same. Whenever there are 10 or more ones, have the child doing the counting regroup 10 ones for 1 ten. When finished, count the tens and ones with the children to find the total number of pockets.

Check for Understanding

■ **Where do you have a pocket?** [Possible responses: shirt, pants]

GUIDED PRACTICE ■ **Working Together** Assign children to work in groups of four or five. Give each group connecting cubes. Tell children that one way to find how many pockets they have in their group is to put a cube in each pocket. [They take the cubes out of their pockets, count the tens and ones, and complete the chart.]

For reteaching, use Alternative Strategy.

3 PRACTICE•APPLY
PRACTICE Have children complete the page. Guide them in developing a plan for finding the total number of pockets.

CLOSE Guide children to summarize the lesson:

■ **How did you find the total number of pockets in the class?**
[Possible response: counted the number of pockets each child has, found the total for each group, then found the total for class]

Problem of the Day

Tim has 2 pockets. Mary has 4 pockets. John has 3 pockets. How many pockets do the three children have? [9 pockets]

AT·A·GLANCE pp. 187-188

LESSON OBJECTIVE
Explore regrouping 10 ones for 1 ten.

ASSIGNMENT GUIDE

COURSE	EXERCISES
Basic	p. 187: 1–4; p. 188: 1–7
Average	p. 187: 1–4; p. 188: 1–7
Challenge	p. 187: 1–4; p. 188: 1–7

MATERIALS
Manipulatives 6 T and 19 O models (or punchouts), Workmat 2 per pair

SKILLS TRACE
2-DIGIT ADDITION

Explore (Concrete) 186, 187–188	Develop/Understand (Transitional/Abstract) 189–190, 191–192, 193–194, 195, 196, 203, 204
Practice 200, 207, 208, 209–210, 213, 224, 245	Apply 197–198, 201–202, 205, 206, 212, 244, 291–292, 351

See **MANIPULATIVES PLUS 31–34**, pp. 184I–184L.

PREPARE **WARM-UP** To prepare children to model numbers, write the following on the chalkboard. Have children identify the number of tens and ones in each number.

14 [1 ten, 4 ones]
25 [2 tens, 5 ones]
81 [8 tens, 1 one]
60 [6 tens, 0 ones]
38 [3 tens, 8 ones]
73 [7 tens, 3 ones]

TEACH **MODELING** Assign each child a partner and give each pair 6 tens and 19 ones models and Workmat 2. Tell children to model the number 17 on their workmats.

■ **How many tens and ones do you have?** [1 ten 7 ones]

ACTIVITY

Regrouping Readiness

Tony and Jan are building a Tens Town.
In Tens Town you must trade 10 ones for 1 ten when you can.

Tony and Jan have 14 ones. ▫▫▫▫▫▫▫▫▫▫▫▫▫▫ (14 ones)

They trade 10 ones for 1 ten. ▬▬▬▬▬ ▫▫▫▫ (1 ten 4 ones)

Trading 10 ones for 1 ten is called **regrouping**.

Working Together

Use 19 ▫ and 1 ▬▬▬▬▬ .
You take some ones models.
Your partner takes some ones models.

How many ones in all?	Do you have enough ones to make a ten?	Regroup when you can. How many tens and ones?
1. ┃Ꮞ	(yes) / no	tens: 1 / ones: 4

For exercises 2–4 answers will vary.

		tens	ones
2. _____	yes / no		
3. _____	yes / no		
4. _____	yes / no		

Repeat with several other 2-digit numbers.

Next have children show 2 tens 14 ones on their mats.

■ **Do you have enough ones to exchange for 1 ten?** [Yes.]

Introduce the term **regroup** as you have children make this exchange.

■ **How many tens and ones do you have now?** [3 tens 4 ones]

Repeat this regrouping with 3 tens 19 ones, 5 tens 12 ones, and 4 tens 13 ones.

PUPIL'S EDITION pp. 187-188

Page 187 Work through the example at the top of the page with the children.

Use Workmat 2. Use 18 ▣ , and 3 ▭ .

Show 1 ten 13 ones on Workmat 2.	Regroup 10 ones as 1 ten.	How many tens and ones are there now?

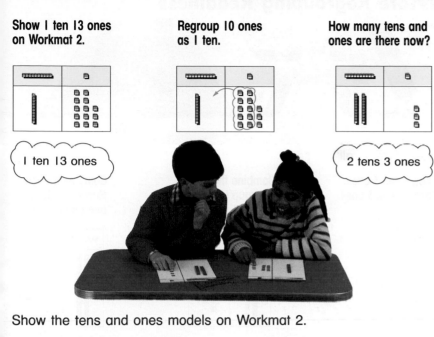

1 ten 13 ones

2 tens 3 ones

Show the tens and ones models on Workmat 2.

Regroup. Write the number.

1. 1 ten 13 ones

tens	ones
2	3

2. 12 ones

tens	ones
1	2

3 10 ones

tens	ones
1	0

4. 1 ten 18 ones

tens	ones
2	8

5. 15 ones

tens	ones
1	5

6. 2 tens 10 ones

tens	ones
3	0

7. Make up more regrouping exercises.
Find the answers.
Answers will vary.

Use your own paper.

For Students Acquiring English (SAE)

Do these pages as a guided lesson. Talk about the children's own experiences with **trading** things. Show the idea of trading for a ten while orally modeling for SAE children the vocabulary in context. Have children work in heterogeneous pairs to complete the lesson.

Activity ALTERNATIVE TEACHING STRATEGY

MATERIALS 6 T and 19 O models (or punchouts), Workmat 2, counting sticks; rubber bands

VISUAL Model 1 ten 13 ones on Workmat 2 using a bundle of 10 counting sticks for ten and 13 sticks for ones. Tell children that there cannot be more than 9 ones in the ones column. Explain that you will regroup 10 of the ones to make 1 ten. Put a rubber band around 10 sticks and place the ten in the tens column. Have a volunteer read the models as 2 tens 3 ones. Repeat with other numbers.

Check for Understanding

■ **What is regrouping?** [trading 10 ones for 1 ten]

WORKING TOGETHER   Assign children to work in pairs. Give each pair 1 ten and 19 ones models.

GUIDED PRACTICE   ex. 1–4: For reteaching, use Alternative Strategy.

Page 188   Go through the steps in the example with the children.

3 PRACTICE·APPLY

PRACTICE   ex. 1–7: For ex. 7 you may want to have children exchange papers and solve each other's problems.

C L O S E   Guide children to summarize the lesson:

■ **What is the number when you regroup 7 tens 12 ones? 13 ones? 4 tens 16 ones?** [82; 13; 56]

Problem of the Day

Albert's pens come in boxes of 10. He has 6 boxes of 10 pens, and 21 single pens. Does he have enough pens to fill 8 boxes? [Yes.]

AT·A·GLANCE pp. 189-190

LESSON OBJECTIVE
Use models to combine two numbers to find a total.

ASSIGNMENT GUIDE

COURSE	EXERCISES
Basic	p. 189: 1–2; p. 190: 1–2
Average	p. 189: 1–2; p. 190: 1–2
Challenge	p. 189: 1–2; p. 190: 1–2

MATERIALS
Manipulatives 5 T, 16 O models (or punchouts), Workmat 2 per pair

Teacher Resources
Reteaching 60   Practice 60   Enrichment 60
MAC Act. 119, 120

SKILLS TRACE
2-DIGIT ADDITION

Explore (Concrete) 186, 187–188	Develop/Understand (Transitional/Abstract) 189–190, 191–192, 193–194, 195, 196, 203, 204
Practice 200, 207, 208, 209–210, 213, 224, 245	Apply 197–198, 201–202, 205, 206, 212, 244, 291–292, 351

See **MANIPULATIVES PLUS 35**, p. 184M.

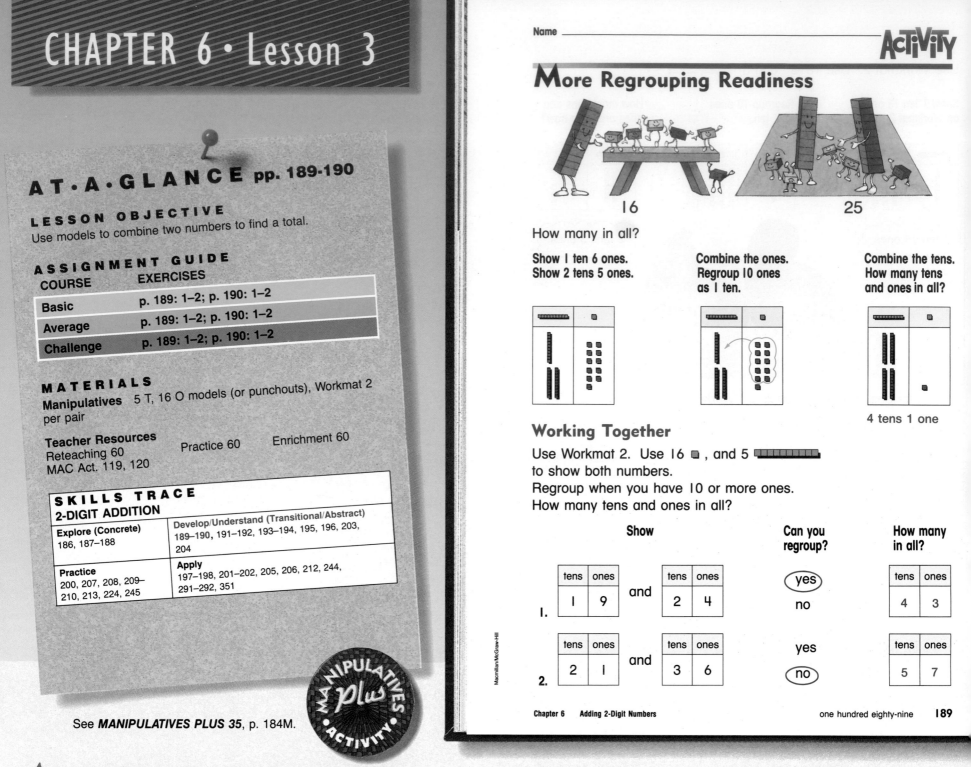

More Regrouping Readiness

16   25

How many in all?

Show 1 ten 6 ones. Show 2 tens 5 ones.	Combine the ones. Regroup 10 ones as 1 ten.	Combine the tens. How many tens and ones in all?

4 tens 1 one

Working Together

Use Workmat 2. Use 16 ▪ , and 5 ▭▭▭▭
to show both numbers.
Regroup when you have 10 or more ones.
How many tens and ones in all?

	Show		**Can you regroup?**	**How many in all?**

1. | tens 1 ones 9 | and | tens 2 ones 4 | (yes) / no | tens 4 ones 3

2. | tens 2 ones 1 | and | tens 3 ones 6 | yes / (no) | tens 5 ones 7

Macmillan/McGraw-Hill

PREPARE

WARM-UP To review regrouping, have children model the following using Workmat 2 and tens and ones models. For each number, have children tell if it is possible to regroup. If so, have them regroup and tell the new number of tens and ones.

2 tens 11 ones [Yes; 3 tens 1 one.]
18 ones [Yes; 1 ten 8 ones.]
3 tens 7 ones [No.]
1 ten 12 ones [Yes; 2 tens 2 ones.]

TEACH

MODELING Assign each child a partner and give each pair of children Workmat 2 and tens and ones models. Tell children to model the numbers 17 and 36, one below the other on their workmats. Tell them to combine and count the ones

models. Remind them that if there are 10 ones or more, they must regroup.

■ **Do you have enough ones to regroup as 1 ten?** [Yes.]

After regrouping 13 ones as 1 ten 3 ones, have children count the tens models to find how many in all. [5 tens 3 ones, or 53]

Repeat this procedure with other pairs of numbers, such as 12 and 34; 16 and 9; 26 and 24. Have children describe the steps followed in combining the models for each pair.

PUPIL'S EDITION pp. 189-190

Page 189 Work through the steps in the example at the top of the page with the children.

Show each number.

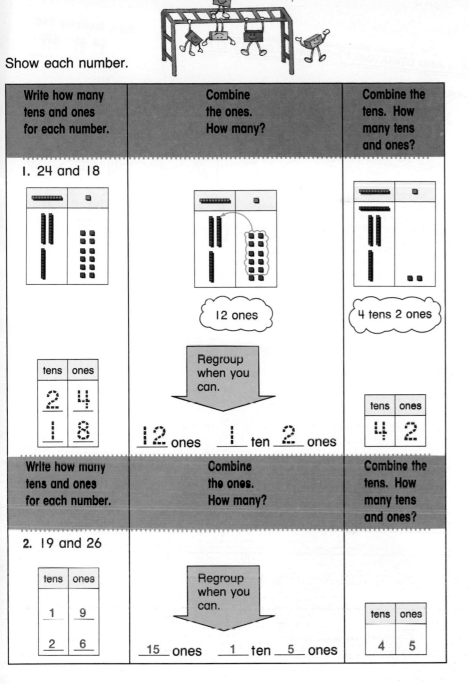

Write how many tens and ones for each number.	Combine the ones. How many?	Combine the tens. How many tens and ones?
1. 24 and 18	12 ones	4 tens 2 ones
tens ones / 2 4 / 1 8	Regroup when you can. / 12 ones 1 ten 2 ones	tens ones / 4 2
Write how many tens and ones for each number.	Combine the ones. How many?	Combine the tens. How many tens and ones?
2. 19 and 26	Regroup when you can.	
tens ones / 1 9 / 2 6	15 ones 1 ten 5 ones	tens ones / 4 5

ONGOING ASSESSMENT

OBSERVATION Determine whether children use models and add numbers correctly in the activity on p. 189.

INTERVIEW Have on hand tens and ones models and Workmat 2. (1) How would you find the answer to 15 + 21? (2) Would you have to regroup when you add 26 + 36? Tell why.

JOURNAL WRITING You may wish to have children record their responses in their math journals.

ACTIVITY Common Error and Remediation

MATERIALS 5 T, 16 O models (or punchouts), Workmat 2

Some children may fail to count the regrouped ten. Work through regrouping examples. Place the regrouped ten in the tens column box on Workmat 2, and have the child describe combining the tens.

ACTIVITY ALTERNATIVE TEACHING STRATEGY

MATERIALS overhead projector; Teacher Aid Transparency 10, Manipulative Kit Transparency 9 (or punchout tens and ones models)

VISUAL Tell children you have 28 books in school and 17 books at home. Explain that you want to find out how many books you have in all. Tell children one way to do this is to model each number, combine the models, and count to find the total. Model both numbers on a workmat transparency. Combine the ones. [15] Have a volunteer tell when to regroup. [When there are 10 or more ones, they should be regrouped as tens and ones.] Regroup 15 ones as 1 ten 5 ones. Combine the tens and have a volunteer give the total. [45] Repeat by combining 23 and 14.

Check for Understanding

■ **How many ones do you need to regroup?** [10 or more]

WORKING TOGETHER Have children work in pairs using Workmat 2 and tens and ones models.

GUIDED PRACTICE ex. 1–2: For reteaching, use Common Error and Remediation or Alternative Strategy.

Page 190 Discuss the example at the top of the page with the children. Read aloud each step in the directions.

PRACTICE·APPLY **PRACTICE** ex. 1–2

CLOSE Guide children to summarize the lesson:

■ **Do you regroup ones when you combine 16 and 33?** [No.] **Why not?** [There are only 9 ones; we need 10 ones to regroup.]

MAC ACTIVITY CENTER

MATH AND LITERATURE ■ *THE MAGIC BEANSTALK*

MAC Activity 120

On Your Own   Pair and Share   In a Group

Materials tens and ones models or punchout tens and ones models, punchout Workmat 2

Help children recall the story "Jack and the Beanstalk." Discuss how quickly the magic beanstalk grew. Have children make up "magic beanstalk" problems that involve combining two numbers. Here is an example.

In one minute the beanstalk grew 28 feet. The next minute it grew 36 feet. How many feet did it grow in the first two minutes? [64 feet]

Have children exchange problems and use tens and ones models on Workmat 2 to combine the two numbers to find the total growth..

MANIPULATIVES ■ *FISHING FOR NUMBERS*

MAC Activity 119

On Your Own   Pair and Share   In a Group

Materials drawing paper, scissors, small boxes, paper clips, string, magnets, punchout Workmat 2, tens and ones models or punchout tens and ones models

Procedure Cut out fish shapes from drawing paper. Write one number from 1 to 50 on each fish. Assign children to groups of four. Give each group a box with 20 fish. Have children attach one paper clip to the "nose" of each fish. Begin the game by having children take turns lowering a magnet into each box to fish for two fish. Then each child finds the total of the two numbers on his or her fish by using models. The members of the group check each other's sums. The child with the greatest total scores one point.

To Win The first child to score five points wins.

▲ **MAC Activity 120:**
Average-to-Challenge

▲ **MAC Activity 119:**
Basic-to-Average

RETEACHING

Name

MORE REGROUPING READINESS

Study

36 and 17

tens	ones
3	6
1	7

6 ones + 7 ones

13 ones

Regroup when you can

13 ones = 1 ten 3 ones

1 ten 3 ones

1 ten 3 ten + 1 ten

tens	ones
5	3

Check

Use models and Workmat 2.
Show each number.

Combine the ones.

1.
tens	ones
2	8
1	3

_____ ones   Regroup when you can   _____ tens _____ ones

tens	ones
4	1

2.
tens	ones
1	5
1	7

12 ones   Regroup when you can   1 tens 2 ones

tens	ones
3	2

3.
tens	ones
4	4
1	9

13 ones   Regroup when you can   1 tens 3 ones

tens	ones
6	3

Macmillan/McGraw-Hill, MATHEMATICS IN ACTION
Grade 2, Chapter 6, Lesson 3, pages 189–190

Reteaching-60

PRACTICE

Name

MORE REGROUPING READINESS

Use models and Workmat 2. Show each number.

Write how many tens and ones for each number.

Combine the ones. How many?

Combine the tens. How many tens and ones?

1. 32 and 19

tens	ones
3	2
1	9

11 ones   Regroup when you can   1 tens 1 ones

tens	ones
5	1

2. 28 and 7

tens	ones
2	8
	7

15 ones   Regroup when you can   1 tens 5 ones

tens	ones
3	5

3. 56 + 13

tens	ones
5	6
1	3

9 ones   Regroup when you can   0 tens 9 ones

tens	ones
6	9

Macmillan/McGraw-Hill, MATHEMATICS IN ACTION
Grade 2, Chapter 6, Lesson 3, pages 189–190

Practice-60

ENRICHMENT

Name

MORE REGROUPING READINESS

On Your Own   Pair and Share   In a Group

DOES NOT BELONG

Draw a line through the number that does not belong.

1.
2 tens 3 ones
23
1 ten 13 ones
~~13~~

2.
75
~~7 tens 15 ones~~
6 tens 15 ones
7 tens 5 ones

3.
~~4 tens 8 ones~~
4 tens 18 ones
58
5 tens 8 ones

4.
66
5 tens 16 ones
~~56~~
6 tens 6 ones

5.
32
3 tens 2 ones
~~2 tens 3 ones~~
2 tens 12 ones

6.
59
5 tens 9 ones
4 tens 19 ones
~~4 tens 9 ones~~

7.
9 tens 1 one
~~8 tens 10 ones~~
91
8 tens 11 ones

8.
~~14 tens~~
1 ten 4 ones
14 ones
14

Macmillan/McGraw-Hill, MATHEMATICS IN ACTION
Grade 2, Chapter 6, Lesson 3, pages 189–190

Enrichment-60

Problem of the Day

The lunchroom seats 75 children. There are 38 children in first grade. There are 43 children in second grade. Can both grades eat in the lunchroom at the same time? [No; possible solution: 38 and 43 total 81; 81 > 75.]

AT·A·GLANCE pp. 191-192

LESSON OBJECTIVE
Use models to add two 2-digit numbers.

ASSIGNMENT GUIDE

COURSE	EXERCISES
Basic	p. 191: 1–2; p. 192: 1–6, Mental Math
Average	p. 191: 1–2; p. 192: 1–6, Mental Math
Challenge	p. 191: 1–2; p. 192: 1–6, Mental Math

MATERIALS
Classroom Materials overhead projector
Manipulatives 9 T and 15 O models (or punchouts), Workmat 2 per child

Teacher Resources
Reteaching 61   Practice 61   Enrichment 61
MAC Act. 121, 122   Calculator 6
Teacher Aids Transparency 6
Computer Software *Mathematics Skills*: Disk 4 Act. 1

SKILLS TRACE
2-DIGIT ADDITION

Explore (Concrete) 186, 187–188	Develop/Understand (Transitional/Abstract) 189–190, 191–192 193–194, 195, 196, 203, 204
Practice 200, 207, 208, 209–210, 213, 224, 245	**Apply** 197–198, 201–202, 205, 206, 212, 244, 291–292, 351

Name _____

2-Digit Addition

Add 14 and 29.

First add the ones.

13 ones

Regroup. Do you know why?

There are more than 9 ones.

1 ten 3 ones

Next add the tens.

4 tens

	tens	ones
	☐ 1	4
+	2	9

	tens	ones
	☐ 1	4
+	2	9
		3

	tens	ones
	☐ 1	4
+	2	9
	4	3

1. What is the sum? 14 + 29 = __43__

2. **Tell why you add ones first.** Possible answer: If you start with tens, you would have to add another ten when you regroup the ones.

Macmillan/McGraw-Hill

PREPARE
WARM-UP To review addition facts and place value, ask children to give the sums for the following exercises. Then have them say how many tens and ones are in each sum.

8 + 6 [14; 1 ten 4 ones]
8 + 8 [16; 1 ten 6 ones]
3 + 9 [12; 1 ten 2 ones]
6 + 9 [15; 1 ten 5 ones]
7 + 4 [11; 1 ten 1 one]

TEACH
MODELING Distribute tens and ones models and Workmat 2 to pairs of children. Tell them to model the number 25 on their workmats. Then have them model 38 below the 25.

Show the following on the chalkboard with an overhead projector or on Teacher Aids Transparency 6.

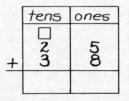

	tens	ones
	☐ 2 3	5 8
+		

Explain to children that this is a way to write an addition for the models on their mats. Guide children through the steps for adding. Tell them that when they add 2-digit numbers, they should always add the ones first. Have children combine the ones models.

■ **How many ones do you have?** [13]

Use Workmat 2. Use 15 ■ , and 9 ▬▬▬▬▬ .
Find the sum.

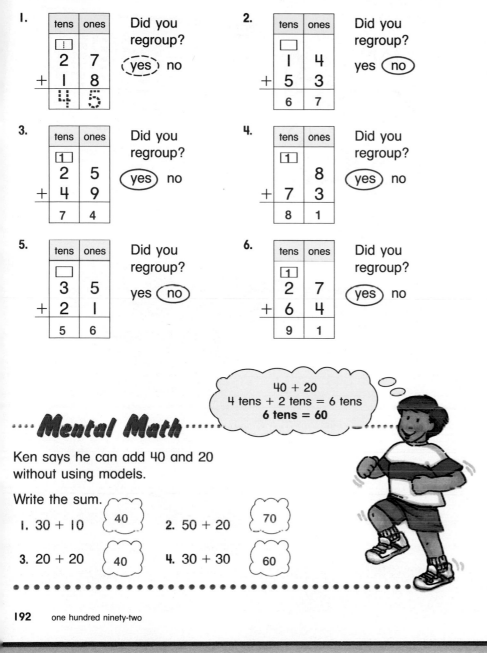

1.

tens	ones
[1]	
2	7
+ 1	8
4	5

Did you regroup? (yes) no

2.

tens	ones
[ ]	
1	4
+ 5	3
6	7

Did you regroup? yes (no)

3.

tens	ones
[1]	
2	5
+ 4	9
7	4

Did you regroup? (yes) no

4.

tens	ones
[1]	
	8
+ 7	3
8	1

Did you regroup? (yes) no

5.

tens	ones
[ ]	
3	5
+ 2	1
5	6

Did you regroup? yes (no)

6.

tens	ones
[1]	
2	7
+ 6	4
9	1

Did you regroup? (yes) no

···· *Mental Math* ·······

40 + 20
4 tens + 2 tens = 6 tens
6 tens = 60

Ken says he can add 40 and 20 without using models.

Write the sum.

1. 30 + 10   40
2. 50 + 20   70
3. 20 + 20   40
4. 30 + 30   60

ACTIVITY *Common Error and Remediation*

MATERIALS 5 bundles of 10 sticks and 19 loose sticks

When adding 2-digit numbers, some children may forget to add the regrouped ten. Prepare sets of addition exercises. Work individually with each child. Have him or her use bundles of sticks and loose sticks as place-value models to model each exercise. Have the child regroup by bundling 10 ones sticks to make a ten and placing the ten in the tens column. He or she should then add it to the number of tens already in the tens column.

For Students Acquiring English (SAE)

On an overhead projector, model the process of adding the ones first and then the tens. For the first problem, guide children through the thinking process and steps orally. Ask *"Did we regroup? How do you know?"* Have SAE children paraphrase what you have just done.

ACTIVITY ALTERNATIVE TEACHING STRATEGY

MATERIALS 9 T, 7 O models (or Manipulatives Kit Transparency 9), Teacher Aids Transparency 10; overhead projector

VISUAL/AUDITORY Display models for 29 + 35 on a transparency. Demonstrate each step, emphasizing the regrouping step. Repeat with another exercise and have volunteers explain each step as you demonstrate with the models.

■ **Do you have more than 10 ones?** [Yes.]

Tell children to regroup 13 ones as 1 ten 3 ones and place these models on the workmat. Record 3 in the ones column and 1 at the top of the tens column. Have children add the tens by combining the models and then have them tell how many tens. Record 6 in the tens column. Read the addition as 25 + 38 = 63.

PUPIL'S EDITION pp. 191-192

Page 191 Work through the steps of the example with the children.

Check for Understanding

■ **How would you add 25 + 17? Explain the steps.** [Add the ones. Next regroup 12 ones as 1 ten 2 ones. Then add the tens to get 42.]

GUIDED PRACTICE ex. 1–2: For reteaching, use Common Error and Remediation or Alternative Strategy.

Page 192 Tell children that they are to use their models on Workmat 2 to do the addition and then write the sum.

PRACTICE•APPLY **PRACTICE** ex. 1–6

MENTAL MATH Discuss the example. Explain to children that they can think of numbers like 40 and 20 as 4 tens and 2 tens.

CLOSE Guide children to summarize the lesson:

■ **How are tens and ones models used to help you add two 2-digit numbers?** [Possible response: First you model each number in the exercise. Then you combine the ones, regroup if necessary, and combine the tens to find the sum.]

MAC Activity 122

On Your Own   Pair and Share   In a Group

ESTIMATION ▪ COMPARING SUMS

Write the following exercises on the chalkboard or chart paper.

1. 12 + 30 = _____   Is the sum < or > 50? [<]
2. 20 + 42 = _____   Is the sum < or > 50? [>]
3. 62 + 21 = _____   Is the sum < or > 99? [<]
4. 57 + 28 = _____   Is the sum < or > 50? [>]
5. 32 + 22 = _____   Is the sum < or > 50? [<]
6. 18 + 29 = _____   Is the sum < or > 99? [<]
7. 53 + 41 = _____   Is the sum < or > 99? [<]
8. 41 + 32 = _____   Is the sum < or > 50? [>]
9. 15 + 40 = _____   Is the sum < or > 50? [>]
10. 50 + 50 = _____   Is the sum < or > 99? [>]

Review the signs for *less than* and *greater than*. Have children estimate each sum and then compare. Have volunteers explain how they got their estimates.

▲ **MAC Activity 122:**
Average-to-Challenge

SPEAKING MATHEMATICALLY ▪ *ADDITION WORDS*

MAC Activity 121

On Your Own   Pair and Share   In a Group

Read the following statements about adding 2-digit numbers. Have children repeat the sentence, filling in the blank. Suggested words are provided, but accept all reasonable answers.

1. I always add the tens _____.   [after the ones]
2. If I have 12 ones, I have to _____.   [regroup]
3. 14 plus 28 equals 42. 42 is the _____.   [sum]
4. I do not have to regroup if I have _____ ones.   [0-9]
5. I _____ the ones and tens to find the sum.   [add]

sum   regroup

▲ **MAC Activity 121:**
Basic-to-Average

RETEACHING

Name

RETEACHING-61

2-DIGIT ADDITION

Study

| Add the ones. | Regroup if you can. | Add the tens. |

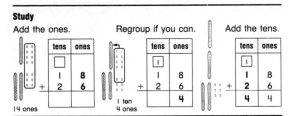

tens	ones
□	
1	8
+ 2	6

14 ones

tens	ones
1	
1	8
+ 2	6
	4

1 ten
4 ones

tens	ones
1	
1	8
+ 2	6
4	4

Check

Use Workmat 2 and models.
Find the sum.

1.

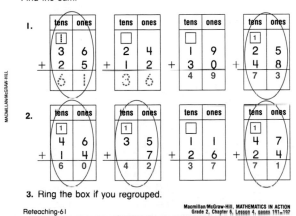

tens	ones
1	
3	6
+ 2	5
6	1

tens	ones
□	
2	4
+ 1	2
3	6

tens	ones
□	
1	9
+ 3	0
4	9

tens	ones
1	
2	5
+ 4	8
7	3

2.

tens	ones
1	
4	6
+ 1	4
6	0

tens	ones
1	
3	5
+	7
4	2

tens	ones
□	
1	1
+ 2	6
3	7

tens	ones
1	
4	7
+ 2	4
7	1

3. Ring the box if you regrouped.

Reteaching-61

Macmillan/McGraw-Hill, MATHEMATICS IN ACTION
Grade 2, Chapter 6, Lesson 4, pages 191–192

PRACTICE

Name

PRACTICE-61

2-DIGIT ADDITION

Use Workmat 2 and tens and ones models.
Find the sum. Ring the sum if you regrouped.

1.

tens	ones
□	
3	9
+ 4	5
(8)	(4)

tens	ones
1	
4	5
+ 1	6
6	1

tens	ones
1	
1	9
+ 2	7
4	6

tens	ones
□	
1	2
+ 1	4
2	6

2.

tens	ones
1	
5	6
+ 1	8
7	4

tens	ones
1	
1	9
+ 4	3
6	2

tens	ones
□	
3	7
+ 3	2
6	9

tens	ones
□	
4	6
+ 5	0
9	6

3.

tens	ones
□	
1	7
+ 2	7
4	4

tens	ones
1	
3	3
+ 2	7
6	0

tens	ones
□	
4	2
+ 2	3
6	5

tens	ones
1	
1	5
+ 2	6
4	1

4.

tens	ones
1	
2	5
+ 2	5
5	0

tens	ones
□	
1	3
+ 5	2
6	5

tens	ones
1	
1	9
+ 1	8
3	7

tens	ones
1	
7	5
+ 1	7
9	2

Practice-61

Macmillan/McGraw-Hill, MATHEMATICS IN ACTION
Grade 2, Chapter 6, Lesson 4, pages 191–192

ENRICHMENT

Name

ENRICHMENT-61

On Your Own   Pair and Share   In a Group

2-DIGIT ADDITION

ADDITION PUZZLER

Work in a group.
Write the addends that equal each sum.
Use the numbers once for each exercise.

Answers will vary.

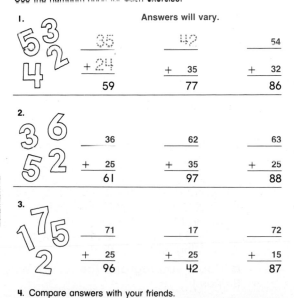

1. 5 3 2 4

35	42	54
+ 24	+ 35	+ 32
59	77	86

2. 3 6 5 2

36	62	63
+ 25	+ 35	+ 25
61	97	88

3. 1 7 5 2

71	17	72
+ 25	+ 25	+ 15
96	42	87

4. Compare answers with your friends.

Enrichment-61

Macmillan/McGraw-Hill, MATHEMATICS IN ACTION
Grade 2, Chapter 6, Lesson 4, pages 191–192

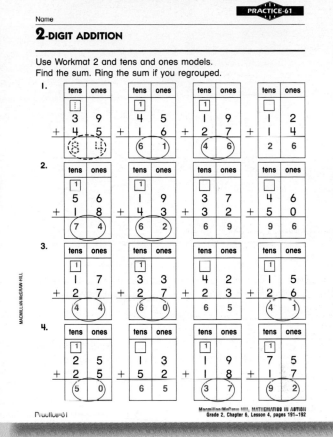

Problem of the Day

Abby has 16 friends at school. She has 7 more friends who live near her. Does she have more than 20 friends?   [Yes. Possible solution: 16 + 7 = 23; 23 > 20.]

CHAPTER 6 • Lesson 5

AT·A·GLANCE pp. 193-194

LESSON OBJECTIVE
Add 2-digit numbers.

ASSIGNMENT GUIDE

COURSE	EXERCISES
Basic	p. 193: 1–4; p. 194: 1–11
Average	p. 193: 1–4; p. 194: 1–11
Challenge	p. 193: 1–4; p. 194: 1–11

MATERIALS
Manipulatives 5 T, 15 O models (or punchouts), Workmat 2 per child

Teacher Resources
Reteaching 62   Practice 62   Enrichment 62
Prob. Solv. 26   MAC Act. 123, 124

SKILLS TRACE
2-DIGIT ADDITION

Explore (Concrete)	Develop/Understand (Transitional/Abstract)
186, 187–188	189–190, 191–192, 193–194 195, 196, 203, 204
Practice	**Apply**
200, 207, 208, 209–210, 213, 224, 245	197–198, 201–202, 205, 206, 212, 244, 291–292, 351

Name _____

More 2-Digit Addition

Add 38 and 27.

Add the ones.	Regroup if you can.	Add the tens.

$$\begin{array}{r} 38 \\ + 27 \\ \hline \end{array}$$

$$\begin{array}{r} 38 \\ + 27 \\ \hline 5 \end{array}$$

$$\begin{array}{r} 38 \\ + 27 \\ \hline 65 \end{array}$$

15 ones   1 ten 5 ones   6 tens

Add.

1.
$$\begin{array}{r} 12 \\ + 38 \\ \hline 50 \end{array}$$

Did you regroup?   (yes)   no

2.
$$\begin{array}{r} 59 \\ + 13 \\ \hline 72 \end{array}$$

Did you regroup?   (yes)   no

3.
$$\begin{array}{r} 22 \\ + 56 \\ \hline 78 \end{array}$$

Did you regroup?   yes   (no)

4.
$$\begin{array}{r} 84 \\ + 6 \\ \hline 90 \end{array}$$

Did you regroup?   (yes)   no

Macmillan/McGraw-Hill

Chapter 6   Adding 2-Digit Numbers   one hundred ninety-three   **193**

PREPARE   **WARM-UP**   To review how to add 2-digit numbers, write on the chalkboard: 27, 19, 42, 66, 71, 50, 83.

■ **If the number 7 was added to each number, would you have to regroup? 27** [Yes.] **19** [Yes.] **42** [No.] **66** [Yes.] **71** [No.] **50** [No.] **83** [Yes.]

Have children explain their reasoning.

TEACH   **MODELING**   Write the following example on the chalkboard. Emphasize how the numbers align.

$$\begin{array}{r} 27 \\ + 18 \\ \hline \end{array}$$

Have children use tens and ones models to model the numbers 27 and 18 on Workmat 2. Tell them to combine the ones models to add the ones.

■ **Could you regroup the ones? Why?** [Yes, because there are more than 10 ones.]

After children model the regrouping, have a volunteer come to the chalkboard and write a 5 under the ones column and a regrouped 1 at the top of the tens column. Then have children combine the tens models to find the sum. Record the 4 on the chalkboard and read the sum, 45. Repeat this procedure with another example that does not require regrouping, such as 32 + 47.

■ **Could you regroup the ones? Why?** [No; because there are only 9 ones.]

193   Chapter 6 • Lesson 5

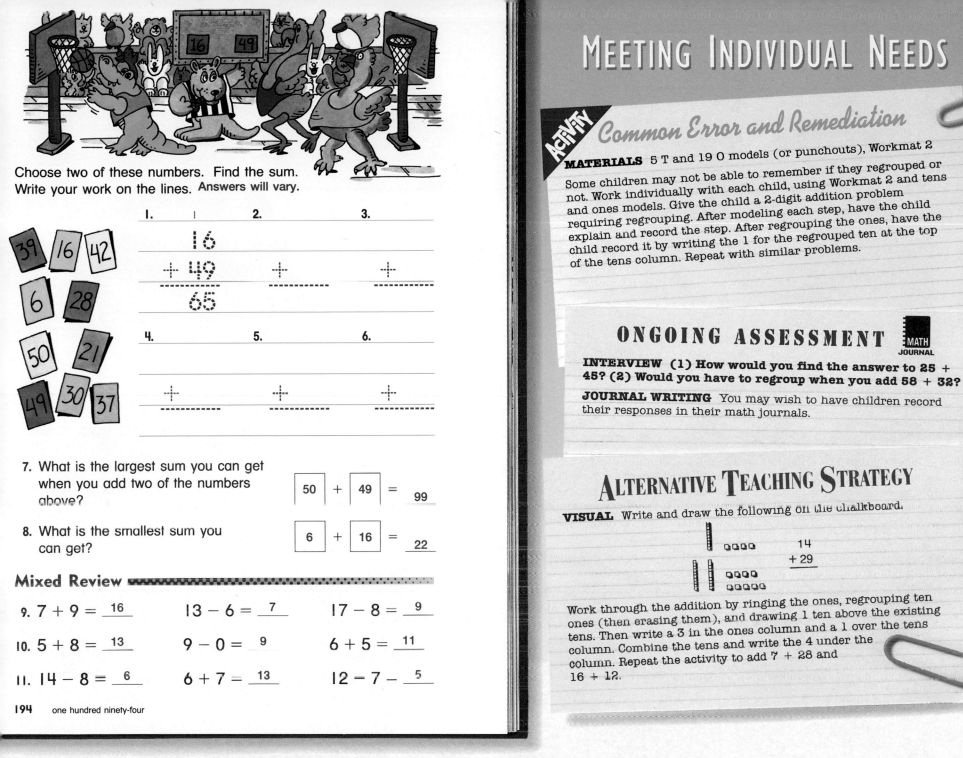

Choose two of these numbers. Find the sum.
Write your work on the lines. Answers will vary.

Cards: 39 16 42 6 28 50 21 49 30 37

1.
```
   16
+  49
------
   65
```

2.
```
+
------
```

3.
```
+
------
```

4.
```
+
------
```

5.
```
+
------
```

6.
```
+
------
```

7. What is the largest sum you can get
   when you add two of the numbers
   above?

   $\boxed{50}$ + $\boxed{49}$ = 99

8. What is the smallest sum you
   can get?

   $\boxed{6}$ + $\boxed{16}$ = 22

Mixed Review

9. $7 + 9 =$ 16 $13 - 6 =$ 7 $17 - 8 =$ 9

10. $5 + 8 =$ 13 $9 - 0 =$ 9 $6 + 5 =$ 11

11. $14 - 8 =$ 6 $6 + 7 =$ 13 $12 - 7 -$ 5

MEETING INDIVIDUAL NEEDS

ACTIVITY Common Error and Remediation

MATERIALS 5 T and 19 O models (or punchouts), Workmat 2

Some children may not be able to remember if they regrouped or not. Work individually with each child, using Workmat 2 and tens and ones models. Give the child a 2-digit addition problem requiring regrouping. After modeling each step, have the child explain and record the step. After regrouping the ones, have the child record it by writing the 1 for the regrouped ten at the top of the tens column. Repeat with similar problems.

ONGOING ASSESSMENT

INTERVIEW (1) How would you find the answer to 25 + 45? (2) Would you have to regroup when you add 58 + 32?

JOURNAL WRITING You may wish to have children record their responses in their math journals.

ALTERNATIVE TEACHING STRATEGY

VISUAL Write and draw the following on the chalkboard.

Work through the addition by ringing the ones, regrouping ten ones (then erasing them), and drawing 1 ten above the existing tens. Then write a 3 in the ones column and a 1 over the tens column. Combine the tens and write the 4 under the column. Repeat the activity to add 7 + 28 and 16 + 12.

PUPIL'S EDITION pp. 193-194

Page 193 Work through the example at the top of the page with the children.

Check for Understanding

■ If I add 6 ones and 8 ones, how many ones do I have after I regroup? [4 ones]

GUIDED PRACTICE ex. 1–4: For reteaching, use Common Error and Remediation or Alternative Strategy.

Page 194 Explain to children that they will use the numbers on the cards to make up their own exercises. Be sure children understand how to write the addition on the lines.

③ PRACTICE·APPLY   PRACTICE ex. 1–11

CLOSE Guide children to summarize the lesson:

■ **Explain the steps to add 29 and 12.** [Add the ones, regroup, and add the tens to find the sum.]

MAC ACTIVITY CENTER

MAC Activity 123:
Basic-to-Average

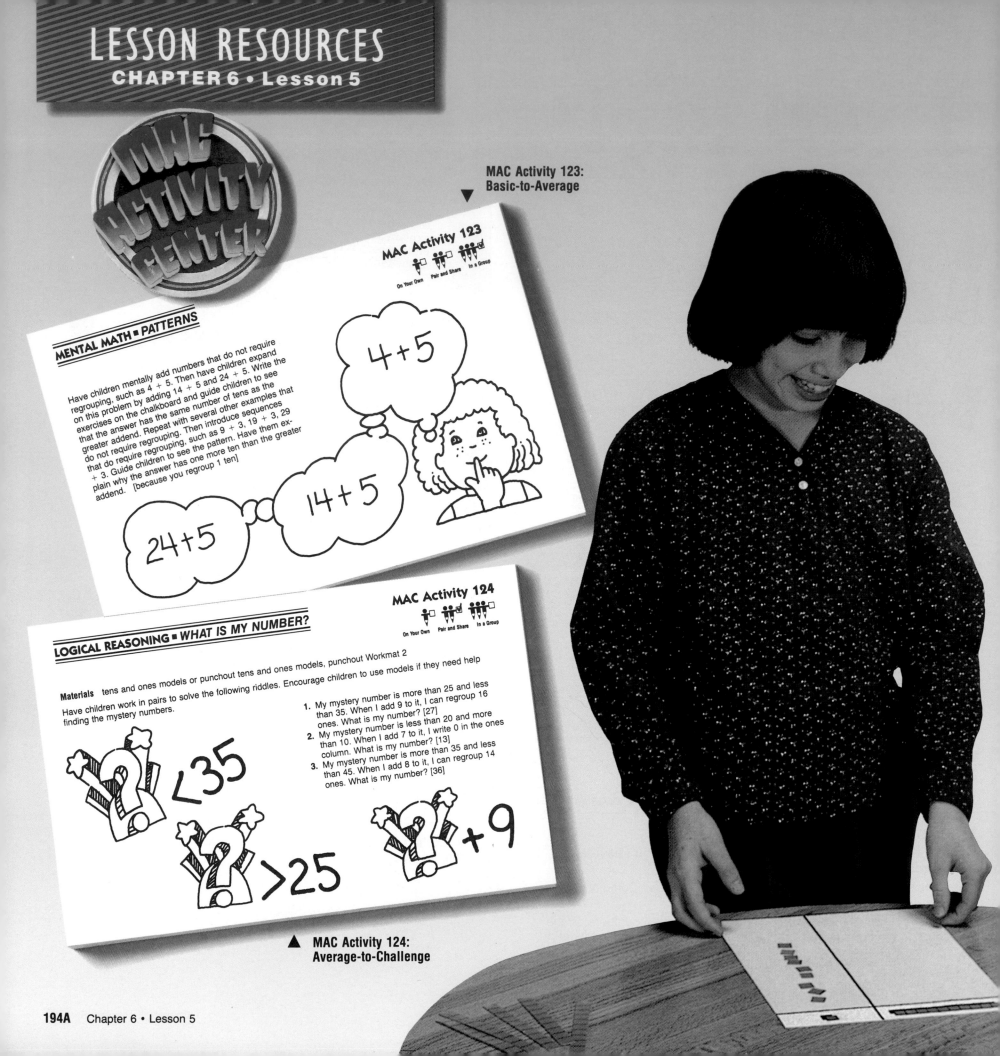

MAC Activity 123

On Your Own   Pair and Share   In a Group

MENTAL MATH ▪ PATTERNS

Have children mentally add numbers that do not require regrouping, such as 4 + 5. Then have children expand on this problem by adding 14 + 5 and 24 + 5. Write the exercises on the chalkboard and guide children to see that the answer has the same number of tens as the greater addend. Repeat with several other examples that do not require regrouping. Then introduce sequences that do require regrouping, such as 9 + 3, 19 + 3, 29 + 3. Guide children to see the pattern. Have them explain why the answer has one more ten than the greater addend.   [because you regroup 1 ten]

4 + 5

14 + 5

24 + 5

MAC Activity 124

On Your Own   Pair and Share   In a Group

LOGICAL REASONING ▪ WHAT IS MY NUMBER?

Materials   tens and ones models or punchout tens and ones models, punchout Workmat 2

Have children work in pairs to solve the following riddles. Encourage children to use models if they need help finding the mystery numbers.

1. My mystery number is more than 25 and less than 35. When I add 9 to it, I can regroup 16 ones. What is my number? [27]
2. My mystery number is less than 20 and more than 10. When I add 7 to it, I write 0 in the ones column. What is my number? [13]
3. My mystery number is more than 35 and less than 45. When I add 8 to it, I can regroup 14 ones. What is my number? [36]

? < 35

? > 25

? + 9

▲ MAC Activity 124:
Average-to-Challenge

RETEACHING-62

Name _____

MORE 2-DIGIT ADDITION

Study

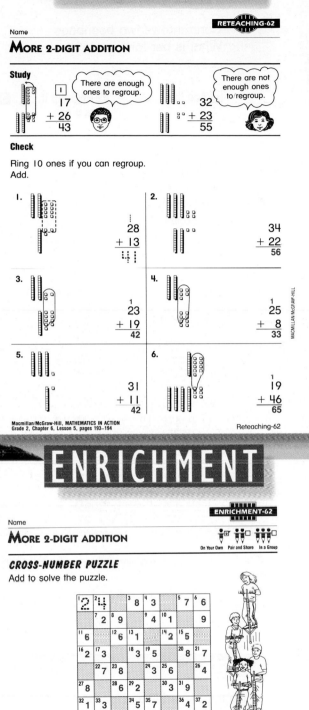

There are enough ones to regroup.

```
  1
  17
+ 26
  43
```

There are not enough ones to regroup.

```
  32
+ 23
  55
```

Check

Ring 10 ones if you can regroup.
Add.

1.
```
  28
+ 13
  41
```

2.
```
  34
+ 22
  56
```

3.
```
  1
  23
+ 19
  42
```

4.
```
  1
  25
+  8
  33
```

5.
```
  31
+ 11
  42
```

6.
```
  1
  19
+ 46
  65
```

Macmillan/McGraw-Hill, MATHEMATICS IN ACTION
Grade 2, Chapter 6, Lesson 5, pages 193–194

Reteaching-62

PRACTICE-62

Name _____

MORE 2-DIGIT ADDITION

Add.

1.
```
  24
+ 39
  63
```
Did you regroup? (yes) no

2.
```
   8
+ 14
  22
```
Did you regroup? (yes) no

3.
```
  44
+ 25
  69
```
Did you regroup? yes (no)

4.
```
  63
+ 27
  90
```
Did you regroup? (yes) no

5.
```
  28
+ 36
  64
```
Did you regroup? (yes) no

6.
```
  15
+ 33
  48
```
Did you regroup? yes (no)

7.
```
  27
+ 48
  75
```
Did you regroup? (yes) no

8.
```
  56
+ 17
  73
```
Did you regroup? (yes) no

Macmillan/McGraw-Hill, MATHEMATICS IN ACTION
Grade 2, Chapter 6, Lesson 5, pages 193–194

Practice-62

ENRICHMENT-62

Name _____

MORE 2-DIGIT ADDITION

On Your Own   Pair and Share   In a Group

CROSS-NUMBER PUZZLE

Add to solve the puzzle.

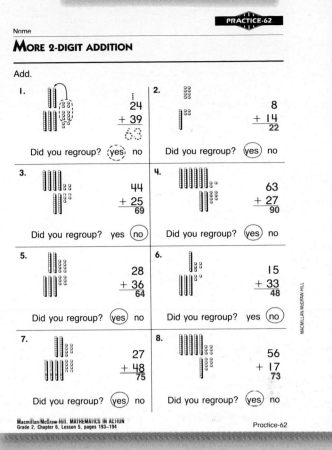

Across

1. 16 + 8
3. 57 + 26
5. 41 + 35
7. 14 + 15
9. 32 + 9
12. 23 + 38
14. 7 + 18
16. 14 + 9
18. 19 + 16
20. 38 + 49
22. 36 + 42
24. 17 + 19
26. 4 + 0
28. 44 + 18
30. 25 + 14
32. 6 + 7
34. 21 + 36
36. 19 + 23
38. 25 + 17
39. 9 + 6

Down

2. 13 + 29
4. 9 + 25
6. 51 + 18
8. 38 + 58
10. 9 + 3
11. 35 + 27
13. 5 + 8
15. 39 + 19
17. 25 + 12
19. 32 + 21
21. 59 + 15
23. 14 + 72
25. 35 + 28
27. 27 + 54
29. 8 + 17
31. 28 + 66
33. 7 + 27
35. 23 + 48
37. 16 + 7

Macmillan/McGraw-Hill, MATHEMATICS IN ACTION
Grade 2, Chapter 6, Lesson 5, pages 193–194

Enrichment-62

Problem of the Day

There are 27 children on the junior swim team.
The senior swim team has 34 members. Is a
66-passenger bus large enough to take both
teams to a swim meet? [Yes; possible solution:
27 + 34 = 61; 61 < 66.]

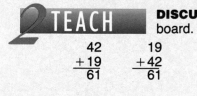

AT·A·GLANCE p. 195

LESSON OBJECTIVE
Practice adding 2-digit numbers.

ASSIGNMENT GUIDE

COURSE	EXERCISES
Basic	p. 195: 1–4
Average	p. 195: 1–4
Challenge	p. 195: 1–4
Extra Practice, p. 200	Practice Plus, p. 208

MATERIALS
Manipulatives 9 T and 18 O models (or punchouts), Workmat
2 per child

Teacher Resources
Reteaching 63   Practice 63   Enrichment 63
MAC Act. 125, 126
Computer Software *Mathematics Skills: Disk 4 Act. 2*

SKILLS TRACE
2-DIGIT ADDITION

Explore (Concrete) 186, 187–188	Develop/Understand (Transitional/Abstract) 189–190, 191–192, 193–194, 195, 196, 203, 204
Practice 200, 207, 208, 209–210, 213, 224, 245	Apply 197–198, 201–202, 205, 206, 212, 244, 291–292, 351

See **MANIPULATIVES PLUS 36**, p. 184N.

Name _____

Addition Practice

Carla throws two beanbags.
What is her total score?

| 46 |
| 39 |
| 25 |
| 24 |
| 9 |

1 Add the ones. **2** Regroup if you can. **3** Add the tens.

$$\begin{array}{r} 2\,5 \\ +\,3\,7 \\ \hline \end{array}$$

$$\begin{array}{r} \overset{1}{2}\,5 \\ +\,3\,7 \\ \hline 2 \end{array}$$

$$\begin{array}{r} \overset{1}{2}\,5 \\ +\,3\,7 \\ \hline 6\,2 \end{array}$$

(12 ones)   (1 ten 2 ones)   (6 tens)

Carla's total score is 62.

Add. Use models if you need help.

1.
$$\begin{array}{r} 37 \\ +\ 9 \\ \hline 46 \end{array}$$
$$\begin{array}{r} 14 \\ +48 \\ \hline 62 \end{array}$$
$$\begin{array}{r} 47 \\ +45 \\ \hline 92 \end{array}$$
$$\begin{array}{r} 7 \\ +36 \\ \hline 43 \end{array}$$
$$\begin{array}{r} 15 \\ +18 \\ \hline 33 \end{array}$$

2.
$$\begin{array}{r} 28 \\ +14 \\ \hline 42 \end{array}$$
$$\begin{array}{r} 81 \\ +\ 6 \\ \hline 87 \end{array}$$
$$\begin{array}{r} 25 \\ +14 \\ \hline 39 \end{array}$$
$$\begin{array}{r} 45 \\ +43 \\ \hline 88 \end{array}$$
$$\begin{array}{r} 55 \\ +\ 5 \\ \hline 60 \end{array}$$

3.
$$\begin{array}{r} 74 \\ +19 \\ \hline 93 \end{array}$$
$$\begin{array}{r} 66 \\ +26 \\ \hline 92 \end{array}$$
$$\begin{array}{r} 28 \\ +62 \\ \hline 90 \end{array}$$
$$\begin{array}{r} 46 \\ +15 \\ \hline 61 \end{array}$$
$$\begin{array}{r} 24 \\ +27 \\ \hline 51 \end{array}$$

4. Ring each exercise where you regrouped.

What shape did your rings make? ___rectangle___

Extra Practice, page 200 *Practice Plus,* page 208   one hundred ninety-five **195**

Macmillan/McGraw-Hill

---

1 PREPARE
WARM-UP To review regrouping, have children do the following.

Regroup 4 tens 18 ones [5 tens 8 ones]
Regroup 3 tens 12 ones [4 tens 2 ones]
Regroup 5 tens 14 ones [6 tens 4 ones]
Regroup 2 tens 16 ones [3 tens 6 ones]
Regroup 1 ten 15 ones [2 tens 5 ones]

2 TEACH
DISCUSSING Write the following on the chalkboard.

$$\begin{array}{r} 42 \\ +19 \\ \hline 61 \end{array} \qquad \begin{array}{r} 19 \\ +42 \\ \hline 61 \end{array}$$

Do the two additions for the children, showing the regrouping.
■ **Are the sums the same?** [Yes.]
Point out that the addends in each exercise are the same, so the sums are the same. Repeat with other exercises.

PUPIL'S EDITION p. 195
Work through the example at the top of the page.

Check for Understanding
■ **Did you have to regroup to get Carla's score?** [Yes.] **Why?** [There were 12 ones.]

GUIDED PRACTICE ex 1: For reteaching, use Common Error and Remediation or Alternative Strategy.

ACTIVITY
Common Error and Remediation

MATERIALS 9 T, 18 O models (or punchouts), Workmat 2

Some children may "regroup" when there are fewer than 10 ones. Work individually with each child using tens and ones models and Workmat 2. Give the child exercises with and without regrouping. After the ones are combined, have the child line up the ones next to a tens model and tell if there are 10 or more ones. Then have the child regroup if possible and complete the addition.

ALTERNATIVE TEACHING STRATEGY

AUDITORY Tell children to write 62 + 19 on a sheet of paper. Have volunteers tell each step of the addition as the rest of the children find the sum. [81] Repeat the activity with 7 + 12, 23 + 38, and 25 + 9.

3 PRACTICE•APPLY   PRACTICE   ex. 2–4

CLOSE Guide children to summarize the lesson:
- **Do you regroup when you add 24 + 15?** [No.]
- **Do you regroup when you add 24 + 17?** [Yes.]

MAC ACTIVITY CENTER

MAC Activity 125:
Basic-to-Average ▼

MAC Activity 125

On Your Own   Pair and Share   In a Group

MANIPULATIVES ■ PROBLEMS, PROBLEMS

Materials tens and ones models or punchout tens and ones models, punchout Workmat 2

Assign children to work in pairs. Give each pair of children tens and ones models and Workmat 2. Tell children they are to work together to solve the problems you will read aloud. After each problem, have a volunteer tell how the problem was solved.

1. Betty made 28 pot holders to sell at the school fair. John made 17 pot holders to sell. How many pot holders did they make in all?   [45]
2. Sonia made 36 muffins to sell. Chuck made 48 muffins to sell. How many muffins did the two children make?   [84]
3. Robert built 16 birdhouses to sell. Tara built 14 birdhouses to sell. Which child built more birdhouses? [Robert]

Continue the activity with similar problems. Include comparing questions, as well as addition questions.

MAC Activity 126:
Average-to-Challenge ▶

MATH AND SOCIAL STUDIES ■ HOW FAR?

MAC Activity 126

On Your Own   Pair and Share   In a Group

Draw the following map on the chalkboard or draw it on paper and duplicate it.

BIG ROCK
31 — WAYNE — 34 — PETERSVILLE
19
59
15 — BAY CITY
OAK TOWN
44 — PINEVILLE — 40 — REMO

Have children solve the following problems.

1. What is the distance from Big Rock to Petersville?   [65 miles]
2. How far is it from Big Rock to Pineville?   [63 miles]
3. How far is it from Oak Town to Bay City?   [74 miles]

To continue the activity, encourage children to write their own problems using information on the map. Then have them exchange problems with another child to solve.

RETEACHING-63

Name

ADDITION PRACTICE

Study

Add the ones. Regroup if you can. Add the tens.

$$\begin{array}{r} 2\ 4 \\ +\ 4\ 8 \\ \end{array} \rightarrow \begin{array}{r} 4 \\ +\ 8 \\ \hline 12 \end{array} \qquad \begin{array}{r} ^1 24 \\ +\ 48 \\ \hline 2 \end{array} \qquad \begin{array}{r} ^1\,2\ 4 \\ 4\ 8 \\ \hline 7\ 2 \end{array}$$

Check

Add. Use models if you need help.

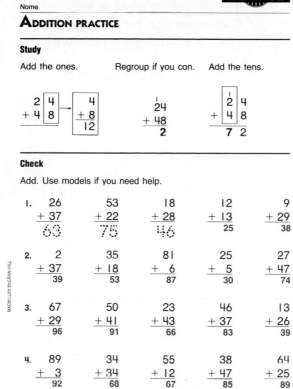

1.
$$\begin{array}{r} 26 \\ +37 \\ \hline 63 \end{array} \quad \begin{array}{r} 53 \\ +22 \\ \hline 75 \end{array} \quad \begin{array}{r} 18 \\ +28 \\ \hline 46 \end{array} \quad \begin{array}{r} 12 \\ +13 \\ \hline 25 \end{array} \quad \begin{array}{r} 9 \\ +29 \\ \hline 38 \end{array}$$

2.
$$\begin{array}{r} 2 \\ +37 \\ \hline 39 \end{array} \quad \begin{array}{r} 35 \\ +18 \\ \hline 53 \end{array} \quad \begin{array}{r} 81 \\ +6 \\ \hline 87 \end{array} \quad \begin{array}{r} 25 \\ +5 \\ \hline 30 \end{array} \quad \begin{array}{r} 27 \\ +47 \\ \hline 74 \end{array}$$

3.
$$\begin{array}{r} 67 \\ +29 \\ \hline 96 \end{array} \quad \begin{array}{r} 50 \\ +41 \\ \hline 91 \end{array} \quad \begin{array}{r} 23 \\ +43 \\ \hline 66 \end{array} \quad \begin{array}{r} 46 \\ +37 \\ \hline 83 \end{array} \quad \begin{array}{r} 13 \\ +26 \\ \hline 39 \end{array}$$

4.
$$\begin{array}{r} 89 \\ +3 \\ \hline 92 \end{array} \quad \begin{array}{r} 34 \\ +34 \\ \hline 68 \end{array} \quad \begin{array}{r} 55 \\ +12 \\ \hline 67 \end{array} \quad \begin{array}{r} 38 \\ +47 \\ \hline 85 \end{array} \quad \begin{array}{r} 64 \\ +25 \\ \hline 89 \end{array}$$

Reteaching-63

Macmillan/McGraw-Hill, MATHEMATICS IN ACTION
Grade 2, Chapter 6, Lesson 6, page 195

PRACTICE-63

Name

ADDITION PRACTICE

Add. Then color to match sums.

20 to 29	red	40 to 49	blue
50 to 59	green	60 to 69	yellow
80 to 89	orange	90 to 99	purple

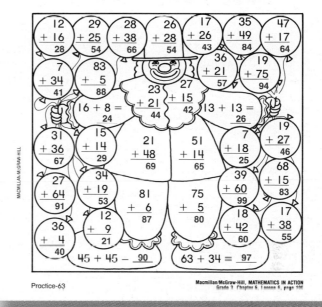

$$\begin{array}{r} 12 \\ +16 \\ \hline 28 \end{array} \quad \begin{array}{r} 29 \\ +25 \\ \hline 54 \end{array} \quad \begin{array}{r} 28 \\ +38 \\ \hline 66 \end{array} \quad \begin{array}{r} 26 \\ +28 \\ \hline 54 \end{array} \quad \begin{array}{r} 17 \\ +26 \\ \hline 43 \end{array} \quad \begin{array}{r} 35 \\ +49 \\ \hline 84 \end{array} \quad \begin{array}{r} 47 \\ +17 \\ \hline 64 \end{array}$$

$$\begin{array}{r} 7 \\ +34 \\ \hline 41 \end{array} \quad \begin{array}{r} 83 \\ +5 \\ \hline 88 \end{array} \quad \begin{array}{r} 36 \\ +21 \\ \hline 57 \end{array} \quad \begin{array}{r} 19 \\ +75 \\ \hline 94 \end{array}$$

$$16 + 8 = 24 \qquad \begin{array}{r} 23 \\ +21 \\ \hline 44 \end{array} \quad \begin{array}{r} 27 \\ +15 \\ \hline 42 \end{array} \qquad 13 + 13 = 26$$

$$\begin{array}{r} 31 \\ +36 \\ \hline 67 \end{array} \quad \begin{array}{r} 15 \\ +14 \\ \hline 29 \end{array} \quad \begin{array}{r} 21 \\ +48 \\ \hline 69 \end{array} \quad \begin{array}{r} 51 \\ +14 \\ \hline 65 \end{array} \quad \begin{array}{r} 7 \\ +18 \\ \hline 25 \end{array} \quad \begin{array}{r} 19 \\ +27 \\ \hline 46 \end{array}$$

$$\begin{array}{r} 27 \\ +64 \\ \hline 91 \end{array} \quad \begin{array}{r} 34 \\ +19 \\ \hline 53 \end{array} \quad \begin{array}{r} 81 \\ +6 \\ \hline 87 \end{array} \quad \begin{array}{r} 75 \\ +5 \\ \hline 80 \end{array} \quad \begin{array}{r} 39 \\ +60 \\ \hline 99 \end{array} \quad \begin{array}{r} 68 \\ +15 \\ \hline 83 \end{array}$$

$$\begin{array}{r} 36 \\ +4 \\ \hline 40 \end{array} \quad \begin{array}{r} 12 \\ +9 \\ \hline 21 \end{array} \quad 45 + 45 - 90 \qquad \begin{array}{r} 18 \\ +42 \\ \hline 60 \end{array} \quad 63 + 34 = 97 \quad \begin{array}{r} 17 \\ +38 \\ \hline 55 \end{array}$$

Practice-63

Macmillan/McGraw-Hill, MATHEMATICS IN ACTION
Grade 2, Chapter 6, Lesson 6, page 195

ENRICHMENT-63

Name

ADDITION PRACTICE

On Your Own   Pair and Share   In a Group

EXTRA NUMBERS

Draw an X on the extra number in the exercise.

1. $6 + \cancel{3} + 4 = 10$ $8 + 7 + \cancel{X} = 15$

2. $\cancel{18} + 50 + 12 = 62$ $23 + 29 + \cancel{48} = 52$

3. $43 + 35 + \cancel{29} = 78$ $13 + \cancel{15} + 31 = 44$

4. $28 + \cancel{57} + 62 = 90$ $81 + 6 + \cancel{75} = 87$

5. $86 + 12 + \cancel{19} = 98$ $\cancel{35} + 25 + 14 = 39$

Make up your own exercises.
Have your partner solve them.

Exercises will vary.

6. _____ + _____ + _____ = _____

7. _____ + _____ + _____ = _____

8. _____ + _____ + _____ = _____

9. _____ + _____ + _____ = _____

Enrichment-63

Macmillan/McGraw-Hill, MATHEMATICS IN ACTION
Grade 2, Chapter 6, Lesson 6, page 195

Problem of the Day

Dan planted 57 pots of ivy and 37 pots of marigolds. Carolyn planted 36 pots of violets and 58 pots of daisies. Who planted the most pots? [Both planted the same number of pots. Possible solution: 57 + 37 = 94; 36 + 58 = 94.]

Checking Addition

The basketball score is tied.
Each team has the same total.
What are the missing numbers?

Work with a partner to find out.

Points Scored

	Team A	Team B
1st Half	35	46
2nd Half	46	
Total		81

1. First find the sum.
   Then find the number that
   is missing.

$$\begin{array}{r} 35 \\ + 46 \\ \hline 81 \end{array} \qquad \begin{array}{r} 46 \\ + \boxed{35} \\ \hline 81 \end{array}$$

 Use ▭▭▭▭ ▫ , mental math, paper and pencil, or a 🖩 .

2. Tell how the numbers you added are the same and different. Possible answer: The addends are the same, but in a different order; the sum is the same in both examples.

3. Can you add the other way to check your answer? Make up your own addition pairs.

   Use a 🖩 to find the sums.

Add. Check your answer.

4. $\begin{array}{r} 18 \\ + 54 \\ \hline 72 \end{array}$ $\begin{array}{r} 54 \\ + 18 \\ \hline 72 \end{array}$ $\begin{array}{r} 27 \\ + 69 \\ \hline 96 \end{array}$ $\begin{array}{r} 69 \\ + 27 \\ \hline 96 \end{array}$ $\begin{array}{r} 7 \\ + 38 \\ \hline 45 \end{array}$ $\begin{array}{r} 38 \\ + 7 \\ \hline 45 \end{array}$

Check the sum. Correct it if you need to.

5. $\begin{array}{r} 47 \\ + 16 \\ \hline \cancel{62} \\ 63 \end{array}$ $\begin{array}{r} 16 \\ + 47 \\ \hline 63 \end{array}$ $\begin{array}{r} 5 \\ + 79 \\ \hline \cancel{74} \\ 84 \end{array}$ $\begin{array}{r} 79 \\ + 5 \\ \hline 84 \end{array}$ $\begin{array}{r} 82 \\ + 9 \\ \hline \cancel{92} \\ 91 \end{array}$ $\begin{array}{r} 9 \\ + 82 \\ \hline 91 \end{array}$

Common Error and Remediation

MATERIALS place-value computation boxes (Teacher Aid 10)

Some children may not be able to write a 2-digit addition exercise and align the digits properly. Work individually with each child. Provide a worksheet with place-value boxes for the child to use when rewriting an addition exercise. Give the child exercises in both vertical and horizontal format. Observe the child as he or she copies the exercises to make sure that the digits are aligned correctly.

ALTERNATIVE TEACHING STRATEGY

VISUAL/AUDITORY Write the following exercises on the chalkboard.

```
  75        18
+ 10      + 75
[93]      [93]
```

Tell children that they should always check their addition. Explain that to do this, they should reverse the order of the addends and add again. As you work through each addition, emphasize the order of the addends; for example, 5 + 8 = 13, 7 + 1 + 1 = 9; 8 + 5 = 13, 1 + 1 + 7 = 9.

PUPIL'S EDITION p. 196

Guide children through the example at the top of the page. Discuss that the chart shows the points scored for each team in the first half, second half, and the total points. Have children relate the numbers in the chart to the examples in ex. 1.

GUIDED PRACTICE ex. 1–3: Distribute calculators, ones models, tens models, and Workmat 2 to pairs. Discuss that children may choose a method (models, mental math, paper and pencil, or a calculator) to find the missing numbers in ex. 1. Children will use calculators in ex. 3 to add their own 2-digit examples, reverse addends, and discover the order property can be used to check a sum.

Check for Understanding

■ **How can you check the sum of an addition example?** [by reversing the order of the addends and adding again]

PRACTICE·APPLY **PRACTICE** ex. 4–5: Discuss that the exercises in row 5 may have an incorrect sum written in. Children should add the other way to check each sum and correct it if they need to.

CLOSE Guide children to summarize the lesson:

■ **How could you check the sum for 32 + 47 = 79?** [Reverse the addends and add 47 + 32.]

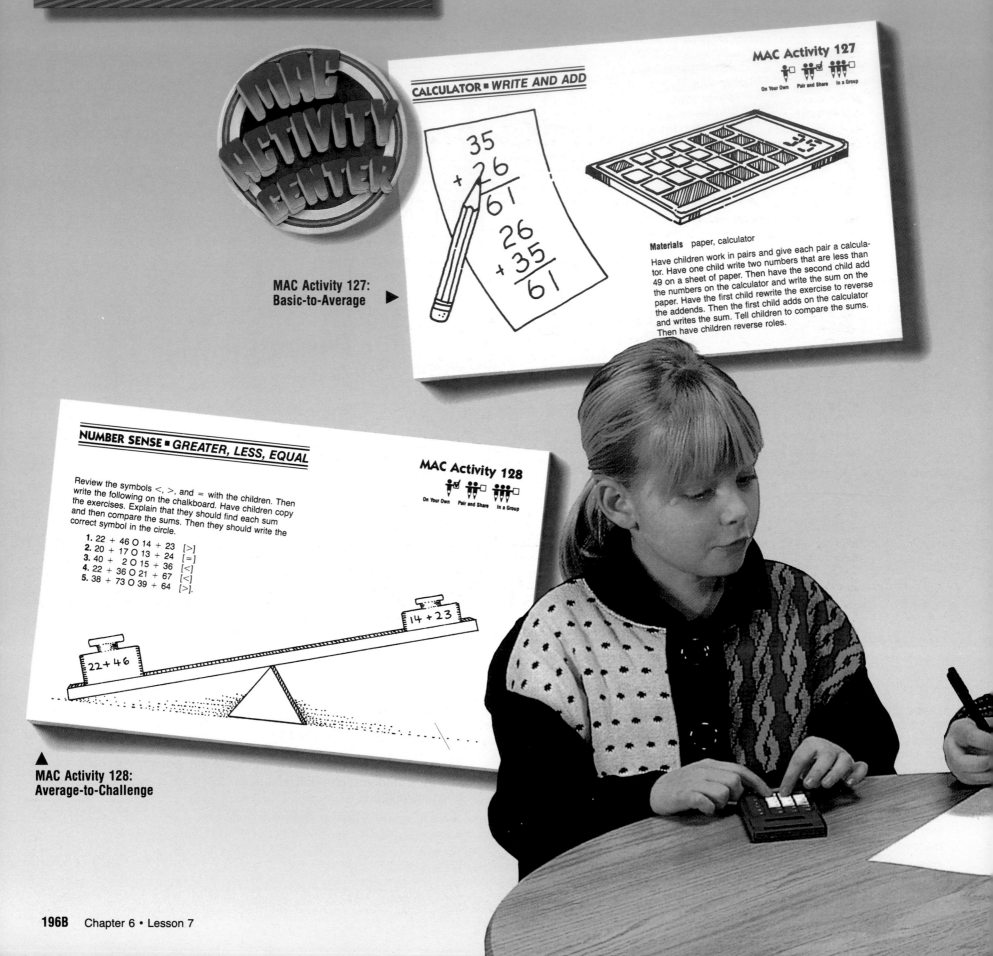

MAC Activity 127:
Basic-to-Average ▶

CALCULATOR ■ WRITE AND ADD

MAC Activity 127

On Your Own   Pair and Share   In a Group

$$\begin{array}{r} 35 \\ + 26 \\ \hline 61 \end{array}$$

$$\begin{array}{r} 26 \\ + 35 \\ \hline 61 \end{array}$$

Materials   paper, calculator

Have children work in pairs and give each pair a calculator. Have one child write two numbers that are less than 49 on a sheet of paper. Then have the second child add the numbers on the calculator and write the sum on the paper. Have the first child rewrite the exercise to reverse the addends. Then the first child adds on the calculator and writes the sum. Tell children to compare the sums. Then have children reverse roles.

NUMBER SENSE ■ GREATER, LESS, EQUAL

MAC Activity 128

On Your Own   Pair and Share   In a Group

Review the symbols $<$, $>$, and $=$ with the children. Then write the following on the chalkboard. Have children copy the exercises. Explain that they should find each sum and then compare the sums. Then they should write the correct symbol in the circle.

1. $22 + 46 \bigcirc 14 + 23$ $[>]$
2. $20 + 17 \bigcirc 13 + 24$ $[=]$
3. $40 + 2 \bigcirc 15 + 36$ $[<]$
4. $22 + 36 \bigcirc 21 + 67$ $[<]$
5. $38 + 73 \bigcirc 39 + 64$ $[>]$.

14 + 23

22 + 46

▲
MAC Activity 128:
Average-to-Challenge

RETEACHING-64

Name ___

CHECKING ADDITION

Study

Add the ones. Regroup if you can. Add the tens. Check.

```
   35            35            35         18
 + 18          + 18          + 18       + 35
(13 ones)        3            53         53
           (1 ten 3 ones)   (5 tens)   (Sums are the
                                         same.)
```

Check

Add. Then check the answers.

```
1.   17    26      2.  28    39      3.  56    14
   + 26  + 17        + 39  + 28        + 14  + 56
     43    43          67    67          70    70

4.   47    22      5.  19    57      6.  44    47
   + 22  + 47        + 57  + 19        + 47  + 44
     69    69          76    76          91    91

7.   19    56      8.  21    48      9.  26    69
   + 56  + 19        + 48  + 21        + 69  + 26
     75    75          69    69          95    95
```

Macmillan/McGraw-Hill, MATHEMATICS IN ACTION
Grade 2, Chapter 6, Lesson 7, page 196

Reteaching-64

PRACTICE-64

Name ___

CHECKING ADDITION

Add. Check your answer.

```
1.   49    14       2.  83    7       3.  27    54
   + 14  + 49         + 7  + 83         + 54 + 27
     63    63           90    90          81    81

4.   38    8        5.  19    17      6.  48    15
   + 8   + 38         + 17  + 19        + 15  + 48
     46    46           36    36          63    63

7.   28    67       8.  35    31      9.  42    9
   + 67  + 28         + 31  + 35         + 9  + 42
     95    95           66    66          51    51

10.  30    40      11.  74    16     12.  45    38
   + 40  + 30         + 16  + 74        + 38  + 45
     70    70           90    90          83    83

13.   5    16      14.  48    33     15.  15    35
   + 16  + 5          + 33  + 48        + 35  + 15
     21    21           81    81          50    50
```

Macmillan/McGraw-Hill, MATHEMATICS IN ACTION
Grade 2, Chapter 6, Lesson 7, page 196

Practice-64

ENRICHMENT-64

Name ___

CHECKING ADDITION

On Your Own   Pair and Share   In a Group

DOUBLE CHECK

Using a nomograph is another way to check addition

Use a straight edge to connect two addends.
The line crosses the sum.
This nomograph shows 26 + 29 = 55.

```
25  26  27  28  29  30  31  32  33  34  35   addend

50 51 52 53 54 55 56 57 58 59 60 61 62 63 64 65 66 67 68 69 70   sum

25  26  27  28  29  30  31  32  33  34  35   addend
```

Find each sum.
Use the nomograph to check.

```
1.   25    32    33    31    28    26
   + 26  + 34  + 27  + 35  + 32  + 30
     51    66    60    66    60    56

2.   30    28    29    32    25    29
   + 34  + 26  + 31  + 27  + 35  + 34
     64    54    60    59    60    63

3.   28    33    25    34    30    33
   + 35  + 29  + 26  + 35  + 31  + 28
     63    62    51    69    61    61
```

Macmillan/McGraw-Hill, MATHEMATICS IN ACTION
Grade 2, Chapter 6, Lesson 7, page 196

Enrichment-64

Problem of the Day

Tony had 14 stamps and he used 7 of them. Then he bought 25 more stamps. How many stamps does Tony have now? [32. Possible solution: 14 − 7 = 7; 7 + 25 = 32.]

Name _____

Problem Solving

UNDERSTAND / PLAN / TRY / CHECK / EXTEND

Using Data from a Table

Sue and Tom recorded their gym exercises on this table.
Sue's exercises are under her name.
Tom's are under his name.

Write the numbers. Solve.

Exercises We Did

	Sue	Tom
Somersaults	8	14
Jumping Jacks	12	9
Stretch-ups	26	38
Toe Taps	48	35

1. Sue did __48__ toe taps.

   Tom did __35__ toe taps.

   How many toe taps did they do in all? __83__ toe taps

2. Sue did __8__ somersaults.

   Sue did __12__ jumping jacks.

   How many somersaults and

   jumping jacks did Sue do? __20__

3. Sue did __12__ jumping jacks.

   Tom did __9__ jumping jacks.

   Who did fewer jumping jacks? _____Tom_____

   How many fewer? __3__ fewer jumping jacks

4. Sue wants to do 14 somersaults.

   How many more does she have to do? __6__ somersaults

Chapter 6   Adding 2-Digit Numbers   one hundred ninety-seven   **197**

Macmillan/McGraw-Hill

PREPARE
WARM-UP To prepare children to solve a problem using data from a table, have them give the following sums and differences:

34 + 25 [59]   15 − 7 [8]   12 + 6 [18]   17 − 9 [8]

TEACH
QUESTIONING Write this table on the board:

THINGS WE COLLECT

	Lee	Bob
Baseball Cards	32	45
Shells	9	15
Rocks	11	4

Explain to children that a table is a way to organize information or data so that it is easy to read.
- **What does this table tell us?** [It tells how many baseball cards, shells, and rocks Lee and Bob have collected.]
- **How many shells does Bob have?** [15]
- **How many shells does Lee have?** [9]
- **What do we do to find how many more shells Bob has than Lee?** [Subtract 9 from 15; 6.]
- ■ **How do we find how many baseball cards Lee and Bob have altogether?** [Find the number of cards they each have, then add; 32 + 45 = 77.]
- ■ **How do we find how many more rocks Bob needs to collect to have as many as Lee?** [Subtract to find the difference between 11 and 4.]

Team A and Team B had a gym contest.

Exercises Completed

	A	B
Cartwheels	12	5
Jumping Jacks	7	16
Push-ups	47	38
Knee Bends	28	13

Write the numbers. Solve.

1. Team A did __47__ push-ups.

 Team B did __38__ push-ups.

 How many push-ups did the teams do in all? __85__ push-ups

2. Team B did __5__ cartwheels.

 Team A did __12__ cartwheels.

 How many cartwheels did both teams do? __17__ cartwheels

3. Team B did __13__ knee bends.

 The gym teacher asked them to do 15 more.

 How many knee bends did Team B do in all? __28__ knee bends

4. Think of some exercises you and a friend could do.
 Use this table to tell about the exercises.

 Answers will vary.

5. Write a problem about your exercises. Solve it.

Extra Practice, page 200

PUPIL'S EDITION pp. 197-198

Page 197 Read the information at the top of the page.

■ **What do you need to do?** [Read the table to find the numbers of exercises.]

■ **What do the numbers on the table tell you?** [The numbers tell how many of each exercise Sue and Tom did.]

■ **How do you find out how many stretch-ups Tom did?** [You look under Tom's name and find the number next to "Stretch-ups."]

■ **How do you find out how many stretch-ups were done in all by both children?** [Add the number of stretch-ups they each did.]

■ **What did you learn?** [Possible response: Sometimes you need data from a table to solve problems.]

Encourage children to explain other ways to solve this problem.

Check for Understanding

■ **What if Sue did 3 more jumping jacks than the chart shows? How many jumping jacks would it show that Sue had done?** [15]

GUIDED PRACTICE ex. 1–4: Work through problem 1 with the children. Make sure they understand how to use data.

Page 198 Read the information at the top of the page.

 **PRACTICE•APPLY** **PRACTICE** ex. 1–5

C L O S E Guide children to summarize the lesson:

■ **How do you use data on a table to solve problems?** [Possible response: You find the information you need to complete the problem.]

Chapter 6 • Lesson 8 **198**

TEACHER to TEACHER

COOPERATIVE LEARNING TIP My class uses a variety of methods to gather data, such as **people hunts, group challenges,** and **charts with tallies.** Then we organize the data. In small groups, children talk about appropriate categories for the tables, using the cooperative skill **making suggestions.** I then call on groups, asking someone at random to speak for his or her group. When a class list of suggested categories is compiled, groups can set up tables, write the data collected from the class, and post them in their sections of the bulletin board for others to read.

For Students Acquiring English (SAE)

Scan the pages for vocabulary that may be new to SAE children. Introduce new words by using visuals, gestures, and body movements to convey meaning. Ask questions frequently to check comprehension. Enlarge the table on an overhead projector or the chalkboard. Ask questions similar to those on the page orally. Pair SAE and non-SAE children to complete the pages.

MAC ACTIVITY CENTER

MAC Activity 129:
Basic-to-Average ▼

LOGICAL REASONING ▪ FIND THE NUMBER

MAC Activity 129

On Your Own   Pair and Share   In a Group

Materials tens and ones models or punchout tens and ones models, punchout Workmat 2

Setup Copy the following table on the chalkboard:

Sticker Sales

	Jan	Ted
Stars	32	28
Hearts		16
Bears	43	

Procedure Assign children to work in pairs. Give each pair a workmat and a set of tens and ones models. Explain to children they are to use the data on the table and their models to solve problems you will read aloud. Ask volunteers to write the missing numbers on the table.

1. Jan and Ted sold stickers at the school fair. Jan sold 32 star stickers. Ted sold 28 star stickers. How many stars did they sell in all? [60]
2. Jan sold 9 fewer heart stickers than Ted did. How many heart stickers did Jan sell? [7]
3. Ted sold 29 more bear stickers than Jan did. How many bear stickers did Ted sell? [72]

MAC Activity 130:
Average-to-Challenge
▼

WRITING MATHEMATICS ▪ WINNING ACROBATS

MAC Activity 130

On Your Own   Pair and Share   In a Group

Setup Copy the following table on the chalkboard:

Gym Show

	Suns	Flyers
Handstands	17	9
Backflips	44	37
Cartwheels	39	52
Leapfrogs	8	15

Procedure Have children play in small groups with two teams in each group. Tell them that the Suns and Flyers put on a gymnastic show. The table shows how many exercises each team did. Explain that you will read some problems. Each team solves the problem on paper and announces the answer. The first team in each group to announce the correct answer wins a point.

1. The Flyers did 7 more of what exercise? [leapfrogs]
2. How many backflips did both teams do? [81]
3. How many more handstands did the Suns do than the Flyers? [8]
4. How many cartwheels and backflips did the Suns do? [83]
5. How many leapfrogs did both teams do? [23]

Continue with similar questions.

To Win The team with more points at the end of play wins.

RETEACHING-65

Name

PROBLEM SOLVING:
USING DATA FROM A TABLE

Study

How many puppets did Jake and Amy make in all?

Find the word *Puppets* on this table. Go across the row to find the numbers under Jake and Amy.

Add to find how many in all.

THINGS WE MADE

	Jake	Amy
Car Models	15	7
Clay Animals	9	13
Puppets	17	24
Paper Flowers	35	26

17 + 24 = 41
41 puppets

Check

Use the table.
Write the numbers. Solve.

1. Jake made __15__ car models.   15

   Amy made __7__ car models.   7

   Who made fewer cars? __Amy__
   How many fewer?   __8__ fewer

2. Jake wants to make 13 clay animals.   13

   He has already made __9__ animals.   − 9
   How many more does he have to do?   4 more

3. Jake made __35__ flowers.   35

   Amy made __26__ flowers.   + 26
   How many flowers did they make in all?   __61__ flowers

Reteaching 65

Macmillan/McGraw-Hill, MATHEMATICS IN ACTION
Grade 2, Chapter 6, Lesson 8, pages 197–198

PRACTICE-65

Name

PROBLEM SOLVING:
USING DATA FROM A TABLE

Ray and Kimi helped their parents recycle at home. They made this table to show what they collected. Ray's recycled items are under his name. Kimi's recycled items are under her name.

Things We Recycled

	Ray	Kimi
Cans	36	47
Glass Jars	15	9
Newspaper Bundles	21	29
Plastic Bottles	6	11

Write the numbers. Solve.

1. Ray tied __21__ newspaper bundles.

   Kimi tied __29__ newspaper bundles.

   How many bundles did they tie in all? __50__ bundles

2. Ray collected __15__ glass jars.

   Kimi collected __9__ glass jars.

   Who collected fewer jars? __Kimi__

   How many fewer? __6__ fewer glass jars

3. Ray collected __36__ cans.

   Kimi collected __47__ cans.

   How many cans did they collect in all? __83__ cans

4. Ray found __6__ plastic bottles.
   His mother gave him 15 more.
   How many plastic bottles did he have? __21__ bottles

Practice-65

Macmillan/McGraw-Hill, MATHEMATICS IN ACTION
Grade 2, Chapter 6, Lesson 8, pages 197–198

ENRICHMENT-65

Name

PROBLEM SOLVING

On Your Own   Pair and Share   In a Group

SALES FOR THE DAY

Rachel and Sam worked at the Used Toy Booth. They want to know how many things they sold. Use the clues to help them find out. Write the numbers on the table.

THINGS WE SOLD

	Sam	Rachel
Toys	6	15
Puzzles	60	33
Marbles	39	61
Race Cars	9	6

Clues

1. Rachel sold 16 puzzles in the morning. She sold 17 puzzles in the afternoon.

2. Rachel sold 15 toys. Sam sold 9 fewer toys than Rachel did.

3. Sam sold 27 more puzzles than Rachel sold.

4. The children had 17 race cars to sell. Sam sold 9 race cars. They had 2 race cars left at the end of the day.

5. Sam sold 39 marbles. Rachel sold 22 more marbles than Sam sold.

6. Who sold the most puzzles? __Sam__

7. Who sold the most marbles? __Rachel__

Enrichment-65

Macmillan/McGraw-Hill, MATHEMATICS IN ACTION
Grade 2, Chapter 6, Lesson 8, pages 197–198

Problem of the Day

Juan and Tim made a table to show how many cans and bottles they collected for recycling. Juan found 32 cans and 19 bottles. Tim found 23 cans and 28 bottles. Who collected more cans and bottles? [Both children collected the same number of cans and bottles; 32 + 19 = 51 and 23 + 28 = 51.]

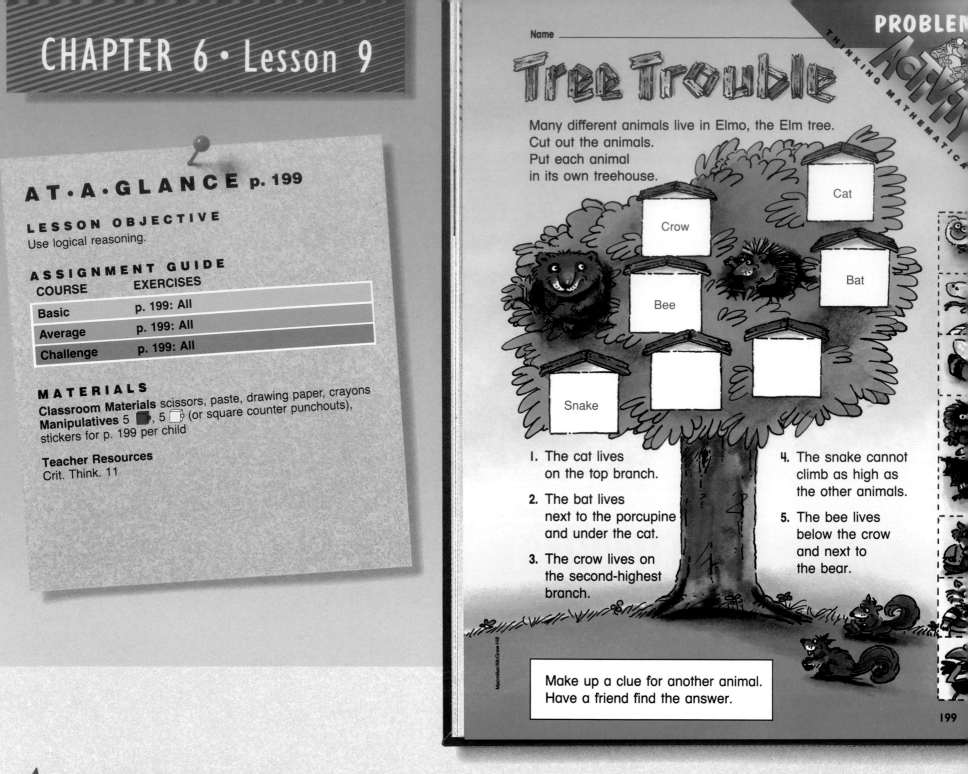

AT·A·GLANCE p. 199

LESSON OBJECTIVE
Use logical reasoning.

ASSIGNMENT GUIDE

COURSE	EXERCISES
Basic	p. 199: All
Average	p. 199: All
Challenge	p. 199: All

MATERIALS
Classroom Materials scissors, paste, drawing paper, crayons
Manipulatives 5 ▮, 5 ▯ (or square counter punchouts),
stickers for p. 199 per child

Teacher Resources
Crit. Think. 11

Tree Trouble

Many different animals live in Elmo, the Elm tree.
Cut out the animals.
Put each animal
in its own treehouse.

Cat
Crow
Bee
Bat
Snake

1. The cat lives
   on the top branch.

2. The bat lives
   next to the porcupine
   and under the cat.

3. The crow lives on
   the second-highest
   branch.

4. The snake cannot
   climb as high as
   the other animals.

5. The bee lives
   below the crow
   and next to
   the bear.

Macmillan/McGraw-Hill

Make up a clue for another animal.
Have a friend find the answer.

Name _____

199

PLAN

AIMS AND ATTITUDES This lesson develops logical reasoning involving clues about position. In the lesson, children make choices about where to place cutouts or stickers after considering clues presented.

Encourage children to develop their own methods for solving the problems. Some children may be able to retain the clues mentally. Others may find it helpful to draw and revise pictures as new information is obtained. Still others may find it helpful to manipulate physical models. Accept all methods as valid and encourage children to verbalize their reasoning.

MANAGEMENT The activity is intended for all children and has been designed for independent work. It is appropriate for pairs of children as well. If pairing children for this activity, teaming a child having

strong language and problem-solving skills with a child having weaker skills may be particularly effective.

GUIDE

Before beginning the activity on page 199, ask children to model the following problem.

Give each child 5 red and 5 yellow cubes. Tell them to make a tower of cubes according to the following instructions.

1. Use a red cube for the top cube and the bottom cube.
2. Place a yellow cube under the top cube and above the bottom cube.
3. Place three red cubes in the middle.

■ **What is the order of the cube tower from top to bottom?** [red, yellow, red, red, red, yellow, red]

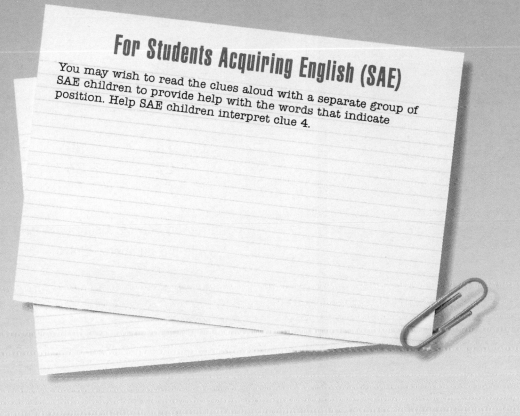

For Students Acquiring English (SAE)

You may wish to read the clues aloud with a separate group of SAE children to provide help with the words that indicate position. Help SAE children interpret clue 4.

Read the directions at the top of page 199 with the children. Identify each animal cutout at the side of the page. Have children cut out the pictures of the animals or use stickers. Tell them to read the clues and use them to decide where to paste each animal. Discuss the placement of the animals with children. Ask volunteers to describe the method they used to solve each problem.

Then have children write their own clues about one of the animals not used so far in the activity and exchange them with classmates to solve.

3 EXTEND Ask children to work in pairs. Distribute drawing paper and crayons to each pair. Ask one child to draw a tree and four treehouses similar to the drawing on page 199. The other child selects four animal stickers or cutouts (whichever were not used for page 199). Each child takes a turn thinking of a clue for one of the animals. The other partner places the animal in the correct treehouse.

EXTRA PRACTICE

Extra Practice items are provided so that children may have an opportunity for further practice.

The *Additional Practice* section also provides practice you may wish to assign.

Extra Practice

Addition Practice, page 195 ....

Add.

1.
$$\begin{array}{r} 49 \\ +13 \\ \hline 62 \end{array}$$
$$\begin{array}{r} 25 \\ +26 \\ \hline 51 \end{array}$$
$$\begin{array}{r} 31 \\ +42 \\ \hline 73 \end{array}$$
$$\begin{array}{r} 55 \\ +15 \\ \hline 70 \end{array}$$
$$\begin{array}{r} 2 \\ +6 \end{array}$$

2.
$$\begin{array}{r} 42 \\ +36 \\ \hline 78 \end{array}$$
$$\begin{array}{r} 53 \\ +29 \\ \hline 82 \end{array}$$
$$\begin{array}{r} 15 \\ +19 \\ \hline 34 \end{array}$$
$$\begin{array}{r} 37 \\ +38 \\ \hline 75 \end{array}$$
$$\begin{array}{r} 2 \\ +4 \end{array}$$

3.
$$\begin{array}{r} 18 \\ +27 \\ \hline 45 \end{array}$$
$$\begin{array}{r} 54 \\ +36 \\ \hline 90 \end{array}$$
$$\begin{array}{r} 82 \\ +11 \\ \hline 93 \end{array}$$
$$\begin{array}{r} 20 \\ +49 \\ \hline 69 \end{array}$$
$$\begin{array}{r} 1 \\ +2 \end{array}$$

Problem Solving: Using Data from a Table, pages 197–198 ....

Write the numbers. Solve.

Birds We Saw

	Beth	Ar
Robins	14	8
Blue Jays	7	27
Sparrows	41	29

1. Art saw __8__ robins.

Beth saw __14__ robins.

How many robins did they

see? __22__ robins

2. Beth saw __7__ blue jays.

Art saw __27__ blue jays.

How many blue jays did

they see? __34__ blue jays

ADDITIONAL PRACTICE

p. 195 *Add.*

1.
$$\begin{array}{r} 61 \\ +37 \\ \hline [98] \end{array}$$
$$\begin{array}{r} 57 \\ +38 \\ \hline [95] \end{array}$$
$$\begin{array}{r} 42 \\ +27 \\ \hline [69] \end{array}$$
$$\begin{array}{r} 14 \\ +49 \\ \hline [63] \end{array}$$

2.
$$\begin{array}{r} 13 \\ +16 \\ \hline [29] \end{array}$$
$$\begin{array}{r} 29 \\ +33 \\ \hline [62] \end{array}$$
$$\begin{array}{r} 58 \\ +21 \\ \hline [79] \end{array}$$
$$\begin{array}{r} 80 \\ +15 \\ \hline [95] \end{array}$$

Add.

3.
$$\begin{array}{r} 71 \\ +19 \\ \hline [90] \end{array}$$
$$\begin{array}{r} 42 \\ +36 \\ \hline [78] \end{array}$$
$$\begin{array}{r} 16 \\ +39 \\ \hline [55] \end{array}$$
$$\begin{array}{r} 27 \\ +23 \\ \hline [50] \end{array}$$

4.
$$\begin{array}{r} 69 \\ +18 \\ \hline [87] \end{array}$$
$$\begin{array}{r} 51 \\ +34 \\ \hline [85] \end{array}$$
$$\begin{array}{r} 18 \\ +63 \\ \hline [81] \end{array}$$
$$\begin{array}{r} 53 \\ +19 \\ \hline [72] \end{array}$$

p. 197 *Write the numbers. Solve.*

TICKETS SOLD

	Carol	Dan
Monday	20	25
Tuesday	8	13
Wednesday	36	41

1. Carol sold [20] tickets on Monday. Dan sold [25] tickets on Monday. How many tickets did they sell on Monday?
   [45] tickets

2. Dan sold [13] tickets on Tuesday. He sold [41] tickets on Wednesday. How many tickets did he sell in two days?
   [54] tickets

CHAPTER 6 • Lesson 10

AT·A·GLANCE pp. 201-202

LESSON OBJECTIVE
Use estimation to solve problems.

ASSIGNMENT GUIDE

COURSE	EXERCISES
Basic	p. 201: 1; p. 202: 1–3
Average	p. 201: 1; p. 202: 1–3
Challenge	p. 201: 1; p. 202: 1–3

Teacher Resources
Reteaching 66   Practice 66   Enrichment 66
Prob. Solv. 28   MAC Act. 131, 132

Problem Solving

UNDERSTAND / PLAN / TRY / CHECK / EXTEND

Strategy: Using Estimation

Sometimes you can estimate to find
about how many in all.

Kate wants to make 70 pies for the fair.
She made 21 pies yesterday.
She made 38 pies today.
About how many pies did she make?

Is 21 nearer to 20 or 30?   Is 38 nearer to 30 or 40?

```
←─┼──┼──┼──┼──┼──┼──┼──┼──┼──┼──┼──┼──┼──┼──┼──┼──┼──┼──┼──┼─→
  20 21 22 23 24 25 26 27 28 29 30 31 32 33 34 35 36 37 38 39 40
```

> 21 is nearer to 20.

> 38 is nearer to 40.

$$20 + 40 = 60$$

Kate made about __60__ pies.

Did she make enough pies for the fair? __No.__

Write your estimate. Solve.

```
←─┼──┼──┼──┼──┼──┼──┼──┼──┼──┼──┼──┼──┼──┼──┼──┼──┼──┼──┼──┼─→
  10 11 12 13 14 15 16 17 18 19 20 21 22 23 24 25 26 27 28 29 30
```

1. Todd needs 50 apples to make some pies.
   He has 12 red apples.
   He has 27 yellow apples.

   About how many apples does he have? __40__ apples

   Does he have enough apples for the pies? __No.__

Macmillan/McGraw-Hill

---

1 PREPARE

WARM-UP To prepare children for using estimation to solve problems, have children give the following sums:

    20 + 10 [30]   30 + 20 [50]   40 + 30 [70]   30 + 50 [80]

2 TEACH

DISCUSSING On the board, draw a number line from 20 through 30. Read the following problem:

    Ben bought 27 stickers yesterday. He bought 23 stickers today. About how many stickers does Ben have in all?

■ **Is the question asking *exactly* how many or *about* how many stickers Ben has in all?** [*about* how many in all]

Explain to children that finding *about how many* means making an estimate. Tell children that to make an estimate, they can find numbers close to the 27 and 23 in the problem and add them. Point out that children can use a number line to find the numbers that are close. Have a volunteer point to the 27 on the number line on the board.

■ **Is 27 nearer to 20 or 30?** [It is nearer to 30.]

Have the volunteer point to the 23 on the number line.

■ **Is 23 nearer to 20 or 30?** [It is nearer to 20.]

■ **What is 30 + 20?** [50]

■ **About how many stickers does Ben have in all?** [about 50 stickers in all]

PUPIL'S EDITION pp. 201-202

Page 201 Have a volunteer read the information and the problem at the top of the page.

Write your estimate. Solve.

```
10 11 12 13 14 15 16 17 18 19 20 21 22 23 24 25 26 27 28 29 30 31 32 33 34 35 36 37 38 39 40
```

1. The Western Train Ride
   can hold 50 children.
   37 boys are on line.
   21 girls are on line.
   About how many children are on line? __60__ children

   Can the Western Train Ride hold all the children? __No.__

2. The Future Space Ride
   can hold 60 children.
   14 children get on the ride.
   Then 26 children get on the ride.
   About how many children are on the ride? __40__ children

   Can the Future Space Ride hold all the children? __Yes.__

3. Wilt needs to score
   50 points to win a prize.
   He scored 22 points.
   Then he scored 33 points.
   About how many points did he score? __50__ points

   Does he have enough points for a prize? __Yes.__

202   two hundred two

TEACHER to TEACHER

COOPERATIVE LEARNING TIP 👥 My children benefited from working in small groups when using estimation to solve problems. They checked each other's estimates by using number lines. After they decided on an answer, they discussed whether the answer made sense.

■ **What do you know?** [Kate wants to make 70 pies. She made 21 pies yesterday and 38 pies today.]

■ **What do you need to find out?** [You need to find out about how many pies Kate made.]

Discuss the example. Guide children to see that they can use the number line to estimate the number of pies Kate made each day. Have children trace the answer. Discuss the final question and have children trace the answer.

■ **What did you learn?** [You can estimate to solve a problem.]

Check for Understanding

■ **If Kate made 32 pies yesterday, would she have enough pies?** [Yes, 32 is close to 30 and 38 is close to 40. 30 + 40 = 70.]

GUIDED PRACTICE   ex. 1: Work through problem 1 with the children. Make sure they understand how to solve the problem using estimation.

Page 202   Read the directions at the top of the page. Discuss the number line and have children identify the range of numbers shown.

PRACTICE·APPLY   **PRACTICE**   ex. 1–3

C L O S E   Guide children to summarize the lesson:

■ **When can you use estimation to solve a problem?** [Possible response: when the problem asks you to find *about how many*]

MAC ACTIVITY CENTER

MAC Activity 131

On Your Own   Pair and Share   In a Group

ESTIMATION ▪ ON LINE

Materials   mural paper

Setup   Tape a long sheet of mural paper to the floor. Draw a number line showing the numbers 20 to 60.

Procedure   Assign children to work in groups of three. Tell children you will read a problem to each group. Have two members of a group stand on the number line or on the floor to show the numbers in the problem. Tell them to estimate the numbers by moving to the nearest 10. The third member of the group adds the two numbers and stands on the estimated sum. The group then answers the final question.

1. The bus has seats for 50 children. 23 second-graders are waiting for the bus. 38 third-graders are waiting for the bus. About how many children are waiting for the bus? [One member stands on 23, another on 38; they move to 20 and 40 respectively. The third member stands on 60.] Are there enough seats for the children? [No.]

2. Brenda wants to make 40 paper flowers for the party. She makes 13 flowers one day. She makes 39 flowers the next day. About how many flowers did she make? [50] Did she make enough flowers for the party? [Yes.]

Continue the activity with similar problems.

◀ **MAC Activity 131:
Basic-to-Average**

**MAC Activity 132:
Average-to-Challenge** ▶

SPEAKING MATHEMATICALLY ▪ ESTIMATION TALES

MAC Activity 132

On Your Own   Pair and Share   In a Group

13   38   books   50

Materials   index cards

Setup   Prepare Number, Word, and Estimate game cards as follows. Write the numbers 11 through 44 on one set of cards. Leave out 15, 20, 25, 30, 35, and 40. On another set of 15 cards write such words as toys, apples, books, boxes, cookies, seats, and blocks. On a third set of cards, write the numbers 10, 20, 30, 40, 50, 60, 70, and 80.

Procedure   Assign chidren to work in pairs. Have each pair team up with another pair. Provide each team with a set of Estimate cards. Place the Number and Word cards facedown on a table. Have one pair from each team come forward and choose two Number cards and one Word card. Have the pair make up a problem for the other team using the information from the three cards. For example, if the children chose 31, 42 and *blocks*, a problem could be: "We needed 70 blocks to build a model house. We made a pile of 31 blocks. We made another pile of 42 blocks. Do we have enough blocks?" The second team estimates the answer and shows the appropriate Estimate card.

The second team then comes forward and chooses two Number cards and a Word card to make up a problem. Each team that uses the cards correctly scores 2 points. Each team that gives the correct answer scores 1 point.

To Win   The team with more points at the end of play wins.

RETEACHING

RETEACHING-66

Name _____

PROBLEM SOLVING STRATEGY: USING ESTIMATION

Study

Mary made 12 name cards for the party.
Then she made 18 more name cards.
About how many cards did she make?

10 11 (12) 13 14 15 16 17 (18) 19 20 21 22 23 24 25 26 27 28 29 30

| 12 is close to 10. | | 18 is close to 20. |

Add. $10 + 20 = 30$

Mary needs 40 cards for the party. She does not have enough cards.

Check

Write your estimate. Solve.

1. Bill needs 40 cups for the party.   11 is about __10__ cups.
   He has 11 cups in one box.   29 is about __30__ cups.
   He has 29 cups in another box.
   About how many cups does he have?   __40__ cups
   Does he have enough cups?   __yes__

2. Juan needs 50 plates.
   He finds 13 plates on a shelf.
   He finds 17 plates on another shelf.
   About how many plates does he have?   __30__ plates
   Does he have enough plates?   __no__
   Juan's mother brought 29 more plates.
   About how many plates are there now? __60__ plates
   Are there enough plates?   __yes__

Macmillan/McGraw-Hill, MATHEMATICS IN ACTION
Grade 2, Chapter 6, Lesson 10, pages 201–202

Reteaching-66

MACMILLAN/McGRAW-HILL

PRACTICE

PRACTICE-66

Name _____

PROBLEM SOLVING STRATEGY: USING ESTIMATION

Write your estimate. Solve.

10 11 12 13 14 15 16 17 18 19 **20** 21 22 23 24 25 26 27 28 29 **30** 31 32 33 34 35 36 37 38 39 **40**

1. The bus can hold 50 children.
   28 children get on the bus.
   13 children get on the bus.   __40__ children
   About how many children are on the bus?
   Can the bus hold all the children?   __yes__

2. A row of theater seats can hold 40 people.
   22 children sit down in their seats.
   17 children sit down in their seats. __40__ children
   About how many children sit down?
   Can all of the children sit in one row? __yes__

3. The usher has 30 play programs.
   23 children ask for a program.
   31 children ask for a program.   __50__ children
   About how many children want programs?
   Does the usher have enough programs? __no__

4. The teacher wants to get snacks for 40 children.
   He buys 18 apples.
   He buys 27 boxes of raisins.   __50__ snacks
   About how many snacks does he buy?
   Does he have enough snacks for the children? __yes__

Macmillan/McGraw-Hill, MATHEMATICS IN ACTION
Grade 2, Chapter 6, Lesson 10, pages 201–202

Practice-66

MACMILLAN/McGRAW-HILL

ENRICHMENT

ENRICHMENT-66

Name _____

PROBLEM SOLVING

On Your Own   Pair and Share   In a Group

WIN A PRIZE

The children want to win the top prize.
Each child has 2 turns to make the
ring go up high.
See how many points they made.

Win a bicycle.   **70**

Win a radio.   **60**

Win a baseball mitt.   **50**

40

30

20

10

1. Andy hit the ring to 12.
   Then he hit the ring to 39.
   About how many points did he make?
   __50__ points
   Did he make enough to win a prize?
   __yes__
   What did he win? __baseball mitt__

2. Lynn hit the ring to 23.
   Then she hit the ring to 19.
   About how many points did she make?
   __40__ points
   Did she win a prize? __no__

3. Bob hit the ring to 13 and 32.
   Dana hit the ring to 43 and 28.
   José hit the ring to 29 and 33.
   About how many points did each one make?
   Bob __40__ Dana __70__ José __60__
   Who won the top prize?
   __Dana__

Macmillan/McGraw-Hill, MATHEMATICS IN ACTION
Grade 2, Chapter 6, Lesson 10, pages 201–202

Enrichment-66

MACMILLAN/McGRAW-HILL

Problem of the Day

Jean made 22 muffins on Monday. She made
37 muffins on Tuesday and 19 muffins on
Wednesday. About how many muffins did she
make in all? [80; 20 + 40 + 20 = 80]

AT·A·GLANCE p. 203

LESSON OBJECTIVE
Add money amounts.

ASSIGNMENT GUIDE

COURSE	EXERCISES
Basic	p. 203: 1–5
Average	p. 203: 1–5
Challenge	p. 203: 1–5
Extra Practice, p. 207	

MATERIALS

Manipulatives 7 T, 12 O models (or punchouts) for demonstration; 7 D, 15 P coins (or punchouts), Workmat 2 per child

Teacher Resources
Reteaching 67   Practice 67   Enrichment 67
Prob. Solv. 29   MAC Act. 133, 134
Math Anthology, pp. 162–165

SKILLS TRACE
2-DIGIT ADDITION

Explore (Concrete) 186, 187–188	Develop/Understand (Transitional/Abstract) 189–190, 191–192, 193–194, 195, 196, 203, 204
Practice 200, 207, 208, 209–210, 213, 224, 245	**Apply** 197–198, 201–202, 205, 206, 212, 244, 291–292

MANIPULATIVES plus ACTIVITY

See **MANIPULATIVES PLUS 37**, p. 184O.

Name _____

Adding Money

What is the total cost
of a bear and a balloon?

$$\begin{array}{r} 28\cent \\ + \ 6\cent \\ \hline 34\cent \end{array}$$

37¢   28¢   43¢   6¢

Add to find the total amount.

1.

40¢	47¢	23¢	50¢	79¢	36¢
+ 26¢	+ 33¢	+ 16¢	+ 30¢	+ 9¢	+ 15¢
66¢	80¢	39¢	80¢	88¢	51¢

2.

62¢	85¢	48¢	49¢	28¢	54¢
+ 30¢	+ 7¢	+ 29¢	+ 48¢	+ 5¢	+ 9¢
92¢	92¢	77¢	97¢	33¢	63¢

3.

36¢	59¢	7¢	60¢	39¢	45¢
+ 34¢	+ 25¢	+ 13¢	+ 37¢	+ 26¢	+ 35¢
70¢	84¢	20¢	97¢	65¢	80¢

Solve.

4. Eva buys a car and an elephant.

What is the total cost? 80¢

$$\begin{array}{r} 37\cent \\ + 43\cent \\ \hline 80\cent \end{array}$$

5. Julio buys a bear and a car.

What is the total cost? 65¢

$$\begin{array}{r} 28\cent \\ + 37\cent \\ \hline 65\cent \end{array}$$

Macmillan/McGraw-Hill

Extra Practice, page 207

two hundred three   **203**

PREPARE   **WARM-UP**   To review money amounts, remind children that 10 pennies equal 1 dime. Then read the following money amounts and have children use punchout pennies and dimes to show each amount.

47¢   25¢   16¢   30¢

TEACH   **MODELING**   Explain to children that pennies can be thought of as ones, and dimes can be thought of as tens. Write the following exercise on the chalkboard and then tell the story.

47¢
+25¢

Tim bought a kit for 47¢. He bought a ball for 25¢. How much money did he spend in all? [72¢]

Demonstrate how the punchout dimes and pennies can be used as place-value models to find this sum. Have the children use dimes and pennies to model 47¢ + 25¢ on Workmat 2. Guide them through the regrouping.

Model the problem again for children using tens and ones models instead of dimes and pennies.

■ **Why are the answers to the two exercises the same?** [same numbers]

Point out that the operation of adding money is no different than the addition children have been doing. The only difference is the cent sign.

Common Error and Remediation

MATERIALS 1 T, 6 O models (or punchouts), Workmat 2

Some children may add the ones digit twice when adding a 1-digit and a 2-digit number. Work individually with each child. Show the child 4¢ and 12¢ written in vertical format. Have the child model the numbers on the workmat. Tell the child to add the ones and write 6 in the ones column. Then have the child say what should be done next. If the child says to add the 4 and the 1, refer to the models. Have the child combine the ones to see that there are 6. Guide the child to see that there is only 1 ten.

For Students Acquiring English (SAE)

SAE children may need to have the story problems (ex. 4 and 5) read to them to ensure comprehension.

ALTERNATIVE TEACHING STRATEGY

MATERIALS 6 D, 14 P coins (or punchouts)

VISUAL Display 4 dimes 6 pennies and 2 dimes 8 pennies. Explain that you want to find the total amount of money. Suggest that you could count the dimes by tens and count the pennies. Then note that another way to find the total is to add. Tell children that since dimes are tens and pennies are ones, you can quickly count 46¢ in one group and add the 28¢ in the other. Show the addition to find the sum. [74¢]

PUPIL'S EDITION p. 203

Work through the example at the top of the page with the children.

Check for Understanding

■ **What is the total cost of a toy car and a balloon?** [43¢]

GUIDED PRACTICE ex. 1: Remind children to write a cent sign for each sum. For reteaching, use Common Error and Remediation or Alternative Strategy.

Mathematics and Literature

3 PRACTICE·APPLY **PRACTICE** ex. 2–5: For ex. 4 and 5, have children use the pictures at the top of the page to find the prices of the items.

Tell children that they will hear a story in which three boys figured out a plan for making some money. Distribute pennies and dimes to each pair of children. Then read *A Hot Thirsty Day*. Have children use the coins to find the total amount of money the boys made. They can model each amount mentioned in the story (24¢, 6¢, 45¢), then add or count to find the total. [75¢]

CLOSE Guide children to summarize the lesson:

■ **How is adding money amounts different from adding numbers?** [The operation of adding money is the same; the cent sign is the only difference.]

MAC ACTIVITY CENTER

MATH AND CONSUMERS ▪ *LESS MONEY*

MAC Activity 133

On Your Own   Pair and Share   In a Group

Materials   punchout pennies and dimes, game board, beanbags

Procedure   Make a game board for each group of children as shown.

Provide each group with a game board, punchout pennies and dimes, and two beanbags. Tell children they are to toss the two beanbags, one at a time, and then write the two amounts as an addition exercise. Have them add the two amounts using punchout coins as needed. Tell group members to compare their sums after every child has had a turn throwing the beanbags. The child with the least amount says "I paid less money" and scores one point.

To Win   The first child to score five points wins the game.

15¢	32¢	21¢	37¢	29¢	11¢
24¢	16¢	40¢	25¢	43¢	18¢

▲ **MAC Activity 133:**
Basic-to-Average

CALCULATOR ▪ MORE THAN A DOLLAR

MAC Activity 134

On Your Own   Pair and Share   In a Group

Materials   calculator

Write the following exercises on the chalkboard. Give each child a calculator and guide children in entering the first exercise into the calculator. Remind them to put a decimal point in front of each number. Have them read the sums as dollars and cents.

$.74	$.29	$.62	$.57	$.98
+.28	+.84	+.95	+.38	+.23
[$1.02]	[$1.13]	[$1.57]	[$.95]	[$1.21]

$1.13 $.95 $1.02

▲ **MAC Activity 134:**
Average-to-Challenge

RETEACHING-67

Name

ADDING MONEY

Study

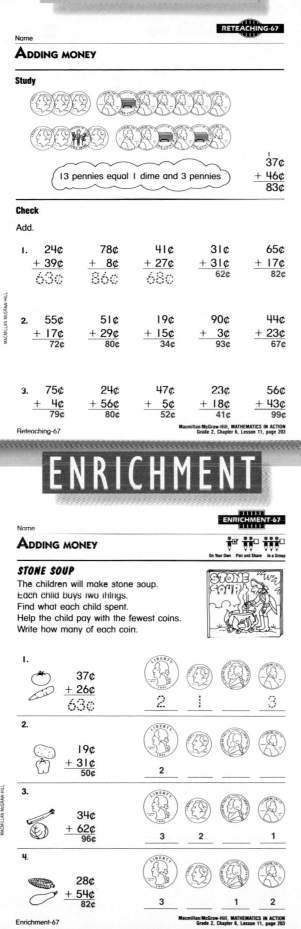

13 pennies equal 1 dime and 3 pennies

$$\begin{array}{r} 1 \\ 37¢ \\ + 46¢ \\ \hline 83¢ \end{array}$$

Check

Add.

1.
$$\begin{array}{r} 24¢ \\ + 39¢ \\ \hline 63¢ \end{array}$$
$$\begin{array}{r} 78¢ \\ + 8¢ \\ \hline 86¢ \end{array}$$
$$\begin{array}{r} 41¢ \\ + 27¢ \\ \hline 68¢ \end{array}$$
$$\begin{array}{r} 31¢ \\ + 31¢ \\ \hline 62¢ \end{array}$$
$$\begin{array}{r} 65¢ \\ + 17¢ \\ \hline 82¢ \end{array}$$

2.
$$\begin{array}{r} 55¢ \\ + 17¢ \\ \hline 72¢ \end{array}$$
$$\begin{array}{r} 51¢ \\ + 29¢ \\ \hline 80¢ \end{array}$$
$$\begin{array}{r} 19¢ \\ + 15¢ \\ \hline 34¢ \end{array}$$
$$\begin{array}{r} 90¢ \\ + 3¢ \\ \hline 93¢ \end{array}$$
$$\begin{array}{r} 44¢ \\ + 23¢ \\ \hline 67¢ \end{array}$$

3.
$$\begin{array}{r} 75¢ \\ + 4¢ \\ \hline 79¢ \end{array}$$
$$\begin{array}{r} 24¢ \\ + 56¢ \\ \hline 80¢ \end{array}$$
$$\begin{array}{r} 47¢ \\ + 5¢ \\ \hline 52¢ \end{array}$$
$$\begin{array}{r} 23¢ \\ + 18¢ \\ \hline 41¢ \end{array}$$
$$\begin{array}{r} 56¢ \\ + 43¢ \\ \hline 99¢ \end{array}$$

MACMILLAN McGRAW-HILL

Reteaching-67

Macmillan/McGraw-Hill, MATHEMATICS IN ACTION
Grade 2, Chapter 6, Lesson 11, page 203

PRACTICE-67

Name

ADDING MONEY

Add.

1.
$$\begin{array}{r} 16¢ \\ + 3¢ \\ \hline 19¢ \end{array}$$
$$\begin{array}{r} 27¢ \\ + 36¢ \\ \hline 63¢ \end{array}$$
$$\begin{array}{r} 9¢ \\ + 39¢ \\ \hline 48¢ \end{array}$$
$$\begin{array}{r} 25¢ \\ + 5¢ \\ \hline 30¢ \end{array}$$
$$\begin{array}{r} 4¢ \\ + 16¢ \\ \hline 20¢ \end{array}$$

2.
$$\begin{array}{r} 29¢ \\ + 9¢ \\ \hline 38¢ \end{array}$$
$$\begin{array}{r} 81¢ \\ + 6¢ \\ \hline 87¢ \end{array}$$
$$\begin{array}{r} 17¢ \\ + 29¢ \\ \hline 46¢ \end{array}$$
$$\begin{array}{r} 53¢ \\ + 22¢ \\ \hline 75¢ \end{array}$$
$$\begin{array}{r} 89¢ \\ + 9¢ \\ \hline 98¢ \end{array}$$

3.
$$\begin{array}{r} 27¢ \\ + 47¢ \\ \hline 74¢ \end{array}$$
$$\begin{array}{r} 12¢ \\ + 13¢ \\ \hline 25¢ \end{array}$$
$$\begin{array}{r} 58¢ \\ + 7¢ \\ \hline 65¢ \end{array}$$
$$\begin{array}{r} 2¢ \\ + 27¢ \\ \hline 29¢ \end{array}$$
$$\begin{array}{r} 29¢ \\ + 35¢ \\ \hline 64¢ \end{array}$$

Solve.

4. Terry bought an apple for 35¢.
She bought a banana for 29¢.
How much did Terry spend? __64¢__

5. Jon spent 43¢ for paper.
He spent 29¢ for paste. How much did Jon spend? __72¢__

6. Kim bought a stamp for 25¢
and a card for 55¢. How
much did she spend? __80¢__

MACMILLAN McGRAW-HILL

Practice-67

Macmillan/McGraw-Hill, MATHEMATICS IN ACTION
Grade 2, Chapter 6, Lesson 11, page 203

ENRICHMENT-67

Name

ADDING MONEY

On Your Own   Pair and Share   In a Group

STONE SOUP

The children will make stone soup.
Each child buys two things.
Find what each child spent.
Help the child pay with the fewest coins.
Write how many of each coin.

1.
$$\begin{array}{r} 37¢ \\ + 26¢ \\ \hline 63¢ \end{array}$$
2   1   3

2.
$$\begin{array}{r} 19¢ \\ + 31¢ \\ \hline 50¢ \end{array}$$
2

3.
$$\begin{array}{r} 34¢ \\ + 62¢ \\ \hline 96¢ \end{array}$$
3   2   1

4.
$$\begin{array}{r} 28¢ \\ + 54¢ \\ \hline 82¢ \end{array}$$
3   1   2

MACMILLAN McGRAW-HILL

Enrichment-67

Macmillan/McGraw-Hill, MATHEMATICS IN ACTION
Grade 2, Chapter 6, Lesson 11, page 203

Problem of the Day

Kira bought a pear for 15¢, a peach for 37¢, and a banana for 15¢. How much did she spend in all for fruit? [97¢]

AT·A·GLANCE p. 204

LESSON OBJECTIVE
Add three 2-digit numbers.

ASSIGNMENT GUIDE

COURSE	EXERCISES
Basic	p. 204: 1–2, Calculator
Average	p. 204: 1–2, Calculator
Challenge	p. 204: 1–2, Calculator
Extra Practice, p. 207	Practice Plus, p. 208

MATERIALS

Calculator
Manipulatives 9 T and 15 O models (or punchouts), Workmat
2 per child

Teacher Resources
Reteaching 68   Practice 68   Enrichment 68
MAC Act. 135, 136

SKILLS TRACE
2-DIGIT ADDITION

Explore (Concrete) 186, 187–188	Develop/Understand (Transitional/Abstract) 189–190, 191–192, 193–194, 195, 196, 203, 204
Practice 200, 207, 208, 209–210, 213, 224, 245	Apply 197–198, 201–202, 205, 206, 212, 244, 291–292

See **MANIPULATIVES PLUS 38**, p. 184P.

Adding Three Numbers

1 Add the ones.   **2** Regroup.   **3** Add the tens.

```
  36                      ¹                      ¹
  13     Look for a      36                     36
+ 14     10 to help.     13                     13
                       + 14                   + 14
                          3                     63
```

(13 ones)   (1 ten 3 ones)   (6 tens)

Add.

1.
```
   21      13      35      24      15       3
   17      27       5       6      24      43
 + 19    + 38    + 16    +  6    +  1    + 12
   57      78      56      36      40      58
```

2.
```
   40      24      16       3      42       4
   12      54      41       6      35       3
 + 39    + 15    + 20    + 57    + 12    + 73
   91      93      77      66      89      80
```

····Calculator····

Find two more numbers to make a sum of 70. **Answers will vary. Possible answers:**

First guess. Then use your calculator to test.

57 [+] [12] [+] [1] [=] 70   38 [+] [22] [+] [10] [=] 70

Extra Practice, page 207 *Practice Plus,* page 208

---

1 PREPARE

WARM-UP To prepare children for adding three 2-digit numbers, have children find the sums for the following exercises.

```
  4      6      3      2      8
  3      2      7      5      1
+ 2    + 1    + 4    + 3    + 9
 [9]    [9]   [14]   [10]   [18]
```

2 TEACH

MODELING Write the following exercise on the chalkboard and have children model it with tens and ones models on Workmat 2.

```
  36
  42
+ 16
 [94]
```

Guide children through each step of the addition, adding the ones, regrouping the ones if possible, and then adding the tens. Have a volunteer record each step on the chalkboard. Repeat the activity with other exercises, such as 24 + 16 + 25 [65], 31 + 18 + 13 [62], 26 + 12 + 22 [60]. As you work through each exercise, remind children to look for number combinations that make 10 (4 + 6), easy facts (1 + 3), and also doubles (2 + 2).

ACTIVITY

Common Error and Remediation

MATERIALS 9 T and 15 O models (or punchouts), Workmat 2

Some children may forget to regroup when adding more than two numbers. Work individually with each child. Provide exercises similar to those in the lesson. Tell the child to model each number in the exercise. Have the child explain each step as he or she adds the three numbers. Emphasize the regrouping step by having the child repeat the number of ones being regrouped and the resulting number of tens and ones.

ALTERNATIVE TEACHING STRATEGY

VISUAL Write the following exercises on the chalkboard.

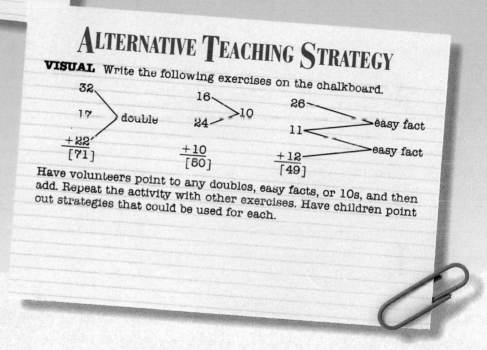

Have volunteers point to any doubles, easy facts, or 10s, and then add. Repeat the activity with other exercises. Have children point out strategies that could be used for each.

PUPIL'S EDITION p. 204

Work through the example at the top of the page with the children.

Check for Understanding

■ **Can you regroup when you add 14 + 3 + 12?** [No.]

GUIDED PRACTICE ex. 1: For reteaching, use Common Error and Remediation or Alternative Strategy.

PRACTICE•APPLY

PRACTICE ex. 2

CALCULATOR Tell children that there is more than one answer to the problems.

CLOSE Guide children to summarize the lesson:

■ **What strategies can you use when adding three numbers?** [Look for 10, doubles, or easy facts.]

MAC Activity 135:
Basic-to-Average

MAC Activity 135

On Your Own   Pair and Share   In a Group

LOGICAL REASONING ■ MAGIC SQUARES

Reproduce the following magic squares and distribute copies to the children. Have children work in pairs. Explain that in a magic square, the sum is the same when they add across, down, or diagonally. Demonstrate how to complete the first square.

84

[27]	32	25
26	28	[30]
31	[24]	29

63

[20]	25	18
19	[21]	23
24	17	[22]

72

25	[20]	[27]
26	[24]	22
[21]	28	[23]

39

14	[9]	16
[15]	[13]	11
10	[17]	[12]

MAC Activity 136

On Your Own   Pair and Share   In a Group

LOGICAL REASONING ■ NUMBER EATER

Write the following exercises on the chalkboard. Tell children that the "Number Eater" has swallowed some of the numbers. Have children copy each exercise and be a "Number Detective" and find the missing addends.

```
   31        26        42        15
   12         ?        34      + 21
 + ?      + 11      + ?         72
  96        60        91       [36]
 [53]      [23]      [15]
```

Then assign one child to be the "Number Eater." He or she should write a missing addend exercise. Have the other child be the "Number Detective" and find the missing addend. Then have children reverse roles.

```
 31
 12
+53
───
 96
```

▲ MAC Activity 136:
Average-to-Challenge

Name

ADDING THREE NUMBERS

Study

Add the ones.
Regroup if you can.

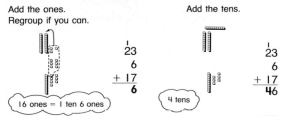

$$
\begin{array}{r} 1 \\ 23 \\ 6 \\ + 17 \\ \hline 6 \end{array}
$$

Add the tens.

$$
\begin{array}{r} 1 \\ 23 \\ 6 \\ + 17 \\ \hline 46 \end{array}
$$

16 ones = 1 ten 6 ones

4 tens

Check

Add. Use models if you need help.

1.
18	26	31	24	21	33
31	42	18	13	6	10
+ 10	+ 8	+ 11	+ 25	+ 12	+ 34
59	76	60	62	39	77

2.
12	31	24	1	23	35
35	18	46	46	34	30
+ 23	+ 34	+ 3	+ 32	+ 14	+ 28
70	83	73	79	71	93

3.
11	18	34	6	36	21
47	12	13	18	31	5
+ 41	+ 33	+ 13	+ 3	+ 26	+ 47
99	63	60	27	93	73

Macmillan/McGraw-Hill, MATHEMATICS IN ACTION
Grade 2, Chapter 6, Lesson 12, page 204

Reteaching-68

Name

ADDING THREE NUMBERS

Add to find the sum.

1.
36	7	15	24	53	11
22	42	2	24	16	45
+ 29	+ 27	+ 19	+ 24	+ 12	+ 23
87	76	36	72	81	79

2.
76	8	7	20	5	42
3	9	42	19	20	35
+ 17	+ 22	+ 25	+ 17	+ 23	+ 14
96	39	74	56	48	91

3.
47	3	13	58	6	19
30	28	20	23	53	21
+ 12	+ 55	+ 19	+ 7	+ 8	+ 17
89	86	52	88	67	57

4.
8	7	48	21	32	13
71	33	31	22	4	45
+ 19	+ 27	+ 6	+ 23	+ 16	+ 34
98	67	85	66	52	92

Solve.

5. Connie saw 15 bluebirds and
12 redbirds. Bob saw 26
birds. How many birds did
the two children see?   53

Macmillan/McGraw-Hill, MATHEMATICS IN ACTION
Grade 2, Chapter 6, Lesson 12, page 204

Practice-68

Name

ADDING THREE NUMBERS

On Your Own   Pair and Share   In a Group

3-DIGIT SUMS
Add. Then color.

sums greater than 200 — blue
sums between 175 and 200 — red
sums between 150 and 175 — yellow
sums between 125 and 150 — purple
sums between 100 and 125 — orange
sums less than 100 — green

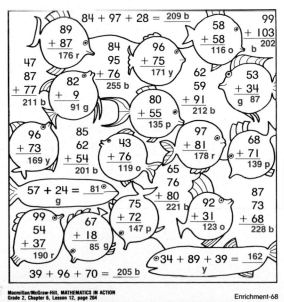

Macmillan/McGraw-Hill, MATHEMATICS IN ACTION
Grade 2, Chapter 6, Lesson 12, page 204

Enrichment-68

Problem of the Day

Phyllis found 14 white shells at the beach. She
also found 27 blue shells and 38 black shells.
How many shells did she find in all?   [79]

AT·A·GLANCE p. 205

LESSON OBJECTIVE
Make decisions using information.

ASSIGNMENT GUIDE

COURSE	EXERCISES
Basic	p. 205: 1–4
Average	p. 205: 1–4
Challenge	p. 205: 1–4

Teacher Resources
Crit. Think. 12   Prob. Solv. 30

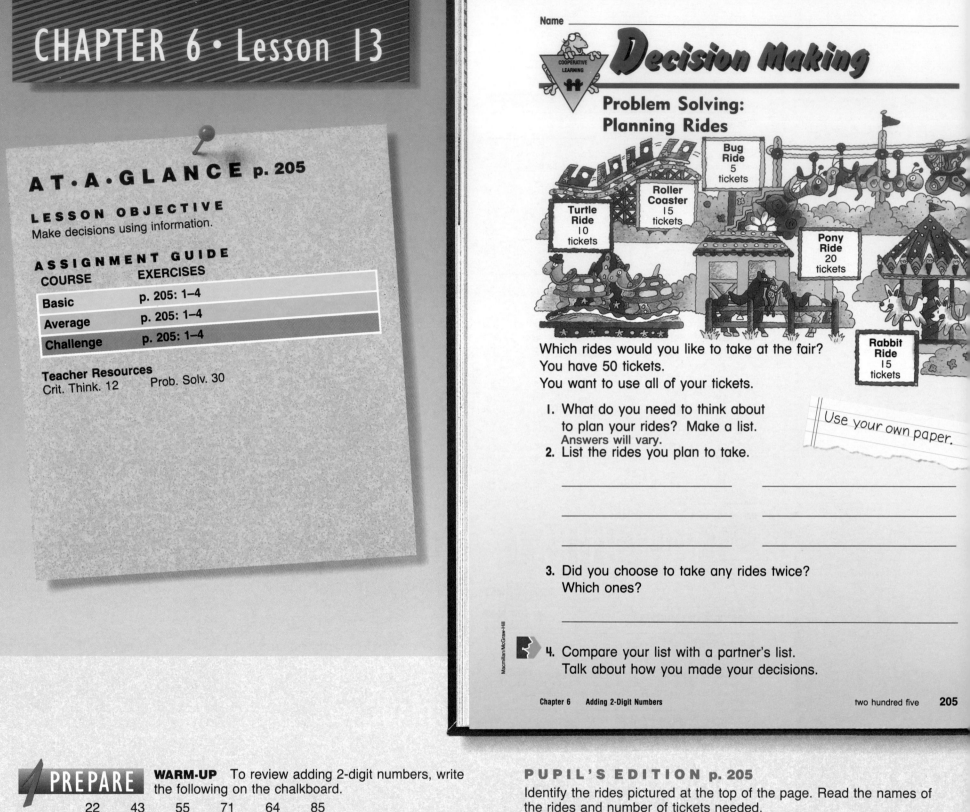

Name _____

Decision Making

COOPERATIVE LEARNING

Problem Solving: Planning Rides

Bug Ride 5 tickets

Roller Coaster 15 tickets

Turtle Ride 10 tickets

Pony Ride 20 tickets

Rabbit Ride 15 tickets

Which rides would you like to take at the fair?
You have 50 tickets.
You want to use all of your tickets.

1. What do you need to think about
   to plan your rides? Make a list.
   Answers will vary.

2. List the rides you plan to take.

   Use your own paper.

   _____   _____

   _____   _____

   _____   _____

3. Did you choose to take any rides twice?
   Which ones?

   _____

4. Compare your list with a partner's list.
   Talk about how you made your decisions.

Macmillan/McGraw-Hill

Chapter 6   Adding 2-Digit Numbers   two hundred five **205**

PREPARE
WARM-UP To review adding 2-digit numbers, write
the following on the chalkboard.

22	43	55	71	64	85
+14	+20	+31	+ 6	+34	+11
[36]	[63]	[86]	[77]	[98]	[96]

Have volunteers write the sums. Continue with other facts as needed.

TEACH
DISCUSSING Have children tell about their experiences at a fair or amusement park. Discuss the
kinds of rides that are usually found at these places. List children's
responses on the chalkboard. Read the completed list with the children, and have volunteers name their favorite rides.

PUPIL'S EDITION p. 205
Identify the rides pictured at the top of the page. Read the names of
the rides and number of tickets needed.

Check for Understanding
■ **For which ride are 20 tickets needed?** [pony ride]
■ **How many tickets would you need to ride on the roller coaster
and the turtle ride?** [25]

PRACTICE·APPLY
Have children complete ex. 1–4. Call
on volunteers to tell how they would
use all 50 tickets. Have children tell how they decided on which rides
to take.

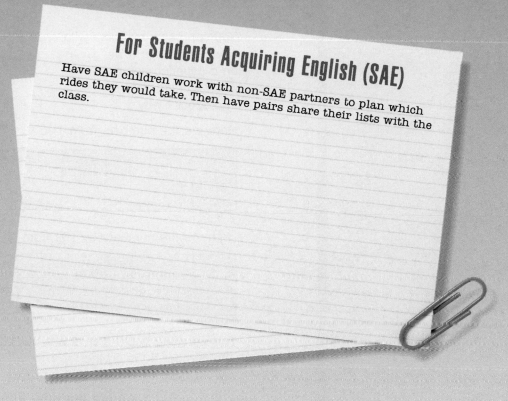

For Students Acquiring English (SAE)

Have SAE children work with non-SAE partners to plan which rides they would take. Then have pairs share their lists with the class.

CLOSE Guide children to summarize the lesson:

■ **What should you do before deciding on which rides to take at a fair?** [Find out how many tickets are needed for each ride and then decide which rides to take.]

CLASS PROJECT

Materials mural or butcher paper, paint, brushes

Have children work in small groups to make a mural of an amusement park. Remind children to think about the events, rides, and games that are found at an amusement park. Then provide each group with a sheet of mural or butcher paper, paint, and brushes. Have children paint a mural of a fair or an amusement park.

When groups have finished their project, display their murals in the classroom. Discuss each mural with the children.

AT·A·GLANCE p. 206

OBJECTIVE
Represent numbers through 99 using a place-value system of rods.

MULTICULTURAL OUTCOME
Introduce children to Chinese *chou* (counting rods) and the Chinese counting board.

MATERIALS
Classroom Materials toothpicks and 1 × 2 counting boards

Curriculum Connection

Math and Social Studies

People use tools to work with numbers. In China, people used counting rods called *chou*.

You can show numbers with *chou*. *Chou* are put in rows on a counting board. Each number is formed in a special way.

Here are the numbers from 1 to 9.

Here are the numbers by 10s from 10 to 90.

This counting board shows two numbers. The number 40 is on the top row. The number 4 is on the bottom row.

Here is the number 26.

$20 + 6 = 26$

Working Together

Use a counting board and toothpicks. Show 62. What other numbers can you show? Take turns.

206 two hundred six

---

1 PREPARE

WARM-UP Prior to the lesson, make 1 × 2 counting boards to represent part of a Chinese counting board. Make the squares large enough (7 cm or 3 in.) to hold toothpicks.

Discuss the tools people use to show or work with numbers such as an abacus, a calculator, and counters. Have children compare and contrast the tools in as many ways as possible.

Tell the children that they will be learning about a Chinese tool for showing and working with numbers.

2 TEACH

DISCUSSING Discuss the *chou* in the top row. Ask:

■ **What pattern can you see in the numbers 1 to 5?** [vertical rods put side by side]

■ **What pattern can you see in the numbers 6 to 9?** [one horizontal rod stands for 5, with enough vertical rods placed below it to show each number]

Continue analyzing the *chou* patterns in the bottom row. Ask:

■ **What can you say about how to show the number 10?** [One rod is placed horizontally instead of vertically.]

■ **How are the rods on both charts alike? How are they different?** [Numbers use 5 or fewer rods; 1–5 is like 10–50, but rods for ones are vertical, and rods for tens are horizontal. Rods for 6–9 and 60–90 use one rod in the opposite direction to show 5 or 50 with however many other rods are needed to show the greater numbers.]

CULTURAL DIVERSITY

CHINESE COUNTING RODS

The Chinese counting board uses a base-10 system to represent numbers. Traditional rods (*chou*), made of bamboo or ivory, were placed on rows of the counting board according to place-value rules—the place farthest to the right is ones, then tens, and so on. Rod orientation is an essential aspect of this system. Rods in ones place are vertical, rods in tens place are horizontal, rods in hundreds place are vertical, and so on. Numbers such as 40, 500, or 820 show rods only in the necessary places, leaving places vacant as appropriate.

BIBLIOGRAPHY

Ifrah, Georges. *From One to Zero: A Universal History of Numbers.* New York: Viking, 1985. ISBN 0-670-37395-8. (For teacher reading)

Compare the 4 and the 40, as shown on the page. Guide children to notice the place value position of the rods as well as the different orientation.

3 PRACTICE•APPLY

Give 10 toothpicks and one 1 x 2 counting board to each child. Explain that Chinese counting boards have more squares, but the small counting boards will help them practice making numbers. Have children use toothpicks to form the numbers 1–9 in the right-hand square. When they make the numbers 10–90, they must place the toothpicks in the left-hand square to reinforce the place value.

WORKING TOGETHER Divide the class into pairs. Within pairs, both children form numbers using the toothpicks and counting boards. Have them describe how the *chou* show 26. Then ask:

■ **How is 26 like 62? How is it different? How would you show 62 with the *chou*?** [Accept all reasonable answers.]

After both partners have formed and read several numbers, they can reverse the task; each child builds any number up to 99 that the partner asks for. Partners switch roles.

CLOSE Guide children to summarize the lesson:

■ **How can you use Chinese *chou* and a counting board to show the number 5? 50? 86?** [Check the children's answers.]

Extra Practice items are provided so that children may have an opportunity for further practice.

The *Additional Practice* section also provides practice you may wish to assign.

Name _____

Adding Money, page 203 . . . .

Add.

1.	52¢ + 39¢ 91¢	12¢ + 41¢ 53¢	47¢ + 34¢ 81¢	23¢ + 56¢ 79¢	34¢ + 64¢ 98¢
2.	19¢ + 13¢ 32¢	42¢ + 23¢ 65¢	51¢ + 38¢ 89¢	36¢ + 14¢ 50¢	27¢ + 26¢ 53¢
3.	18¢ + 25¢ 43¢	24¢ + 53¢ 77¢	65¢ + 27¢ 92¢	24¢ + 35¢ 59¢	79¢ + 18¢ 97¢

Adding Three Numbers, page 204 . . . .

1.	24 31 + 17 72	46 19 + 22 87	57 13 + 25 95	31 49 + 16 96	15 25 + 35 75
2.	62 12 + 14 88	20 38 + 26 84	11 55 + 22 88	34 43 + 14 91	52 18 + 23 93

ADDITIONAL PRACTICE

p. 203 *Add.*

1.	63¢ +29¢ [92¢]	45¢ +32¢ [77¢]	16¢ +27¢ [43¢]	**3.**	47¢ +16¢ [63¢]	25¢ +66¢ [91¢]	35¢ +19¢ [54¢]
2.	59¢ +17¢ [76¢]	38¢ +25¢ [63¢]	14¢ +78¢ [92¢]	**4.**	28¢ +12¢ [40¢]	52¢ +16¢ [68¢]	78¢ +17¢ [95¢]

p. 204 *Add.*

1.	14 16 +29 [59]	23 36 +15 [74]	54 11 +22 [87]	15 11 +37 [63]
2.	30 28 +41 [99]	67 12 +10 [89]	45 31 +12 [88]	31 20 +18 [79]

Practice Plus

Key Skill: 2-Digit Addition, page 195 . . . .

Add.

1.
31	64	58	14	23
+ 57	+ 17	+ 33	+ 26	+ 66
88	81	91	40	89

2.
19	42	44	27	16	23
+ 29	+ 29	+ 51	+ 35	+ 18	+ 67
48	71	95	62	34	90

3.
32	47	35	55	30	46
+ 52	+ 19	+ 39	+ 11	+ 61	+ 12
84	66	74	66	91	58

Key Skill: Adding Three Numbers, page 204 . . . .

Add.

1.
31	54	31	12	61	38
17	12	19	43	13	20
+ 21	+ 28	+ 25	+ 34	+ 17	+ 35
69	94	75	89	91	93

2.
11	31	14	29	19	24
46	51	36	30	20	15
+ 23	+ 12	+ 30	+ 12	+ 21	+ 47
80	94	80	71	60	86

208   two hundred eight

ADDITIONAL PRACTICE

p. 195 *Add.*

1.
49	31	13	54
+ 43	+ 16	+ 80	+ 27
[92]	[47]	[93]	[81]

2.
46	18	25	79
+ 27	+ 65	+ 17	+ 14
[73]	[83]	[42]	[93]

p. 204 *Add.*

1.
18	49	39	25
11	16	18	51
+ 14	+ 27	+ 15	+ 10
[43]	[92]	[72]	[86]

2.
11	21	58	41
67	17	27	31
+ 15	+ 30	+ 11	+ 17
[93]	[68]	[96]	[89]

3.
21	64	19	41
56	10	19	22
+ 12	+ 17	+ 19	+ 31
[89]	[91]	[57]	[94]

4.
15	44	29	37
20	23	24	41
+ 31	+ 18	+ 23	+ 10
[66]	[85]	[76]	[88]

PRACTICE **PLUS**

Practice Plus is provided to supply additional practice for the two key skills in this chapter.

Key Skills
Page 195: Addition Practice
Page 204: Adding Three Numbers

The *Additional Practice* also provides practice you may wish to assign for key skills in this chapter.

CHAPTER 6

AT·A·GLANCE pp. 209-210

OBJECTIVE
Review/test the concepts and skills presented in Chapter 6.

6A. Add 2-digit numbers with and without regrouping.
6B. Add three 2-digit numbers.
6C. Add money amounts to 99¢.
6D. Solve problems including those that involve using data from a table.

Teacher Resources
Testing Program, pp. 61–72

Name _____

Chapter Review/Test

Language and Mathematics
Choose the correct word.

1. When you add 2-digit numbers,

   first you add the _____ones_____ .

   Then you add the _____tens_____ .

   | regroup |
   | tens |
   | ones |

2. When you add 26 and 16,

   you need to ____regroup____ the ones.

Concepts and Skills
Add. Did you regroup? Ring *yes* or *no*.

3.	24 + 57 81	(yes) no	4.	15 + 65 80	(yes) no
5.	36 + 41 77	yes (no)	6.	83 + 2 85	yes (no)
7.	78 + 19 97	(yes) no	8.	51 + 28 79	yes (no)
9.	44 + 25 69	yes (no)	10.	38 + 17 55	(yes) no

Macmillan/McGraw-Hill

Chapter 6   Adding 2-Digit Numbers   two hundred nine   **209**

USING THE CHAPTER REVIEW/TEST

The Chapter Review/Test may be used as a review to survey children's knowledge and understanding of the chapter material. Or it may be used as a test to formally assess children's understanding of the concepts and skills taught in the chapter. If used as a test, you may wish to assign one or more of the resources listed in *Reinforcement and Remediation* on p. 210 after reviewing children's test results.

If the Chapter Review/Test is used as a review, you may wish to have children work in pairs to complete it. Then, you can use the Chapter Tests—Forms A, B, and C—provided in the *Testing Program Blackline Master and Teacher's Manual* for testing purposes. Any of these forms may be used for pretesting, posttesting, or retesting.

A performance assessment activity for the key concept in this chapter is provided on page 211.

209   Chapter 6 • Chapter Review/Test

Add.

11.
35¢	46¢	58¢	14¢	27¢
+ 27¢	+ 19¢	+ 36¢	+ 65¢	+ 38¢
62¢	65¢	94¢	79¢	65¢

12.
14	9	23	42	16
5	20	26	17	11
+ 36	+ 54	+ 29	+ 33	+ 47
55	83	78	92	74

Problem Solving

Write the numbers. Solve.

Tim and Ida are collecting empty cans.

Empty Cans Collected

	Tim	Ida
Food	27	34
Juice	12	35
Soda	56	17

13. Tim has __12__ juice cans.

Ida has __35__ juice cans.

How many juice cans in all? __47__ juice cans

14. Ida has __34__ food cans.

Tim has __27__ food cans.

Who has fewer cans? __Tim__

How many fewer? __7__ fewer cans

15. Lynn sold __35__ dolls.

She sold __38__ cars.

How many dolls and cars did she sell?

__73__ dolls and cars

Toys Sold

	Ira	Lynn
Games	16	9
Dolls	27	35
Cars	37	38

MEETING INDIVIDUAL NEEDS

Reinforcement and Remediation

CHAP. OBJ.	TEST ITEMS	PUPIL'S EDITION pp.			TEACHER'S EDITION pp.	TEACHER RESOURCES	
		Lesson	Extra Practice	Practice Plus	Alt. Teaching Strategy	Reteaching	Practice
6A	1–10	187–196	200	208	188, 190, 192, 194, 195A, 196A	60, 61, 62, 63, 64	60, 61, 62, 63, 64
6B	12	204	207	208	204A	68	68
6C	11	203	207		203A	67	67
6D	13–15	197–198	200			65	65

For Students Acquiring English (SAE)

Before beginning the Chapter Review/Test with SAE children, scan the pages for any unfamiliar vocabulary that should be pretaught. You may wish to pair or group SAE children with non-SAE children. You may also wish to repeat some of the activities and techniques for SAE children that were suggested earlier in this chapter.

AT·A·GLANCE p. 211

OBJECTIVE
Assess whether children can add 2-digit numbers (with and without regrouping), including money values, in a problem.

MATERIALS
Manipulatives Workmat 2, 4 T and 12 O models (or punchouts) per pair

Teacher Resources
Performance Assessment booklet, pp. 27–29

For Students Acquiring English (SAE)

Before beginning the performance assessment with SAE children, scan the page for any unfamiliar vocabulary that should be pretaught. You may wish to pair or group SAE children with non-SAE children. You may also wish to repeat some of the activities and techniques for SAE children that were suggested earlier in this chapter.

Performance Assessment

Work with a partner.

Your friend was absent from school one day.
How would you show your friend how to add these numbers?

$$\begin{array}{r} 24 \\ + 18 \\ \hline \end{array}$$

Write what you would say to your friend.
Draw pictures if you want.

You may put this page in your Portfolio

USING PERFORMANCE ASSESSMENT
The Performance Assessment activity may be used to informally assess children's understanding of the key concept(s) of the chapter. Additional assessment activities and Math Journal Options are provided in the *Performance Assessment* booklet.

Performing the Activity
Assign children to work in pairs. Distribute tens and ones models and Workmat 2. Have children work together to explain, using models if they want, how to add the 2-digit numbers. Let them record their explanations individually.

Evaluation Guidelines
Use these criteria to help determine the holistic score for each child. The holistic scoring scale can be found in the Teacher's Reference Section.

- Do children use the models to explain their reasoning?
- If they do use models, do children use them correctly?
- Can children explain how to regroup the ones in the problem?

[Example Response: 4 + 8 = 12 or 1 ten and 2 ones, add the 1 ten to the tens column, 1 + 2 + 1 = 4; the answer is 42]

If children do not have a full understanding of the key concept(s), you may wish to use the Alternative Teaching Strategies or the MAC Activities within the chapter.

 Portfolio

You may wish to have children put their final revised work in their portfolios.

A formal assessment of the concepts and skills taught in this chapter is provided on pages 209–210.

Enrichment For All

Solving a Simpler Problem

Jackie did 23 sit-ups on Sunday.
She did 15 sit-ups on Monday.
She did 34 sit-ups on Tuesday.
How many sit-ups did
Jackie do?

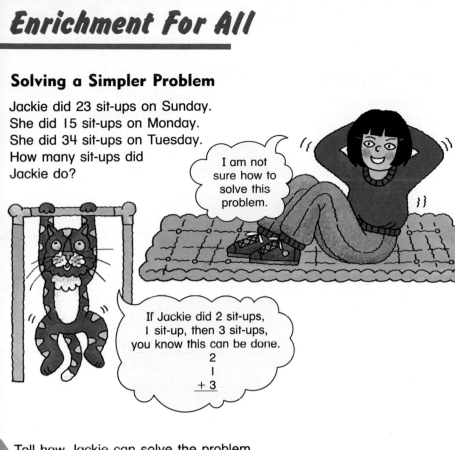

I am not
sure how to
solve this
problem.

If Jackie did 2 sit-ups,
1 sit-up, then 3 sit-ups,
you know this can be done.

$$\begin{array}{r} 2 \\ 1 \\ + 3 \\ \hline \end{array}$$

Tell how Jackie can solve the problem.
By adding the three 2-digit numbers.

Solve. Use a simpler problem first
if you need to.

1. The gym has 18 basketballs.
   It has 13 volleyballs.
   It has 32 tennis balls.
   How many balls does the
   gym have?

   _63_ balls

2. There are 16 players on
   Team 1.
   11 players are on Team 2.
   9 players are on Team 3.
   How many players are
   on all the teams?

   _36_ players

AT·A·GLANCE p. 212

OBJECTIVE
Solve a problem by using a simpler problem.

ASSIGNMENT GUIDE

COURSE	EXERCISES
Basic	p. 212: 1–2
Average	p. 212: 1–2
Challenge	p. 212: 1–2

PREPARE

WARM-UP To prepare children to do mental math
computations, have them do the following:

2 + 3 + 4	[9]	3 + 4 + 2	[9]
1 + 4 + 5	[10]	2 + 1 + 5	[8]
8 − 4	[4]	7 − 6	[1]
9 − 3	[6]	4 − 2	[2]

TEACH

DISCUSSING Discuss the problem at the top of
the page. Guide children to understand that sometimes a problem with larger numbers may confuse them. Explain that
by changing larger numbers to smaller numbers, the problem is made
easier and can then be solved the same way that easier problems are
solved.

■ **What did Jackie do to solve her problem?** [She changed numbers to smaller ones.]

Have children discuss how Jackie solved her problem by adding. Point
out that by making the numbers simpler, it is often easier to see *how*
to solve the problem.

PRACTICE·APPLY

 Have children complete ex. 1–2.

CLOSE Guide children to summarize the lesson:

■ **How can you make a problem simpler?** [Possible response:
Change larger numbers to smaller numbers.]

Chapter 6 • Enrichment For All   **212**

AT·A·GLANCE p. 213

OBJECTIVE
Review and maintain previously learned concepts and skills.

Name _____

Cumulative Review

Fill in the ○ to answer each question.

1.

$$2 + 5 + 8 = \underline{\ ?\ }$$

10	12	13	15
○	○	○	●

2. How long?

```
 0  1  2  3  4
centimeter
```

1 cm	2 cm	3 cm	4 cm
○	○	●	○

---

3. Complete.

3, 6, 9, __?__

10	11	12	18
○	○	●	○

4.

$$\begin{array}{r} 19 \\ + 19 \\ \hline \end{array}$$

40	39	38	18
○	○	●	○

---

5. Which number is 6 tens 3 ones?

36	60	63	65
○	○	●	○

6.

$$\begin{array}{r} 15 \\ -\ 8 \\ \hline \end{array}$$

6	7	8	13
○	○	●	○

---

7. John had 36¢ in his bank.
His mother gave him 55¢.
How much money did he have then?

- ○ 19¢
- ○ 81¢
- ○ 90¢
- ● 91¢

Macmillan/McGraw-Hill

USING THE CUMULATIVE REVIEW

The Cumulative Review is presented in a multiple-choice format to provide practice in taking a standardized test. It gives children an opportunity to review previously learned skills. An answer sheet, similar to those used when taking standardized tests, can be found in the *Testing Program Blackline Masters and Teacher's Manual.*

The table that follows correlates the review items to the lesson pages on which the skills are taught.

Review Items	Text Pages	Review Items	Text Pages
1	111	5	57–58
2	153–154	6	108
3	62	7	203
4	191–195		

Testing Program Blackline Masters
In addition to the Cumulative Review in the Pupil's Edition, there are quarterly Cumulative Tests and an End-Year Test. These tests are multiple choice and provide additional opportunities for children to practice taking standardized tests.

Cumulative Tests measure children's performance on major skills and concepts taught during the previous quarters. The **End-Year Test** measures children's performance on major skills and concepts taught throughout the year.

Home Activity

Your child has been learning to add 2-digit numbers. There is a game you can play to practice this skill.

Players:
2 to 4

Materials:
2 counters
paper and pencil

Directions:
Take turns dropping the counters on the gameboard. Add the numbers in the boxes where the counters land. Compare your sums. The player with the greatest sum scores 1 point. The first player to reach 5 points wins the game.

15	36	42	14
30	23	12	38
24	9	47	22
49	18	5	50

Score Cards

GAME 1

Player	Score

GAME 2

Player	Score

GAME 3

Player	Score

AT·A·GLANCE p. 214

OBJECTIVE
Give family members an opportunity to share in their child's mathematics learning.

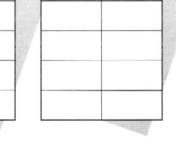

For Students Acquiring English (SAE)

Before assigning this Home Activity to SAE children, find out if someone at home will be able to work with them in English. If not, prepare them to complete the activity independently at home. Explain the directions of the activity and ask SAE children to restate them so you can check comprehension. Scan the page and preteach any difficult vocabulary or phrases that they may not know. If you feel that an SAE child will need extra help with the activity, you might assign that student a non-SAE partner and arrange a time for them to work on the activity in or out of school.

USING THE ACTIVITY

Have children look at the page. Explain that the page has a game that an adult in the family can help them complete. Read the page with the children, making sure that they understand what needs to be done. Tell children that they will do this page at home.

Picture Glossary

calendar

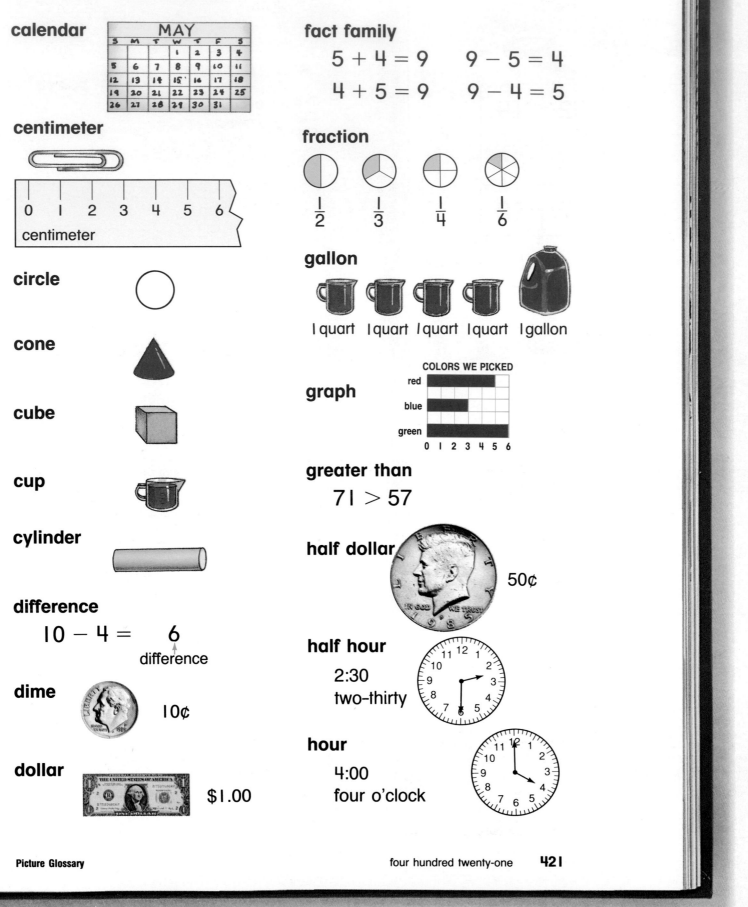

	MAY					
S	M	T	W	T	F	S
				1	2	3	4
5	6	7	8	9	10	11
12	13	14	15	16	17	18
19	20	21	22	23	24	25
26	27	28	29	30	31	

centimeter

0 1 2 3 4 5 6
centimeter

circle

cone

cube

cup

cylinder

difference

$$10 - 4 = 6$$
difference

dime

10¢

dollar

$1.00

fact family

$$5 + 4 = 9 \qquad 9 - 5 = 4$$
$$4 + 5 = 9 \qquad 9 - 4 = 5$$

fraction

$\frac{1}{2}$ $\frac{1}{3}$ $\frac{1}{4}$ $\frac{1}{6}$

gallon

1 quart 1 quart 1 quart 1 quart 1 gallon

graph

COLORS WE PICKED
red
blue
green
0 1 2 3 4 5 6

greater than

$$71 > 57$$

half dollar

50¢

half hour

2:30
two-thirty

hour

4:00
four o'clock

Macmillan/McGraw-Hill

inch

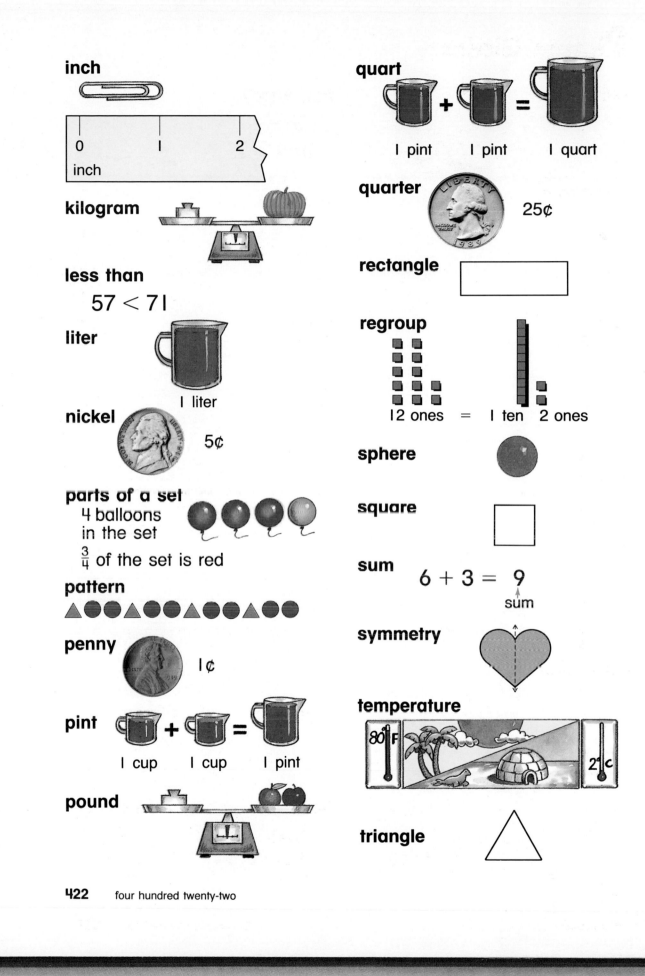

kilogram

less than

$$57 < 71$$

liter

I liter

nickel

5¢

parts of a set

4 balloons
in the set

$\frac{3}{4}$ of the set is red

pattern

penny

I¢

pint

I cup I cup I pint

pound

quart

I pint I pint I quart

quarter

25¢

rectangle

regroup

12 ones = I ten 2 ones

sphere

square

sum

$$6 + 3 = 9$$

sum

symmetry

temperature

triangle

SCOPE and SEQUENCE

This section contains the Scope and Sequence for Mathematics in Action. The following mathematical strands are covered:

NUMERATION AND NUMBER THEORY	K	1	2	3	4	5	6	7	8
Count	▨	▨	▨	▨	▨				
Skip-count	▨	▨	▨	▨	▨				
Ordinal numbers	▨	▨	▨	▨					
Place value									
whole numbers	▨	▨	▨	▨	▨	▨	▨	▨	▨
decimals				▨	▨	▨	▨	▨	▨
Compare and order	▨	▨	▨	▨	▨	▨	▨	▨	▨
whole numbers	▨	▨	▨	▨	▨	▨	▨	▨	▨
decimals					▨	▨	▨	▨	▨
fractions and mixed numbers				▨	▨	▨	▨	▨	▨
integers							▨	▨	▨
rational numbers							▨	▨	▨
Round									
whole numbers			▨	▨	▨	▨	▨	▨	▨
decimals				▨	▨	▨	▨	▨	▨
fractions and mixed numbers						▨	▨	▨	▨
Exponents							▨	▨	▨
Scientific notation								▨	▨
Squares and square roots							▨	▨	▨
Other numeration systems			▨	▨	▨	▨	▨	▨	▨
Common factors/greatest common factor (GCF)					▨	▨	▨	▨	▨
Common multiples/least common multiple (LCM)					▨	▨	▨	▨	▨
Divisibility rules				▨	▨	▨	▨	▨	▨
Even and odd numbers			▨	▨	▨	▨	▨	▨	▨
Prime and composite numbers					▨	▨	▨	▨	▨
Prime factorization					▨	▨	▨	▨	▨

DECIMALS	K	1	2	3	4	5	6	7	8
Concepts									
Place value				▨	▨	▨	▨	▨	▨
Equivalent decimals				▨	▨	▨	▨	▨	▨
Compare and order				▨	▨	▨	▨	▨	▨
Round				▨	▨	▨	▨	▨	▨
Convert decimals and fractions				▨	▨	▨	▨	▨	▨
Convert decimals and percents						▨	▨	▨	▨
Terminating and repeating							▨	▨	▨
Nonrepeating								▨	▨
Scientific notation								▨	▨
Rational numbers								▨	▨
Real numbers									▨
Computation									
Add decimals				▨	▨	▨	▨	▨	▨
Subtract decimals				▨	▨	▨	▨	▨	▨
Estimate sums and differences					▨	▨	▨	▨	▨
Multiply by whole number					▨	▨	▨	▨	▨
Multiply by decimal						▨	▨	▨	▨
Estimate products						▨	▨	▨	▨
Divide by whole number						▨	▨	▨	▨
Divide by decimal						▨	▨	▨	▨
Zeros in quotient and dividend						▨	▨	▨	▨
Estimate quotients						▨	▨	▨	▨
Mental math strategies						▨	▨	▨	▨
Compute with rational numbers								▨	▨
Solve equations								▨	▨

GRADE 2
NUMERATION AND NUMBER THEORY
Count
  understand numbers
    to 100: 52, 60, 87
    to 1,000: 276, 299
Skip-count
  by 10s, 56, 60, 89
  by 2s, 61-62, 64, 68, 84, 85, 86, 87, 301
  by 5s, 61, 84
  by 3s, 62, 68, 84, 85, 87, 213
  by 4s, 62, 68, 84, 85, 87, 123
Ordinal numbers
  to twentieth, 77-78, 83, 86, 87
Place value
  whole numbers
    expanded form, 88
      tens and ones, 53-54, 55-56, 57-58, 74, 87, 88,
        89, 98, 213, 278
      hundreds, tens, and ones, 277-278, 279-280,
        281-282, 286, 296, 297-299, 331, 361
Compare and order
  whole numbers, **using > and <**
    to 100: 59, 68, 73-74, 75-76, 83-84, 85-86, 87, 123,
      136, 149, 273, 277-278, 279-280, 286, 297, 298,
      331, 361
    to 1,000: 287-288, 289-290, 295, 296, 298, 299,
      306, 361, 419
Round
  whole numbers, 300
Other numeration systems
  Chinese numerals, 82
  Roman numerals, 48
Even and odd numbers, 63-64, 68, 85

Red type denotes introduction of skill.

WHOLE NUMBER COMPUTATION	K	1	2	3	4	5	6	7	8
Addition									
Meaning of addition	▪	▪	▪	▪	▪	▪	▪		
Properties		▪	▪	▪	▪	▪	▪		
Basic facts	▪	▪	▪	▪	▪	▪	▪		
Fact families		▪	▪	▪	▪	▪	▪		
Missing addends		▪	▪	▪	▪	▪	▪		
Add 2- and 3-digit numbers			▪	▪	▪	▪	▪		
Add greater numbers				▪	▪	▪	▪		
Add money amounts			▪	▪	▪	▪	▪		
Mental math strategies			▪	▪	▪	▪	▪		
Estimate sums			▪	▪	▪	▪	▪		
Solve equations					▪	▪	▪	▪	▪

GRADE 2
WHOLE NUMBER COMPUTATION
Addition

Meaning of addition, 9, 10
  count on to add, 23, 31-32, 46, 60, 97
  sentences, 11, 17, 19, 21, 23, 25, 28, 31, 33, 35, 39-40, 43, 46, 47, 49, 93, 95, 101

Properties
  order, zero, 15
  grouping, 31-32, 43, 44, 46, 47, 49

Basic facts
  to 5, 11, 45, 46, 47, 49
  to 6, 19-20, 32, 46, 47, 89
  to 7, 21-22, 28, 32, 44, 45, 46, 47
  to 8, 29-30, 32, 46, 47, 60, 183, 245, 301
  to 9, 33-34, 45, 46, 47, 49, 60, 105, 123
  to 10, 10, 35-36, 38, 43, 44, 46, 47, 60, 89, 102, 111, 123, 138, 149
  to 11, 93-94, 118, 119, 121, 138, 168, 194
  to 12, 95-96, 119, 121, 138
  to 13, 99-100, 119, 120, 121, 149, 168, 194
  to 14 and 15, 101-102, 118, 119, 120, 121, 168, 183, 224
  to 16, 17, and 18, 92, 107-108, 117, 118, 119, 121, 123, 194, 245, 273
  add with doubles, 30, 32, 89, 102, 111, 121, 123, 149, 168, 224
  add three numbers, 31-32, 43, 44, 46, 47, 49, 111, 117, 118, 120, 121, 123, 204, 207, 208, 210, 211, 213, 361, 419

Fact families, 13-14, 20, 22, 28, 30, 34, 36, 43, 44, 45, 94, 95, 99, 102, 106

Missing addends, 27, 98, 196, 204

Add 2- and 3-digit numbers
  2-digit numbers, 186, 191-192, 193-194, 195, 197-198, 200, 208, 209, 210, 211, 212, 213, 224, 234, 235-236, 239, 243, 245, 252, 301, 331, 338, 419
  3-digit numbers, 392, 395-396, 397-398, 402, 414, 415, 416, 417, 419

Add money amounts, 37, 112, 183, 203, 207, 210, 211, 213, 245, 418

Mental math strategies, 97, 396

Estimate sums, 36, 108, 201-202, 282, 406

Red type denotes introduction of skill.

WHOLE NUMBER COMPUTATION	K	1	2	3	4	5	6	7	8
Subtraction									
Meaning of subtraction	■	■	■						
Properties		■	■	■					
Basic facts	■	■	■						
Fact families		■	■	■					
Subtract 2- and 3-digit numbers		■	■	■	■	■	■		
Subtract greater numbers			■	■	■				
Subtract money amounts		■	■	■	■	■	■		
Mental math strategies			■	■	■	■	■		
Estimate differences			■	■	■	■	■		
Solve equations			■	■	■	■	■	■	■
Multiplication									
Meaning of multiplication			■	■					
Properties			■	■	■				
Basic facts			■	■	■				
Fact families			■	■	■				
Missing factors			■	■	■	■			
Multiply 3 factors				■	■	■	■		
Multiply powers of 10				■	■	■	■		
Multiply by 1-digit multiplier			■	■	■	■			
Multiply by 2-digit multiplier				■	■	■	■		
Multiply greater numbers					■	■	■	■	
Multiply money amounts				■	■	■	■	■	
Mental math strategies				■	■	■	■		
Estimate products				■	■	■	■		
Solve equations				■	■	■	■	■	■
Division									
Meaning of division			■	■					
Properties				■	■	■			
Basic facts				■	■	■	■		
Fact families				■	■	■			
Divide powers of 10					■	■	■		
Divide by 1-digit divisor				■	■	■	■		
Divide by 2-digit divisor					■	■	■	■	
Divide by 3-digit divisor						■	■	■	
Zeros in quotient					■	■	■		
Short division					■	■	■		
Divide money amounts					■	■	■	■	
Mental math strategies				■	■	■	■		
Estimate quotients				■	■	■	■		
Solve equations				■	■	■	■	■	■

GRADE 2
WHOLE NUMBER COMPUTATION

Subtraction
Meaning of subtraction, 9, 10
  count back to subtract, 24, 60
  sentences, 12, 18, 19, 21, 24, 26, 33, 35, 39-40, 43,
  46, 47, 49, 93, 95, 101
  number line, 231-232
Properties
  zero, 16
Basic facts
  to 5: 12, 32, 45, 46, 47, 49
  to 6: 19-20, 46, 47, 49, 102
  to 7: 21-22, 28, 32, 44, 45, 46, 47, 49
  to 8: 29-30, 32, 34, 46, 47, 102, 149
  to 9: 33-34, 45, 46, 47, 60, 89, 102, 105, 183, 194
  to 10: 10, 35-36, 38, 43, 44, 46, 47, 60, 89, 102
  to 11: 93-94, 96, 119, 121
  to 12: 95-96, 119, 121
  to 13: 99-100, 168, 194
  to 14 and 15: 101-102, 119, 121, 123, 128, 138, 149,
    168, 213
  to 16, 17, and 18: 92, 107-108, 117, 118, 119, 121, 138,
    168, 183, 194, 331
Fact families, 13-14, 20, 22, 28, 30, 34, 36, 43, 44, 45,
  94, 95, 99, 102, 106
Subtract 2- and 3-digit numbers
  2-digit numbers, 216, 221-222, 223-224, 225, 230,
    234, 235-236, 239, 240, 241-242, 243, 245, 273, 288,
    301, 331, 338, 361, 398, 419
  3-digit numbers, 405-406, 407-408, 413, 414, 415,
    416, 417
Subtract money amounts, 37, 112, 233, 239, 240, 242,
  243, 245
Mental math strategies, 98, 222, 406
Estimate differences, 406

Multiplication
Meaning of multiplication, 363-364
  sentences, 365-366
Properties
  order, zero, one, 369-370
Basic facts
  by 2 and 3: 365-366, 369-370, 372, 385, 386, 387
  by 4 and 5: 367-368, 369-370, 372, 384, 385, 386, 387
  by 0: 370

Multiply by 1-digit multiplier, 365-366, 367-368,
  369-370, 372, 379-380, 384, 385, 386, 387, 389

Division
Meaning of division, 364
  equal groups, 375-376, 377-378, 383, 384, 385,
    386, 387
  sentences, 388

Red type denotes introduction of skill.

FRACTIONS AND MIXED NUMBERS	K	1	2	3	4	5	6	7	8
Concepts									
Meaning of fractions	■	■	■	■	■	■	■	■	■
Equivalent fractions				■	■	■	■	■	■
Simplest form				■	■	■	■	■	■
Least common denominator (LCD)					■	■	■	■	■
Compare and order			■	■	■	■	■	■	■
Round					■	■	■	■	■
Convert improper fractions and mixed numbers				■	■	■	■	■	■
Find fraction of a number					■	■	■	■	■
Density property								■	■
Reciprocals							■	■	■
Computation									
Add fractions				■	■	■	■	■	■
like denominators				■	■	■	■	■	■
unlike denominators					■	■	■	■	■
Add mixed numbers					■	■	■	■	■
Estimate sums					■	■	■	■	■
Subtract fractions				■	■	■	■	■	■
like denominators				■	■	■	■	■	■
unlike denominators					■	■	■	■	■
Subtract mixed numbers					■	■	■	■	■
Estimate differences					■	■	■	■	■
Multiply fractions						■	■	■	■
Multiply mixed numbers						■	■	■	■
Estimate products						■	■	■	■
Divide fractions						■	■	■	■
Divide mixed numbers							■	■	■
Estimate quotients							■	■	■
Convert fractions and decimals					■	■	■	■	■
Convert fractions and percents						■	■	■	■
Solve equations								■	■

GRADE 2
FRACTIONS AND MIXED NUMBERS
Concepts

Meaning of fractions, 334, 337, 342

halves, 335-336, 343, 345, 356, 357, 358, 359, 376

fourths, 337-338, 343, 344, 345-346, 354, 356, 357, 358, 359, 376

thirds, 339-340, 344, 346, 354, 356, 357, 359, 376

sixths, 341-342, 344, 345-346, 355, 356, 358, 359, 361

parts of a set, 347-348, 355, 356, 358, 359

parts of a whole, 334, 335-336, 337-338, 339-340, 341-342

using half inches, 360

Red type denotes introduction of skill.

MEASUREMENT, TIME, MONEY	K	1	2	3	4	5	6	7	8
Measurement									
Estimate and measure length		■	■	■	■	■	■	■	
nonstandard units	■	■	■						
metric/customary units		■	■	■	■	■	■	■	■
Estimate and measure capacity		■	■	■	■	■	■	■	
metric/customary units		■	■	■	■	■	■	■	■
Estimate and measure weight (mass)		■	■	■	■	■	■	■	
metric/customary units		■	■	■	■	■	■	■	■
Convert units				■	■	■	■	■	■
Compute with denominate numbers					■	■	■	■	■
Temperature		■	■	■	■	■	■	■	■
Perimeter			■	■	■	■	■	■	■
Circumference						■	■	■	■
Area			■	■	■	■	■	■	■
Surface area							■	■	■
Volume			■	■	■	■	■	■	■
Precision								■	■
Indirect measurement								■	■
Time									
Read a calendar	■	■	■	■					
Estimate and tell time		■	■	■	■	■	■	■	■
Convert units				■	■	■	■	■	■
Compute with denominate numbers					■	■	■	■	■
Find elapsed time		■	■	■	■	■	■	■	■
Money									
Find values of coins and bills	■	■	■	■					
Make change		■	■	■	■	■	■	■	■
Compare and order		■	■	■	■	■	■	■	■
Round				■	■	■	■	■	■
Estimate and compute with money amounts		■	■	■	■	■	■	■	■
See Problem Solving—Consumer Math	■	■	■	■	■	■	■	■	■

GRADE 2
MEASUREMENT, TIME, MONEY

Measurement
Estimate and measure length
  nonstandard units, 152
  metric units, 153-154, 155-156, 164, 178, 179, 180,
    181, 213, 330
  customary units, 5, 152, 165-166, 167-168, 176, 177,
    178, 180, 181, 360
Estimate and measure capacity
  compare: holds more, less, 157
  metric units, 157-158, 164, 179, 181
  customary units, 169-170, 177, 180, 181, 382
Estimate and measure weight (mass)
  metric units, 159, 164, 179, 180, 181
  customary units, 171, 177, 180, 181
Temperature
  Celsius, 160, 164, 180, 181, 245
  Fahrenheit, 172, 177, 180, 181, 301
Perimeter, 315-316, 325, 326, 328, 329
Area, 317, 325, 328, 329
Volume, 318

Time
Read a calendar, 261-262, 266, 267, 270, 271
Estimate and tell time
  hour, 249-250, 254, 269, 271, 308
  half hour, 251-252, 254, 268, 269, 271, 301, 308
  quarter hour, 257-258, 270, 271, 361
  five minutes, 259-260, 267, 268, 269-270, 273, 308
  A.M. and P.M., 272
Find elapsed time, 253, 255-256, 260, 265, 285

Money
Find values of coins and bills
  penny, 7, 126, 127-128, 145, 146, 147, 148, 149, 156,
    183, 273
  nickel, 7, 126, 127-128, 145, 146, 147, 148, 149,
    156, 183
  dime, 7, 126, 127-128, 145, 146, 147, 148, 149, 156,
    183, 273
  quarter, 129-130, 134, 144, 145, 147, 148, 156, 183,
    273
  half dollar, 130
  dollars and cents, 135-136, 137-138, 143, 144,
    145-146, 147, 156, 183, 331
Make change, 148
Estimate and compute with money amounts
  add/subtract, 37, 112, 183, 203, 207, 210, 211, 213,
    233, 238, 239, 240, 242, 243, 245, 418
See Problem Solving—Consumer Math

Red type denotes introduction of skill.

GEOMETRY	K	1	2	3	4	5	6	7	8
Patterns	■	■	■	■	■	■	■	■	■
Points, lines, line segments, rays, angles			■	■	■	■	■	■	■
Classify angles				■	■	■	■	■	■
Measure and estimate angles					■	■	■	■	■
Identify plane figures	■	■	■	■	■	■	■	■	■
Identify space figures	■	■	■	■	■	■	■	■	■
Classify polygons				■	■	■	■	■	■
Classify triangles				■	■	■	■	■	■
Classify quadrilaterals				■	■	■	■	■	■
Similarity					■	■	■	■	■
Congruence		■	■	■	■	■	■	■	■
Symmetry	■	■	■	■	■	■	■	■	■
Circles				■	■	■	■	■	■
Use geometric formulas					■	■	■	■	■
Constructions						■	■	■	■
Tessellations				■	■	■	■	■	■
Translations, reflections, and rotations				■	■	■	■	■	■
Coordinate geometry					■	■	■	■	■
Pythagorean theorem						■	■	■	■
Special right triangles								■	■
Tangent, sine, cosine ratios									■

GRADE 2
GEOMETRY
Patterns, 3, 142, 313, 321-322
Identify plane figures
  circle, triangle, rectangle, square, 307-308, 309-310, 314, 326, 327, 329, 419
  open and closed figures, 310
Identify space figures
  cone, cylinder, sphere, rectangular prism, cube, 305-306, 314, 327, 329
Congruence, 320, 324, 325, 328
Symmetry, 319, 324, 325, 328, 329

Red type denotes introduction of skill.

PROBLEM SOLVING	K	1	2	3	4	5	6	7	8
Strategies and Skills									
Use the five-step process			■	■	■	■	■	■	■
Use/draw a picture/diagram	■	■	■	■	■	■	■	■	■
Find a pattern	■	■	■	■	■	■	■	■	■
Identify extra information		■	■	■	■	■	■		■
Find needed information		■	■	■	■	■	■	■	■
Make an organized list		■	■	■	■	■	■	■	■
Use/make a graph	■	■	■	■	■	■	■	■	■
Choose operation/write a number sentence		■	■	■	■	■	■		
Write and solve an equation					■	■	■	■	■
Use a physical model	■	■	■	■	■	■	■	■	■
Use/make a chart/table		■	■	■	■	■	■	■	■
Guess, test, and revise		■	■	■	■	■	■	■	■
Use estimation			■	■	■	■	■	■	■
Solve a simpler problem			■	■	■	■	■	■	■
Use number sense		■	■	■	■	■	■	■	■
Work backward			■	■	■	■	■	■	■
Solve two-step problems			■	■	■	■	■	■	■
Solve multistep problems				■	■	■	■	■	■
Check for a reasonable answer				■	■	■	■	■	■
Conduct an experiment or simulation					■	■	■	■	■
Interpret the quotient and remainder					■	■	■	■	■
Use a proportion						■	■	■	■
Use a formula						■	■	■	■
Use different strategies				■	■	■	■	■	■
Use more than one strategy					■	■	■	■	■
Strategies review	■	■	■	■	■	■	■	■	■
Thinking Mathematically									
Investigate patterns	■	■	■	■	■	■	■	■	■
Apply mathematics	■	■	■	■	■	■	■	■	■
Use number concepts	■	■	■	■	■	■	■	■	■
Visual reasoning	■	■	■	■	■	■	■	■	■
Measuring	■	■	■	■	■	■	■	■	■
Collect and interpret data	■	■	■	■	■	■	■	■	■
Logical reasoning	■	■	■	■	■	■	■	■	■
Experiment and predict	■	■	■	■	■	■	■	■	■
Consumer Math									
Interpret consumer information sources		■	■	■	■	■	■	■	■
Spend/buy		■	■	■	■	■	■	■	■
Save/invest					■	■	■	■	■
Percent applications						■	■	■	■
Misleading statistics						■	■	■	■
Decision making		■	■	■	■	■	■	■	■

GRADE 2
PROBLEM SOLVING
Strategies and Skills
Use the five-step process, 17-18

Use/draw a picture/diagram, 131-132, 134, 311-312, 345-346, 355, 358, 359

Find a pattern, 69-70, 83, 86, 87, 123, 280

Identify extra information, 227-228, 230, 242, 243

Make an organized list, 79-80, 283-284, 286, 298, 299

Use/make a graph, 6, 71, 72, 113-114, 117, 120, 121, 176, 182, 311-312, 314, 328, 329

Choose operation/write a number sentence, 25-26, 28, 39-40, 43, 46, 47, 49, 89, 103-104, 106, 116, 120, 121, 149, 173-174, 177, 180, 181, 235-236, 239, 242, 243, 245, 273, 301, 331, 361, 379-380, 383, 386, 387, 389, 398, 408, 419

Use a physical model, 321-322

Use/make a chart/table, 82, 176, 196, 197-198, 200, 206, 210, 211, 226, 253

Guess, test, and revise, 139-140, 373-374

Use estimation, 201-202, 231-232

Solve a simpler problem, 212

Use number sense, 65-66, 161-162, 263-264, 267, 270, 271, 409-410, 413, 416, 417

Work backward, 255-256

Solve two-step problems, 399-400, 402, 416, 417

Strategies review, 291-292, 351-352

Thinking Mathematically
Investigate patterns, 2, 3, 313, 371

Apply mathematics, 106, 220, 263

Use number concepts, 7, 27, 67, 343

Visual reasoning, 163, 199, 401

Measuring, 5

Collect and interpret data, 6

Logical reasoning, 4, 8, 285

Experiment and predict, 133

Consumer Math
Interpret consumer information sources, 41, 131-132, 139-140, 141, 293, 353, 373-374, 381

Spend/buy, 7, 37, 127-128, 129-130, 131-132, 135-136, 137-138, 139-140, 148, 183, 203, 216, 233, 234, 400, 418

Decision making
  planning a craft, 41
  planning a game, 81
  choosing a classroom pet, 115
  planning a collection, 141
  planning a garden, 175
  planning rides, 205
  choosing a prize, 237
  planning a class trip, 265
  planning a recycling drive, 293
  planning a bulletin board, 323
  planning a pizza order, 353
  planning a catalog order, 381
  planning tickets, 411

Red type denotes introduction of skill.

MATHEMATICAL REASONING	K	1	2	3	4	5	6	7	8
Thinking Mathematically	■	■	■	■	■	■	■	■	■
Decision making	■	■	■	■	■	■	■	■	■
Critical thinking			■	■	■	■	■	■	■

ESTIMATION	K	1	2	3	4	5	6	7	8
Strategies									
Round		■	■	■	■	■	■	■	■
Front-end				■	■	■	■	■	■
Compatible numbers				■	■	■	■	■	■
Clustering					■	■	■	■	■
Computation									
Whole numbers									
sums and differences		■	■	■	■	■	■	■	■
products and quotients				■	■	■	■	■	■
Decimals									
sums and differences				■	■	■	■	■	■
products and quotients					■	■	■	■	■
Fractions / mixed numbers									
sums and differences					■	■	■	■	■
products and quotients						■	■	■	■
Percents							■	■	■
Measurement									
Length, weight (mass), capacity	■	■	■	■	■	■	■	■	■
Time		■	■	■	■	■	■	■	■
Temperature		■	■	■	■	■	■	■	■
Perimeter, area, volume				■	■	■	■	■	■
Angle measure					■	■	■	■	■
Problem Solving									
Check for reasonableness			■	■	■	■	■	■	■
Over- and underestimates			■	■	■	■	■	■	■

MENTAL MATH	K	1	2	3	4	5	6	7	8
Count on or back	■	■	■	■		■	■	■	■
Use doubles		■	■	■	■		■	■	■
Make ten		■	■	■					
Skip-count		■	■	■	■	■	■	■	■
Work left to right						■	■	■	■
Break apart numbers					■	■	■	■	■
Use fact families		■	■	■	■	■	■	■	■
Use properties		■	■	■	■	■	■	■	■
Use patterns	■	■	■	■	■	■	■	■	■
Use compensation				■	■	■	■	■	■
Multiply and divide by powers of 10				■	■	■	■	■	■
Scale up or down						■	■	■	■
Solve equations							■	■	■
Find percent of a number							■	■	■
Find fraction of a number							■	■	■

GRADE 2
MATHEMATICAL REASONING
Thinking Mathematically, See Problem Solving
Decision making, See Problem Solving—Consumer Math

ESTIMATION
Strategies
Round, 282, 300, 406

Computation
Whole numbers
  sums and differences, 36, 108, 201-202, 282, 406

Measurement
Length, weight (mass), capacity, 153-154, 155-156,
  157-158, 159, 165-166, 167-168, 169-170, 171, 177, 178,
  179, 180, 181
Time, 248, 260, 267, 270, 271
Temperature, 160

MENTAL MATH
Count on or back, 23-24, 60, 85, 87, 96
Use doubles, 30
Make ten, 35-36, 97-98
Skip-count, 56, 60, 61-62, 64, 68, 84, 85, 86, 87, 89,
  123, 213, 301
Use fact families, 13-14, 20, 22, 28, 30, 34, 36, 43, 44,
  45, 94, 95, 99, 102, 106
Use properties, 15-16, 31-32, 43, 44, 46, 47, 49, 369-370
Use patterns, 15-16, 109-110

Red type denotes introduction of skill.

ALGEBRA	K	1	2	3	4	5	6	7	8
Expressions, Equations, Inequalities									
Patterns, relations, functions	▪	▪	▪	▪	▪	▪	▪	▪	▪
Inverse operations		▪	▪	▪	▪	▪	▪	▪	▪
Properties		▪	▪	▪	▪	▪	▪	▪	▪
Use order of operations					▪	▪	▪	▪	▪
Evaluate algebraic expressions							▪	▪	▪
Write/solve number sentences/equations	▪	▪	▪	▪	▪	▪	▪	▪	▪
Solve 2-step equations							▪	▪	▪
Solve equations in 2 variables								▪	▪
Graph equations									▪
Inequalities		▪	▪	▪	▪	▪	▪	▪	▪
Graph inequalities									▪
Positive/Negative Numbers									
Integers					▪	▪	▪	▪	▪
meaning of					▪	▪	▪	▪	▪
properties							▪	▪	▪
absolute value							▪	▪	▪
compare and order							▪	▪	▪
add and subtract							▪	▪	▪
multiply and divide							▪	▪	▪
graph							▪	▪	▪
Rational numbers								▪	▪
meaning of								▪	▪
properties								▪	▪
compare and order								▪	▪
compute with								▪	▪
Irrational numbers									▪
Real numbers									▪
Negative exponents								▪	▪
Law of exponents								▪	▪

GRADE 2
ALGEBRA

Expressions, Equations, Inequalities

Patterns, relations, functions, See Patterns, Relations, Functions

Inverse operations, 13-14, 27

Properties, 15, 16, 31-32, 43, 44, 46, 47, 49, 109-110, 369-370

Write/solve number sentences/equations, 14, 17-18, 25-26, 27, 98, 101-102, 107-108, 122, 196, 226, 388-389

Inequalities

use >, < symbols, 75-76, 83, 84, 86, 87, 136, 149, 290, 295, 298, 299, 306

PROBABILITY AND STATISTICS	K	1	2	3	4	5	6	7	8
Probability									
Meaning			■	■	■	■	■	■	■
Conduct an experiment/simulation			■	■	■	■	■	■	■
Simple events				■	■	■	■	■	■
Mutually exclusive events							■	■	■
Independent events					■	■	■	■	■
Dependent events							■	■	■
Theoretical/experimental probability					■	■	■	■	■
List outcomes				■	■	■	■	■	■
Tree diagrams					■	■	■	■	■
Counting principle					■	■	■	■	■
Predict outcomes			■	■	■	■	■	■	■
Sample space					■	■	■	■	■
Random numbers							■	■	■
Permutations							■	■	■
Combinations							■	■	■
Statistics									
Collect and organize data	■	■	■	■	■	■	■	■	■
Conduct a survey		■	■	■	■	■	■	■	■
Conduct an experiment or simulation			■	■	■	■	■	■	■
Tally		■	■	■	■	■	■	■	■
Make a table/graph	■	■	■	■	■	■	■	■	■
Interpret data	■	■	■	■	■	■	■	■	■
Find mean, median, mode, and range				■	■	■	■	■	■
Effects of change on data					■	■	■	■	■
Misleading statistics/deceptive graphs					■	■	■	■	■
Use statistical sampling							■	■	■

GRADE 2
PROBABILITY AND STATISTICS

Probability
Meaning, 349-350
Conduct an experiment/simulation, 349-350

Statistics
Collect and organize data
   from a picture, 131-132, 134
   make a list, 79-80, 283-284, 286, 298-299
   from a table, 82, 176, 182, 197-198, 200, 206, 210, 211, 253
Conduct a survey, 182
Conduct an experiment or simulation, 349-350
Tally, 71, 182
Make a table/graph, 182, 198, 206, See Graphing
Interpret data
   from a map, 42, 330
   from a graph, See Graphing

Red type denotes introduction of skill.

GRAPHING	K	1	2	3	4	5	6	7	8
Pictographs	■	■	■	■	■	■	■	■	■
Bar graphs	■	■	■	■	■	■	■	■	■
Line graphs				■	■	■	■	■	■
Circle graphs						■	■	■	■
Frequency tables and histograms					■	■	■	■	■
Scattergrams							■	■	■
Line plots					■	■	■	■	■
Stem-and-leaf plots						■	■	■	■
Box-and-whisker plots							■	■	■
Deceptive graphs							■	■	■
Coordinate graphing		■	■	■	■	■	■	■	■

PATTERNS, RELATIONS, FUNCTIONS	K	1	2	3	4	5	6	7	8
Patterns									
Number patterns	■	■	■	■	■	■	■	■	■
Sequences	■	■	■	■	■				
Geometric/spatial patterns	■	■	■	■	■	■	■	■	■
Relations									
Graphing and ordered pairs		■	■	■	■	■	■	■	■
Functions									
Meaning							■	■	■
Function tables							■	■	■
Graph functions							■	■	■

RATIO, PROPORTION, PERCENT	K	1	2	3	4	5	6	7	8
Ratio									
Meaning					■	■	■	■	■
Equal ratios						■	■	■	■
Rate						■	■	■	■
Tangent, sine, cosine ratios									■
Proportion									
Meaning							■	■	■
Solve proportions							■	■	■
Scale drawings						■	■	■	■
Similar figures							■	■	■
Scale up or down							■	■	■
Indirect measurement							■	■	■
Percent									
Meaning						■	■	■	■
Convert fractions and percents						■	■	■	■
Convert decimals and percents						■	■	■	■
Percents greater than 100% and less than 1%							■	■	■
Percent of a number							■	■	■
Percent one number is of another							■	■	■
Find number when percent of it is known								■	■
Estimate percents							■	■	■
Mental math							■	■	■
Percent increase and decrease								■	■
Percent applications							■	■	■
circle graphs							■	■	■
simple/compound interest								■	■
discount/sale price								■	■
commission									■

GRADE 2
GRAPHING
Pictographs, 72
Bar graphs, 6, 71, 113-114, 117, 120, 121, 176, 182
Coordinate graphing, 311-312, 314, 328, 329

PATTERNS, RELATIONS, FUNCTIONS
Patterns
Number patterns, 56, 61-62, 68, 84, 85, 87, 123, 213
   addition/subtraction, 15-16, 109-110, 244
   multiplication, 369-370
Geometric/spatial patterns, 3, 313, 321-322

Relations
Graphing and ordered pairs, 311-312

Red type denotes introduction of skill.

TECHNOLOGY	K	1	2	3	4	5	6	7	8
Calculator									
Patterns									
Computation									
Choose a calculation method									
Order of operations									
Fractions and decimals									
Special keys									
Computer									
Logo									
Spreadsheets									
Patterns									
Simulations									
Functions									
Graphs									

GRADE 2
TECHNOLOGY

Calculator
Patterns, 294, 368
Computation
   addition/subtraction, 38, 62, 196, 204, 226,
      373-374, 412
   multiplication, 368
Choose a calculation method, 38, 103, 131, 139, 173,
   196, 226, 228, 235, 379, 380
Special keys
   C , 294

Computer
Logo, 116, 324
Spreadsheets, 238
Patterns, 142
Graphs, 176

Red type denotes introduction of skill.

T28

TEACHER'S REFERENCE SECTION

This section contains the following:

BIBLIOGRAPHY

Books for Teachers

Ashlock Robert B., et al. *Guide Each Child's Learning of Mathematics.* Columbus, OH: Merrill, 1983.

Beaumont, Vern, et al. *How to Teach Perimeter, Area, and Volume.* Reston, VA: National Council of Teachers of Mathematics, 1986.

Beyer, Barry K. *Practical Strategies for the Teaching of Thinking.* Boston: Allyn and Bacon, 1987.

Billstein, R., et al. *A Problem Solving Approach to Mathematics for Elementary School Teachers.* Menlo Park, CA: Benjamin Cummings, 1987.

Brisby, Linda-Sue, et al. *Measurement: A "Hands On" Approach to Teaching.* Solvang, CA: Hands On, Inc., 1968.

———. *Patterns and Functions: A "Hands On" Approach to Teaching.* Solvang, CA: Hands On, Inc., 1990.

Copeland, Richard W. *How Children Learn Mathematics: Teaching Implications of Piaget's Research.* New York: Macmillan, 1984.

Farrell, Margaret A., ed. *Imaginative Ideas for the Teacher of Mathematics.* Reston, VA: National Council of Teachers of Mathematics, 1988.

Feinberg, Miriam M. *Solving Word Problems in the Primary Grades: Addition and Subtraction.* Reston, VA: National Council of Teachers of Mathematics, 1988.

Forseth, Sonia D. *Creative Math-Art Activities for the Primary Grades.* Englewood Cliffs, NJ: Prentice-Hall, 1984.

Graph Paper Masters. Palo Alto, CA: Dale Seymour Publications, 1989.

Grossnickle, Foster E., et al. *Discovering Meanings in Elementary School Mathematics,* 7th ed. New York: Holt, Rinehart and Winston, 1983.

O'Daffer, Phares G., ed. *Problem Solving: Tips for Teachers.* Reston, VA: National Council of Teachers of Mathematics, 1988.

Reys, Robert, Marilyn N. Suydam, and Mary N. Lindquist. *Helping Children Learn Mathematics.* Englewood Cliffs, NJ: Prentice-Hall, 1984.

Skolnick, Joan, Carol Langbort, and Lucille Day. *How To Encourage Girls In Math and Science: Strategies for Parents and Educators.* Englewood Cliffs, NJ: Prentice-Hall, 1982.

Slavin, R., et al., eds. *Learning to Cooperate, Cooperating to Learn.* New York: Plenum Press, 1985.

Worth, Joan, ed. *Preparing Elementary School Mathematics Teachers: Readings from the Arithmetic Teacher.* Reston, VA: National Council of Teachers of Mathematics, 1988.

Grade 2

Books for Students

Chapter 1 — Adding and Subtracting Facts to 10

Grossman, Virginia. *Ten Little Rabbits.* San Francisco: Chronicle, 1991. ISBN 0-87701-552-X. **(Average)**

Peek, Merle. *Roll Over: A Counting Song.* New York: Clarion Books, 1981. ISBN 0-395-29438-X. **(Easy)**

Wolkstein, Diane. *The Banza.* New York: Dial Books for Young Readers, 1981. ISBN 0-8037-0428-3. **(Average)**

Chapter 2 — Understanding Numbers to 100

Cutler, Daniel Solomon. *One Hundred Monkeys.* New York: Simon & Schuster, 1991. ISBN 0-671-73564-0. **(Average)**

MacCarthy, Patricia. *Ocean Parade: A Counting Book.* New York: Dial Books for Young Readers, 1990. ISBN 0-8037-0780-0. **(Easy)**

Moore, Margaret. *Fifty Red Nightcaps.* San Francisco: Chronicle Books, 1988. ISBN 0-87701-520-1. **(Average)**

Mora, Pat. *A Birthday Basket for Tia.* New York: Macmillan Publishing Co., 1992. ISBN 0-02-767400-2. **(Average)**

Sloat, Teri. *From One to One Hundred.* New York: Dutton Children's Books, 1991. ISBN 0-525-44764-4. **(Challenging)**

Chapter 3 — Adding and Subtracting Facts to 18

Carle, Eric. *The Rooster Who Set Out to See the World.* New York: Franklin Watts, Inc., 1972. ISBN 0-88708-042. **(Average)**

Gackenbach, Dick. *A Bag Full of Pups.* New York: Clarion, 1981. ISBN 0-395-30081-9. **(Average)**

Merriam, Eve. *12 Ways to Get to 11.* New York: Simon and Schuster Books for Young Readers, 1992. ISBN 0-671-75544-7. **(Challenging)**

Pittman, Helena Clare. *Miss Hindy's Cats.* Minneapolis: Carolrhoda Books, Inc., 1990. ISBN 0-87614-368-0. **(Average)**

Chapter 4 — Money

Caple, Kathy. *The Purse.* Boston: Houghton Mifflin Company, 1986. ISBN 0-395-4182-6. **(Average)**

Hoban, Russell. *A Birthday for Frances.* New York: Harper & Row, Publishers, 1968. ISBN 0-06-022338-3. **(Challenging)**

Hoban, Tana. *26 Letters and 99 Cents.* New York: Scholastic, Inc., 1987. ISBN 0-688-06361-6. **(Average)**

Schwartz, David. *If You Made a Million.* New York: Lothrop, Lee & Shepard, 1989. 0-688-07017-5. **(Challenging)**

Viorst, Judith. *Alexander, Who Used to be Rich Last Sunday.* New York: Atheneum, 1978. ISBN 0-689-30602-4. **(Average)**

Zaslavsky, Claudia. *Count on Your Fingers African Style.* New York: Thomas Y. Crowell, 1987. ISBN 0-690-03864-X. **(Challenging)**

Chapter 5 — Measurement

Briggs, Raymond. *Jim and the Beanstalk.* New York: Coward-McCann, Inc., 1970. ISBN 0-698-20641-X. **(Challenging)**

Dahl, Roald. *Esio Trot.* New York: Viking, 1990. ISBN 0-670-83451-3. **(Challenging)**

Gibbons, Gail. *Weather Forecasting.* New York: Macmillan Publishing Company, 1987. ISBN 0-02-737-250-2. **(Challenging)**

Lionni, Leo. *Inch by Inch.* New York: Astor-Honor, Inc., 1960. ISBN 0-8392-3010-9. **(Easy)**

Morimoto, Junko. *The Inch Boy.* New York: Viking Kestrel, 1986. ISBN 0-14-050677-2. **(Challenging)**

Myller, Rolf. *How Big is a Foot?* New York: Atheneum, 1969. **(Challenging)**

Pluckrose, Henry. *Length.* New York: Franklin Watts, 1988. ISBN 0-531-10618-7. **(Average)**

Ziefert, Harriet. *A New Coat for Anna.* New York: Alfred A. Knopf, Inc., 1986. ISBN 0-394-97426-3. **(Average)**

Chapter 6 — Adding 2-Digit Numbers

Hoban, Tana. *26 Letters and 99 Cents.* New York: Scholastic, Inc., 1987. ISBN 0-688-06361-6. **(Average)**

Chapter 7 — Subtracting 2-Digit Numbers

Caple, Kathy. *The Purse.* Boston: Houghton Mifflin Company, 1986. ISBN 0-395-4182-6. **(Average)**

Hoban, Lillian. *Arthur's Funny Money.* New York: Harper & Row, Publishers, 1981. ISBN 0-06-022343-X. **(Average)**

Viorst, Judith. *Alexander, Who Used to be Rich Last Sunday.* New York: Atheneum, 1978. **(Average)**

Chapter 8 — Time

Baden, Robert, reteller. *And Sunday Makes Seven/Y Domingo Siete.* IL: Albert Whitman & Co., 1990. ISBN 0-8075-0356-8. **(Average)**

Gould, Deborah. *Brendan's Best-Timed Birthday.* New York: Bradbury, 1988. ISBN 02-737390-8. **(Challenging)**

Singer, Marilyn. *Nine O'Clock Lullaby.* New York: HarperCollins, 1991. ISBN 0-06-025648-6. **(Average)**

Chapter 9 — Understanding Numbers to 1,000

Anderson, Lonzo, and Adrienne Adams. *Two Hundred Rabbits.* New York: Viking Penguin, 1968. **(Average)**

Birch, David. *The King's Chessboard.* New York: Dial Books, 1988. ISBN 0-8037-0367-8. **(Challenging)**

Gag, Wanda. *Millions of Cats.* New York: Coward-McCann, 1928. ISBN 0-698-20637-1. **(Easy)**

Sharmat, Marjorie Weinman. *The 329th Friend.* New York: Four Winds Press, 1992. ISBN 0-02-782259-1. **(Average)**

Chapter 10 — Geometry

Feldman, Judy. *Shapes in Nature.* Chicago: Children's Press, 1991. ISBN 0-516-05102-4. **(Easy)**

Fisher, Leonard Everett. *Look Around: A Book About Shapes.* New York: Viking Kestrel, 1987. ISBN 0-670-80869-5. **(Easy)**

Grifalooni, Ann. *The Village of Round and Square Houses.* Boston: Little, Brown, 1986. ISBN 0-316-32862-6. **(Average)**

Tompert, Ann. *Grandfather Tang's Story.* New York: Crown Publishers, Inc., 1990. ISBN 0-517-57487-X. Gr. 2, Ch. (10) **(Challenging)**

Tucker, Sian. *The Shapes Game.* New York: Henry Holt and Company, 1989. ISBN 0-8050-1280-X **(Average)**

Chapter 11 — Fractions

Anno, Mitsumasa. *Anno's Math Game III.* New York: Philomel Books, 1989. ISBN 0-399-21615-4. **(Challenging)**

Pomerantz, Charlotte. *The Half-Birthday Party.* Boston: Houghton Mifflin, 1984. ISBN 0-89919-273-4 **(Easy)**

Watson, Clyde. *Tom Fox and the Apple Pie.* New York: Crowell, 1972. **(Challenging)**

Chapter 12 — Explore Multiplication and Division Facts

Anno, Mitsumasa, and Masaichiro Anno. *Anno's Mysterious Multiplying Jar.* New York: Putnam/Philomel, 1983. ISBN 0-399-21615-4. **(Challenging)**

Blia, Xiong. *Nine-in-One-Grrr!: A Folktale from the Hmong People of Laos.* Adapted by Cathy Spagnoli. San Francisco: Children's Book Press, 1989. ISBN 0-89239-048-4 **(Challenging)**

Giganti, Paul, Jr. *Each Orange Had Eight Slices.* New York: Greenwillow Books. 1992. ISBN 0-688-10429-0. **(Challenging)**

Hulme, Joy. *Sea Squares.* **(Challenging)**

Chapter 13 — Explore Adding and Subtracting 3-Digit Numbers

Birch, David. *The King's Chessboard.* New York: Dial Books, 1988. ISBN 0-8037-0367-8. **(Challenging)**

Pittman, Helena Clare. *A Grain of Rice.* New York: Hastings House, 1986. ISBN 0-8038-2728-8. **(Challenging)**

Sharmat, Marjorie Weinman. *The 329th Friend.* New York: Four Winds Press, 1992. ISBN 0-02-782259-1. **(Average)**

HOLISTIC SCORING SCALE

Below is given a general scoring scheme for open-ended activities. The method is called "holistic" because it focuses on all the work that the student does, rather than solely on the correctness of the final solution.

One recommended way to begin holistic scoring is to divide your class's work into three groups:

🖊 **Superior Work** (**6** or **5**)

🖊 **Capable Work** (**4** or **3**)

🖊 **Insufficient Work** (**2, 1,** or **0**)

Then each of the three groups can be redivided into subgroups using the scoring scheme described below.

Seven-Point Assessment Scheme

SCORE	EXPLANATION
Superior ⎰ **6**	**Exemplary Response** - student gives a complete response with a clear, coherent, and unambiguous explanation.
5	**Effective Response** - student gives a fairly complete response with clear explanations.
Capable ⎰ **4**	**Satisfactory** - student gives a fairly complete response but the explanation may be somewhat unclear or incomplete.
3	**Nearly Satisfactory** - student begins the activity appropriately and shows progress, but fails to complete it or omits significant parts of it. Explanation fails to show full understanding of mathematical ideas involved.
Insufficient ⎰ **2**	**Begins, But Fails to Carry Through** - student cannot go beyond the early stages of the activity. Explanation is not understandable. Student shows no understanding of problem situation.
1	**Unable to Begin Effectively** - student response does not correspond to the activity. Response indicates complete lack of understanding of mathematical ideas involved.
0	**No Attempt**

Page numbers in italic type indicate references in the Teacher's Edition.

INDEX

INDEX

Celsius, 160, *160–160C*
centimeter, 153–156, 164, 178–180, *153–156B*
decimeter, 155–156, *150J, 155–156B*
gram, *150M*
kilogram, 159, *150M, 159–159C*
liter, 157–158, 164, *157–158B*
mass, 159, *150L, 150M, 159–159C*
meter, 155–156, *150J, 155–156B*
standard units of, *150B*

Mental Math
in Author Notes, *90B*
counting on and back, 23–24, *8O, 23–24B*
in MAC Activities, *16A, 30A, 32A, 34A, 36A, 76A, 98A, 110A, 111B, 140A, 194A, 232A, 378A*
in Manipulatives Plus, *8O, 90K*
in Pupil's Edition, 14, 30, 96, 192, 222, 396. *See also* same pages in Teacher's Edition
strategies, 97–98, *97–98B*

Meter (m), 155–156, *150J, 155–156B*
Minute hand, 249–250, *246I, 249–250B*
Minutes, 249–250, *246M, 249–250B. See also* Five minutes
Mixed Review, 20, 32, 60, 74, 98, 136, 138, 156, 168, 194, 224, 252, 278, 288, 306, 308, 338, 348, 376, 398, 408
Money
adding, 37, 112, 203, 207, 418, *37–37C, 112–112C, 184O, 203–203C, 418*
change, making, 148, *148*
comparing, 137–138, *124L, 137–138B*
concept of, 125–126, *125–126*
counting, *124B, 124J*
counting with, 127–130, 144–146, *127–130B*
dime, 7, 127–128, *7, 127–128B*
dollars and cents, 135–138, 143–146, *124K, 135–138B*
nickel, 7, 127–128, *7, 127–128B*
penny, 7, 127–128, *7, 127–128B*
problems involving, 7, 131–133, 139–140, *7, 131–133A, 139–140B*
quarter, 129–130, 134, *129–130B*
regrouping with, *124I, 214L*
subtracting, 37, 112, 239, *37–37C, 112–112C, 214O*

Multiplication
concept of, 363–364, *362B, 362I, 363–364*
4 and 5, 367–368, 372, 385, *367–368B*
joining sets, 365–368, *365–368B*
order property of, 369–370, *369–370B*
patterns, 369–370, 372, 384, *362J, 369–370B*
properties of, *362K*
sentence, 365-366, *362B, 365–366B*
sign, 365-366, *365-366B*
2 and 3, 365-366, 385, *365-366B*
Music, math and
in MAC Activities, *12B, 54A, 250A*

N

National Council of Teachers of Mathematics (NCTM)
Standards, *8C–8D, 50C–50D, 90C–90D, 124C–124D, 150C–150D, 184C–184D, 214C–214D, 246C–246D, 274C–274D, 302C–302D, 332C–332D, 362C–362D, 390C–390D*
Nickel, 7, 125–128, *7, 125–128B*
Number line, *8N, 74, 246K*
Numbers. *See* Fractions; Whole numbers
Number sense. *See also* Thinking Mathematically

---

in MAC Activities, *59B, 60B, 64A, 72A, 98A, 100A, 108A, 158A, 196B, 225B, 234B, 366A, 368A, 406A, 408A*
in problem solving, 65–66, 161–162, 263–264, 267, 270, 409–410, 413, 416, *65–66B, 161–162B, 263–264B, 409–410B*
Number sentence, 122, 388, *122, 388. See also* Addition; Subtraction

O

Odd numbers, 63–64, *63–64B*
One less, 59, *59–59C*
One more, 59, *59–59C*
Ones
concept of place, *50K*
counting by, 60, *60–60C*
to 100, 53–54, 57–58, *53–54B, 57–58B*
to 1,000, 277–282, *277–282B*
regrouping
concept of, 185–186, 215–216, *184B, 185–186, 214B, 215–216*
for subtraction, 407–408, *407–408B*
as tens, 187–194, 397–398, *184K, 184L, 187–194B, 397–398B*
tens as, 217–224, *214I, 214J, 214K, 214L, 217–224B*
Ongoing Assessment, *14, 36, 56, 62, 74, 100, 108, 130, 136, 159A, 170, 190, 194, 220, 224, 250, 262, 280, 290, 306, 317A, 320A, 340, 348, 370, 378, 396, 404*
Order of whole numbers, 59, 287–288, *5B, 59–59C, 274B, 274K, 287–288B*
Order property
of addition, 15–16, *8L, 8M, 15–16B*
of multiplication, 369–370, *369–370B*
Ordinal numbers, 77–78, 83, 86, *77–78B*
Ounce, *150P*

P

Part-part-whole model, 11, 19–20, *8B, 8I, 8J, 11–11A, 19–20B*
Patterns
addition, 15–16, 109–110, 244, *15–16B, 109–110B, 244*
counting, *59B*
finding, 69–70, 83, 85–86, 142, *69–70B*
multiplication, 369–370, *369–370B*
ordered pairs, 106, 108–110, 118, 371, *108–110B, 371*
shape, 142, 313, 321, *308A*
skip counting, 61–62, *61–62B*
subtraction, 15–16, 109–110, 244, *15–16B, 109–110B, 244*
using a calculator, 294, 368, *294–294A, 368*
using a computer, 142, *142–142A*
using patterns for predictions, 349–350, 370, 371, *349–350, 370, 371–371A*
using a physical model, 321–322, *321–322B*
Penny, 7, 127–128, *7, 127–128B*
Performance Assessment, 47, 87, 121, 147, 181, 211, 243, 271, 299, 329, 359, 387, 417
Perimeter, 315–316, *302B, 302M, 315–316B*
Physical education, math and
in MAC Activities, *58A, 262A, 282A, 342A*
Pint, 169–170, *169–170B*
Place value, 281–282, *50B, 50L, 274B, 274J, 281–282B*
Planning Guide, *8C, 50C, 90C, 124C, 150C, 184C, 214C, 246C, 274C, 302C, 332C, 362C, 390C*
Pound, 171, *150P, 171–171C*

Practice
Extra, 28, 43, 68, 83, 106, 117, 134, 143, 164, 177, 200, 207, 230, 239, 254, 267, 286, 295, 314, 325, 344, 355, 372, 383, 402, 413. *See also* same pages in Teacher's Edition
Plus, 44, 84, 118, 144, 178, 208, 240, 268, 296, 326, 356, 384, 414. *See also* same pages in Teacher's Edition
Prism, 305–306, *302B, 302I, 305–306B*
Probability, 349–350, *349–350*
Problem formulation, 104, 114, 132, 198, 322
Problem solving
skills
bar graph, using data from, 113–114, 117, *113–114B*
extra information, identifying, 227–228, 230, 242, *227–228B*
five-step plan, using, 17–18, *17–18B*
picture, using, 311–312, 314, 328, *311–312B*
picture, using data from, 131–132, *131–132B*
strategies review, 291–292, 351–352, *291–292B, 351–352B*
table, using data from, 197–198, *197–198B*
strategies
acting it out, *90I*
addition or subtraction sentence, 25–26, 28, 46, *25–26B*
estimation, using, 201–202, 231–232, *201–202B, 231–232B*
generating and extending problems, 104, 114, 132, 198, 322
geometry, 311–312, 321–322, *311–312B, 321–322B*
guess and test, 139–140, 373–374, *139–140B, 373–374B*
lists, making, 79–80, 283–284, 286, *79–80B, 283–284B*
measurement, 161, 162, *161–162B*
number sense, using, 65–66, 161–162, 263–264, 267, 270, 409–410, 413, 416, *65–66B, 161–162B, 263–264B, 409–410B*
operation, choosing, 39–40, 43, 103–104, 106, 173–174, 177, 180, 235–236, 239, 379–380, 383, 386, *39–40B, 103–104B, 173–174B, 235–236B, 379–380B*
patterns, finding, 69–70, 83, 85–86, *69–70B*
physical model, using, 321–322, *321–322B*
picture, drawing, 345–346, 355, 358, *345–346B*
selecting appropriate materials and methods, 38, 103–104, 131, 139–140, 173, 228, 235, 379–380, 412, *38A*
simpler problem, using, 212, *212*
two-step problem, solving, 399–400, 402, 416, *399–400*
working backward, 255–256, *255–256B*
Product, 367–368, *367–368B*
Programming, computer, *220A, 398A*
Projects
in Decision Making lessons, *41A, 81A, 115A, 141A, 175A, 205A, 237A, 265A, 293A, 323A, 353A, 381A, 411A*

Q

Quart, 169–170, *169–170B*
Quarter, 129–130, *129–130B*
Quarter hour, 257–258, *257–258B*

R

Read Aloud

INDEX

CONSULTANTS

MULTICULTURAL AND EDUCATIONAL CONSULTANTS

Rim An

Marcia Ascher

Elsie Babcock

Vicki Chan

Dr. Alejandro Gallard

Zelda Gold

Jerilyn Grignon

Earlene Hall

Susan Lair

Dr. Barbara Merino

Carol Mitchell

James R. Murphy

Gail Lowe Parrino

Yolanda Rodriguez

Claudia Zaslavsky

ASSESSMENT CONSULTANT

Michael Priestley

COOPERATIVE LEARNING CONSULTANT

Liana Nan Graves

ACKNOWLEDGMENTS

The publisher gratefully acknowledges permission to reprint the following copyrighted material:

ARITHMETIC IN VERSE AND RHYME selected by Allan D. Jacobs and Leland B. Jacobs. Drawings by Kelly Oechsli. Copyright © 1971 by Allan D. Jacobs and Leland B. Jacobs. Cover art used by permission of Kelly Oechsli.

THE BANZA by Diane Wolkstein, pictures by Marc Brown. Text, copyright © 1981 by Diane Wolkstein. Pictures, copyright © 1981 by Marc Brown. Reprinted by permission of the publisher, Dial Books for Young Readers.

CLOCKS AND MORE CLOCKS by Pat Hutchins. Reprinted with permission of Macmillan Publishing Company. Copyright © 1970 by Pat Hutchins.

THE DOORBELL RANG by Pat Hutchins. Text copyright © 1986 by Pat Hutchins. By permission of Greenwillow Books (A Division of William Morrow & Co.).

"Homework Machine" from A LIGHT IN THE ATTIC by Shel Silverstein. Copyright © 1981 by Evil Eye Music, Inc. Reprinted by permission of HarperCollins Publishers, Inc.

HOW BIG IS A FOOT? written and illustrated by Rolf Myller. Reprinted with permission of Atheneum Publishers, an imprint of Macmillan Publishing Company. Copyright © 1962 Rolf Myller.

HOW MANY WAYS CAN YOU CUT A PIE? by Jane Belk Moncure. © The Child's World, Inc., Elgin, IL, and used by permission.

NINETY-NINE POCKETS by Jean Myrick. Copyright © 1966 by Jean Myrick. Used by permission of Lantern Press, Inc.

PENELOPE GETS WHEELS by Esther Allen Peterson. Copyright © 1981 by Crown Publishers, Inc. Reprinted by permission of the publishers.

THE RANDOM HOUSE BOOK OF POETRY FOR CHILDREN selected by Jack Prelutsky and illustrated by Arnold Lobel. Copyright © 1983 by Random House, Inc. Cover art used by permission of the publisher.

THE STORY SNAIL by Anne Rockwell. Reprinted with permission of Macmillan Publishing Company. Copyright © 1974 by Anne Rockwell.

"Surprises" by Jean Conder Soule. Used by permission of the author.

TOO MANY BOOKS by Caroline Feller Bauer. Copyright © 1986. Reprinted by permission of Viking Penguin Inc.

TWO HUNDRED RABBITS by Lonzo Anderson and Adrienne Adams. Copyright © 1968. Reprinted by permission of Viking Penguin Inc.

"Using Subtraction" by Lee Blair from ARITHMETIC IN VERSE AND RHYME selected by Allan and Leland Jacobs. Copyright © 1971. Reprinted by permission of Leland B. Jacobs.

COVER DESIGN Designframe Inc. **COVER PHOTOGRAPHY** Pete McArthur

ILLUSTRATION Elizabeth Allen; 11, 12, 233, 234 • Istvan Banyai; 142, 176, 238, 294, 324, 412 • Nina Barbaresi; 87, 101, 147, 154, 181, 329, 387, 399, 400, 407, 408, 409 • Bill Basso; 276, 397, 398 • Christine Beauregard; stickers 2A-D; 19, 20, 46, 96, 230, 231, 232, 239, 254, 257, 258, 266, 267, 286, 291, 292, 373, 374, 385, 386 • Shirley Beckes; 37, 58, 59, 60, 68, 99, 100, 139, 140, 141, 201, 202, 384 • Phillipe Beha; stickers 3B-C; 3, 17, 18, 173, 174, 199 • Patti Boyd; 6 • Stephanie Britt; 23, 24 • Maxi Chambliss; stickers 1A-B; 2, 22, 45, 50, 61, 76, 85, 87, 90, 102, 112, 119, 121, 124, 127, 145, 150, 153, 154, 156, 179, 181, 184, 191, 204, 208, 209, 214, 220, 221, 241, 246, 252, 269, 271, 274, 297, 299, 302, 305, 327, 329, 332, 342, 357, 359, 362, 367, 377, 384, 385, 387, 390, 396, 414, 415, 418 • Lydia Chang; 82 • Luisa D'Augusta; 47 • Fred Daurino; 401 • Jim Delgan; 337, 350 • Suzanne DeMarco; 116, 330 • Susan Dodge; 55, 56, 115, 167, 168 • Kathleen Dunne; 31, 32, 39, 40, 129, 130, 197, 198, 206, 244, 272, 323, 354, 382 • Eldon Doty; 28, 71, 72, 107, 120, 235, 236, 266 • Andrea Eberback; 102, 118, 285 • Lois Ehlert; 52, 92, 126 • Mac Evans; 22, 111, 161, 162, 165, 166, 178, 237, 287, 288, 392, 394, 395, 421, 422 • Don Gambino; 238, 324 • David Garner; 353 • Doreen Gay-Kassel; 7, 27, 61, 62 • Marvin Glass; 122, 148 • Steve Henry; 25, 26, 41, 42, 67, 75, 76, 147, 193, 194, 243, 251, 252, 254, 302, 335, 377, 381, 382, 417 • Chris Hill; 116, 142 • Tom Huffman; 48, 88 • Marilyn Janovitz; stickers 3D, 4A; 216, 277, 278 • Dave Joly; 313 • Brian Karas; 225, 226 • Elliot Kreloff; 69, 70, 134, 143, 314, 325 • Lingta Kung; 253 • Claude Martinot; 15, 16, 86, 133, 146, 175, 179, 180, 200, 242, 255, 256, 263, 264, 269, 270, 300, 330, 359, 416 • Hima Pamoedjo; 354 • Dennis Panek; 13, 14, 17, 18, 95, 169, 170, 192, 227, 228, 279, 280, 296, 341, 348, 356, 411 • Jerry Pavey; 371 • Charles Peale; 135, 136 • Judith Pfeiffer; stickers 4D, 159, 160, 311, 312, 403, 404 • Debbie Pinkney; 28, 43, 82, 103, 104, 113, 176, 345, 346, 372, 379, 380, 383, 402 • Norman Rainock; 33, 34, 44, 79, 80, 223, 224, 305, 306, 307, 308, 318, 319, 320, 321, 322, 327, 351, 352, 360, 388 • Chris Reed; 81 • Tim Robinson; 84, 171, 172, 222, 240, 259, 260, 268, 326 • Doug Roy; 83, 90, 106, 124, 164, 177, 183, 332, 420 • Joanna Roy; 206 • Joshua Schreier; 315, 316 • Bob Shein; stickers 4B-C; 229, 339, 340 • Jerry Smath; 63, 64 • Linda Solovic; punchouts 3, 4, 7, 19; 10, 20, 22, 30, 34, 36, 97, 98, 127, 128, 187, 195, 196, 205, 212, 217, 218, 219, 265, 282, 290, 293 • Dorothy Stott; stickers 1D; 35, 36, 77, 78, 94, 109, 110, 153, 155, 156, 186, 248, 249, 283, 284, 309, 310, 409, 410 • Peggy Tagel; 73, 74, 343 • Arnie Ten; 42, 152, 182 • Randy Verougstraete; 8, 29, 30, 157, 158, 250, 344, 369, 375, 376 • Michael Waldman; 6, 418 • John Wallner; 50, 54 • Vicki Wehrman; punchout 20 • Fred Winkowski; 137, 138, 144, 189, 190, 261, 262, 364 • Leslie Wolf; 4 • Rusty Zabransky; stickers 1C; 64, 70, 116, 266 • Jerry Zimmerman; stickers 3A; 65, 66, 105, 131, 132, 163, 334, 365, 366, 368, 405, 406
CONTENTS: Bob Shein

PHOTOGRAPHY Animals Animals / Mantis Wildlife, 51 • Bruce Coleman Inc. / Jane Burton, 275B, D; Hans Reinhard, 275C; Tom Stack, 9B, C; Norman O. Tomalin, 9D • Ken Cavanaugh, 38 • Bob Cass, 1C-D, 9A, 52, 91, 93, 125, 126, 151, 169, 185, 196, 215, 247, 249, 275A, 303, 333, 363, 391 • Rob Gray, punchouts 3, 4, 5, 6, 9, 10, 11 12; 3, 7, 11, 12, 37, 101, 127, 128, 129, 130, 133, 134, 135, 136, 137, 138, 143, 144, 145, 146, 147, 148, 149, 156, 179, 183, 273, 331, 347, 421, 422 • Scott Harvey; 85, 95, 147, 266 • Richard Hutchings, 1A-B, 11, 12, 21, 65, 92, 153, 154, 188, 226, 289, 304, 307, 317, 336, 347, 349, 368, 369, 370, 378 • The Image Bank / Grant V. Faint, 9 • J. Gerard Smith, 57, 108, 412
CONTENTS: Clara Aich, ivB, v, viT, viB, viiiT, viiiB, ivT, xT • Bob Cass, iiiB, xB • Lillian Gee, ivB • Richard Haynes, iiiT, ivT • Richard Hutchings, viiB

Production: Textart, Inc.

All photographs are by the Macmillan/McGraw-Hill School Division (MMSD) except as noted below.

Manipulative Workshop pages and manipulatives all by Scott Harvey for MMSD. Hand shots and performance assessment pages by Scott Harvey for MMSD; and Ken Karp for MMSD. Author photos all by Ken Karp for MMSD except: Audrey Jackson by James Visser for MMSD.

Setup photography for MAC Activity and Manipulatives Plus pages: Clara Aich

4/C illustration for Problem Solving pages: Deb Troyer Bunnell

Line illustration for MAC Activity and Manipulatives Plus pages: Shirley Beckes, Rick Cooley, Daniel DelValle, Julie Durrell, Judith Fast, Felipe Galindo, G. Brian Karas, Kathie Kelleher, Jane F. Kendall, Vickie Learner, Kathi McCord, Karen Pellaton, Marcy Dunn Ramsey, Dana C. Regan, Joel Synder, Lynn Sweat

Technical illustration: Network Graphics